mœopathy in the USA

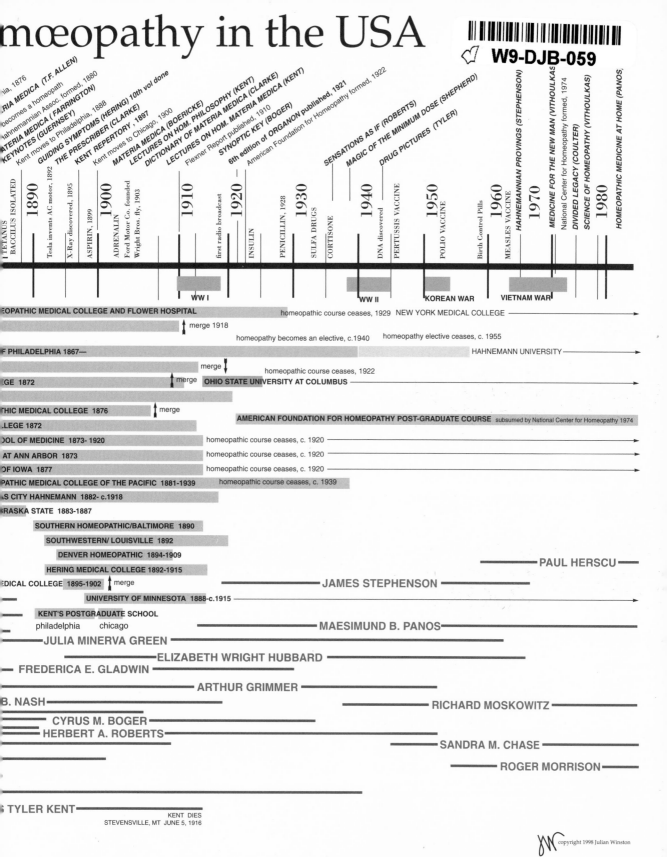

THE FACES
OF
HOMŒOPATHY

THE FACES
OF
HOMŒOPATHY

An Illustrated History of the First 200 Years

by

Julian Winston

Great Auk Publishing
Tawa, New Zealand

Great Auk Publishing
PO Box 51-156
Tawa, Wellington 6230
NEW ZEALAND
e-mail: jwinston@actrix.gen.nz

First Printing, March 1999

Printed by the RR Donnelley and Sons Company
Oakland, California, USA

Cover Photograph by David Hamilton
Book Design by Julian Winston
Index by Deborah Patton
This book was designed on a Macintosh 6100 using QuarkXpress,
Adobe Photoshop, and a Hewlett Packard Scanjet IIcx

ISBN 0–473–05607–0

single copies may be had from the publisher or through homœopathic booksellers

for multiple copies or bulk orders contact the publisher at the above address

This book is dedicated
to the memory
of all the grand homœopaths
mentioned within these pages
and
especially to the memory of
Raymond Seidel, MD, HMD, DHt
1908-1980

Acknowledgements

There are a number of people without whom this book would have been an impossible task. Barbara Williams and Judy Baker at the Hahnemann Archives let me spend many hours browsing through the storehouse of memorabilia and artifacts, and Barbara always knew where to look for that bizarre detail; Bill Kirtsos at Homeopathic Resources and Services in Old Chatham, New York, who played "yes, but have you seen THIS" for endless hours; Chris Ellithorp in Johnstown, New York, with his uncanny collector's ability shared his treasures freely with me and provided information that would have taken me years of searching to find; Patty Smith who kept asking me of the video, "When will it be a book?" and never let up; Greg Bedayn who encouraged me in the project, asked very good questions to keep me on track, and was a wonderful companion on the pilgrimage to Kent's house in Stevensville, Montana; Roger Savage who found a photo of Dorothy Shepherd after years of searching; The Robert Bosch Institute in Stuttgart who preserved so much of the ephemera of Hahnemann; the staff and Board of the National Center for Homeopathy who have been encouraging all along; Joe Lillard, a grand friend, whose Homeopathy Works in Berkeley Springs, West Virginia, preserves the legacy of Mr. Furr and the Washington Homeopathic Pharmacy; Richard Moskowitz, MD, whose library, companionship, and understanding what all this craziness is about was most helpful; Harris Coulter who started me on all this and filled in many details of the 1960-70s; the late Glenn Hill who told me stories about people and details until late into the night; Maisie Panos who answered many of my questions through several long phone calls; Bill Gray who allowed me to probe his "unused databanks" and retrieved many things that shed light on the recent history; Roger Morrison who answered questions about the development of homœopathy in the Berkeley area; Dana Ullman who furnished a number of wonderful artifacts of the early times in the Bay Area; Georgiana Neiswander who said, "I don't know if this would help, but..." giving me several very valuable earfuls about the 1950s; Catherine Coulter who gave me some "jumping off points"concerning modern history; Alain Naudé who answered many questions; the late Ralph Packman who candidly discussed "the great unpleasantness" over pastrami and rye sandwiches; Christine Zack who was gracious enough to take time to look at the recent history and provide her insights; Lester Steward and Harvey Biegelsen, MD, who told me all about Arizona; Stephen Barrett, MD, who so graciously proofed my chapter on "the quackbusters"; Wenda Brewster O'Reilly, whose comments made the work even better; Pam Sutton who carefully proof–read and edited a manuscript I thought was finished; Deborah Patton who said, "I can index that!"; Robin Meyer who guided me through the printing business; Simon Diplock who lent an ear and eye to my page-layout ideas; all those who helped me glean information about the history of homœopathy in their countries: Dr. Jorge Valdez from Argentina, John Francis and Alan Jones from Australia, Dr. Christopher Kurz from Austria, Raaja Swetta from Bahrain, Dr. Michael Van Wassenhoven from Belgium, Vera Maria Moreiota from Brazil, Dr. Paikov from Bulgaria, Patty Smith and Rudi Verspoor from Canada, Denis Fornier from Quebec, Dr. Ewald Finsterbusch from Chile, Giovanni Zapata Gutiérrez from Columbia, Rogielo Arce from Costa Rica, Tatjana Dunatov from Croatia, Rogelio Fernandez from Cuba, Jiri Cehovsky from the Czech Republic, Nasser Gamal from Egypt, Michel Eytan and Jean Claude Ravalard from France, Sue Mann, Louise Kunkle, and Ulrike Kessler from Germany, Anna Theodoraki from Greece, Dr. M. Kamalan and Dr. Anil Singhal from India, Dr. J. Rozencwajg, Yanai Lev-Or, Maralyn Dunbar, and Danny Altman from Israel, Bruno Galeazzi from Italy, Paul Wagener from Luxembourg, Suryia Osman and Nik Omar from Malaysia, Dr. Kim Sikorski from Mexico, Renee Koenders from the Netherlands, Petter Viksveen from Norway, Ajmal Khan from Pakistan, Lourdez Gonzaga from the Philippines, Leonid V. Kosmodemiansky and Andre Popen from Russia, Rangarao Padmanaban from Singapore, Vladimir Petroci from Slovakia, Paul Booyse and Dr. Florrie Kerschbaumer from South Africa, Carles Amengual Vicens from Spain, Ingrid High and Stephanie Arnberg Bengtsson from Sweden, Alain Jean-Mairet and Stefan Sterchi from Switzerland, Shukri Bensale from Tunisia, Angelique Perez from the UAR, Sergey Kearaéjev from the Ukraine, and Edgar Ordóñez García from Venezuela; Jeremy Sherr who saw me well enough to find a good remedy; and, lastly, my wonderful wife, Gwyneth Evans, without whose help, support, and guidance I could never have completed this book.

Table of Contents

Foreword

Homœopathy's principles have remained unchanged for 200 years, and its ten generations of practitioners therefore constitute one of the largest groups of physicians ever to profess allegiance to a single doctrine. While a minority in any given generation, they represent a powerful force in the history of world medicine.

We who have devoted our lives to this movement, some as physicians, others in a less exalted capacity, thus feel strong kinship and solidarity with colleagues distant in both space and time.

Ties of friendship unite us with homœopaths in nearly all countries of the world, and we sense a profound indebtedness to the founders and early leaders in the United States and Europe.

But these ancestors have always seemed somewhat pale and ghostly. We have read their books and articles, we have admired their amazing cures, we have been astonished by their capacity to study, to treat patients, to translate from German and French, to write books of their own, and to propagate homœopathy in *partibus infidelium*. But they were still disembodied figures — "dead white males" in dark suits and long beards.

Julian Winston's *The Faces of Homœopathy* shows they were not all males by any means; homœopathy opened its doors to women just as early as allopathy and much more hospitably. Nor are they as dead now as they used to be.

Julian offers a new perspective on Hahnemann and his circle and on the Anglo-American movement. He shows us the circumstances in which these physicians lived— and in which we ourselves live— their wives, husbands, and families; their students, teachers, and disciples; their organizations and lack of organization; their personal and professional hardships and triumphs.

On every aspect of homœopathy's history we are given

new insights. Take the "high-low split," for instance. Kent called Hughes, "that skunk, Dicky Hughes," and now we know the "low potency" leader a little better. We knew that the American Institute of Homœopathy and the International Hahnemannian Association were on opposite sides of the barricades, but we never realized there was an ultra-classical Society of Homœopathicians sniping at the IHA from behind the lines. We knew that Kent was a bulwark of the "highs," but we never knew he resigned from the IHA in 1900, charging that it had "not done any useful work for 10 years." (He rejoined a few years later.) Surprise after titillating surprise!!

Julian is a recognized artist, in addition to his other talents, and his artist's eye and ear inform these pages. Whether it is William Tod Helmuth's wonderfully comical ode, "How I Became a Surgeon," or Kent's engrossing account of how he undertook to write his *Repertory,* or T. C. Duncan's essay (so alien to our way of thinking) on "How to be Plump," or John Henry Clarke and the origins of British Fascism, or a short sketch of Melanie Hahnemann, or… ? Every one of these vignettes arouses a fierce curiosity to learn more and more about these figures, their lives, their ideas, and the times they lived in.

Since I start my working day at 5 a.m., it is my wont to retire at about 10 p.m. When the preliminary manuscript of *The Faces of Homœopathy* first arrived in the mail, I picked it up at bedtime for a brief look before closing my eyes, and, to my astonishment, read the whole book in one sitting. At 2 a.m. I was still perusing the final pages. I urge all future readers and lovers of homœopathy to choose an appropriate moment to dip into this book. Otherwise, friends and lovers will be left on street corners, brides and grooms at altars, and patients in waiting rooms.

Harris L. Coulter, PhD
May 1997

Introduction

I was introduced to homœopathy the way many people are. A friend suggested that I see her doctor. It was in 1970 and I had just moved to Philadelphia, Pennsylvania. Ray Seidel, MD, HMD, had been practicing medicine in Philadelphia since his graduation from Hahnemann Medical College in 1935. He was a homœopath. I was impressed with his wall of medicines and even more impressed by the clinical results he achieved. Ray became my physician.

Over the next ten years, Ray taught me the fundamentals of homœopathy. In 1980 Ray suggested I attend the National Center for Homeopathy's Summer School at Millersville, Pennsylvania. I knew that there were books to go with the medicine, and I finally got to see about 200 old volumes that summer. As much as I had come to depend on homœopathy as medicine, I became fascinated with its rich history.

By 1982 I was a member of the board of directors of the National Center, and had volunteered to catalog its library of 2,000 volumes. Many of the books contained pictures of the authors, and the familiar names soon became faces. I photographed them as a way of cataloging the rich visual history of homœopathy. With the help of friends across several continents I began to fill in the "image gaps" and have found many likenesses that have never before been seen.

A friend once said that I was a folklorist. I guess I am. I'm fascinated by the minutiae of homœopathy — that Hering loved limburger cheese, that E. B. Nash had a clear tenor voice, that the gruff looking H. C. Allen had a great sense of humor. When I read (in Nash's *Leaders*–under *Magnesium phosphoricum*) that, "I habitually prescribe the 55m made by myself upon the gravity potentizer," I was more interested in what the potentizer was than in the reasons for the choice of the remedy (and I *did* find out about the potentizer — see page 100).

Along the way, I've been lucky. I've been in the right place at the right time. I showed an interest in old books and ephemera at a time when many old doctors were passing on and their treasures wound up in my possession. I became friends with the Borneman family (John, Jack, and Jay) who filled my mind with information and my

The author, kneeling on the right. Maesimund Panos, MD, standing center. NCH summer school, 1980

home with treasures. I spent time with Don Lee and Gus Tafel of Boericke and Tafel, and was there to catalog their library and to help them sort their treasures when they vacated the Philadelphia premises. I was there to find the history, in person.

When I was asked to fill the footsteps of Harris Coulter (and large footsteps they were!) as the one who presented the "history of homœopathy" lecture to the class at the NCH summer school, I began to sprinkle the lecture with slides of images of the people who made the history.

Soon, the "slide show" took on a life of its own. Between 1990 and 1995 I worked on turning the slide show into a self-standing video, *The Faces of Homœopathy*, which is now distributed by the National Center for Homeopathy.

Though the video is just an hour long, when I presented it "live" it often took three hours— a result of my digressions about the material being discussed.

After completing the video, many people asked when was I going to "write the book?" They all begged me to take the plethora of information I carry in my head and get it out in some form. This book is the result of those requests.

In 1905, William Harvey King edited (with the help of Thomas Lindsley Bradford, the Librarian at Hahnemann Medical College) the four–volume *History of Homœopathy and Its Institutions in America*. After that, there was little published in the way of homœopathic history. Martin Kaufman gave us some insights in his 1971 *Homeopathy: The Rise and Fall of a Medical Heresy*, and Harris Coulter gave us his magnificent *Divided Legacy Volume III*, in 1973.

More recently there have been other works— short papers which are presented at conferences of historians— but while the minutiae discussed in them is of possible interest to me, the information certainly is not designed to be of interest to many others.

History is composed of people, not facts. It is the people who can give us insights into the deeds which become describable incidents.

The chances of King's four–volume *History* or Bradford's *Pioneers of Homœopathy* being republished are slim. Yet when I read these works I find myself wishing others could read them as well. I have extracted much of the

Letter from Elizabeth Wright Hubbard to Julia M. Green.
Dated January 25, 1960

Dear Dr. Green:
We are eager to have our elder members write for us their reminiscences of the masters of homeopathy whom most of us did not have the privilege of knowing such as Kent, Hering, H. C. Allen, Nash, T. F. Allen, J. H. Allen, E. A. Farrington, etc. A word portrait of these men, a knowledge of their birthdays, mannerisms, anecdotes about them, whatever makes them rare, strange and peculiar, is what we want.
If there are any others whom you know of who might have been acquainted with these men, please let me have their names and addresses.
With great anticipation of what you have done for the cause of homeopathy and almost envy of you knowledge and wisdom,

Faithfully yours,
Elizabeth Wright Hubbard, MD

cc: Drs. A. Holcomb, W. W. Sherwood, Grimmer, Slabaugh, Peck, Royal, Griggs.

information from those volumes and included it in these pages to give a sense of the buried treasure trove of information. It brings me great joy to share it with you. In some sense I am offering a "Reader's Digest" version of the cream of the homœopathic literature.

Assembled before you is not a dry historical text. The sources are given when I know them, but a great deal of the information presented here has been communicated to me by others (upholding the oral tradition) or it has been filed in my memory banks long before I began to note where I was reading or hearing the information.

It is the vogue, in these times of political correctness, to sanitize all we see and hear, and that includes history. I am neither a follower nor a believer in this effort. I like calling the large circular opening that we find upon our roadways "manholes" rather than "personal sewerage access points." Likewise, the people who were outraged that the "floating plumbing valve and spigot" was a "ball-cock" had little understanding that the original name had nothing to do with the male sexual anatomy.

The history of homœopathy is filled with rugged individualists who often spoke their mind, and did not worry about offending others. Their behavior, too, can tell much about them as people. I am not about to sanitize our history. I want to see it "warts and all."

It saddens me to find the letter quoted here (left), and realize the task was either never done or, if it was, all records have been lost. At the May 1971 meeting of the American Institute of Homeopathy, it was said, "There should be a history written of homœopathy in the past four or five years." Unfortunately, that task too was never done. I trust that this book will serve as an answer to the two requests of years past.

There are some regrets under the heading of "useless worries." I regret I never met Elizabeth Wright Hubbard, although I lived in New York City, not far from her office— (though I knew nothing of homœopathy at that time!). I regret I didn't press to talk to William Gutman or James Stephenson, both of whom told me they were too busy to talk at the several times I phoned them. I regret that I didn't ask Ray Seidel so much more.

As I was compiling the material I realized how few of these historical personages would have even spoken to me— much less any of a number of homœopaths I know.

Many of these people were medical doctors who believed only medical doctors should practice homœopathy. They would not talk to laymen. If we conjured up Kent or Boger would they talk to the RSHoms? I doubt it.

Aside from the work of Kaufman, very little has been written about our contemporary history. Some of it has been so wrapped in the personalities that, until now, it would have been difficult to talk about. Many old wounds were still smarting. The current history (from 1965 to the present), therefore, appears here for the first time. Only after I put it together did I go back and look at Kaufman's work. I found we had very different "takes" on the subject. Kaufman was the historian, the detached observer, who got the information from the written records. I was *there*. Those who were the players I knew as people, not as names on the page.

It is not the intent of this book to explain homœopathy or its principles. As I was writing the biography of Hahnemann I realized I could discuss in great detail his methodology, his concept of miasms, the development of the potentization scales through the LM or Q potencies, and the whole question of how Hahnemann practiced in his last years. But that is another work, and it has already been written by several people. Likewise, Kent's writings all are available and speak for themselves. The information I am presenting fits into a matrix of the theory and practice of homœopathy. If a reader wishes to understand more about homœopathy, I have included a list of beginning books and the Internet link to all homœopathic information in the **Bibliography and References**.

So what follows is not "what is homœopathy" as much as "who is homœopathy"— and that from an Anglo–American viewpoint. It is seen from my particular (and peculiar) vantage-point, showing strong biases about many issues. It is *not* a scholarly tome (although it has enough elements of that) but, rather, a book to be read, absorbed, and enjoyed on many levels.

Julian Winston
Tawa, New Zealand
January 1999

That's me talking...

I've tried to find a way of separating the personal "I" from the editorial "we" within the context of the book. I have found it nigh impossible. The book is not only a historical journey but it is my personal journey as well. After debating what to do, I have decided to leave the "I" in place. If you find a sentence that begins "I thought..." and it is not credited to anyone else, it's me— the author— commenting on the topic at hand.

The detached observer

I once asked Martin Kaufman if he had ever tried using homœopathy. He told me he had not, and wouldn't because it would prevent him from being "objective." I then asked him if he used conventional medicine. He admitted he did. So much for being a "detached observer."

I have no delusions about where I stand. I am certainly and unabashedly in the homœopathic camp. I've used it. It works. And I make no apologies.

What do we know?

What do we know of medicine in the late 1800s? Pictures are firmly embedded in our minds by the things we have seen on television and things we have read. The homœopath is mentioned in Alcott's Little Women, *but to the uninitiated the reference would mean little. We learn about the medicine of the time from* Dr. Quinn: Medicine Woman *or by the doctor in any number of westerns:*

Someone rushes in to the bar. "Doc! Come quick, there's been a shooting!" Doc, getting up from the card game, replies, "Carry him to my office." The scene cuts to Doc, emerging from behind the curtain in his office. "It was close, but I think he'll be OK," says Doc on the way back to the bar.

We think to ourselves, "They hardly had medicine then."

A quick look at the history of the states in **Appendix D** *will show that in the move west, homœopathic doctors were among the first to settle in. A conventional physician of today would have little to discuss with a conventional physician on the frontier in 1885, but a homœopath of today would feel right at home in the office of Dr. Gorham in Cheyenne, Wyoming at that time, or the office of Dr. Fetterman, in Tombstone, Arizona, a few years later. ("Well, doc... how would you differentiate between Pulsatilla and Sulphur in this case?")*

A Note About the Times

Homœopathy flowered in the early 1820s. For those wanting a clear picture of Hahnemann's time, a viewing of the movie *Amadeus* would suffice. Mozart was born in 1756 and Hahnemann in 1755— they were contemporaries.

In the 1820s there were not many amenities. For Lewis and Clark, their exploration of the wilds of the USA was not that much different than their daily life. Toilet facilities were about as crude in the city as they were in the wild, most cooking was done by boiling, roasting, or frying; there were no artificial lights to be had in or out of the city, and the ground with a blanket was not that much different than a horsehair mattress.

Everyone traveled by horseback or wagon, and while Frankford, Pennsylvania is now within the city limits of Philadelphia— a 20 minute drive from Center City— Guernsey noted that when Hering came from Philadelphia to visit him in Frankford it was a 16 mile drive costing him the whole day.

We look at Allen's *Encyclopedia* or Hering's *Guiding Symptoms* and wonder, "How did these people have the time to do all that work?"

"Well, they didn't have MTV or radio," is the quick answer. But it is more than that. They had fewer distractions, and they also had servants. The Hering household consisted of Hering, his wife, several children, George (his full-time coachman), a full-time cook, a full-time waitress, and a "door-girl" who spoke both German and English. Hering also employed Dr. Knabe, an "elderly man" who transcribed all Hering's case-notes into legible manuscript.

When living in that style there was no need to cook, clean, or to do washing. It was all done by others. Most of the well-to-do homœopathic doctors had similar life-styles.

Between 1800 and 1900, most USA cities saw the birth of electric lighting, indoor plumbing, and faster communication via the telephone and the telegraph.

When Kent bought his vacation home in Montana in 1912, it was wired for electricity, although electric service did not reach the area until 1926. There was a hand pump in the kitchen and kerosene lamps or candles gave light at night. Even in a large city like Philadelphia, many fire stations were still using horse-drawn equipment through the 1920s.

They were slower times, when an evening of entertainment

consisted of having a story read or performing a play with friends. Conversation was something one engaged in and enjoyed. Many homœopaths received a classical education and were versed in Latin and Greek, and literature in those languages. Many of them also learned German to read Hahnemann, or came from German backgrounds.

It was a time of discovery, and everyone was a "closet scientist." Many homœopaths were inveterate collectors of natural history. They had more than a passing interest and understanding of the natural and physical sciences.

We learn homœopathy through the language of the repertory and think of the heartbroken woman as, "Love, unrequited, ailments from." After delving for so many years in the homœopathic journals I find I have come to enjoy the "style." I hope the "antiquated" or "quaint" way of expressing oneself that is found within these pages is understood in the context of the time.

We read a part of Dr. John C. Morgan's eulogy to Hering:

"But the long, long past stretches forward until this day. Homœopathy writes beneath that noble galaxy the names of a new constellation— a group of heroes as glorious as they; few in number but of imperishable fame. Antiquity overtakes us. Hahnemann, Gram, Jahr... these have gone over to the reunion of the great. One by one has the heroic Past inscribed them upon her scroll. We, too, are acquiring a history— short it may be in time; but long in all that makes time venerable; ages old, in the truth spoken, and in deeds performed.

Ye Homœopaths, behold these your heroes! Measure the territory; glory in the fame they have won for you; emulate their exalted worth. Mark well, too, the noble souls who yet remain with us, to pile still loftier mountains of grand doing upon the heights attained by them."

To say:

"Many of the important figures of the past are dead. Remember them. Recognize those who are still alive and build upon their work," just doesn't have the same ring!

"œ"

The word "homœopathy" derives from two Greek words homoios (ομοιου) and pathos (παϕος) meaning "similar" and "suffering." The word, often because of the lack of proper type on the part of type-setters, has become "Americanized" to "homeopathy"— often giving the novice the sense that this "opathy" has something to do with the "home." This is regrettable.

I have made the decision to use the classical form of "homœopathy"— keeping the "œ" (a ligature digraph which was the Latin way of writing the "oi" of Greek) in the text. I will use the original spelling throughout, keeping the newer spelling only for those books and/or organizations that have dropped the ligature digraph from the word.

Read the books

I've presented, in the following pages, a very condensed picture of the history of homœopathy— primarily in the United States. To get a much fuller view of this subject I strongly suggest both Kaufman's book, Homeopathy: The Rise and Fall of a Medical Heresy, *and Coulter's Volume III of* Divided Legacy.

The Pictures

I have looked not only for information but also for pictures of all these folk. We know their work, but do we know them? How much can we understand of them through their likenesses? It lets us meditate upon them in a special way. How did Timothy Field Allen manage to keep his hair up like that? How long did it take him to do up the fancy collar and buttoned shoes? Why did Kent grow a beard in 1884? When did he cut it off? Why? The few pictures we have are about as close as we will ever get to these folks. So… look at them and converse with them. They were interesting people, all worthy of knowing. Maybe H. C. Allen will tell you a joke!

The Signatures

All the engraved portraits in Cleave's Biography *have signatures appended. I thought, "Well, I have one or two, maybe I can get more." And the search began in earnest. Of all the people pictured in these pages I am lacking only a few signatures. Some of the signatures were found in Bradford's* Scrapbooks *at the Hahnemann Collection in Philadelphia. Some were in Glasgow, Scotland. Some were buried under my nose in my own library.*

For those interested in graphology, these signatures may give another insight into these wonderful people.

The Biographies

Some people had volumes written about them. With others I could barely find a three-line obituary. With some, I found such interesting or beautifully written information that I felt it would be a sin not to share it.

The Structure

This book is, for the most part, an expansion of the video *Faces of Homœopathy*. I first attempted to lay it out as the "script" of the video, but it did not translate well as the information grew.

I also found, as we approached the current day, the video commentary lacked some in-depth information about the underlying issues of the time.

The book is structured, basically, chronologically. I struggled with putting all the "organizations" into a single chapter, but they all grew from the needs of the times. And the needs in 1844 were quite different than those in 1880. So I've kept to a generalized time-line. Of course some names will come up out of sequence. I hope readers will have the patience to move forward in the text for a fuller story.

The material has been garnered from many sources, primarily Bradford's *Pioneers of Homœopathy*, Cleave's *Biographical Cyclopædia of Physicians and Surgeons*, and King's *History of Homœopathy and Its Institutions in America*. Other sources include a myriad of journals and copies of articles and ephemera in my personal collection. A general bibliography is included at the end of this book.

I have included a number of appendices:

- The first is a collection of stories, anecdotes, and ephemera I found funny, interesting, informative, whatever, and wished to share but found no logical place to do so, within the main text, without interrupting the flow.
- The second is three expanded histories: "the great unpleasantness," Kent's Post–Graduate School, and of an organization that came and went in 1984.
- The third is a statistical study of the homœopathic graduates and practitioners.
- The fourth is a brief history of homœopathy in each state.
- The fifth is a listing of all the United States homœopathic hospitals from 1880-1960.
- The sixth is a very brief history of homœopathy in the countries in the world.

The Beginnings

Hahnemann and his family
Hahnemann's lost son
Hahnemann's pupils

As seen below, I once tried to build a family tree of homœopathy: this person taught that person, who taught these persons, etc. But it soon grew less like a tree, with limbs branching off a single trunk, and more like a spreading weed, seeding itself through chance encounters across the country. It was spread by those who used it and told others, and by those who investigated the claims through the written literature which was mainly Hahnemann's writings and the *Repertory* of Jahr. The spread of homœopathy was world–wide but since so much of its literature and practice came from "the golden age" of homœopathy in the late 1800s in the United States, this book will focus on the history of homœopathy in the United States, with a short detour to Britain.

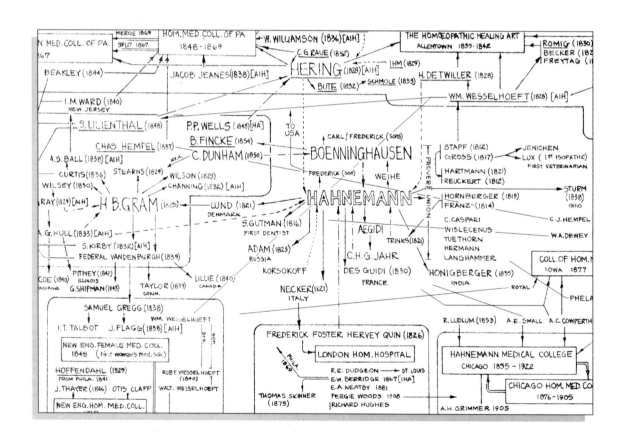

Hahnemann

"There is a reason why homœopathy spoke clear and advanced words from the beginning. Its fluency came from somewhere. Out of the labyrinth of ancient languages, remote peoples, and the ignored works of obscure botanists and physicians of different nations, Hahnemann made a synthesis utterly different from any of its parts… Any translation involves a highly scientific and disciplined meditation on the structure of language, the roots of meaning, and the transformations between codes. Homœopathy resembles the codes of its origins more than it does standard medicine… In the brief and almost silent hiatus between the end of academic hermeticism and the birth of professional science, Hahnemann coaxed a single child from their unrecorded union… From his brain, which had so long been coalescing bizarre and discontinuous elements, came the resolution of homœopathy."

— Richard Grossinger in *Planet Medicine*

Christian Friedrich Samuel Hahnemann, MD
April 10, 1755 — July 2, 1843

Samuel Hahnemann was the third child in a family of three boys and two girls. Hahnemann's father was a porcelain painter in the city of Meissen, Germany. The town was plundered by Frederick the Great at the onset of the Seven Year War (1756–1763), and the Hahnemann family was left destitute. Young Samuel was educated at home, and under the tutelage of his strict father, he acquired an ability for self-developed study. Eventually, the local school, noticing his academic excellence, gave him free tuition. By the age of 12 he was tutoring Greek. Says Richard Haehl, "A happy carefree youth was entirely denied him; from early days he was constrained to unceasing work."

At 20 Hahnemann left for Leipzig and attended, he said, "the lectures I found useful," at the University. Within a year he left for Vienna where, arriving destitute, he was taken under the wing of Joseph von Quarin, one of the noted physicians in the city. Quarin found young Samuel a position with Baron von Brukenthal, the Governor of Transylvania (now Romania). Hahnemann was hired to

This photograph of Hahnemann was taken by M. Faucault in Paris on September 30, 1841. It was an overcast day, and Hahnemann had to remain motionless for the 20 minutes it took to make the exposure. He was suffering from a slight cold at the time, and his case-books show he did not work the following day.

William Cullen's,

b. A. D. Professors der praktischen Arzneikunde auf der Universität zu Edinburg, ersten Leibarztes des Königs für Schottland, des königl. Kollegiums der Aerzte zu Edinburg, der königl. Gesellschaften zu London und Edinburg, der königl. Gesellschaft der Aerzte zu Paris, des königl. Kollegiums der Aerzte zu Madrit, der amerikanischen philosophischen Gesellschaft zu Philadelphia, der arzneilichen Gesellschaft zu Copenhagen, der arzneilichen Gesellschaft zu Dublin, der königl. arzneilichen und der königl. physikalischmedicinischen Gesellschaften zu Edinburg Mitglieds

Abhandlung

über die

Materia medika

nach der nunmehr von dem Verfasser selbst ausgearbeiteten Originalausgabe,

übersetzt und mit Anmerkungen

von

Samuel Hahnemann,

der Arzneikunde Doktor.

Erster Band.

Leipzig,
im Schwickertschen Verlage 1790.

"I took, for several days, as an experiment, four drams of good China twice daily. My feet and finger tips, etc. at first became cold. I became languid and drowsy; then my heart began to palpitate; my pulse became hard and quick; an intolerable anxiety and trembling (but without a rigor); prostration in all the limbs; then pulsations in the head, redness of the cheeks, thirst… all those symptoms which are typical of intermittent fever… This paroxysm lasted for two to three hours every time, and recurred when I repeated the dose, and not otherwise. I discontinued the medicine and I was once more in good health."

—*Footnote by Hahnemann in Cullen's* Materia Medica.

put the Baron's library in order and to act as the family physician. Brukenthal also introduced Hahnemann to the Freemason's Lodge in Hermannstadt of which Hahnemann became a member.

In 1779 Hahnemann returned to Germany, where he completed his medical degree at Erlangen. After a brief sojourn in Hettstadt, he moved to Dessau in 1781, a town which Hahnemann said had "better social intercourse" and "facilities for acquiring knowledge." It was here, in 1782, he met his first wife, Johanna Henriette Küchler.

Hahnemann was appointed the Medical Officer to the town of Gommern. He supplemented his income by translating books, many of them about chemistry. In 1785 he moved to Dresden, the first of many moves with his increasingly larger family. In the next 20 years he would move 20 times. In Dresden he became occupied with chemistry and translating — all but giving up his meager medical practice. His medical writings show he was increasingly interested in the powers of diet and in non-interventionist therapies.

By 1789 he moved to Leipzig, and by 1790 had abandoned medical practice. In 1790, while translating Cullen's *Materia Medica* from English into German, he became interested in the relationship between the curative effects of *Cinchona* and its poisoning symptoms. It was this interest that led him to his first "proving"— the testing of the *Cinchona* upon himself — and eventually led him to his "New Principle" in 1796.

In 1792 he spoke out vehemently against the medical profession who had enabled Emperor Leopold II of Austria to be bled to death. Later that year he was given charge of a mental hospital in Georgenthal that contained a single patient, Herr Friedrich Klockenbring, the Minister of Police, who was suffering with insanity. Hahnemann cured him with a regimen of diet, hygiene, and rational discourse.

In the summer of 1793 Hahnemann left Georgenthal and, as Haehl says, "sought everywhere for an anchorage." On the way from Georgenthal, the hired carriage overturned. His youngest son, the newborn Ernst, died shortly after as a result of the injuries. It was the beginning of very difficult times. By 1805, when he again settled in Dessau-Torgau, he and his family had moved ten times.

His moves did not halt his literary output. In 1796 he

wrote his "Essay on a New Principle For Ascertaining The Curative Powers of Drugs, and Some Examination of the Previous Principles," and homœopathy was born.

Between 1799–1800 he again took up medicine, this time using his new methodology. In 1801 he wrote his essay on the "Cure and Prevention of Scarlet Fever" in which he begins to use "the smallest dosages," a concept he first introduced in 1798. In these years his literary output was more than 5,500 pages.

He bought a home in Torgau in 1805 and contributed the article, "The Medicine of Experience," to *Heufeland's Journal*. By 1810 he had written the first edition of *The Organon of Rational Healing*.

In 1811, at age 56, he again moved to Leipzig. The University of Leipzig would grant faculty status to anyone who could defend a thesis in Latin in a public forum, and Hahnemann applied. While many thought Hahnemann's presentation would be a rant against conventional medicine, Hahnemann presented a long, detailed paper about the use of *Hellebore* by the ancients— speaking in Latin and quoting his sources in their eight original languages— including Hebrew and Arabic.

Once accepted at the university, he began to lecture on homœopathy. His lectures, said student Franz Hartmann, "…poured forth a flood of abuse against the older medicine and its followers…" Some described him as "a raging hurricane." He gained few converts. While he desired to interest physicians in this new therapy, he found few who were interested in "forgetting" the knowledge they had, to spend time learning an entirely new system of therapeutics. Hahnemann's best pupils were the young medical students, most of whom had to withstand pressure from their colleagues and faculty for associating with Hahnemann. It was a small group that became his "provers union."

By 1813, when typhus was raging in Leipzig after the battle between Prussian forces and the Army of Napoleon who were in retreat from Moscow, Hahnemann, using potentized medicines, was able to cure 178 of the 180 typhus cases presented to him. The allopathic mortality rate was between 20 and 30 percent.

By 1820, Hahnemann's stay in Leipzig was becoming more difficult. He was constantly attacked in the papers by the city's doctors. Prince Swarzenburg came from Austria to be treated by Hahnemann, but after a brief remission of

This first edition of the Organon *belonged to Constantine Hering. It is in the Hahnemann Collection in Philadelphia, Pennsylvania. When I wanted to photograph it there was not enough light in the Archive room. Librarian Judy Baker and I walked the book down to the street where I photographed it, in daylight, resting on a milk crate next to a hot-dog vendor's cart outside the school on 15th Street. I wondered what Hering would have thought of it all. It was a surreal experience.*

Organon

The Greek word Organon *denotes an instrument for acquiring knowledge; a body of methodological doctrine comprising principles for scientific or philosophical procedures or investigation. It is also the name given to the six logical treatises of Aristotle. Francis Bacon (1561-1626) called his work* Novum Organum, *in the belief that he had discovered new principles of inductive logic. Based on the example of these two previous works, Hahnemann called his work the* Organon of Rational Healing.

"A" or "E"?

Hahnemann used the phrase "similia similibus curentur" to describe the main concept of homœopathy. Usually translated as "let likes cure likes," the word "curantur" is often substituted.

The Latin word "curare" means to cure. The verb form "curantur" is the third person plural in passive voice— "they are cured," referring to the "similia," which means "similar things." Hence, "similia similibus curantur" is translated as "likes cures likes."

The verb form "curentur" is also the third person plural, passive voice, but this time in the subjunctive. In Latin, the subjunctive is used to express fullfillable wishes of the present time. This is usually best translated as "let them be cured" or "are to be cured." The proper translation of "similia similibus curentur" is therefore "Let likes be cured with likes."

The second word in the sentence, "similibus" is in casus ablativus pluralis *(a special noun form with no direct correspondence in English). In this context it means "by similar things."*

Both versions are proper Latin and convey the same general message but "curentur" expresses the statement as a wish, or demand, whereas "curantur" just states it as a matter of fact.

Hahnemann, the astute language scholar, chose to state it as a guiding principle ("are to be cured") rather than a fundamental doctrine ("are cured").

his illness, slipped back into heavy drinking habits, and began to alternate homœopathy with allopathic methods. When Hahnemann arrived one day to treat him, the other doctors of the Prince had just finished bleeding him. Hahnemann, in anger, left. The Prince died five weeks later, and the failure of homœopathy was implicated in his death. At the same time, Hahnemann was brought to court for encroaching on the apothecary's domain of "dispensing medicine."

He applied to Duke Ferdinand, of Anhalt–Köthen, for permission to settle in his Duchy to practice medicine and dispense remedies. The Duke had been a patient of Hahnemann's and was also a Freemason. Hahnemann moved to Köthen in June 1821, with eleven wagons of goods, his wife, and seven daughters. In effect, the Duke gave him sanctuary.

While in Köthen he continued writing, continued his provings and in 1828, published *Chronic Diseases*, in which he suggests the concept of the inherited miasm. He also maintained an increasingly busy practice.

His wife died in the spring of 1830, and Hahnemann, at 75, became a recluse, looked after by his two daughters.

Homœopathy produced many cures during the European cholera epidemic of 1831-32, and was becoming well known. However, Hahnemann was increasingly critical of those who called themselves homœopaths and yet used allopathic treatments on occasion. To Hahnemann, you either were a homœopath or you weren't— there was no middle ground.

In 1832 there was a move in Leipzig to establish a homœopathic school and hospital. It was about ready to open when Hahnemann wrote an open letter to the newspaper, addressed to the "Half-Homœopaths in Leipzig," heaping scorn on those who would allow patients to choose between the systems, and calling the person who was to head the hospital, Moritz Müller, "a bastard-homœopath." The hospital, amidst the invective, lasted only a few years.

In October 1834, Melanie D'Hervilly traveled from Paris to Köthen to consult Hahnemann. By January of the following year they were married, and by June they had moved to Paris.

Melanie became a quick pupil, and together they maintained a lively practice. In April 1843, Hahnemann came down with bronchitis, and despite homœopathic treatment, became weaker. He was confined to bed and died on July 2, with Melanie at his side.

He had written six editions of the *Organon,* although the 6th, finished in 1842, was not printed until 1920. He compiled the *Materia Medica Pura* between 1811 and 1821, and published *The Chronic Diseases* in 1828. He proved 106 remedies during his life.

The "sixth edition"

The *Organon* went through six editions. The first was published in 1810; the second in 1819; the third in 1824; the fourth (the first to be translated into English) in 1829; and the fifth in 1833. The sixth edition was readied for printing in 1842, but Hahnemann died before it could be printed. Melanie kept the manuscript and only made its presence known when several other versions were being claimed to be "the sixth." Melanie began negotiations for publication in Germany, but the Prussian/Austrian war in 1865 intervened.

In 1865 negotiations to obtain the book were conducted between Melanie and Hering, Lippe, and Raue, but nothing materialized.

During the Franco-Prussian War of 1870-71, all of Hahnemann's papers were moved from Paris to Westphalia and watched over by Melanie's adopted daughter who had married Karl Boenninghausen.

Carroll Dunham was negotiating for the purchase of the *Organon* in 1877, but he died before completing the process. In 1877, Dr. Bayes, from the London School of Homeopathy asked to publish the manuscript. Melanie said that she would be willing to supervise the translation so there could be "no malicious or deceptive alterations of the text," and she asked for a sum, the yearly interest of which would equal her yearly professional income. The matter was then dropped.

In 1880, Dr. H. N. Guernsey met Madam Boenninghausen while in Europe and he attempted to raise $10,000 from the American homœopathic community for the purchase, but funds were not forthcoming.

Just before the turn of the century, Dr. Richard Haehl contacted the Boenninghausen family, and Dr. William Boericke offered to buy the book were it ever available. Hahnemann's papers were again nearly lost during the military occupation of Westphalia during the period of 1914-18. Shortly after this, Haehl negotiated the purchase of the *Organon* from the Boenninghausen family. Drs. William Boericke and James William Ward paid the $1,000 being asked, and Dr. Haehl brought the manuscript to the United States. The sixth edition finally appeared in print in Germany in 1921 and in the United States in 1922.

The death of Hahnemann

"At the end of his life Hahnemann realized the seriousness of his condition and gave me some instructions. The terrible sorrow caused by the prospect of having to lose him soon, instead of weighing my soul down, illumined it and made it soar to a higher level where it became equal to these terrible circumstances. Two days before leaving me he said to me: 'I have chosen you among all my disciples and I leave you my scientific heritage which is of such importance to humanity. Continue to work as we have done for such a long time, carry on my mission; you know Homœopathy and you know how to cure as well as I do.' I replied: 'But I am a woman, my body has grown tired, my hair has become white under the strain of this difficult work, I have well earned a little rest.' 'Rest!' said Hahnemann, and raised himself up in his bed, 'Have I ever rested? Forward, ever forward against the wind, struggle against the strain, always cure and everywhere, and by constantly curing you will compel justice to be done to you; current opinion will support you respectfully after having opposed you on your path. Call faithful disciples to your side, teach them all that I could not tell them, what you alone now know; hand on my tradition, and when your hour to leave the earth has arrived come and join me where I shall await you. Your body will be put in the same coffin as mine, not beside mine, but inside and they will write on our tomb:

Heic nostro cineri cinis, ossibus ossa sepulcro, Miscentur vivos ut sociavit amor.'

(As love united us in life, so does the tomb, Ashes to ashes and bones to bones.)

I promised all he wanted; then he added: 'God will recompense you,' and five minutes before he departed he said to me full of tenderness: 'You will be mine in eternity.' These were his last words."
— Melanie Hahnemann, 1846

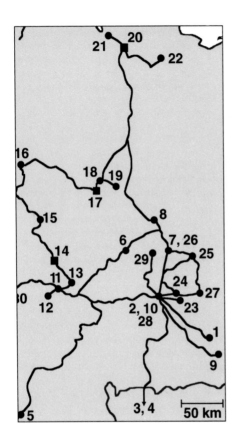

The peripatetic Hahnemann

PLACE	DATE	AGE
1. Meissen	1755 born	
2. Leipzig	1775-77 schooling	20-22
3. Vienna	spring to September 1777	22
4. Hermanstadt	(Sibiu, Romania) 1777-79	22-24
5. Erlangen	1779 degree (It is unknown where Hahnemann spent his time between graduation and settling in Hettstedt)	
6. Hettstedt	1780-81 first job as doctor	25-26
7. Dessau	1781-82 met wife	26-27
8. Gommern	1782-84 medical officer	27-29
9. Dresden	1785-89	30-34
10. Leipzig	1789-92 (living in Stötteritz, a suburb 4km from the city)	34-37
11. Gotha	spring 1792	37
12. Georgenthal	June '92- July '93	37-38
13. Molschleben	1793-94 spent 10 months	38-39
14. Mühlhausen	carriage accident	
15. Göttingen	spring through September 1794	
16. Pyrmont	October 1794-spring 1795	39-40
17. Wolfsbutel	passed through	
18. Brunswick	1795-96	40-41
19. Konigslutter	1796-spring 1799	41-43
20. Hamburg	passed through	
21. Altona	summer 1799-1800	43-44
22. Mölln	Sept 1800- 1801	44-45
23. Machern	spring 1801	
24. Eilenburg	summer 1801	46
25. Wittenburg	1802 (?)-1804	47-49
26. Dessau	1804	
27. Torgau	1805-1811	50-56
28. Leipzig	1811-1821	56-66
29. Köthen	1821-1835	66-80
30. Paris	1835-1843	80-88

The way we now know where Hahnemann lived is through the letters he left that still survive. We often know his intentions of where he was going and, through town records, when he arrived. But some locations are not very time specific.

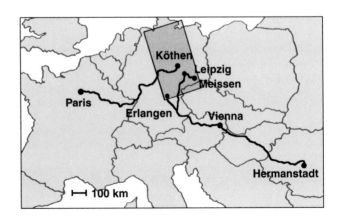

November 3rd, 1832: A word to the half-homœopaths of Leipzig

I have heard for a long time and with displeasure, that some in Leipzig, who pretend to be Homœopaths, allow their patients to choose whether they shall be treated homœopathically or allopathically. Whether it is that they are not yet so grounded in the true spirit of the new doctrine, or that they are lacking in true love for their fellow mortals, or that, contrary to their better convictions, they do not scruple to dishonour their profession for the sake of sordid gain-- let them at any rate, not require of me that I should recognise them as my true disciples. It is remarkable and a splendid indication of the power of the new system for improvement, that in no place where this system has even moderately flourished, are there such homœopathic-allopathic mongrels to be found, it grieves me to say it, as in Leipzig, a town hitherto so dear to me. Blood-letting, the application of leeches and Spanish flies, the use of fontanels and setons, mustard plasters and medicated bags, embrocations with salves and aromatic spirits, emetics, purgatives, various sorts of warm baths, pernicious doses of calomel, quinine, opium and musk, are some of the quackeries by which, when used in conjunction with homœopathic prescriptions, we are able to recognise the crypto-homœopath, trying to make himself popular, as we recognise the lion by his claws. They swagger in the cradle of the homœopathic science (as they choose to call Leipzig) where its founder first stepped forward as a teacher. But behold ! I have never yet acknowledged you; away from me, ye medical _____!

Either be honourable allopaths of the old fraternity, ignorant as yet of anything better, or pure homœopaths intent on curing your suffering brethren. Once more I exhort you, and this, for the last time to abandon this course and to give those abroad a better example one more worthy of imitation.

But he who from this day forward hesitates to follow this faithful advice, to prove himself in word and deed a homœopath, let him never come again to Köthen while I behold the light of day, for he may look for no friendly reception. But if ye will persist in that behaviour, then may _____ be meted out to you alone. Now, when an institution is about to be founded for an undeceptive practical demonstration before the eyes of the whole world, of the unsurpassable efficacy of the only genuine, purely homœopathic treatment— now the matter becomes infinitely more serious. On such an occasion I consider it my duty to raise my voice aloud, lest these scandalous abuses should impart in this prospective hospital and clinic a disreputable character to the whole system. Hence I most solemnly protest against the employment of such a bastard-homœopath, whether as teacher or medical attendant. Let no one of this description enter upon the sacred offices of our divine art in this hospital— no one of this type!

For, should any false doctrines be taught under the honourable name of homœopathy, or should patients be treated otherwise than by pure homœopathy (with no trace of this allopathic muck), you may depend upon it I that shall raise my voice aloud honestly and to its utmost. In all the public papers far and near I shall warn a world already weary of deceit against such treachery and degeneracy, which deserves to be branded and avoided. Today my paternal admonition sounds through this journal within the precincts of Leipzig, hoping for your improvement.

Bas-reliefs of Hahnemann's life from the Hahnemann Monument in Washington, DC. From Top: As a student, as a chemist, as a teacher, as a physician

Hahnemann the man

Politics

Haehl says, "What Hahnemann really lacked in his nature was an interest in politics in the widest sense of the term, when we mean a real, personal interest for the general social economics of his countrymen. He was thoroughly non-political… coming from an outlandish little spot on the German map, he was destined to spend the greater part of his life within these narrow provincial conditions. He was thus deprived of a wider vision for larger political events… He regarded the incidents of war merely as obstacles in the way of his work of reform and as disturbances of the economic life compelling him to inactivity."

Smoking

Hahnemann's only habit of self-indulgence was pipe-smoking. The Reverend Everest once asked him why he smoked, and Hahnemann replied: "Oh, it's an idle habit contracted when I had to sit up every other night in order to get bread for my children, while I was pursuing my own investigations by day."

His daily life

The house in Köthen had a small, narrow piece of land in the back of the house surrounded by a tall wall. Hahnemann called this his "garden" and walked in it every day. Often, at night, he would walk up and down with a lantern in his hand. When a visitor commented on how small the garden was, Hahnemann replied, "You are right. My garden is small. But see how high it is!"

Hahnemann's daily work routine was strictly regulated. He rose at 6 a.m. in the summer and 7 a.m. in the winter, drank a few cups of warm milk, and went to walk in his garden. At 10 a.m., if the season permitted, he ate some fruit. At noon he had a meal of strong beef-tea, roasted beef or mutton, or chicken, roasted larks, or a similar food. He was very fond of roast veal and pork, and a dish in order to be to his taste must be very sweet. The only vegetables he ate were new beans, cabbage, and spinach. He often used cake instead of bread. Although he drank wine when he had guests, his normal drink was sweetened gose, a kind of mild beer.

After eating he slept an hour on the sofa, and then saw patients until 7 p.m. after which he had a supper of warm milk. In the summer he had gose and bread.

After supper he walked in his garden with his small pet dog, which also sat next to him at the table. After walking he sat in the sitting room, then went to his office where he wrote until 1 a.m.

He never slept in artificially warmed rooms.

Although he was passionately fond of chess, he rarely played for lack of time.

Johanna Leopoldine Henriette Küchler
January 1, 1764 — March 31, 1830

The step-daughter of a Dessau pharmacist, Hahnemann met Johanna when she was seventeen. They were married on November 17, 1782.

They had 11 children: Henriette (1783), Friedrich (1786), Wilhelmine (1788), Amalie (1789), Karoline (c. 1792), Ernst (1794— died as an infant), Friederike (1795) and twin sister stillborn, Elanore (1803), Charlotte (1805), Luise (1806).

"Frau Henriette," as she was called by Hahnemann, "watched with tender care over the domestic happiness, the tranquil peace of the great master, so that he only felt happy in his home, in his family, and seldom left them…"

Described as a "tall and stout wife" another writer says, "It was she who often caused dissension between him and his most faithful pupils…Not withstanding this, Hahnemann used to call this scolding Xanthippe, who took pleasure in raising a storm in the house, 'the noble companion of his personal life.'"

Said his pupil Hartman: "When Hahnemann was called for dinner a third time, he remarked: 'Now I shall get a black look.'"

Melanie d'Hervilly Gohier Hahnemann
February 2, 1800 — May 27, 1878

Melanie was born in Paris to a family of "liberal nobility." At a time when most young girls were educated at home in "domestic things," Melanie was receiving a more liberal education. She had many quarrels with her mother, and her father sent her to live with the family of her painting teacher, Guillaume Guillon-Lethière, when she was 15. By the time she was 20 she was enjoying modest success as a painter.

During the 1820s Melanie wrote poetry and became involved with the complex politics of the Republican wing of French political life. She undoubtedly knew many of the poets and writers of the time. She had tea with Alexander Dumas and lived near George Sand. She began to write poetry to and for Louis Jérôme Gohier, a well known political figure. When Gohier died aged 84 in 1830, he left Melanie both money and his name "so that his name would be spoken of with an esteem equal to hers."

"All my friends have been telling me, for the last few months, that I look twenty years younger. Melanie has just painted my portrait in oils, and completed it in nine days, and everyone expresses surprise at its perfect likeness and finished execution—(three years ago she was considered the most celebrated poetess and painter in France) but on account of her illness— a kind of tic douloureux in the right hypogastrium, she had not touched a brush for three years— now she can paint again without discomfort; that is the extent to which I have improved the health of my angelic wife!"

— *S. Hahnemann*

Seeing the failure of medicine to help many of her acquaintances, and seeing the success of Dr. Quin (then in Paris) who treated the victims of the 1832 cholera epidemic with homœopathy, Melanie became interested in this new medicine. She found a copy of the 4th edition of the *Organon* and read it. Sadness for her many departed friends was causing her physical pain, and she left for Köthen to seek help from Hahnemann. Dressing herself in men's clothing, Melanie undertook the 15-day journey and arrived in Köthen on October 7, 1834.

She found the widowed Hahnemann living with his two daughters. At age 79, he had not left his house or garden for more than a year. Within three days of meeting, Hahnemann proposed to her.

Referred to as a "second George Sand," Melanie stayed at Köthen with a friend of Hahnemann's. She was seen, dressed in male attire, and said, "I prefer going about with men, for no sensible word can be addressed to a woman." While in Köthen she painted, rode horse-back, practiced pistol-shooting, and hunted.

Permission to wed was received from Melanie's father. Melanie, a Catholic, learned the Lutheran creed to be married to Hahnemann, and on January 18, 1835, the couple were married.

To quash the rumors that Melanie had married Hahnemann for his fortune, Hahnemann made a will that left everything to his children, with the proviso that should he have children with Melanie, they too would have a share of his estate.

After living in Köthen for a while, they left for Paris on June 7, arriving on June 21.

Hahnemann was granted permission to practice medicine in Paris, and over the next eight years Hahnemann enjoyed a wonderful life and a busy practice. Melanie became his star pupil and shared the practice with him. Often, she would prescribe and he would supervise. Many of those seeking his advice were the *crème de la crème* of Parisian Society. Balzac and Pagannini were among his patients.

Hahnemann enjoyed a grand social life and often went to the concerts or the opera with Melanie and her father. He was often seen with Melanie walking to have ice cream at a local cafe.

On July 2, 1843, Hahnemann died after a brief illness. He was embalmed, and Melanie lay next to him for almost a week. His body was then placed in the small vault at Montmartre where she had buried both Gohier and Guillaume Lethière. The aftermath was not pleasant, with much acrimony between the Hahnemann daughters and Melanie.

Melanie continued to practice homœopathy, and on February 20, 1847, was brought to court for practicing without qualification. Melanie claimed she had the right to call herself a "doctor of Homœopathy" because she had been granted a diploma from Allentown, Pennsylvania in 1840. Dr. Croserio, who supervised her cases, spoke on her behalf, but she was found guilty, fined 100 francs, and told to cease practice.

It took a while before she began to practice again, very discreetly. The trial had taken a great toll on her. She was extremely sad and lonely, and mistrusting of many. She visited Hahnemann's grave and begged he send her a "friend." The "friend" arrived in the person of Baptiste Ambrose Marcelin Jobard, a publisher and inventor. She began to go out again, but refused Jobard when he proposed marriage although they remained friends and carried on a correspondence.

In 1843, shortly before Hahnemann's death, Melanie adopted Sophie, the five–year–old daughter of the musician Anton Böhrer, a patient and friend of Hahnemann. In 1857, Sophie married Karl Boenninghausen, the son of the noted homœopath. It was, to all extents, an arranged marriage. Melanie procured permission for Karl to practice medicine in Paris, and she began to practice again under Karl's supervision.

Karl and Sophie left Paris amid anti-German sentiment in 1871, and moved to Westphalia where Melanie would visit on occasion.

Melanie died alone in Paris and was buried in Montmartre next to Hahnemann.

In 1898 an international committee exhumed the body of Melanie and the body of Hahnemann from the Lethière vault and removed them to their present resting place in Père la Chaise cemetery.

Hahnemann's grave at Père la Chaise

Medallion inscribed:
"Melanie Hahnemann, Paintre,
Poet, & Homœopath, Paris,
1839, E. Woltrek"

In Melanie's words

Smart women who are gifted, at times find favour with men because they have become their toys, and men are fond of that which they own; even when these have become faithless, when they have committed adultery, men try to defend them, or pretend not to see. I say, at times, because whilst extending an interested protection, man never allows woman to overstep the barrier that his tyrannical spirit has erected in the intellectual field into which he was powerless to prevent her entering. Women do not need man's permission to become musicians, painters, poets, writers, mathematicians, astronomers, or scientists, but man has arrogated to himself the right to forbid them the practice of certain liberal professions, in which they might even excel, occasionally.

— Melanie Hahnemann, 1846

On learning homœopathy

Hahnemann associated me with his work; I served as interpreter and secretary when patients came to consult him, because he wrote everything; as his doctrine rests entirely upon the expression of symptoms it cannot be practiced without written notes. He made me learn his *Materia Medica Pura*, a dry and difficult study; but as I possess an extraordinarily good memory it remained so well and so completely impressed upon my mind that whilst the patient told his symptoms I pointed out, in German to the doctor, the remedies in which this symptom was to be found. In this way I considerably shortened for him the search that every homœopath however capable is obliged to make if he wishes to cure. Hahnemann had created the *Materia Medica* but he did not remember all the single details so well as I did. When he once had the few remedies which I indicated to him and from which he always made his selection, his work became so easy that he could see a larger number of patients without becoming tired out each time. It gave him inexpressible joy to disclose to me all the mysteries of his science of healing. I must have been very stupid if I had not made rapid progress with such a teacher. He entrusted me entirely with the treatment of the poor who came at four o'clock and frequently numbered more than a hundred. Hahnemann sometimes looked in at this consultation hour more for the sake of enjoying the benedictions which were showered upon me, and for the sake of seeing me distribute the alms which I gave to the working people, who in their illness lacked necessaries, than in order to solve medical difficulties which might impede my work; for the good results were constant. The large afflux of patients proved it. All that I did in those days passed for his work, and I was quite satisfied that it should be so, and when he said to me: "Really I could not do better myself, I wish the world could know what a good homœopath you are," (this was written by his own hand) I used to reply:

My life to you is as closely bound,
To your happiness devoted,
My place in your noble heart I found,
No other in this world I do desire.

— Melanie Hahnemann, 1846

Melanie Hahnemann, circa 1870

On doing provings

In addition to making me work as hard as I have just said, and sometimes I was dead tired, Hahnemann gave me medicines in order to experiment upon me as he had done upon himself; I resigned myself to these painful experiences, partly in order to work at the *Materia Medica* and partly in order to prevent Hahnemann having to experience himself the torments of the experiments; for his great age and his health required medicines which he had not taken hitherto. I now suffered as he had once suffered and an important work which is not yet finished will be the result of it. It will be of great use to homœopathic science by filling in the empty spaces in the provings which were already known, and by making known many new remedies to be experimented with; that is why I am still obliged to see patients and the reason which makes me desire to keep in touch with them.

— Melanie Hahnemann, 1846

A glimpse of Hahnemann in Paris

"At the head of a long table sat a lady, dressed in the most recherché demi-toilette, with a gold pen in her hand, and piles of books and papers strewn around her. She might have been forty years old; but I am no judge of ages. Her form was finely rounded, and her face still fresh and handsome. Her brow was remarkably high, and the hair, thrown back from her temples, fell in long, light curls upon her shoulders. Her complexion was brilliantly clear, and her blue eyes had a deeply-thoughtful expression. She rose to receive me, and it was not until she resumed her seat that a shriveled, little, old man became visible. He was reclining in a sumptuous arm chair, with a black velvet skullcap on his head, and in his mouth a richly-enameled pipe, that reached almost to his knees. His face reminded me of a ruddy apple that had been withered by the frost; but the small, dark eyes, deeply set in his head, could scarcely have glittered with more brilliancy in his lusty youth. As I took the seat which Mrs. Hahnemann designated, he noticed me with a look rather than a bow, and removing the pipe from his mouth, deliberately sent a volume of smoke across the table— probably in token of greeting.

"Mrs. Hahnemann addressed me, and wrote down my answers to her numerous questions, but at the conclusion of the interview declined prescribing until the invalid made the effort to appear in person. Hahnemann sat puffing away as though his existence depended upon the amount of smoke with which he was surrounded, and apparently intent alone upon his pleasant occupation. But when I spoke of a long visit to Germany, he suddenly took the pipe from his mouth. 'Sprechen sie Deutsche?' were the first words he addressed to me.

"I had only to utter 'Ya wohl,' when a species of Promethean fire seemed to shoot through the veins of the smoking automaton; he laid down his pipe and commenced an animated conversation in his own language.

"He spoke of Germany and her institutions with enthusiasm; he asked me many questions concerning America, and expressed his admiration of the few Americans with whom he was acquainted. As soon as politeness permitted, I led back the subject to the point from which we originally started— Mr. Mowatt's illness in Germany. At the first medical question, the pipe returned to its former position, the expanded countenance shriveled up again, the distended muscles relaxed, the erect form sank back into a withered heap, and was quickly enveloped in smoke— he was the wearied–out old man again."

Autobiography of an Actress by Anna Ogden Mowatt Ritchie. (1854)

Hahnemann's lost son:
The strange case of Friedrich Hahnemann

Friedrich Hahnemann was born November 30, 1786. In 1812 he received his medical degree from Leipzig. Says Dudgeon: "He contracted a matrimonial alliance with a widow… but according to what I have heard, was not well qualified to make his married life happy. This marriage gave great offense to his father, and led to an estrangement between them which was never removed."

He suffered rickets as a child which left him high-chested and with a spinal curvature. He suffered persecution of the medical community, and left his wife and became a wanderer. He wrote to his parents once in 1818 from Holland. A letter from London in 1819 was so bizarre in appearance that Hahnemann said, "My poor son is certainly insane." It is reported Friedrich spoke English, Latin, Greek, German, French, and Italian, and had a passing knowledge of Arabic. He was a fair musician, playing the guitar and piano.

He was reported in Dublin, Ireland in 1823 and described as humpbacked and eccentric in dress, manner, and habits.

In 1851, Frederick Humphreys reported that when he went to practice in upstate New York in 1841 he found someone had already practiced homœopathy there, in Ludlowville in 1828. The practitioner had a German accent and a hunchback appearance. His age was about 40 and his complexion very dark, almost copper colored. He was very quick and vivacious in his movements and conversation, and exceedingly irritable and passionate in his temperament and disposition. His dress was peculiar, exhibiting but little regard for the fashions of the day, his face unshaved, his beard long, and generally attired in an old morning-gown, giving him anything but an inviting exterior. He said he was the son of Hahnemann.

Humphreys describes the case of a little nine-year-old girl who had been treated by conventional physicians for some two years for dropsy:

"Upon an examination of her case Hahnemann decided that this dropsy was only symptomatic, and that the real affection was a disease of the heart; and that the former would disappear upon the cure of the latter. The application of his first powder entirely relieved her of a pain in her left side which had existed from before the appearance of the dropsy, and which all the medicines she had taken utterly failed to reach.

"He gave her very particular directions in reference to her diet, habits, etc. She was to have her own plate, spoon and knife, and on no account was she to use any other. She was not to sit or sleep with an aged person. Her diet was rigidly prescribed in quantity and quality; she was to smell of no flowers, or perfumes, and neither camphor nor acids were to be used about her, and if anyone smoking or chewing tobacco came into the room he was instantly to be expelled.

"The treatment appeared successful, as the child seemed to become healthier, but the swelling persisted. The child's mother was very anxious to see the 'bloat go down,' and to her continued entreaties Hahnemann only answered, 'It will do no good.' Finally he yielded to her solicitations, all the while protesting that no benefit would result. He gave a powder, and the old lady declares that while she yet looked the swollen edematous skin became corrugated and in a little time every vestige of it had disappeared.

"At the next visit the child was worse. He began earnestly to question the mother in a passionate manner if the minute details of all his directions had been severally complied with. The old lady, irritated by his manner beyond endurance, pettishly replied that she thought it was high time that something more was done besides attending to his whims. At the mention of this last word the doctor broke into a passion of ungovernable rage. His fury knew no bounds. 'Whim, whim!' he yelled; 'Hah! hah! you call my doctrine whim! Hah! Hah! Whim! Whim! I will not doctor her more, hah! hah! She will go to the fools and asses, hah! hah! She will die! Whim! Hah! Hah!' yelled he as he stalked back and forth with the language and manner of a lunatic. When excited, as was often the case, he had a passion for throwing in this word 'hah! hah!' between his sentences, and with such violence as to resemble more the barking of a small dog than the voice of a human being.

"Finally unable longer to contain himself he seized his hat and rushed from the house into darkness and storm, repeating his 'hah, hah' and 'whim, whim' until the sound was lost in the distance; he made his way to a neighboring house where he hired a person to convey him to the village, some miles distant, that night amid the rain and darkness."

The mother instituted a suit against him to reclaim her money, and Hahnemann boarded a boat, never to be seen again.

Sometime in 1832–33 when the cholera epidemic was raging in the midwest, a strange individual came from the lead mines at Galena, Missouri. He was dark-complexioned, a hunchback, and attired in long-flowing robes. He cured several hundred people with medicine he gave them from a small vial. It was the last he was seen. His fate is unknown.

When Humphreys described this person to Hering, he was told that it was Hahnemann's long lost son.

Hahnemann's pupils

While teaching at Leipzig, Hahnemann formed his Prover's Union— a group of students who would be his "inner circle." The group consisted of Gross, Stapf, Hornburg, Franz, Wislicensus, Teuthorn, Hermann, Rückert, Langhammer, and Hartmann.

Gustav Wilhelm Gross, MD
September 6, 1794 — September 18, 1847

Gross earned his medical degree in 1817, shortly before meeting Hahnemann. Hartmann says of him:

"When I first saw him at Hahnemann's house, I took him for a patient who wished to submit himself to homœopathic treatment, since his whole outer man, his yellowish-gray complexion, his bloated countenance, his backwardness in conversation were all expressive of a diseased condition. As he left the room, however, before I did, I learned from Hahnemann that Gross had engaged in homœopathy with zeal, and that he bade fair to be one of his best pupils; he earnestly recommended me to seek his intimacy, and I never had occasion to regret having followed his advice. It was necessary entirely to disregard his exterior, for by this he gained the affections of none, and consider only the inner man, the very kernel itself, for there one would soon find his benevolent and warm disposition… Gross was the most skilled prover of us all, and the symptoms observed by him have a great practical value." He was a prover of 28 remedies, including *Chamomilla*.

Rapou says:

"Gross is a man of many parts. I entered his dwelling and introduced myself to a man, bilious, jaundiced, of a hypochondriacal manner, who immediately penetrated to the purpose of my visit; he said to me in a tone but little affable: 'Monsieur, you ask without delay that which you wish to know because I have only about twenty minutes to give you.' Twenty minutes to a confrere who had come three hundred leagues to visit him."

Rummel recounts, "…his greenish-gray color of his somewhat puffed up cheeks, then already gave warning of the unseen enemy which was to end his life."

Gross introduced the horse–man, Julius Jenichen, to

homœopathy, and encouraged Jenichen to manufacture high potencies. Gross was the first to introduce to homœopathy the mineral waters, writing about *Teplitz* and *Karlsbad* waters. He became estranged from Hahnemann when, after the death of one of Gross' children, Gross suggested that homœopathy could not cure everything.

In 1845 the liver condition from which he suffered "increased to a frightful extent, and so altered his appearance that he looked like an old man of eighty." On September 16, 1847 he said, "I now have no more hope for on earth, the account is closed, my path now tends upward." He died in his sleep two days later.

Johann Ernst Stapf, MD
September 9, 1788 — July 11, 1860

In 1811, Stapf was the first to embrace the principles of Hahnemann. He was converted to homœopathy after reading the *Organon*, soon after its publication in 1810. Hahnemann referred to him as "my brightest and best." Stapf was a prover of 32 medicines. In his later years he employed only olfaction of the higher dilutions to administer the remedies.

Lorbacher says:

"Endowed with brilliant talents, a wealth of knowledge, and personal amiability, he was the active and vivifying element in the small circle, for which his peculiar and somewhat mercurial vivacity and his sparkling wit eminently qualified him. That both the above named qualifications remained to him in a high degree in advanced life I had an opportunity of becoming personally convinced during a visit I paid him at Naumburg. The hours I passed in his company are among the pleasantest recollection of my life."

Stapf, in 1822, started the first homœopathic journal in the world, *Archiv für die homöopathische Heilkunst*, and remained editor until 1839.

In 1835 he was called to England to prescribe for the Queen.

When the monument to Hahnemann was unveiled in Leipzig in 1851, Boenninghausen led him, as Hahnemann's oldest student, in placing the first wreath at the monument.

Homœopathy Comes to the USA

The beginnings in New York
The Germans in Pennsylvania
The arrival of Hering
The first school
The first wave
The first repertories

The beginnings in New York

Hans Burch Gram, MD
July 13, 1787 — February 26, 1840

The story is told that when Gram was in Copenhagen he was present when a full grown lion at a zoo attacked its keeper and attempted to escape from the cage. Gram, armed with a large iron fork, "sprang toward the animal, placed his hand on the lion's shoulder holding the instrument pointed at his mouth and fixed his eyes firmly on those of the beast, maintaining an unshaken look of commanding firmness; their eyes were thus engaged for a few moments when the lion cowed before the look of intense bravery and sovereignty which Gram gave him, turned meekly away and walked into the cage. Dr. W. says Gram was afraid of nothing earthly except doing wrong."

—Bradford, Pioneers *pg. 299*

Hans Burch Gram was born in Boston, the son of a Danish sea captain who had settled in Boston after marrying the daughter of the proprietor of the boarding house where he was staying.

The elder Gram died just before he was to leave for Copenhagen to acquire his father's estate. Young Hans Gram, at the age of 18, went to Copenhagen. The estate gave him enough money for a good education and he was enrolled in the Royal Medical and Surgical Institute. After several years as a military surgeon, Gram settled into general practice. He was introduced to homœopathy in about 1823 by Dr. Lund, who had studied with Hahnemann. Gram returned to America in 1825, settling in New York City.

In 1825 he published a small pamphlet about homœopathy. Says Bradford, "Unfortunately, Gram's long disuse of the English language, comprising over twenty years of his residence in Denmark, gave his pamphlet so quaint a construction and style as to render it a very difficult task to read it intelligently." Although Hering said that he had never seen a copy of the tract and doubted the existence of it, Bill Kirtsos has a copy of it in his collection.

In 1828 Gram was elected a member of the New York Medical and Philosophical Society, and was elected president the following year.

"Broken in heart by the misfortunes and death of his only brother upon whom he lavished all the estate he brought back from Europe," Gram's health failed. He suffered a stroke in May, 1839, and died February 26, 1840.

He was buried at the St. Mark's Burial Grounds in Manhattan. In 1862, his remains were moved to the plot of John Gray in Greenwood Cemetery in Brooklyn, New York. According to Gray, "Gram was a Christian of the Swedenborgian faith."

Like many of the founding fathers of the United States, Gram was a Freemason, and, as such, was socially acquainted with many doctors, lawyers, and bankers.

While tutoring a businessman, Ferdinand Wilsey, in Masonic matters, Wilsey confided he'd been suffering from indigestion for a number of years, and his doctor couldn't help the condition. Gram cured him with homœopathy.

The Folger Manuscript

Dr. Gram met Dr. Robert Folger at a Masonic Lodge meeting on May 25, 1826. Bradford reports Dr. Folger introduced Gram to Ferdinand Wilsey so that Gram, "might instruct Wilsey in certain important Masonic points."

Folger was the first person to learn homœopathy from Gram, but never felt confident enough to practice it without Gram present. Folger went into business in 1828 and gave up practicing medicine.

A piece of this period is preserved in the *Folger Manuscript*. Written in a strange hieroglyphic-like cipher it has been known in Masonic circles for a number of years. On its first page it has the name of Dr. Hans B. Gram at the top and another name, crossed out, underneath. In the hand of Dr. Folger is the request that upon his death the book be given to Dr. Gram. If Dr. Gram was already deceased, the book should go to— and here the name is again removed.

In 1990 I received a call from Masonic historian S. Brent Morris who was working on a text of the *Folger Manuscript*. Discovering Gram was a homœopath, Morris found the National Center for Homœopathy, and was referred to me. Knowing the history surrounding Gram, I was immediately able to surmise the missing name was Ferdinand Wilsey. Brent Morris went back to his research. Another piece of history's puzzle had been solved.

It appears this manuscript was the very Masonic rite Gram was teaching Wilsey— and which had been transcribed by Folger. In a time of great internal turmoil within the Masonic Lodges, Folger was suspended from the Grand Lodge in New York in 1853. It is most likely that Wilsey spoke out against Folger at the time, resulting in his name being removed from the document.

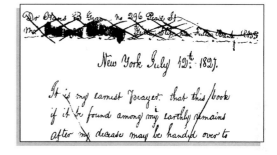

The Folger Manuscript. The first page heading at the top, a portion of the main text is below.

Ferdinand Wilsey's doctor, John Gray, curious about his patient's cure with this new medicine, came to see Gram and presented him with three more difficult cases. Gram cured them all. John Gray became his pupil, and the second homœopathic practitioner in the United States.

John Gray, MD
September 24, 1804 — June 6, 1882

Gray received his doctorate in medicine from the College of Physicians and Surgeons in New York. He began practicing homœopathy shortly after meeting Gram. Along with his brother-in-law, Dr. Amos Gerald Hull, he edited *The American Journal of Homœopathy*, the first homœopathic journal in America. He was also one of the American Institute of Homœopathy's founders in 1844. He died of senile gangrene at the age of 77.

Federal Vanderburgh, MD
May 11, 1788 — January 23, 1868

Another pupil of Gram was Federal Vanderburgh. Dr. Vanderburgh stood at more than six feet and his mere entrance into a sick room, it was said, dispelled many a dark and heavy cloud. At the age of 80, while travelling through Rhinebeck, New York, he was persuaded to stay the night with some friends. His hosts asked, "Well, what can we do to entertain you?" To which Vanderburgh replied, "Oh, show me some sick folks!"

Dr. Vanderburgh, the 17th of 19 children (his father married twice), taught himself Latin to get through medical training. He studied with Dr. Wright, an eminent physician in New Milford, Connecticut, then studied in New York, and obtained his medical license at the age of 19. Subject to attacks of pulmonary hemorrhage, he moved to dryer weather in Geneva in the western part of New York state. He returned to New York City about 1830, met Gram, and began homœopathic practice.

In an obituary, the *American Homeopathic Observer* said:

"Dr. Vanderburgh's mind was peculiar; his conclusions were so often the result of intuition... His advice was sought at his home, on the highway, in the railroad station, in the rail-car, on the steamer, at his dinner, at the hotel in the city, in bed and out of bed. He never turned a deaf ear to 'a case'... He was proverbial for punctuality, and woe betide the man who kept him waiting in the consultation room."

He was born during the adoption of the US Constitution, and a young lawyer suggest the infant be called Federal Constitution Vanderburgh, "but his mother objecting, the 'Constitution' was omitted."

Although the year of his birth is generally agreed upon, Dr. Vanderburgh told someone in 1865 that he was 84 years old— which would put his birth in 1781.

It was Vanderburgh who introduced homœopathy to the first doctors to use it in Indiana, Illinois, Connecticut, and Massachusetts.

Vanderburgh's conversion

"I was attending a gentleman on Pearl Street, one of whose toes were set at right angles with his foot by a contraction of the tendon. I wished him to have it divided, and he assented unwillingly. The next day Dr. Gray and myself met according to the agreement, and he discharged us both. Thirty days afterwards I met him walking down the street with his toe adjusted. I asked him how it was done, and he said Dr. Gram had given him some sugar pellets the size of a mustard seed, and thus straightened the toe. Having no prejudice to encounter I straightway introduced myself to Dr. Gram. I found him using a gigantic intellect with the simplicity of a child, entirely unconscious of its power. He seemed to be learned beyond the books and with his capacious mind was working out the problems and primal facts of science from his own standpoint. I saw at a glance that he dwarfed my proportions immeasurably, and that I had been creeping in a labyrinth while he was walking in the noonday sun."

Charles Julius Hempel, MD
September 5, 1811 — September 24, 1879

Born in Prussia, Hempel immigrated to the United States in 1835, arriving on his 24th birthday. He received his medical education at the New York University Medical College. Hempel's interested in homœopathy was through many of his social acquaintances. He worked for William Radde, a homœopathic bookseller, translating all of Hahnemann's and Jahr's writings into English and thus making them accessible to the English-speaking world. He was paid ten cents per page.

In 1896 Hahnemann's *Chronic Diseases* was re-translated by Professor Louis Tafel who suggested that Hempel's prior translation was "somewhat inexact" and had arbitrarily left out symptoms present in the original edition. After this, most of Hempel's homœopathic translations were questioned.

Hempel also translated into English all the works of Schiller that had not already been translated. As a follower of Swedenborg, Hempel wrote *The True Organization of the New Church*.

Hempel held the chair of materia medica and therapeutics at the Homœopathic Medical College of Pennsylvania for three years.

After the death of his father-in-law, Hempel moved to Grand Rapids, Michigan to tend to family business. He was appointed to the chair of homœopathy at University of Michigan at Ann Arbor, but machinations by Hering and Lippe rendered the appointment ineffectual and he never filled the post. He maintained a busy practice until his health failed and he became blind.

"Wherever he lived, his gentle manners and genial disposition, his large acquirements and ready discourse, attracted the association of the wise and the admiration of all." (obituary by Henry D. Paine, *American Institute of Homœopathy Transactions*, 1880, page 150)

"Hempel posed as a scholar in Materia Medica. He was extremely ignorant in general practice and scarcely knew the difference between two medicines. He did a lot of translating and brought out a huge volume on Materia Medica... When he was Professor of Materia Medica in Philadelphia, he wrote a New Organon in which he defended free love. There were but a limited number of copies printed, some twenty or forty, which later went for waste-paper.

"It was reported later when Hempel was in the West, that he had an affair with a divorced woman, which resulted in the birth of twins, that soon died after being taken to Hempel's home, with symptoms of Aconite poisoning. Not long after, the mother died of similar symptoms.

"Hempel opposed everything that came from Dr. Hering; even the Lachesis was condemned as being 'no remedy,' an assertion made by Hempel in his Materia Medica."

— C. Hering, May 6, 1869

Note: It should be understood that, at the time, "free love" was defined as the right of a woman to decide whether or not she wanted to become pregnant. —JW

The Germans in Pennsylvania

During the American Revolution, many German mercenaries recruited by the British, were given land in Pennsylvania by the revolutionary forces, in return for leaving British ranks. Soon other Germans joined their friends and relations. By the 1820s, the German presence in eastern Pennsylvania was firmly established by those seeking a better life in the United States.

William Wesselhoeft, MD
1794 — September 1, 1858

Wesselhoeft was born in Saxe-Weimar, Germany. As a child, he was tutored by the philosopher Goethe. He qualified for Doctor of Medicine in 1820. He worked for a year in Goethe's observatory, sketching cloud formations—as Goethe was attempting to forecast the weather by studying the formations of clouds.

While at University, William and his brother, Robert, became active in the movement to unite Germany under a single government. Both brothers were arrested as "political offenders" and sent to prison. William escaped after two months and attempted to go to Greece to aid a revolution there. Though he was thwarted in that attempt he spent time in Switzerland, and eventually fled to America.

Settling in Bath, Pennsylvania, a town with a large German population, and still corresponding with many German classmates from University, he learned of Hahnemann's method from his friend Stapf, who sent him an *Organon*, a *Materia Medica Pura*, and a box of remedies. Wesselhoeft met several other physicians in the area and they all began studying and using homœopathy.

When Hering arrived in the United States, he heard of Wesselhoeft's practice, sought him out, and together they established the Allentown Academy.

William's brother Robert was eventually released from prison. He became interested in the mineral baths and water cures at Carlsbad, Germany. Robert emigrated to Cambridge, Massachusetts, established a water-cure sanitarium and gymnasium and, in 1842, his brother William joined him.

I had been in search of a portrait of Wesselhoeft. Somehow, there isn't even a sketch of his likeness. While searching in the Hahnemann Collection, I found a silhouette of Wesselhoeft in Hering's family album. At the time, before the advent of photography, silhouettes were a popular way of recording someone's likeness. It is as close as we can get to seeing what Wesselhoeft looked like!

Pulsatilla

Henry Detwiller, MD
December 13, 1795 — April 21, 1887

Born in Switzerland, Detwiller migrated to the United States in 1817. On the voyage over he was the ship's doctor. He settled in Hellertown, Pennsylvania in 1818. He met Wesselhoeft, and in 1828 they began studying homœopathy. Shortly after Detwiller prescribed *Pulsatilla* to a woman patient, and became Pennsylvania's first homœopath.

In 1836 Detwiller visited Europe, and met Hahnemann in Paris. Never having been granted his degree because he was too young, he returned to his Alma Mater with his 1816 examinations, and was granted a formal diploma.

In September 1886 he attended the dedication of the new Hahnemann College: "A bright-eyed and rosy-faced, but bowed and gray-haired man, sat in one of the airy halls of the beautiful Hahnemann College and Hospital building last night, looking smilingly around him on hundreds of men and women. It was Dr. Henry Detwiller, of Easton, and the one man who in all that throng had spoken to the great apostle of homœopathy, Hahnemann himself."

Detwiller took an active interest in many business enterprises, and accumulated a large fortune. He was also president of the North Penn Iron Company.

Aged 92, being the oldest homœopathic physician in the United States, he fell while on his morning walk and struck his head on the pavement. Three days later he fell ill and was confined to his bed. He died two weeks later, having given "minute directions as to the treatment of his patients and superintended the preparation of the medicines" until the end.

Legality in 1835

Throughout the early 1800s, American medical practice was a veritable patchwork quilt of rival orthodoxies. Competing with conventional doctors were practitioners of botanical medicine, hydrotherapists, eclectic doctors, and, of course, homœopaths.

By 1835 it became so difficult to control the practice of "medicine," that the individual states began to drop any laws governing such practice. Botanical doctors and "root doctors" often had better successes than the conventional physician who was still "bleeding" and "purging" his patients.

Yet, of all the other medical practices of the time, homœopathy posed the greatest threat to the "regulars," because it not only had an integral and coherent doctrinal basis for its therapeutics, but it recruited most of its practitioners from their own ranks.

THE

AMERICAN BOTANIST,

AND

FAMILY PHYSICIAN:

IN WHICH
The medical virtues of the Mineral, Animal and Vegetable productions of North America are exhibited; together with their uses in the practice of Physic and Surgery; some of which are selected from Dr. STEARNS, and other Authors, but mostly original.

COMPREHENDING
A Treatise upon the principal disorders of the climate; together with directions for preparing, compounding, and applying proper medicines for their cure.

......Likewise......
A LARGE NUMBER OF INDIAN DISCOVERIES IN THE MEDICAL ART, NEVER BEFORE PUBLISHED.

By John Monroe.

COMPILED BY SILAS GASKILL.

WHEELOCK, (VT.) PUBLISHED BY JONATHAN MORRISON,

1824.
Danville—Eben'r. Eaton, Printer.

A typical botanical self-help book of the times. The author, a medical graduate of the University of Pennsylvania, learned of the healing properties of plants from several "Indian teachers."

A typical remedy kit of the era. This one contains 200 remedies in corked bottles. The bottles are about 4mm in diameter and 18mm long. The kit was made in about 1840 by the Leipzig Homœopathic Pharmacy.

The Three Fates

According to Greek legend, your fate— the thread of your life— was allotted by the gods. These gods were personified as three old women: Clotho, who held the thread; Lachesis, who spun the thread; and Atropos, who cut the thread.

The arrival of Hering

In 1833, Constantine Hering arrived in the United States and homœopathy found its charismatic and energetic leader.

The history of homœopathy is made of many people, all working on their part of the whole. But Constantine Hering stands as a Colossus. His contributions were inestimable. Any single one would have sufficed— the 104 provings done upon himself; his introduction of *Lachesis*, *Psorinum*, and *Glonoine*; his 10 volume *Guiding Symptoms*— but from a single man?

His son-in-law, Calvin B. Knerr, summed him up: "I began to suffer under the strain of trying to keep up with the man of iron constitution, who never seemed to tire, or to need time for rest and relaxation..."

He was a worthy successor to Hahnemann, who Hering said, "called me his 'John.'"

Dr. Henry N. Guernsey describes his first meeting when Hering visited the anatomy lab at the University of Pennsylvania: "His erect commanding figure, his eager and piercing eye, his massive brow, his well-shaped head, with long, black hair, and his whole appearance so clothed with dignity as to render him apparently unapproachable. At our first interview, I discovered my mistake; for he proved so genial, so friendly, and so communicative that we fraternized at once."

Constantine Hering, MD
January 1, 1800 — July 23, 1880

Hering was born at Oschatz, Saxony, on the first day of the new century. From an early age he had an extreme desire to investigate all things. Later in life he said: "At the age of nine or ten I had found the caterpillar Sphynx Atropos on my father's grapevine, which was the beginning of my studies in natural history. Later came Lachesis, and finally Clotho, the third of the three fates which are supposed to sway the lives of men; thus coming into my life in reverse order."

He entered the University of Leipzig, under the tutelage of the eminent surgeon Robbi.

Asked to write a paper exposing homœopathy, he decided

to repeat Hahnemann's experiment with *Cinchona*. He asked the druggist for *Cinchona*, "For the purpose of proving it, in order to more thoroughly attack the new folly." The druggist replied, "Let it alone, Hering. You are stepping on dangerous ground." To which Hering replied, "I have no fear of the truth."

Shortly after, in 1821, he received a dissecting wound in his right index finger. Amputation was offered, but he declined the option. A friend persuaded him to try a "ridiculously minute dose of *Arsenicum*. When the various symptoms of recovery from this terrible affliction began to pervade me, there vanished the last obstacles interposed between my eyes and the rising sun of the new healers. The finger is still my own… To Hahnemann who restored it was given the hand, even more the man, body and soul."

He wrote his first letter to Hahnemann in 1824, and Hahnemann replied (in part), "your active zeal for the beneficent art delights me… I would like to become better acquainted with you." Thus began a lifetime correspondence.

Hering graduated with his medical degree from the University of Wurzburg in 1826.

He worked, briefly, as an instructor in natural history. He then received a commission from the King of Saxony to serve as the botanist on a botanical and zoological expedition to Surinam.

In 1827 he sent his first letter to Stapf's *Archive*. The court physician, finding out about this, asked the King to send a letter to Hering, telling him to tend to his botanical duties and to let medical matters alone. Hering promptly resigned his appointment, and settled in to Surinam as a homœopathic physician.

A miniature portrait of Hering at about the time he left for Surinam. The original work is about the size pictured here. It is painted in oils on ivory.

Hering, on finding out about homœopathy

"My enthusiasm grew. I became a fanatic. I went about the country, visited inns, where I got up on tables and benches to harangue whoever might be present to listen to my enthusiastic speeches on homœopathy. I told the people that they were in the hands of cut-throats and murderers. Success came everywhere. I almost thought I could raise the dead."

It was in Surinam, in 1828, that Hering became interested in the use of snake poisons as remedies. He obtained a large surukuku, or bushmaster, from the natives, and milked the venom from it. He then triturated it with milk sugar to obtain a homœopathic potency, and did the first of many provings of the remedy *Lachesis*.

Drawing found in a book in the Moravian Library, titled, "Surinam, 1828"

Myth and Fact: The proving of *Lachesis*

The story is told in Clarke's *Materia Medica*, that Constantine Hering had the natives of the Upper Amazon bring him a surukuku snake. Says Clarke:

"At last one was brought in a bamboo box, and those who brought it immediately fled, and all his native servants with them.

"Hering stunned the snake with a blow on the head as the box opened, then, holding its head in a forked stick, he pressed its venom out of the poison bag upon sugar of milk.

"The effect of handling the virus and preparing the lower attenuations was to throw Hering into a fever with tossing delirium and mania — much to his wife's dismay.

"Towards morning he slept, and on waking his mind was clear. He drank a little water to moisten his throat, and the first question this indomitable prover asked was: 'What did I do and say ?' His wife remembered vividly enough.

"The symptoms were written down, and this was the first installment of the proving of *Lachesis*. The natives crept back one by one next day, and were astonished to find Hering and his wife alive."

It is certainly a good story. But…

A translation of Hering's own account of his first meeting with the famed bushmaster snake was published in *Simillimum*, winter, 1991. According to Hering's account, he was living in Paramaribo, Surinam, and had been looking for a good snake specimen. The natives brought him one that had been run over by a cart at the edge of town. Hering untied the snake and noticed it was still alive. He extracted some venom and began to triturate it with milk sugar. He accidentally ingested some, and the first proving began. It is worth recounting:

"A very peculiar sensation, almost like a scratching in the back of my throat. After an hour I felt a pain in my neck. It was like a pinching of a very circumscribed area at the right of my neck's base, as if on the side of my throat. This pain was not increased by swallowing, but it was by pressure. After a few hours, going by cart, in the fresh air, a feeling of anxiety as if a great tragedy was happening far away; it was like a painful oppressive feeling. I was excessively distressed during the next hour. Toward evening, a quite unaccustomed disposition to a jealousy akin almost to delirium, and as insane as it was unconquerable. During this state of somnolence, or half sleep, I developed a peculiar disposition to loquacity. I spoke a lot, I wanted to talk without sitting up; my words soon turn into an endless babble and I immediately become conscious that I am ranting. I take hold of myself then but soon I am starting to do the same thing again, and so on. Half the evening is spent this way…After having gone to bed very sleepy, I can't sleep; soon I am completely awake…Having fallen asleep very late, I wake up very early in the morning…"

No wife mentioned. No notetaking, save for Hering's own.

A drawing of Hering and *Lachesis* by Herman Faber, a friend of Hering's.

The snake

When Constantine Hering immigrated to the United States, he brought with him his entire biological and botanical collection from Surinam. The lot was donated to the Academy of Natural Sciences in Philadelphia, Pennsylvania. Hering's insect collection comprises a large part of the Academy's South American insect collection, and many of their South American plants are listed in the large leather bound catalogue index as donated by "Dr. Hering." The catalogue list two snakes from Dr. Hering: a male Lachesis mutus, number 7039 and a female, number 7040.

The male specimen is the one from which Hering procured the venom for the remedy. Both snakes are preserved whole in a container of alcohol. When fully extended, the male snake measured six feet, three inches. When alive, it was probably six inches longer. It was about six inches across, or as large around as the thigh of a young man. The fangs were a bit over one inch long. Hering wrote of "dispatching" the snake with a pistol after milking the venom. Snake number 7039 has a single bullet hole though the head.

"Die milde macht ist gross"-- "the gentle action is the powerful." Hering circa 1845.

In Paramaribo, Hering was living in a Moravian community. There he met a young German-American missionary, George Bute. Bute learned homœopathic medicine from Hering and returned to the United States to practice in Pennsylvania. In 1833 he persuaded Hering to move to Pennsylvania where "the land was like Germany, and the people were free."

On contemplating leaving Surinam, Hering said: "The wine must have a winter, and so must you after living six years in a winterless country!"

The Moravians were unhappy with Hering's leaving. "They brought out their lottery machine, provided with acorns cut in half, on which were printed numbers which referred to Bible verses. According to the reading of these was to depend the outcome. I submitted to the ruling of this game of chance, particularly because I had postponed my going for a whole year; mainly because I did not have the means. One is only paid at the beginning of the year for one's services. Consequently I agreed to suffer myself to be led by Bible verses. Amid the most solemn surroundings, I drew a number. I believe it was the number 113. As soon as the man saw the number he exclaimed, 'Oh! Doctor, we will have to let you go!' The verse read: 'Depart in peace, good and faithful servant, thou hast been faithful over little and shall be placed over much.' All of them consented to let me depart in peace. The women began at once to make shirts for me, and to get everything ready for the journey."

Hering's ship was bound for Salem, Massachusetts, but ran aground near Rhode Island and put in at Martha's Vineyard in January 1833. There was snow on the ground, the first Hering had seen in years. "I took it up," he said, "and was happy."

George Bute
May 27, 1792 — February 13, 1876

Bute emigrated from Germany to the United States in 1819. Settling in Pennsylvania, he married the daughter of a Moravian missionary, and received a special commission to do missionary work in Surinam in 1828.

The records at the Moravian Library in Bethlehem, Pennsylvania, has but a single reference to George Bute. There is mention that, "A young missionary, George Bute, and his wife," had arrived from Pennsylvania. It was felt that his knowledge of English would be a valuable asset to the community.

While in Surinam, Bute was cured of a fever by Hering and subsequently studied medicine under Hering. He returned to Philadelphia where, in 1833, Hering joined his practice.

Bute was the first prover of the indigenous American plants: *Sanguinaria, Chimaphila (umbellata* and *maculata), Rhus glabra, Rhus venenata*. A lady whom he had cured with *Daphne mezereum* gave him a twig of *Daphne indica* with a request that he prove it. He did.

The Moravians

The Moravian Church was founded in Bohemia in the mid-1400s, with the Bible as their one rule of faith and life. In 1620, during the Thirty Year War, all its churches, Bibles and hymn books were destroyed and its members driven into exile. The church reappeared in Germany in the early 1700s and was joined by various German Lutherans. In 1732 foreign missions were begun that have remained the predominant concern of the Moravian Church. The first Moravian mission in America was among slaves in the West Indies in 1732. The Moravians came to Pennsylvania in 1740, and settled the towns of Bethlehem, Nazareth, and Lititz. It was from these centers that missionaries went abroad. The full name found on the journals of the time was "The Society of Brethren for the Advancement of the Gospel Among the Heathen." The Moravian Colony was begun in Paramaribo, Surinam in the early 1820s.

One day Henry Williams presented me with a car-load of boxes he had in his basement. "Might be some stuff you'll find of interest," he said.

One of the items was a German 3rd Edition of the Organon. *Upon opening it I found this picture opposite the title page. It was signed "Geo. Bute." I spoke to Dr. Williams, and he has no idea of the trail this book took from Bute to him. The book is now in my private collection.*

The first school

Less than a year after Hering's arrival in Philadelphia, he was approached by Wesselhoeft, Detwiller, and Romig, who were representing the Homœopathic Society of Northampton and Counties Adjacent, with a proposal to establish a homœopathic school, with Hering as the President and principal instructor at a salary "equal to that of a first class Allentown clergyman."

The school was opened on Hahnemann's birthday— April 10, 1835. A stock company was formed, and a number of subscribers raised enough money to buy a tract of land in Allentown. On May 27, the cornerstone was laid for the world's first homœopathic school— The North American Academy of the Homœopathic Healing Art, commonly referred to as the "Allentown Academy." All the courses were taught in German, the language of the homœopathic literature of the time. Students who were not fluent in German were taught the language.

In the troublesome period ending with the 1837 financial crash, the banker with whom the school's endowment fund was deposited made a "bad failure," and the money was lost. Said Hering (page 63 of *Life of Hering*): "A dishonest local banker finally wrecked the institution. He died a miserable death."

The school continued for a few years, and ceased when Wesselhoeft moved to Boston in 1842. Many believe the school would have attracted more students were the courses not conducted in German. The school, through "The Academical Bookstore," published both Hahnemann's *Organon* and Jahr's *Manual* in the English language, but by that time the financial difficulties were overtaking the institution. Although the school only lasted six years, it trained the core group who became the first wave of American educators and practitioners.

The "Allentown Academy"

A list of the graduates of the Allentown Academy. A note appended to the list said: "This is Dr. Detwiller's writing."

The first wave

Adolph Lippe, MD
(Adolph Graf zur Lippe-Weissenfield)
May 11, 1812 — January 23, 1888

"Adolph Lippe was born on the family estate of 'See,' near Goerlitz, in Prussia. Dr. Lippe was educated at Berlin, and it was intended he should follow the legal professions but his natural taste and talents inclining him to medicine, he came to America in 1837. He studied at the homœopathic college at Allentown, and received his diploma on 27th of July, 1841. He first settled at Pottsville and practiced for a time there, but subsequently established himself at Carlisle, where he remained for six years. Having distinguished himself through his treatment of the epidemics prevalent in the Cumberland Valley, he came to Philadelphia, beginning then his brilliant career in this city as a homœopathic practitioner and teacher. Dr. Lippe was remarkably successful in the practice of the healing art, seeming to be peculiarly fitted by nature for his profession. Indeed, it has fallen to the lot of a few physicians to practice medicine so successfully as Dr. Lippe. His many wonderful cures during a practice of forty-six years have won for him a grand reputation, besides giving relief and comfort to hundreds whom less skilled physicians had abandoned in despair.

"From 1863 to 1868, Dr. Lippe filled the chair of materia medica in the old Homœopathic Medical College of Pennsylvania, which his rare knowledge of materia medica enabled him to do with peculiar success.

"He was the prime mover in establishing several homœopathic journals. Among them may be mentioned the late *Organon,* the *Hahnemannian Monthly,* and this journal [*the Homœopathic Physician*]. Even to mention by title his numerous papers would require almost a volume, so unceasing were his labors.

In his style he was positive, even to being dogmatic; the reason for this is readily found, it being due to the wonderful success he had for a lifetime, in curing, or at least relieving, all manner of sickness by a strict adherence to the Law of Similars. Therefore, to doubt its efficacy in any case of disease was, in his eyes, almost a crime. And few would be more tolerant who had his unique experience.

"On January 1st, 1885, Dr. Lippe lost his oldest son, Dr. Constantine Lippe; having two weeks previously (December, 1884) lost his only daughter. He never recovered from the severe shock of this double bereavement.

[Constantine Lippe died of pneumonia resulting from wounds he received while serving in the Civil War some 20 years earlier. He was 45.— JW]

"Having exposed himself during the past few days of raw, inclement weather, a bad cold was contracted which speedily developed into a severe case of typhoid pneumonia, which medicines were powerless to check. From the first initial chill to within a few moments of death, Dr. Lippe retained consciousness and never seemed to have any hope of recovery. He said just a few hours before he died: 'The medicines do no good. They only palliate.' And so it seemed. During the last two days Dr. Lippe, though so ill, was all the time throwing out hints for the treatment of his case. For instance, he would say this symptom indicates, *Nux mosch* or this one *Natrum mur*; and so he would go through a list of remedies, pointing out with such rare skill their characteristics. But all without avail. Taken sick at 3 a.m. Saturday morning, he died Monday, January 23rd at 9:45 a.m."

—Excerpt from the obituary in *The Homœopathic Physician*

Sprechen sie Deutsch?

We forget most of the original homœopaths spoke English as a second language— with a very heavy German accent. We see this from Tyler's Drug Pictures:

"Old Wesselhoeft thought he had Lippe at a disadvantage. He said, 'Dr. Lippe, I have a woman patient who got this peculiar symptom: She felt as though she were walking around on the ends of the bones of her legs and didn't have any feet, as though the feet were gone. What remedy did I give her?'

"Lippe said, 'You gave her der Chamomilla, by Gott!' "

Charles Neidhard, MD
April 19, 1809 — April 17, 1895

Born in Germany, Neidhard came to the United States upon the insistence of his friend, General Layfayette. He studied medicine at the University of Pennsylvania.

Neidhard became interested in homœopathy after becoming ill and being treated by Wesselhoeft. Neidhard graduated from Allentown in 1837. He was appointed Professor of Clinical Medicine at the Homœopathic College of Pennsylvania, holding the post for three years. Neidhard co-edited with Hering the *Philadelphia Journal of Homœopathy*, and was a founding member of the American Institute of Homœopathy. He was one of the first provers of *Eupatorium perfoliatum*.

C. Neidhard

Dr. Wilhelm Sturm.

Joseph Hypolyte Pulte, MD
October 6, 1811 — February 14, 1884

Born in Germany, Pulte completed his medical studies at the University of Marburg. He accompanied his older brother to America in 1834. Heading for St. Louis, he stopped in Northampton, Pennsylvania to visit friends, and met Dr. Wesselhoeft. He studied homœopathy under Wesselhoeft, and worked with Hering in organizing the Allentown Academy.

In 1840 he again headed for St. Louis, and stopped in Cincinnati, Ohio. A fellow traveler was skeptical of the claims of homœopathy, so Pulte set up a small clinic as proof. The news of his successful cures spread through the community, and within six weeks of his arrival he was in full practice, the second homœopath to establish a practice in Cincinnati, Ohio. The first was Wilhelm Sturm, a pupil of Hahnemann, who had settled there in 1839.

In 1850, Pulte published *Pulte's Domestic Practice*, a self-care manual which, by 1892, had been translated into five languages and had more than 100,000 copies in circulation. He filled the chair of clinical medicine and homœopathy at the Cleveland Homœopathic College. He became wealthy enough to endow The Pulte College in Cincinnati, which opened in 1872 and, in 1911, merged with the Cleveland Homœopathic College.

Pulte proposed a plan for a "round the world" telegraph in 1848, but could not get governments interested in the idea. Pulte was recommended as Ambassador to Austria by President Andrew Johnson, but did not assume the position.

It is told that when a distinguished Greek visitor came to Cincinnati, Pulte was the only person able to converse with him in his native language.

When Pulte began practicing in Cincinnati, many people were so angered by a homœopath being in town that they pelted his house with eggs and drove logs through his carriage wheels. He was becoming discouraged enough to think of leaving. His wife said, "Joseph, do you believe in the truth of homœopathy?" He replied in the affirmative. "Then," she said, "you will stay in Cincinnati."

Shortly after, when the cholera epidemic swept through, Pulte was able to boast of not having lost a single patient, and he was accepted into the community. In the epidemic of 1849, people crowded to his door and stood in the street because the waiting room was full.

The first repertories:
Jahr and Boenninghausen

When one has pages and pages of proving symptoms, one needs an index. In 1834, Hahnemann wrote, "Only the Dictionary [repertory] would give the seeker more complete information." Hahnemann had tried to construct a repertory and, of the effort said, "My repertory was an alphabetical record which could only be of great service in looking up the necessary symptoms of medicine, if very complete and this perfection is not yet to be found in mine. It is therefore not to be regretted that it remains unpublished."

It fell to Jahr and Boenninghausen to construct the first usable repertories— the index to the symptoms of the materia medica.

George Heinrich Gottlieb Jahr
January 30, 1800 — July 11, 1875

Born and raised in Neudietendorf, Saxony, Jahr became interested in homœopathy, after Julius Aegidi, a pupil of Hahnemann's who was practicing in Dusseldorf, cleared Jahr of a recurrent illness. Aegidi suggested Jahr study medicine, and introduced him to Hahnemann. Jahr worked with Hahnemann from about 1825, helping to arrange the pathogenesis of symptoms in Hahnemann's *Materia Medica Pura*, and later doing the same with *The Chronic Diseases*.

In 1834 Jahr produced his *Manual* which served as the best repertorial index to Hahnemann's works for a good many years. It was translated into English from German by Hering in 1838.

Through book sales Jahr financed his way through medical school at the University of Bonn, although he never completed his exams. He followed Hahnemann to Paris in 1835, and the local authorities allowed him to practice medicine because he was "an approved medical author," an exception similar to that made for Hahnemann himself.

His literary output (over 250 works) was not confined to homœopathy; rather it included a wide range of subjects.

Jahr's wife wrote:

"How many times on learning that a work has been finished and sent to the printer have I pronounced the words 'at last' with a sigh of relief? At last, a little repose. I have said— a little life in common with family and friends— some readings, a little relaxation. But alas! I always found myself indulging in an illusion, a vain hope; the next day a new work— a new memoir— took its place upon his writing table, and absorbed all his time."

Jahr practiced in Paris until the Franco-German War of 1870 forced him to leave France. He settled in Belgium, but the Belgian government did not allow him to practice medicine because he did not possess a Belgian diploma. Prohibited from earning his living, he retired to his literary work, a broken man, and died soon after.

---

468   *5. Affections of the mind.*

Jocoseness, Croc. *Ign.* Lach. Men. Plat. Sulph. Tar.

Joyfulness (Fröhlichkeit), Cann. Carb. a. Croc. Men. Zinc. (comp. "hilarity".)

— in the evening or at noon, Zinc.

Joylessness (Freudelosigkeit, Unheiterkeit), *Anac.* Calc. c. Cham. Laur. *Nitr. ac.* Ol. *Phos.* Sabin. Sil. Sod. chl. (comp. "dejection".)

Irksomeness (Verdriesslichkeit), Aeth. Alum. Amm. c. Amm. m. Ant. s. Asar. Aur. Carb. a. Cinch. Cyc. *Evon. Grat.* Guaj. Hydr. Ind. Kram. Lach. *Led.* Mgn. m. *Mang.* Mar. Mez. Mur. ac. Oleand. *Phos. ac.* Puls. Rhm. Sabin. Samb. Sass. Scill. Sod. s. Stann. *Staph. Stront. Sulph. ac.* Thuy. Tong. Verb. Zinc. (comp. "fretfulness, ill humor &c.")

— in the evening, Mgn. c. Puls. *Zinc.*

— in the morning, Amm. c.

— in the open air, Aeth. Sabin.

Mania a potu, Ars. Hyosc. Nux v. *Op. Stram.*

Meditation (Nachdenklichkeit), Phell. *Thuy.*

Melancholy, Agn. Anac. *Ars.* Asar. *Aur.* Calc. c. *Caust.* Cocc. Cupr. *Hell.* Hyosc. Jod. Lyc. Phos. *Plumb.* Puls. Sec. Sel. *Sen.* Sep. Sil. Sod. chl. *Stram. Sulph.* Sulph. ac. Tab. Verat. (comp. "dejection, despair, grief, pensiveness, sadness".)

— religious, Lyc. Sulph.

Memory, acute, Cyc.

— loss of, Bry. Camph. Hyosc. Petr. Pot. c. Sil. Stram. Verat.

— weakness of, Acon. *Alum.* Anac. Aur. Berb. *Bov.* Calc. s. Carb. v. Caust. Colch. Con. Cyc. Dig. Guaj. Hell. Hydr. *Laur.* Mez. Myr. Oleand. Plumb. Sabin. *Sep.* Sil. *Sod. chl. Spig. Staph.* Sulph. Tox. Verb. *Viol. od.* Zinc.

— — sudden and periodical. Carb. v.

A page from G. H. G. Jahr's *Manual of Homœopathic Medicine.* This first edition was translated by Hering and published in 1836 by the Academical Bookstore, Allentown, Pennsylvania. Note that some of the rubrics have German translations.

Clemens Maria Franz Von Boenninghausen
March 12, 1785 — January 26, 1864

Next to Hahnemann, Boenninghausen is, perhaps, the brightest star in the homœopathic constellation. Born in Overssel, the Nederlands, Boenninghausen trained in law. He was appointed King's Auditor, and held the position until King Louis Napoleon of Holland resigned in 1810. He returned to his estate to devote himself to studying agriculture, and started corresponding with Germany's most prominent agriculturists.

When the Prussian Provinces of Rhineland and Westphalia were reorganized, he became President of the Provincial Court of Justice. He was subsequently appointed General Commissioner of Appraisements, a job which took him around the provinces. In 1824, he became the director of the Botanical Gardens at Münster.

In 1827 Boenninghausen contracted tuberculosis. When all hope of recovery was lost, he wrote farewell letters to his friends, one of whom was a physician named Weihe. Boenninghausen knew Weihe only as a botanist. He was unaware Weihe was a student of Hahnemann's and was the first homœopath in Westphalia. Weihe asked for more details of the case and mailed Boenninghausen a remedy. Within a few months Boenninghausen was considered cured.

Boenninghausen dove straight into homœopathy, soon practicing and converting physicians to this new method. Not having a medical degree, much of his work remained literary. On July 11, 1843, King Friedrich Wilhelm IV granted Boenninghausen the right to practice medicine in the province.

Of his seven sons, Karl and Friedrich became homœopaths. Karl married Melanie Hahnemann's adopted daughter Sophie, and most of Hahnemann's work (including the manuscript for the 6th edition of the *Organon*) passed into the Boenninghausen family.

Boenninghausen has been credited with developing the first homœopathic repertory, *The Repertory of the Anti-Psoric Remedies*, in 1832. He constantly communicated with Hahnemann from 1830 on.

Boenninghausen, through Gross, was introduced to high potencies and used, almost exclusively, the 200th prepared by Lehrmann.

Maria…I just met a man named Maria…
—Bruce Barwell

His literary work includes *Treatment of Intermittent Fevers, The Therapeutic Pocket Book*, and *The Treatment of Whooping Cough*. His massive *Characteristics* was finally translated into English by Cyrus Boger in 1905. However, the crowning literary work of his life was the *Aphorisms of Hippocrates, with the Glosses of a Homœopathist*, a "large octavo volume so full of learning and of sagacious observation as to have won enthusiastic commendation from the entire allopathic press." It was to be translated into English, but the disturbances caused by the American Civil War saw the project abandoned.

On January 23, 1864, Boenninghausen suffered a stroke that paralyzed his left side. Although he and his son Friedrich prescribed for the condition, Boenninghausen's lungs were not up to the task and he died three days later.

Carroll Dunham on Boenninghausen

Dr. Carroll Dunham often travelled from the United States to visit Boenninghausen. In the *American Homœopathic Review* of April, 1864, Dunham shares his memories of Boenninghausen:

"Although deeply learned in ancient and modern philosophy, his mind was essentially of a practical turn. Those subjects had most attractions for him which presented the problem of definite labor for definite results. The theories and speculations and system-making, which have charms for many homœopathists, seemed to Boenninghausen to have but a secondary importance.

"He perceived that the matter of prime necessity was such a study of the materia medica as should bring out into bold relief the characteristic peculiarities of each individual remedy, so that the practitioner might easily and surely single out that remedy which might be most similar in its symptoms to the disease under treatment. To such a study he devoted himself. The success of his practice is the measure of the success of these studies as well as an indication of Boenninghausen's sagacity in selecting this as the most important subject of study...

"*The Therapeutic Pocket Book* was translated into French and into English. But Boenninghausen pointed out to the writer the fact that the French translation was so carelessly made that the lists of remedies in several cases are placed under different headings from those under which they properly belong, thus making the work a false guide. This was done by Dr. Roth, the same who in his studies of materia medica is now making such charges of inaccuracy and carelessness against Hahnemann, and whom Dr. Hering has just convicted of grossly careless misquotation in his remarks upon *Sabadilla*. The English translation by Dr. Laurie has the same faults, having been translated from the 'improved French' translation, and not from the original German. In America, two translations have appeared by Dr. Hempel and Dr. Okie.

"It was his custom to record every case for which he prescribed. In 1862, he informed the writer that he had just begun the 112th volume of his 'Clinical Record.' Of these 112 volumes, it is safe to estimate that at least 80 contain records of cases treated almost exclusively with high potencies. A rich mine of experience for the conscientious and intelligent explorer!

"Boenninghausen adhered closely to Hahnemann's practical rules in prescribing. He was careful never to repeat the remedy until the effects of the dose already given were exhausted. He thoroughly disapproved of alternation of remedies.

"On resigning the offices which he held under the Prussian Government, Boenninghausen removed to Münster, where he built the house in which he lived when the writer visited him and in which he died. In this house it was his custom to receive patients daily from 9 a.m. to 2 p.m. From 2 to 5 p.m., he spent in diversion, generally in walking about the suburbs, or along the beautiful promenade which surrounds the city, occupying the site of the former ramparts, or else in the Botanical Garden attached to the Ducal Residence. It was in these hours of relaxation that his genial social qualities, his wit and his full and varied knowledge were seen to best advantage. The writer will

A lost treasure

Dr. Henry N. Guernsey wrote of having in his possession a copy of the Repertory of Boenninghausen *that was given to him by Carroll Dunham. The repertory contained all the additions that Boenninghausen had made and which were hand copied into the book by Dunham.*

The present location of the book is unknown. It is believed to be lost.

ever remember how, in the course of one of these walks, Boenninghausen, having gently rallied him on some evidences of home sickness which he thought he had detected, gravely told him that he would take him to see a compatriot who resided in Münster. He accordingly led the way to the Botanical Garden, and there, with charming courtly ceremony, presented the writer to a stately tulip tree (*Liriodendron tulipifera*), which he said he had imported from America 40 years ago, and which he said he believed was the only immigrant from the United States in Westphalia."

Clemens Maria Franz Von Boenninghausen

Homœopathy: 1835 –1870

The detractors (part 1)
The founding of the AIH
The backlash
The college in Philadelphia
The politics of the time

A
AB
ABR
ABRA
ABRAC
ABRACA
ABRACAD
ABRACADA
ABRACADAB
ABRACADABR
ABRACADABRA

An "abracadabra"

The Fronticepiece of William Leo-Wolf's book

The detractors

The tiny pills of the homœopath were ridiculed by the "regulars" of the medical profession, who viewed them as no better than an "abracadabra"— an incantation, written in a triangular pattern, worn as an amulet to ward off illness.

Books and articles against homœopathy appeared as soon as Hahnemann wrote his first article on the possible use of the principle of similars in medicine.

Bradford's *Bibliography* of 1892 lists 70 known works criticizing homœopathy. *The Abracadabra of Homœopathy* written by William Leo-Wolf in 1835, was supposed to entirely overthrow the homœopathic system. Other books critical of homœopathy were Thomas Blatchford's 1842 *The Homœopathic System: a Germanic Reverie of Transcendental Nonsense*, David Reese's 1838 *Humbugs of New York*, and Oliver Wendell Holmes's 1842 *Homœopathy and Kindred Delusions*.

In 1850, Worthington Hooker, MD, in his book, *Lessons from the History of Medical Delusions*, says: "He [the homœopath] attributes palpable results to doses of medicine which are so small that they cannot produce any perceptible effect except by miracle." He proceeds to quote from the proving of *Calcarea carbonica* ("tickling sensation at the outer edge of the palm of the left hand") and says, "The most wild and fertile imagination, set loose from reason, to roam where it listeth, could not collect a more incongruous and ridiculous farrago, than is found in Jahr's *Manual* under the guise of scientific observations of the effect of remedies."

But via its successes (for example, during the 1832 cholera epidemic), homœopathy spread throughout the United States.

The founding of the American Institute of Homœopathy

In 1844, in response to the lack of national medical standards, a group of homœopaths from New York, Boston, and Philadelphia, formed the American Institute of Homœopathy, the first national medical organization. Their aim, as can be seen from the minutes of the session reproduced below, was to develop a sound program of medical education and practice.

MINUTES OF THE SESSIONS OF 1844 AND 1845.

"THE NEW YORK HOMŒOPATHIC PHYSICIANS' SOCIETY," in July, 1843, in view of the benefit to be derived from a mutual cultivation of the art by the various members of our school throughout the United States, appointed a committee to draft and send suitable invitations to them. They performed the duty assigned them, and on the 10th of April, 1844, a convention of the practitioners of Homœopathy of the United States, took place in the city of New York, at the Lyceum of Natural History, upon the anniversary of the birth of the illustrious Hahnemann.

Dr. CONSTANTINE HERING, of Philadelphia, was elected President; Dr. JOSIAH F. FLAGG, of Boston, Dr. WILLIAM CHANNING, of New York, Vice Presidents, and HENRY G. DUNNEL, Secretary.

A preamble and resolutions in these words were adopted, viz:

Whereas, a majority of the allœopathic physicians continue to deride and oppose the contributions to the materia medica that have been made by the Homœopathic School; and whereas, the state of the materia medica in both schools is such as imperatively to demand a more satisfactory arrangement and greater purity of observation, which can only be obtained by associate action on the part of those who seek diligently for truth alone; and, inasmuch as the state of the public information respecting the principles and practice of Homœopathy is so defective as to make it easy for mere pretenders to this very difficult branch of the healing art to acquire credit as proficients in the same;

Therefore, Resolved, That it is deemed expedient to establish a society entitled "The American Institute of Homœopathy:" and the following are declared to be the essential purposes of said Institute:

1st. The reformation and augmentation of the Materia Medica.

2d. The restraining of Physicians from pretending to be competent to practice Homœopathy who have not studied it in a careful and skilful manner.

The following physicians were the founding members present at the first meeting of the American Institute of Homœopathy in New York, April 10, 1844:
From Philadelphia, Pennsylvania:
Hering, Williamson, Neidhard, Jeanes, Pulte, Kitchen, Green, Lingen
From New York City:
Channing, Gray, Kirby, Ball, Wilson, Dunnel, A. G. Hull, Cook
From Boston, Massachusetts:
Flagg, Wilde, Luther Clark, Francis Clark, W. Wesselhoeft
From Maine:
Eliphalet Clark, John Merrill, Albus Rea. Abraham Okie came from Rhode Island, Gustavus Taft from Connecticut; Gosewisch from Delaware; Felix McManus and Adolph Haynel from Maryland; John Piper from Washington, DC; John Taylor, from Rochester, New York; H. Hull Cator from Syracuse, New York; Erastus Humphreys, from Utica, New York; Williams from Geneva, New York; Robinson from Auburn, New York; H. D. Paine, from Newburgh, New York; Fairchild from New Jersey; and Mose, Spalding, and Pilkin (places not recorded).

The backlash

Three years later, in 1847, the American Medical Association was formed by the "regulars," partially in reaction to the spread of homœopathy. Their charter contained a clause preventing any member from consulting with any practitioner "whose practice is based on an exclusive dogma, to the rejection of the accumulated experience of the profession."

This clause, still seen in medical society applications even in the 1920s, prevented allopathic doctors, at the risk of expulsion from the society, from talking to homœopaths.

Phelan, Richard A.
Autograph Signature *Richard A. Phelan*

APPLICATION FOR MEMBERSHIP.

To the St. Louis Medical Society, 3525 Pine Street.

I hereby make application for........................membership in the ST. LOUIS MEDICAL SOCIETY. If accepted as a member, I agree to support its Constitution and By-Laws and the Principles of Ethics of the American Medical Association, and will not in any way profess adherence or give my support to any exclusive dogma or school. (Annual dues must accompany this application.)

Date *May 20* 19 *18* Signed *Richard. A. Phelan.*
(Name in full)

Residence *6070 Maple* || Office *6070 Maple*

Telephone—Bell *Cd. 4469* Kin *Del 1302* || Telephone—Bell *Cd. 4469* Kin *Del 1302*

Sponsor: *Dr. Geo Kilton* || Sponsor: *Frederick G. Baldwin*

1st Publication *5-30-18* 2nd Publication *6-6-18* 3rd Publication *6-13-18*

Referred to Membership Committee........................ Report of Membership Committee........

Elected.................... || Reinstated.................... || By Transfer from........................

Termination of Membership *Elected 2-12-19*

While searching for traces of Richard Phelan, the physician who introduced homœopathy to James Tyler Kent, I found this application for membership in the records of the St. Louis (Missouri) Medical Society. It is the application of Richard Phelan, the son of the homœopath who taught Kent. The exclusion clause is still in evidence.

The son became an allopath. He died in 1920— a year after this application was made.

The war between the "new school" and the "regulars."

By the mid–1850s all state medical societies except the Massachusetts Medical Society had purged their homœopathic members. In 1856, the American Medical Association resolved that homœopathic works should henceforth no longer be discussed or reviewed in allopathic periodicals. After this time there was no formal communication whatever between the two branches of the profession; allopaths were forbidden to consult with homœopathic physicians or to patronize their pharmacies.

This ban saw several peculiar incidents. In 1856 the students of an allopathic medical college boycotted the graduation ceremonies on hearing they would be addressed by a minister known as a homœopathic sympathizer. In 1867, the Medical Society of Westchester County, New York, expelled a member for purchasing sugar of milk at a homœopathic pharmacy. Who would use sugar of milk but a homœopath? In 1878 a physician was expelled from a local medical society in Connecticut for consulting with a homœopath— his wife.

In Alabama the situation became completely irrational. The (allopathic) state society was granted the right in 1877 to examine all candidates and issue practice licenses. But after certifying homœopathic and eclectic physicians, the allopaths then refused to consult with them on the grounds of their alleged professional incompetence.

The medical schools were the profession's main bastion against homœopathy and were thus governed by especially strict rules. Some announced homœopathically–inclined students would not be accepted for admission; others occasionally denied homœopathic students the right to take the final examinations. When allopathic graduates later adopted homœopathy, they were disowned by their alma maters. A Michigan graduate asked his former (allopathic) professor, "You certified me as a doctor of medicine, and now you call me a quack?" The professor avoided a direct reply. Eventually the regulars attempted to cope with this problem by requiring the graduates of their schools to swear never to take up homœopathy, on pain of forfeiting the degree.

— condensed from *Divided Legacy* by Harris L. Coulter

"Have nothing at all to do with [quacks] professionally or socially, whatever be their name— whether followers of the more crude systems which have sprung up amongst ourselves, or the dreamy stupid impostures of Europe… Do not argue and debate with homœopathic patients; let them distinctly understand that you cannot alternate with the charlatan as their physician."

—Peninsular and Independent Medical Journal, *1860*

"When chance brings you into contact with a genuine homœopathist… ignore him professionally and never allow yourself to fraternize with him in the management of a case… "

— *Cathell*, The Physician Himself, *1882*

"Eclectic Physician"

The "Eclectic School" was founded in principle by Wooster Beach (1794-1868) and several other physicians who were attempting to blend conventional therapeutics of the time with the botanical therapeutics of the "root doctors." The movement gained its first school in Cincinnati, Ohio in 1843. By the mid-1860s the movement was unraveling when it was taken over by John M. Scudder (1829-1924), and brought from its doldrums to a new level of energy by Scudder's thinking— a blend of botanical medicine, homœopathy, and allopathy, into a vitalistic system that eventually supported a number of teaching institutions in several states.

THE FOVNDERS
1848

The college in Philadelphia

For seven years after the collapse of the Allentown Academy, there was no formal homœopathic education in the United States. In 1848, in Philadelphia, Constantine Hering, Jacob Jeanes, and Walter Williamson met to form a new school. The new Homœopathic Medical College of Pennsylvania was one of almost two dozen homœopathic medical colleges to be formed within the next few years. The faculty for this new school were recruited by Hering from among the regulars who had taken up homœopathic practice.

Jacob Jeanes, MD
October 4, 1800 — December 18, 1877

Raised a "Philadelphia Quaker," Jeanes received his Medical Degree from the University of Pennsylvania in 1823. He became attracted to homœopathy by seeing notices of it in journals. He learned German to be able to read the works of Hahnemann. He studied the system for 18 months, and became convinced of its efficacy. In 1838 he wrote the first original work on homœopathy in the English language. He was a founder of the American Institute of Homœopathy and a prover of many remedies, including *Sanguinaria*.

Said Hering: "We owe our knowledge of *Benzoic acid* chiefly to Jeanes."

"Jeanes was satisfied to get one good symptom from a proving on which he could prescribe. Guernsey admits that he got his idea of practicing by the keynote system from Jeanes... Jeanes had a medicine for almost every spot on the body! He classified headaches under the various regions assigned by phrenology."

—C. Hering

Walter Williamson, MD
January 4, 1811 — December 19, 1870

A direct descendant of Daniel Williamson, who came to America with William Penn in 1682, Walter Williamson graduated from the University of Pennsylvania in 1833. He began practicing homœopathy in 1836. In 1843 he wrote a treatise on the application of homœopathy to the diseases of women and children. He was a founder of the American Institute of Homœopathy in 1844, and the first prover of *Podophyllum pelatum*.

James Kitchen, MD
March 8, 1800 — August 19, 1894

Born in Philadelphia, Kitchen received his medical degree from the University of Pennsylvania in 1822. He was the Port Physician in Philadelphia from 1832 to 1836. He intended to go to New Orleans, but his father died and he had promised him that he would stay in Philadelphia. Having suffered chronic liver problems since his student days, he was cured by homœopathy, and began to study the system. In 1839 he started homœopathic practice. He translated Jahr's *Manual of Homœopathic Pharmacopoeia and Posology* in 1842.

He died at the age of 94. He never married, but was "Uncle Doctor" Kitchen to a large family of relations.

A. E. Small

Alvan E. Small, MD
March 4, 1811 — December 31, 1886

Born in Wales, Maine, Small received his medical education at the University of Pennsylvania. While reading some New Church (Swedenborg) literature, he was introduced to the principle of similia, and after a brief study, he took up homœopathic practice. Small occupied the chair of medical practice and jurisprudence at the newly–formed Homœopathic Medical College. He was followed to Philadelphia by his student, H. N. Guernsey.

In 1856 Small moved to Chicago where he became chair of theory and practice of medicine at the Hahnemann Medical College. He eventually became president of that institution, as well as the general manager of the Scamon Hospital.

He also wrote several domestic manuals.

Henry Newell Guernsey

Henry Newell Guernsey, MD
February 10, 1817 — June 27, 1885

Born in Rochester, Vermont, Guernsey studied medicine under Alvan Small, MD, and received his medical degree from New York University in 1842. He moved to Philadelphia in 1856. He became professor of obstetrics at the new Homœopathic Medical College and wrote the classic text, *The Application of the Principles and Practice of Homœopathy to Obstetrics and the Disorders Peculiar to Women and Young Children*, known as "Guernsey's Obstetrics." In his later years, Guernsey was renowned as a teacher of materia medica.

"He was an earnest, honest, and conscientious disciple of Hahnemann and was the reputed author of the 'keynote' method and the first public teacher of the 'single remedy' and the 'high potency'."

It is reported that Guernsey literally overworked himself. His health became impaired in 1879, and he sought relaxation in Europe, but still declined. He was diagnosed with tuberculosis and sank rapidly. During his illness many people tried to prescribe for him and he always gave the same answer: "I wish nothing but the simillimum in my case. As I have lived and practiced for others I will do by myself, for I know it is the right way… If I must die, I wish it recorded that I died true to my principles." The funeral services were held at the Church of the New Jerusalem (Swedenborg). Guernsey is buried in West Laurel Hill Cemetery in Philadelphia.

Plain Talks on Avoided Subjects

One book that would give insight into Guernsey and the times in which he lived would be his little tome *Plain Talks on Avoided Subjects*, published in 1882. Here are some samples of his advice:

"Causes which commonly produce sexual impressions on young children are, allowing them to repose playfully on their belly, to slide down banisters, to go too long without urinating, constipation or straining at stool, cutaneous affection, and worms… The sliding down banisters produces a titillation which is agreeable to the sexual organs. Children of both sexes will constantly repeat this act until they learn to become inveterate masturbators, even at a very early age."

"It should clearly be explained to him [the boy] that true chastity requires the shunning of all indecency and foul language…it should be firmly impressed upon his mind that lascivious actions are a drain upon his whole system and weaken the powers which the Lord has given him to be employed only in the married state."

"When night comes and they [children] go to bed, let them learn to go to sleep at once; no play then— they may be read to sleep but no romping or playing. No strange children should be allowed to sleep with yours; make them occupy separate rooms or at least separate beds; be sure that the sleeping places of your children are sacred to them alone."

[To young women] "Study all men long and carefully, keeping them meanwhile at a respectful distance; never allow one to sit near with his arm about your waist or to hold your hand in his; never allow him to kiss you— the vilest of loathsome diseases may be communicated by a kiss viz: syphilis."

"Young women have not, as a rule, any sexual propensity, or amorous thoughts or feelings. If they have been properly educated and cared for, they are, before marriage, perfect strangers to any such sensations; and yet any young lady who falls, does so by her own hand and she has no one else to blame for it."

An older, less intense, Henry Newell Guernsey.

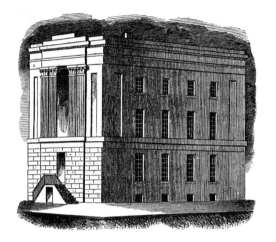

School politics:
The split and the merge

In 1867, the Homœopathic Medical College of Pennsylvania became a corporation controlled by whoever owned the stock's majority. The person who had most of the stock at the time was Dr. Adolph Lippe, and he took over the College.

One of his first moves was to disband the department of pathology, saying that it was unnecessary to know anything other than the law of similars. Dr. Raue, a close friend of Hering, was in charge of pathology, and with Raue's departure, Hering withdrew his support for the school.

Hering found an unused school charter belonging to the Washington Medical College, purchased it, changed the name of the school to the Hahnemann Medical College, and opened for business.

Between 1867 and 1869 there were two homœopathic colleges in Philadelphia.

In 1869, Dr. H. N. Guernsey bought Lippe's stock, and then transferred the stock to Hering. Lippe resigned his position at the school and the two schools merged into the Hahnemann Medical College.

Lippe continued to write and work in Philadelphia, but was no longer connected with the school. The most stalwart of the Hahnemannian homœopaths flocked around him. He formed the "Lippe Club" with E. J. Lee and Walter James, and they met regularly to discuss homœopathy. The minutes of these meetings are in the Hahnemann Collection at the Allegheny University of Health Sciences, Philadelphia, Pennsylvania.

ABOVE LEFT: The second college building at 1105 Filbert Street in Philadelphia. The Homœopathic Medical College operated in this building from 1849 until 1884.
The Hahnemann Medical College operated for two years from rented rooms at 1307 Chestnut Street.
BELOW LEFT: The Hahnemann Medical College of Philadelphia occupied this building on the corner of Race and Broad from 1884.

The politics of the time

When the Republicans swept to Washington in the 1860 election, this new political party provided a new kind of progressive politics *and* its homœopathic doctors. The homœopaths were quick to take advantage of their new–found political visibility. One of the leaders in Washington was Tullio Verdi, the first homœopath appointed to the bureau of health in Washington, DC, and the physician to Secretary of State, William F. Seward. When Lincoln was assassinated, there was also an attempt on the life of Seward. The White House doctor attended Seward, and informed Verdi, when he arrived, of what he had done. For "consulting with a homœopath," the White House doctor was severely censured by the Washington Medical Society.

Tullio Suzzara Verdi, MD
1829 — November 26, 1902

Verdi was born in Mantua, Italy, in 1829. He served in the Sardinian army at a time when the country's political direction was in dispute. When the army of King Albert was routed by the Austrians, Verdi fled to England, and then to America, where he landed with just five dollars in his pocket.

Through the influence of Garibaldi, he secured a teaching position at Brown University in Rhode Island. While there he met Dr. Okie and was introduced to homœopathy.

He attended the Homœopathic Medical College of Pennsylvania and graduated in 1856.

He settled in Washington in 1857 where, as Harris Coulter says, "a fortunate marriage gave him entree to the city's social life. As a specialist in obstetrics and gynecology and a fine-looking Italian with a romantic past, he may be supposed to have exerted much of his peculiarly strong influence on later generations of Washington political figures not only by virtue of his services to them directly, but also through his ascendancy over their wives and daughters."

He was a member of the first Board of Health in the District, and served as Chair of the Sanitary Committee. In 1873 he attended a conference in Europe on sanitary

issues, and upon his return instituted major reforms in the public health and sanitation system in the District.

He was influential in establishing the Washington Homœopathic Hospital, and was a founding member of the Washington Homœopathic Society.

Ill health forced him to retire and, in hopes of regaining his health, he returned to Italy in 1895. He practiced medicine in Milan until his death.

Homœopathic politics in Washington, DC

The fortunes of Washington homœopathy were closely linked with the adventures of two allopaths, Christopher C. Cox and D. Willard Bliss. Cox was appointed Commissioner of Pensions in 1868. The efforts of Cox and Bliss to make capital out of the political antagonisms among Washington's physicians offered opportunities for Verdi to advance the cause of homœopathy.

The troubles started in 1869 when three Negro physicians applied for admission to the DC Medical Society and were rejected.

Cox and Bliss thereupon set about organizing a competing National Medical Society, open to physicians of all races and colors, and asked Congress to recognize it as the only legitimate medical society in Washington, but the bill was never voted on.

Verdi profited from the allopathic division over Negro physicians to apply to Congress for a charter for the homœopaths and provided that any persons "without exception on account of color" could become members of the Washington Homœopathic Medical Society.

To avenge this homœopathic victory, the leaders of the DC Medical Society decided to move against the homœopathic pension examiners. H. Van Aernam, MD, who had succeeded Cox in 1869 as Commissioner of Pensions, announced that only allopathic pension examiners would be countenanced by the federal government. This meant that 38 examiners would lose their jobs. Nineteen of the 38 were homœopaths, and they were dismissed. This move was strongly supported by the allopathic medical societies. The homœopaths, on the other hand, called for the speedy removal of Van Aernam and the restoration of the homœopaths to the federal payroll.

Verdi and his colleagues emphasized that nearly all the homœopathic physicians, and a great part of their patients, were radical Republicans. One of the dismissed homœopaths, a practitioner from upstate New York, wrote to Van Aernam that, "probably nineteen out of twenty practitioners in the country were Republicans."

Verdi wrote to President Grant, stating that, "the non-removal of Dr. Aernam will cost the Republican Party 10,000 votes in that state."

Verdi told the 1871 American Institute of Homœopathy Convention: "The day after this letter was sent, a Cabinet meeting took place, and the name of Dr. Van Aernam's successor was sent to the Senate for confirmation. And you may remain assured that Dr. Van Aernam never knew of his removal until he saw it announced in the evening paper... In two weeks from that time he took leave of his subordinates and left us, forever, I hope."

The dismissed homœopaths were restored to the federal rolls.

Constantine Hering

His collaborators
His family

Hering and his collaborators

At the time of the merger of the two schools, Hering, now 69 years old, was homœopathy's elder statesman. Still in contact with his old students, he spent his time in his medical practice and compiling his major work. A good friend Dr. Charles G. Raue, his son-in-law, Dr. Calvin B. Knerr, and Dr. Charles Mohr, a recent medical graduate, (who went on to become a teacher at Hahnemann) all assisted him. The collaboration resulted in the *Guiding Symptoms*, released as a 10 volume set over a period of years. When some wondered about its size, Hering said, "Who would object to a library because it is too large? If you have good catalogs, you always have a better chance of finding what you are looking for than in a small one." They sat with Hering, in his study, and worked. They had completed three of the volumes when Hering died in 1880.

Although this photo has appeared in several books, I am blessed to have an original print in my collection. When showing it I have often referred to it as "Sulphur in his native habitat."

In his later years, Hering slept on the couch in the study. He saw patients in his office from 10 a.m. till noon, and again from 4 to 6p.m.

After his evening meal he would retire to his study, and spend the night. His wife would come in the morning to help him wash and get dressed.

I have viewed this photo with a magnifying glass many times. Knerr describes many of the items in the photo— including the water-filled glass hemisphere, a device of Hering's design, that served as an intensifier and diffuser for the gas light at his desk.

"I will have to take a day off, stay at home, and put things right in my study. I have made a beginning this morning; no one else can see the change, but I know there is one."
— C. Hering

Augustus Korndoerfer, MD
October 27, 1843 — June 10, 1923

Educated in Philadelphia, Korndoerfer attended the Homœopathic Medical College of Pennsylvania from 1866 to 1867, transferring to the Hahnemann Medical College (with Hering), graduating in 1868.

He and classmate Ernest Farrington, assisted Hering in compiling Hering's *Condensed Materia Medica*.

Korndoerfer was professor of clinical medicine at the Hahnemann Medical College, and worked at most of Philadelphia's homœopathic hospitals. He died, senile, aged 79.

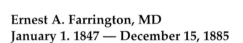

Ernest A. Farrington, MD
January 1. 1847 — December 15, 1885

Born in Williamsburg (now Brooklyn), New York, Farrington was educated in Philadelphia. He graduated first in his class from high school in 1866, preceptored with his brother, H. W. Farrington, MD, and entered the Homœopathic Medical College of Pennsylvania in the fall of 1866. He decided to move to the newly chartered Hahnemann Medical College in 1867 and gained his degree in 1868. In 1874 Farrington became professor of materia medica, filling the vacancy left by Guernsey.

Materia medica was his love. He met daily with "Papa" Hering, who said, "When I am gone, Farrington must finish my *Materia Medica*."

Said Korndoerfer, "His writings all bear the impress of a master mind. Already in 1871, scarcely three years subsequent to his graduation, we find him dealing with the philosophical elucidation of drug prescribing in language indicating depth of knowledge rarely found even among our oldest practitioners."

Farrington was a contributing editor of the *Hahnemannian*

Monthly, and his *Clinical Materia Medica*, transcriptions of his class lectures, was published shortly after his death.

Always of a frail constitution, Farrington sailed to Europe in May of 1885 in hope of regaining his health through relaxation, but after several months he returned home. He died shortly thereafter of malignant lymphoma at the age of 38.

Farrington was a Swedenborgian Christian and a member of the Church of the New Jerusalem. According to the teachings of Emmanuel Swedenborg, the scriptures reveal correspondences between the natural and spiritual world. Farrington found this an attractive theology as did many other homœopaths— Gram, Hempel, Hering, Boericke, Tafel, and Kent. Even on his death-bed, Farrington refused the allopathic help his friends pleaded with him to try, saying, "If I must die, I want to die a Christian."

Charles G. Raue, MD
May 11, 1820 — August 21, 1896

Born in Saxony, Raue immigrated to the United States aged 28, with a referral letter from Hering's brother. Raue gained his medical degree from the Philadelphia College of Medicine, and studied homœopathy under Hering.

He was professor of pathology and diagnosis at the Homœopathic Medical College, and wrote his major work, *Special Pathology and Diagnostics with Therapeutic Hints*, in 1867. He was Hering's personal physician.

Raue and Hering resembled each other so closely that someone said, "You are like the little Hering! You imitate him!" Hering, overhearing the remark, said, "No, you are mistaken. Raue does not imitate me. We are both 'thick heads' that is all."

In dress, Dr. Knerr commented of Raue: "Looks gave way to comfort, fashion to common sense."

In 1889 Raue wrote a book called *Psychology Applied to the Solution of Occult Phenomena*.

On his death-bed, he recognized no one. His last words were spoken in German: "It seems just 100 years ago that Dr. Hering…"

Calvin B. Knerr, MD
December 27, 1847 — September 30, 1940

Knerr's father was a homœopathic lay practitioner near Allentown, Pennsylvania, and his great uncle, Rev. John Helfrich was associated with Hering at the Allentown Academy.

Knerr graduated from Hahnemann Medical College in 1869 and became Hering's assistant. He lived in Hering's house and, in 1874, married Hering's daughter Melitta. While living in the Hering house he kept a diary, and in 1940, when he was 93, the diary was printed under the title of *The Life of Hering.*

Upon Hering's death Knerr became the literary executor of Hering's work and completed the 10 volumes of *Guiding Symptoms* by 1895.

Knerr visited Europe and met with Hahnemann's eldest daughter, as well as with Aegidi, Hartlaub and several other old homœopaths.

On a non-homœopathic note, one of Knerr's sons was the cartoonist who drew the classic comic strip "The Katzenjammer Kids."

Charles G. Mohr, MD
May 2, 1844 — October 31, 1907

Born and raised in Philadelphia, Mohr received his medical degree from Hahnemann Medical College in 1875. Aside from being a trusted student of and assistant to Constantine Hering, Mohr was chief of staff at the Hahnemann Hospital from 1877-1882, General Director of Hahnemann Hospital from 1901, and professor of materia medica and therapeutics from 1885 until his death.

The artist of this beautiful painting, done in oil on wood, is unknown. It resides at the offices of the National Center for Homeopathy in Alexandria, Virginia.

Constantine Hering

His Family

Hering married Charlotte Van Kemper in Surinam in 1829. They had one child, John, before her death in 1831. Hering relates that Charlotte's mother sent her to the country, and thinking nursing would prematurely age her, gave her herbs to suppress the milk, and she died. "I vowed never to be married again to a wife who had a mother," said Hering.

His son stayed with the Van Kemper family in Surinam when Hering came to the United States. Hering brought his son north for schooling, after which the boy returned to Surinam.

Hering married Marianne Husmann in 1834, shortly after arriving in America. From this marriage there were four children, two (Max and Odelia) living past infancy. Marianne died in 1840, and Hering returned to Germany in 1845, intending to stay. There were overtures about his assuming Hahnemann's practice. While in Germany, he met Therese Bucheim, married, and returned to the United States in 1846 after hearing the homœopathic movement was in disarray. This marriage produced eight children, six of whom survived him (Rudolph, Melitta, Walter, Hildegard, Carl, Hermann).

Hering was a prolific author. Bradford's *Bibliography* lists 325 items under his name including his five best known books: *Domestic Physician* (1835), *Comparative Materia Medica* (1867), *Materia Medica* (1873), *Analytical Therapeutics* (1875), *Condensed Materia Medica* (1877), *The Guiding Symptoms of the Materia Medica* (1880).

He was editor of the *North American Homœopathic Journal* (1851–1853); the *Homœopathic News* (1854–56); the *American Homœopathic Materia Medica* (1867–71).

He was working on the third volume of his massive *Guiding Symptoms of the Materia Medica* when he died.

Hering tid-bits (not in cream sauce)

Hering was trying to find out if the color of flowers have anything to do with the spectroscope. Are red flowers right sided? Do the color of the minerals fit in the relationships?

"My daughter got angry when she thought others had stolen my thunder. I replied, 'Let them steal my thunder as long as I am left the lightning.'"

"Eclipses of the sun and moon are occasions which I would like to see observed as national holidays."

Hering's first medicine case contained corked goose quills, as glass vials were not available.

"To begin a proving, I always swallowed the first rinsings from a mortar, after making a trituration."

"Aegidi is opposed to Boenninghausen. Boenninghausen was a layman; Aegidi a thoroughly educated physician. So it was between Lippe and myself."

January 6, 1873— Concerning the death of a patient:
"It is so terrible for me to stand and look on where I cannot help, particularly where it concerns a person for whom I have entertained feelings of affection and respect."

"Hahnemann could easily be made very angry. But he allowed both of his wives to domineer him; not in matters of principle or affairs, but in a general way."

Hering (on his interest in natural history and botany):
"I now think that to be able to cure a man of a toothache is worth more than all the animals in creation."

"A good jest, even though at his own expense, or even against homœopathy, he relished, but a cold and willful expression against the sacred truth of therapeutics he considered unpardonable. After the death of Dr. Watzke, in 1867, I expressed my regret at losing such an able colleague from our ranks; he knit his brow and answered: 'I am not at all sorry; a man who, after finding a truth, can say 'that he is sorry for it', ought to die." — Dr. Negendank

Hering the sleuth

"Radermacher, who lived on Arch Street, was one of the early homœopaths in Philadelphia. His wife was murdered in her room. Dr. Hering secured a piece of wood from a post on which was left the bloody imprint of the murderer's hand. He place this under a microscope and found that the hand, a delicate one, had left particles of shoe-maker's wax in the impress. He said the murderer is a shoe-maker. The murderer, Langenfeld by name, was tried, found guilty, and executed.

"While the criminal was in prison awaiting his execution, Hering suggested that his fingerprints be taken, but this was denied him. After the execution, Hering and some other physicians, were permitted to view the corpse. It was Dr. Hering's intention to take an impression from the hands, in wax, for comparison with the specimens observed under the microscope; but the hands of the cadaver were found cut and mutilated beyond recognition. This piece of vandalism had been committed by an eclectic who was jealous of a homœopath's triumph in a matter of science.

"The Bertillion method was but little practiced at the time of these occurrences. Now we know the lines in the human hand are singular and never duplicated."

—Life of Hering, *page 46*

Hering was a supporter of the Union cause in the Civil War. "In the winter of 1857 in his house, Dr. Hering freely lectured to a class of colored students from Jamaica and Canada, who in those days found no admission into any medical school…" — Herman Faber

Dr. Henry M. Smith of New York asked Hering when he could have some time with him. Hering consulted his schedule. "Quarter of four tomorrow morning," was the reply. And when Dr. Smith came at 3:45 a.m., Hering was up and ready to see him.

Hermann Hering, the youngest son, became a Christian Science practitioner.

A student said:
"I studied general medicine from a homœopathic standpoint in the college; but I really learned homœopathy from Dr. Hering in that back office of his."

"I have often observed that if a man loses his wife by death, who has given him a great deal of trouble during their married life, he will mourn her loss more than if their union had been a happier one."

Hering at home

According to Knerr, the Hering household was always full of life. There were conversations constantly after dinner, either around the table or in the garden, under the grape arbor.

Knerr describes a meeting of Hering and Dunham where Dunham asked questions, Hering gave answers, while Lilienthal (and Knerr) sat and listened.

Herman Faber, an artist friend, described Hering's entrance to a room as: "His step was heavy, elastic; rather large feet 'nicht schön,' as one of his admirers would say."

Dr. C. E. Boyce said: "For his breakfast he had a couple of pieces of zwieback with a cup of coffee or hot chocolate prepared by himself over an alcohol lamp. He never seemed to know when it was time to get ready for the day's business… He was a good listener if one had anything to say of value… I don't remember a time when he was the first to say goodnight."

Dr. George Norton recalled Hering's chief pleasure and relaxations from work were the "meetings on Sunday afternoon, when a circle of old friends assembled in his reception room, and over cigars and coffee compared experiences and discussed various subjects. Neither hot, cold, nor stormy weather interfered with these social gatherings."

Hering's favorite saying was, "Change of occupation is rest."

It is reported that the Hering household had the first German Christmas tree in Philadelphia.

A drawing by Herman Faber of the "roundtable" at Hering's home: (from left) Hering, Dr. August Koch, Therese Hering, Dr. Oswald Seidensticker, Melitta Hering, Dr. Calvin B. Knerr, Herman Faber.

Low potencies and combination remedies

In 1860, Hering wrote a few satires about homœopathy published in German. In one, he wrote of a schoolmaster who, dabbling in homœopathy, had sent for a box of medicines. When the medicines arrived, and the box was opened, he found that all 40 of the vials had broken in transit. The schoolmaster decided to save the pieces, sifted the globules from the paper and broken glass, and put all the globules together in a jar with some dilute alcohol. He labeled the bottle *Universalinum.* He said it was: "the greatest idea of the century. Here was a remedy for every ill. Good-bye to books and hard study!"

"I will not grumble about the low dilutionists. They are bark to the tree. We, the splint, are protected by the bark."
— C. Hering

Hering seemed to thrive on people. I found a letter buried in a book in my collection— written in Hering's hand, in the usual blue-green ink he was fond of using:

Letter from Hering to Professor Samuel Jones, dated March 16, 1876

Dear Colleague
for months letters to you have been written, but as they were not mailed, you could not answer them! But: an early one was the refrain: Come and stay during the Worlds Convention in my house and bring your wife with you. As we will have special meeting, for the women— in the common meeting, they of course are welcome but at the special meeting they must come— tell your wife all about this and also that we have a very plain household and as we take sauerkraut once a meal, but only during the winter, there is nothing to be feared.
Wm. P. Wesselhoeft with his wife will be here, we hope, and an old bachelor, a very scientific physicist, may be quartered= the printing office or the stable. This letter will be mailed and of course answered by Yes I come or its better we come.
yours, C. Hering

"Ailments from bad news"

Dr. J. C. Morgan recalls in the spring of 1861 he did a two–week proving of *Gelsemium*, the results being published in Shipman's *Journal of Materia Medica*. He said: "It was observed by me in April 1861, on reading the telegrams of the firing on Fort Sumter [the start of the American Civil War]; these so disturbed me that I gave up the proving, and stated as a fact that the telegrams produced the effect. But Dr. Hering, with the sagacity which was so peculiar to him, with that keen eye and analytical skill in Materia Medica, in which he was *facile princeps*, seized upon the very thing [diarrhea/ailments from bad news — JW] which I thought was vitiating the proving; said he, 'There is the grand characteristic of the drug'."

An *Aloes* proving

"I remember as if it were but yesterday, the first time we met. It was in his office as physician and patient. He stood and looked at me calmly as I related my symptoms. Then, silently turning to his desk, he prepared three powders and handed them to me with directions. I left him in wonder, for my case had troubled the physician who sent me, and I had expected a long search. The remedy produced a violent aggravation, and I recollect that wonder temporarily gave place to a state of mind akin to resentment.

"Recovery followed, and so did my promised report to the doctor. The recital of the success of his prescription caused his face to smile all over, which ended with a genial laugh, and he said, 'That was *Aloes*; it was low; it was the five-hundredth.' Then seating himself and motioning me to a chair, he went on to relate how he had suffered similarly when proving the drug, and made me promise to write out a history of the case, which I afterwards did, and informed me that the medicine had been potentized for him by Dr. Fincke, from a choice bit of crude material furnished by himself."

— Dr. Edmund Carleton, Jr. at Hering's memorial service

Gelsemium sempervirens

Kill or cure: A favorite case

"A young man who had suffered a long time from intermittent fever came to me with a doleful tale. He wished to marry the daughter of a rich manufacturer. He could only get her on condition that he would be able to fill the position of fireman in her father's establishments. This, he said, was impossible on account of his being harassed by chills and fever. The young fellow was desperate; said he would either drown or shoot himself if he could not be relieved of his malady. He demanded of me a prescription that would 'kill or cure!'

"I hesitated a moment, then gave him the following advice: 'Go to the Schuylkill River when you again feel the attack coming on. Undress. Get some of your friends to tie a rope under your shoulders so that they can suspend you in the water up to your mouth. Jump into the river and force yourself to stay there during the chill. When the fever, which follows the chill, comes on remain there until the sweat appears, then leave the water.'

"My directions were followed to the letter. The patient soon became blue in the face; his friends thought he would die, but he motioned them that he wished to stay in the water. Soon the fever took hold and the poor fellow became so weak that he could scarcely utter a word. His friends again motioned to pull him out, but he decided to stand the ordeal. He had been in the water for two hours when the sweat came on. He now consented to be taken from the river and his friends pulled him to shore and wrapped him into warm blankets and took him home. From that day on he had no return of chills or fever, was happily married to the girl of his choice, and supposedly lived happily ever after.

"If again I should be moved to advise such heroic treatment I would urge the patient to get out of the bath as soon as the fever came on.

"The remedy, in good faith, is one of kill or cure!"

— Constantine Hering, April 22, 1869

Walter's business

One of the ways that Hering could finance the printing of the Guiding Symptoms *was that his son Walter owned the Globe Printing Company, and published the volumes. If you ever get a ticket to an event or even a "coat check" ticket, look to see if there is a little Globe logo. The Globe Printing Company is still in business, and your ticket is a small link back to Dr. Hering.*

Higher potencies

Hering maintained an active interest in homœopathic pharmacy. It was Hering who convinced Dr. Samuel Dubs to make the first "decimal potencies" in the United States, and it was Hering who trained Rudolph Tafel as his personal pharmacist. Hering is often quoted as asking for potencies to be "higher, higher, every year higher!"

One of the earliest makers of high potencies who heeded Hering's call was Julius Caspar Jenichen (1787-1849), a horse–master in Wismar, Germany. Jenichen had been introduced to homœopathy by Wilhelm Gross. He began to experiment with making potencies higher than the 30th, and was convinced the power lay in the succussion rather than completely in the dilution.

Jenichen was a powerful man. It was once reported he rolled up a silver plate at a dinner party and shredded it with his bare hands as if it were paper. He made his potencies at night from 10 p.m. to 3 a.m. Stripped to the waist, he held the vial in his hand in a slanting direction, and gave the bottle a downward stroke with such force that the liquid "would rattle like silver coins." Bradford reports a life–sized portrait of Jenichen in the house of Dr. Stapf showing his Herculean arms and muscular frame.

The early homœopaths were divided on the effectiveness of these new "high" potencies, some as high as 60,000. Hering used them early in his practice. Grafts of Jenichen potencies are still found; I have several in my collection.

Jenichen, in ill health, killed himself in 1849 with, as one of the journals wrote, "an allopathic dose of *Plumbum* by sending a bullet into his brain."

Dudgeon wrote in 1853: "We may make ourselves perfectly easy on this point, and are quite justified in saying that his potencies, so called, were nothing more than a disreputable catch-penny, puffed into unmerited notoriety by a few credulous homœopathists, who should have known better than lend their reputations to the propagation of what five minutes' calm calculation might have convinced them was an impossibility and a cheat."

The Jenichen portrait

Hering refers to Jenichen as "a powerfully built man (as shown in his portrait)." It appears Hering had a painting of Jenichen— probably given to him by Stapf. This painting was passed to Dr. Knerr, who gave it to Dr. Raymond Seidel, along with a painting of Hahnemann.

When I first met Dr. Frederic Schmid in California, he asked me if I knew where the painting was. He had seen it when he visited Seidel in Philadelphia. When Seidel died in 1980, his sister gave the paintings to a Philadelphia auction house to be sold. A student at Hahnemann Medical College was passing the auction gallery and recognized the portrait of Hahnemann. He purchased it and told Barbara Williams at the Archives about it. He said there was a second painting of "someone who looked like Tarzan; a muscular, bearded man, dressed in a leopard skin, and holding a bottle." It was the portrait of Jenichen.

I found out about this event some two years after it transpired. I tried tracking the portrait through the auction house, but their records show only a single "painting, with gilt frame, of an old man." They had no record of the Jenichen painting, and Seidel's sister had no memory of it.

Barbara Williams told me she thought she had seen a photo of it in the Hahnemann Collection, but has been unable to locate it. Yet another treasure of homœopathy is lost to the ages!

The death of Hering

On July 23, 1880, Dr. Hering saw a patient at 6 o'clock. He had supper with his family under the elm tree in the garden, talked for an hour, and then retired to his study to work on volume four of the *Guiding Symptoms*. A little before ten, he rang for his wife and said he was having trouble breathing. She sent for the doctor. Hering said to a friend of the family, "I am dying now," and passed on. By the time Dr. Raue arrived, he could do nothing but turn and walk away in grief.

The funeral was held on July 28, 1880, the 52nd anniversary of his first *Lachesis* proving. The services were conducted by Rev. Seward, the pastor of the Swedenborgian Church of New York City. Hering was buried at Laurel Hill Cemetery and, after the turn of the century, the gravesite was moved to West Laurel Hill Cemetery.

Said Dr. Lilienthal at a memorial service, "Dr. Hering died in harness. At six o'clock on the evening of his death he made his last prescription."

And Dr. Edward Bayard observed, "He ceased to exist, by the withdrawal of his life by the Giver of life, like some locomotive running smoothly upon the track, after exhausting her fuel, slows down and stops— not thrown from the rails by broken machinery and rushing to ruin with terrible violence."

Hering's grave in the family plot at West Laurel Hill Cemetery, Bala Cynwyd, Pennsylvania.

The Division

The 1876 Congress
The retrenching
The founding of the IHA

The division

In 1876, at the Centennial Exposition in Philadelphia, the American Institute of Homœopathy held an international congress. Attended by more than 700 homœopaths from Europe, South America, and the United States, the meeting was organized by Institute president Carroll Dunham.

The published transactions of the Congress of 1876 reveal issues that were to further divide the homœopathic community. The last 20 years had seen many new homœopathic colleges, few of whom were teaching the pure method as promulgated by Hahnemann. Many schools were teaching homœopathy as simply "therapeutics" presenting a "this medicine for that disease" instruction. Many schools were simply commercial establishments, run by conventional physicians. Homœopathy was taught at minimal levels. (For an in–depth look at this, see **Myth and Fact: The decline of homœopathy** on page 226).

The issues that were raised at the Congress included the efficacy of low potencies versus the higher potencies, the usefulness of pathology in prescribing, and the practice of mixing homœopathic medicines with conventional ones.

Dunham, who had spent an enormous amount of energy organizing the Congress, died within the year. It was said that the Congress preparations and the efforts to mediate the different factions within it simply wore him out. Hering, who had been a unifying force between the factions, died a few years later. Although it maintained a number of medical schools and commanded an increasing medical care share, for the first time in 50 years the homœopathic movement had no strong leadership and was becoming increasingly divided over philosophical issues.

Carroll Dunham, MD
October 29, 1828 — February 18, 1877

Dunham was born in New York City, the son of a prosperous merchant. His mother died during the 1834 cholera epidemic, shortly after the family moved to Brooklyn.

As a schoolboy he was reported to have a quiet, studious disposition, more given to reading than play, especially of the rough and noisy sort. At 15 he matriculated at Columbia College, graduating with honors in 1847.

After leaving college, he studied medicine, placing himself under Dr. Whittaker, an old school physician. Having been helped through an illness by homœopathic treatment, he investigated its claims and became a firm believer in its principles and practice.

Nevertheless, he attended the course of instruction at the New York College of Physicians and Surgeons and at the various clinics to which he had access. Dunham received his medical degree in 1850, and left for Europe to continue his studies.

He visited Dublin, where he served a term in the lying–in hospital, as well as Paris, Vienna and other centers of medical science. At Münster, he became a pupil of Von Boenninghausen, daily attending at his office and making careful and elaborate notes of the cases he saw, their treatment, and the results.

Dunham returned to the United States a year later and commenced practicing in Brooklyn, New York. In 1854, he married Harriet Kellog.

After practicing four or five years in Brooklyn with good success, not withstanding some interruptions from sickness (one instance lasting several months) it was deemed necessary for health reasons to take a vacation. He returned to Europe, and again spent several weeks renewing his studies with Boenninghausen, passing the greater part of every day with him.

On returning to the United States he moved to Newburgh, New York and practiced for six years before his poor health forced him to retire again. He visited the West Indies and other foreign parts searching for health or relief. Finally he settled in Irvington-on-the-Hudson, where he lived until his death.

In 1865 Dunham accepted the professorship of materia

February 13, 1996

I had a dream that I found a phone number that would get me in touch with Dunham. In my dream I called the number. It rang. Someone picked up and said, "Dunham here." I thought, "I'm talking to Carroll Dunham! I'm the only person alive who's heard his voice! What do I tell him? That I'm calling from the future?"

I said, "I've read your works, and I was wondering if you'd speculate on the future of homœopathy."

There was a long pause. He said something about the new energy of electricity, and how when we understand what it is we will find that it holds all the secrets— that homœopathy is just a passing phase and electrical therapy will replace it within 50 years.

Then I thought, "How can I be calling Dunham? They didn't have phones in 1860! How could I ring a number that couldn't have existed?" And I awoke.

A rare photo of Dunham from
Hering's Scrapbook

medica in the New York Homœopathic Medical College.
He also served as the college's dean.

In 1874, in such poor health, he resigned all positions
and went to Europe. Upon returning a year later, his health
had substantially improved.

"With a large and well balanced mind, a clear and
discriminating judgment, a great store of learning gathered
from books and observation, with definite views on most
questions of human interest, he combined a wonderful
simplicity and purity of character and an amiable and
cheerful disposition. While his public discourses were
models of clear and concise argumentation, the richness
and sprightliness of his ordinary conversation made him
the charm of the social and domestic circle."

The 1876 AIH meeting in Philadelphia was a turning
point for homœopathy in the United States. On one side
were the stalwart homœopaths like Hering, Lippe, Wells,
Wesselhoeft. On the other were the "mixers," those
already teaching allopathic therapeutics and "this for that"
prescribing.

Dunham's efforts to combine the factions was a severe
strain on his health. Always of a weak constitution, he died
shortly after the 1876 Congress and was buried in
Greenwood Cemetery in Brooklyn. His wife died about a
year later.

The Dunham family plot in
Greenwood Cemetery in
Brooklyn, New York.

The retrenching

In 1880, shortly before the death of Hering, a group of doctors, headed by Henry C. Allen and Adolph Lippe, formed a professional organization outside of the American Institute. The International Hahnemannian Association was formed as a reaction against the increasing lack of homœopathic teaching in the schools which were then in operation and against the poor quality of homœopathy being practiced.

There were several factors leading to its formation.

Dunham's opening of the American Institute of Homœopathy

In 1870, Carroll Dunham asked that the membership of the American Institute be open to all comers, regardless of their stance on homœopathy. Dunham hoped "half-homœopaths" would join the organization, gradually learning homœopathy from the stalwarts. Unfortunately, it was a dream not to be realized. It was "heard with regret and gloomy foreboding by the Hahnemannians present, while it was enthusiastically received by the eclectic wing of the school..."

At the 1874 annual AIH meeting, the word "homœopathy" was stricken from the requirement for membership in the Institute. The 1876 International Meeting in Philadelphia did little to prevent the eventual split of the factions, even though Dunham played the "peacemaker."

In some sense, there was no middle ground. You either did homœopathy as Hahnemann wrote, or you didn't. And those who formed the International Hahnemannian Association had no tolerance for those who did "half-homœopathy"

"It was," as written in the *International Hahnemannian Association Transactions of 1880*, "heretofore thought best by many of the older members of the profession, in order to preserve and perpetuate the inheritance bequeathed to us by the master, to organize an association composed entirely of physicians, who endorsed his theory and practice as set forth in his *Organon of the Healing Art*."

"Excommunication never exterminated heresy"

We have adopted a code of medical ethics which defines with considerable minuteness the duties, as we understand them, of physicians to each other and the public... But we have, besides, a standard which the other school does not possess— a fundamental therapeutic law, which is, to some extent, of the nature of a creed, adhesion to which would seem to be essential to membership in the Institute; and without which it would appear that no physician could entertain views in common with us, or any desire to unite with us...

But as the new practice became popular, men took the name of homœopathic physician who did not accept the homœopathic law as of universal application in therapeutics, or who did not accept the peculiar modes of practice generally known as homœopathic: the single remedy, for instance, and the minimum dose...

Some will say it is vexatious to meet fellow members who are Homœopathists only in name, really ignorant, and giving out their crude assumptions as the science today. It may be equally to some vexatious to meet the stricter Homœopathists. Probably the vexation is not in meeting these men, but rather in fact they exist and practice and talk as they do. Well, if we expel them will they not still exist and talk and practice? If we expel them, we deprive ourselves of every chance to teach them better ways; and there is not an earnest man of them who would not gladly learn!

Let us bear with these trials as it may well be others are patiently bearing with our own short-comings. Let the Institute be an open forum, in which truth shall be so distinctly proclaims, and so persuasively enforced that error shall have no chance...

Carroll Dunham, "Freedom of Medical Opinion and Action: a Vital Necessity and a Great Responsibility," Presidential Address, 1870

The impostors

... And there are among those who call themselves Homœopathists, some who are impostors; men without knowledge and without conscience, who play upon the credulity of mankind... That such men, professing to be of our school, should be regarded by the community as belonging to it... is certainly a misfortune. Yet, that there are so many of them, is, in one sense, a testimony in favor of Homœopathy! For who ever heard of a patent being infringed which was good for nothing? Who ever heard of impostors claiming heirship to an insolvent estate? Should we probably meet with uneducated or knavish persons claiming to be homœopathic physicians, were not the success and consideration which attach to that position something desirable? In some sort, the number of impostors and parasites may be taken as a measure of the value and vitality of that on which they cling!

Carroll Dunham, *"Freedom of Medical Opinion and Action: a Vital Necessity and a Great Responsibility,"* Presidential Address, 1870

The Milwaukee Test

In 1879 the the American Institute of Homœopathy began a project called "The Milwaukee Test," designed to throw doubt upon the teachings and practice of Hahnemann. "The Milwaukee Test," saw a group of 25 provers given 10 vials, one an active substance in the 30th potency, and 9 placebo. The 25 were, during the year, asked to test them and inform the committee which vial was "active." At the end of the year, with only *nine* people reporting, just one person confirmed the active remedy, while the other eight selected the inactive vials. The AIH concluded there was no evidence the 30th potency contained anything other than a placebo.

When the American Institute of Homœopathy held its 1880 annual meeting in Milwaukee, an address by E. W. Berridge, from England, presented "too many wholesome truths and too much homœopathy to be popular with that body." Institute President Dr. T. P. Wilson, talking of the poor homœopathic education provided by the schools said: "If hundreds of such are being turned loose upon the profession yearly, while the old original stock of practitioners is dying out, it will not be difficult to foresee the result of another third of a century to homœopathy in this country."

At the same meeting, several papers presented verified the presence of actual particles of material in a 6X dilution. It was clear the group was moving further and further away from Hahnemann's dynamic thinking.

The founding of the International Hahnemannian Association

Several AIH conference attendees retired to the nearby court-house on the afternoon of June 16 to establish a new organization, and the next day the International Hahnemannian Association was formed. Within two years, the Association grew from the original 16 to 81 members.

Although membership never went much beyond 200 (215 members in 1930), the IHA survived to bring pure homœopathy into the 20th century. It ceased operation in 1959, when its members, all now members of the AIH, voted to merge it with the Institute which, by this time, was once again in the hands of pure homœopaths.

IHA Founding Resolution — June 17, 1880.

Whereas, We believe the *Organon of the Healing Art* as promulgated by Samuel Hahnemann to be the only reliable guide in therapeutics; and

Whereas, This clearly teaches that homœopathy consists in the law of similars, the single remedy, and the minimum dose of the dynamized drug, not singly but collectively; and

Whereas, A number of professed homœopathists, not only repudiate these tenets, but violate them in practice; and

Whereas, An effort has been made on the part of such physicians to unite the allopathic and homœopathic school, therefore

RESOLVED, That the time has come when legitimate Hahnemannian homœopathy should free itself from all such innovations, hurtful alike to its reputation and fatal to the best interests of the sick.

RESOLVED, That the mixing or alternating of two or more medicines displays on the part of the prescriber a lack of skill, besides being a species of empiricism inexcusable and non-homœopathic.

RESOLVED, That in non-surgical cases we regard medicated topical applications and mechanical appliances as relics of defunct customs of past ages, unscientific, non-homœopathic, and often injurious.

RESOLVED, That as "the best dose of medicine is ever the smallest" we cannot recognize as homœopathic the treatment of any physician who administers medicines in such quantities as to suppress symptoms by their primary or toxical action.

RESOLVED, That we have no sympathy in common with those physicians who would engraft onto homœopathy the crude ideas and doses of the eclectics, and we will not hold ourselves responsible for their "fatal errors" and failures in practice.

RESOLVED, That as some self styled homœopathists have taken occasion to traduce Hahnemann as a "fanatic," "dishonest," and "visionary," and his teachings as "not being the standard of the homœopathy today," we denounce all such as being traitors to our cause, and recreant to its best interests.

The original members of the IHA were: Adolph Lippe, George Foote (Stamford, CT), C. Pearson, H. C. Allen (Ann Arbor, MI), O. P. Baer (Richmond, IN), P. P. Wells (Brooklyn, NY), E. W. Berridge (London), W. H. Leonard (Minneapolis, MN), T. F. Pomeroy (Baltimore, MD), J. P. Mills (Chicago, IL), Edward Rushmore (Montclair, NJ), T. F. Smith (New York, NY), E. A. Ballard (Chicago, IL), T. P. Wilson (Ann Arbor, MI), T. Wilhelm Poulson (Council Bluffs, IA), and Edward Cranch (Eire, PA).

The bound *Transactions of the IHA* are a veritable treasure trove of information. Rare as hen's teeth (often only 70 or so were printed and bound), these volumes are an indelible record of Hahnemannian homeopathy in the United States from 1880 through the 1920s.

Henry C. Allen, MD
October 2, 1830 — January 22, 1909

Henry C. Allen was born in Brantford, Ontario, Canada. He was a descendant on the paternal side from Ethan Allen, of American revolutionary fame.

Allen studied medicine at the College of Physicians and Surgeons of Ontario, and homœopathy at the Cleveland Homœopathic College, graduating in 1861. After serving as a surgeon in the Civil War, he was professor of anatomy at the Cleveland Homœopathic Medical College, and later at the Hahnemann College in Chicago. From 1880 to 1885 he was professor of materia medica and clinical medicine in the homœopathic department of the University of Michigan, at Ann Arbor. He organized the Hering Medical College in Chicago; incorporated in 1891, opening for students in 1892. He was its first dean, president of its governing board, professor of materia medica, and teacher of the *Organon*. He was for many years the editor and publisher of the *Medical Advance*, and he was one of the founders of the IHA.

Allen's first published work was the *Therapeutics of Intermittent Fever*. He also edited and partly rewrote the work of Dr. R. R. Gregg on consumption, and added the section on the "Therapeutics of Consumption," and a repertory. This work was published under the title *Gregg on Consumption*, by Allen.

Allen's third work, *Keynotes to the Leading Remedies of the Materia Medica*, has seen several editions.

He was the author of the *Materia Medica of the Nosodes*, which was issued posthumously in 1910.

He died suddenly and quietly January 22, 1909, after a full day's work. He arrived home about 5:30 p.m., saw a patient, had a telephone conversation, and then lay down on the couch, saying he did not feel well. His breathing became difficult, unconsciousness soon followed and he passed on.

"Among his colleagues he was honored for his zeal as a worker; his discretion and practical wisdom as an adviser; his integrity and consistency as a practitioner of pure Homœopathy; and for his affability, magnanimity and unselfishness in all his relations. Never was a man more free from petty professional jealousy, nor one more quick and generous in his recognition of the merits and attainments of his colleagues. He was always frank and hearty in his commendation of the good work of others. But he was brave too as well as kind. He could be severe on occasion. He never hesitated to point out error, but he did it so graciously that he rarely gave lasting offense. He was quick to take the floor in defense of truth, even if it brought him into conflict with men whom he esteemed as personal friends. He was a good fighter, and he never knew when he was whipped. He cherished no enmities, but in a contest involving principle, he would never give up. If he failed at one time, and in one way, he was sure to come back later with some new mode of attack or defense. His was the 'perseverance of the Saints.'

"He traveled much and far in his attendance upon the meetings of societies and colleges. He spared neither time, money nor strength when called upon to lend the influence of his gracious presence and facile speech for the strengthening or upbuilding of his beloved Homœopathy. As organizer, missionary, exhorter and peacemaker-in-general, he was well nigh ubiquitous. Wherever there was a society to be formed or reorganized, a fraternal 'breach of the peace' to be healed, backsliders and weak-kneed brethren to be stirred up and strengthened, there was Dr. Allen to be found. And wherever he went he took with him that genial spirit, that charming presence, that suave address which made him always a welcome and honored guest. He was tactful and diplomatic in his dealings with men and measures. His tactics sometimes puzzled some of his friends who were less experienced in dealing with matters of a quasi-political nature. They were sometimes suspicious of his motives, regarding the appearance instead of the fact. As of old they were inclined to say: 'This man receiveth sinners and eateth with them.' But in reality his life and motives were above reproach, and in his practice he conformed to the highest standards of Homœopathy...

"His spirit was always young, and he kept the appearance of youth and vigor to a surprising degree. At seventy-two he was as erect, as quick, as springy, as active as the average man of half that age— Clean, lean and abstemious, his spirit ruled his body absolutely up to the very end.

"He loved best the family circle and simple social functions. He was at his best in little informal gatherings of friends, lay or professional, especially when the younger element predominated. Quick at repartee, and never at a loss for a quip, a jest or an anecdote, his gaiety and wit made him the life of such a gathering. His presence at the festive board was always a stimulus to that 'feast of reason and flow of soul' which is the essence of the real 'good time.'"

— Excerpts from the obituary of H. C. Allen,
    IHA Transactions, 1909

Adolph Lippe, a guiding light to the homœopathic stalwarts, died within a few years of the founding of the IHA. But the Association remained strong and many of its members guided homœopathy into the next century.

Lippe's grave in the Old Catholic Cemetery in Philadelphia, Pennsylvania. When Lippe died, the small Old Catholic Cemetery was a short distance beyond the edge of the settled city. Located off 48th Street in West Philadelphia, it is now surrounded by rows of housing.

Homœopathic Pharmacy

The rise of the homœopathic pharmacy
The first combinations
Boericke and Tafel
Fincke's high potencies
Dunham's 200s
Skinner's machine
The Work of Swan
The Santee Potentizer
The Kent Potentizer

OUR HOMEOPATHIC REMEDIES.

Our Homœopathic Specifics are prepared under the supervision of an old experienced Homœopathic physician. Great care is taken in preparing them according to the rules laid down by the highest authorities on homœopathy, and only the purest drugs used. Every one of the following specifics is a special cure for the disease named on it. Adults take 6 pellets, children from 1 to 3 according to age, and from two to four doses are to be taken every day according to the severity of the case. We ask the special attention of all our customers to these high grade remedies. If you have them near at hand, we guarantee they will save you many a doctor's bill, and what of more consequence, quickly relieve any suffering member of the family and ward off more serious sickness. We make the price as low as we possibly can in order that they may be within reach of every one of our customers, only 18c each bottle, with the exception of three rare ones which of necessity we require to make a higher price.

OUR $1.50 FAMILY MEDICINE CASE
DR. HAMMOND'S
HOMŒOPATHIC REMEDIES
GUARANTEED
HIGHEST GRADE MADE
SOLD ONLY BY
SEARS ROEBUCK
AND CO. INC.
CHICAGO ILL.

Homœopathic medicines from the Sears, Roebuck Catalog, circa 1900

During the 1850s the United States was fermented with social and economic change. The industrial revolution was under way, while the Civil War was just around the corner. New materials and processes were being developed, and, for the first time, industry was being driven by science and technology.

As homœopathy became popular, the increasing demand for remedies led to the development of the specialized homœopathic pharmacy. Domestic kits were sold, along with books on how to use the remedies. The United States was expanding, and as physicians were few and far between, these domestic kits were often the only form of health care available to the community.

Illustrations of Domestic Cases.

No. 2.

An elegant Mahogany Case with 30 one drachm vials, corked...... .... $3 00
Filled with Medicines, and Morgan's Text Book included......................... .... 5 00

No. 3.

A stout, Mahogany Case of 104 one drachm vials, corked.................... ....… $7 00
Filled with Medicines................ .. .. 12 00
Including Laurie & McClatchey's Domestic... 17 00

Domestic Kits by Boericke and Tafel circa 1875

Notice by William Radde in the back of a *Hull's Jahr*, 1853

The first combinations

Frederick Humphreys, MD
March 11, 1816 — July 7, 1900

Frederick Humphreys, a graduate of the Homœopathic Medical College of Pennsylvania, did the first proving of *Apis* in 1852. Yet, by 1855, his membership in both the American Institute of Homœopathy and the New York State Homœopathic Medical Society was rescinded by both organizations because he had begun to advocate the use of "specifics."

He suggested (as he writes in the introduction to *Humphreys Mentor*) that to find the single remedy based not upon a pathological or physiological similia, but upon a "keynote or fantastic aberration," made the study of homœopathy "a psychological phantasmagoria." He said: "So we seek out the possible law of combination, and adapt our Specific similia to the Pathological Individuality."

Thus, from the mind and hand of Humphreys, were the first homœopathic combination remedies born. As much as they were disapproved of by the homœopathic community, they found quick recognition from the lay public who were then, as now, looking for a "quick fix." Humphreys' Specifics were successful in the marketplace, and are still sold today.

The little manuals published by Humphreys contained minimal indications for "diseases" and suggested the appropriate remedy: "for renal calculi, gravel in the urine, and painful urination, use No. 27." Rarely was there any indication, in the literature, as to what "No. 27" contained (*Pulsatilla, Lycopodium, Sarsaparilla*).

During the 1930s the Humphreys company sponsored a radio show that was broadcast for 15 minutes, four times a week, in eight cities around the country. A mailing from the show appears in the **Appendix** on page 509.

Frederick Humphreys M.D.

Humphreys' veterinary products were used by the Ringling Brothers Circus through the 1930s and, according to the United States Department of Interior, by the United States Cavalry.

The wedding picture of F. E. Boericke and Elise Tafel, 1863.

The only known photo of F. E. Boericke and Adolph Tafel. The original, in Bradford's *Scrapbook,* is about two inches high, a bit smaller than pictured here!

Boericke and Tafel

Francis Edmund Boericke, MD
June 8, 1826 — December 17, 1901

Born in Glauchau, Saxony, Boericke immigrated to the United States in 1849, aged 23. In 1850 he met Rudolph Tafel, then 18, who was translating Le Boys des Guay's *Letters to a Man of the World* into German. Boericke was invited to assist. In 1852, he formally joined the Philadelphia First Society, a New Church (Swedenborg) group. In 1853 Boericke and Tafel opened a book store specializing in New Church literature. On advice of Constantine Hering, they also opened a homœopathic pharmacy as part of the business. Tafel served as Hering's personal pharmacist. Tafel left the business soon after to teach at the Naval Academy in Annapolis, Maryland.

Deciding he needed to learn more about homœopathy, Boericke enrolled at the Hahnemann Medical College of Pennsylvania, graduating with an MD degree in 1863. However, he never practiced medicine. That same year he married Elise Tafel, daughter of Dr. Leonard Tafel, and thus became a brother-in-law to Rudolph L., Louis H., and Adolph Tafel. [See family tree on page 88]

In 1869 he and Adolph Tafel formed the pharmaceutical company "Boericke and Tafel." In 1882 Boericke retired from the pharmacy to run the "Hahnemann Publishing House," the publishing branch of Boericke and Tafel.

In 1887, Boericke, "through a complication from a nervous disease," became an invalid. He remained deeply involved with the New Church until his death. Said John Pitcairn in an obituary: "He had a wonderful memory, was a good conversationalist and even in his illness, when matters of the Church were discussed, he seemed to rise above his bodily sufferings."

The Boericke potentizer

Boericke says he "made a machine" and made five remedies to the MM potency. These potencies were offered gratis in the *Bulletin*. He says, "No superiority nor any special claim was attached to the MM potencies. They were given out for whatever they might be worth."

These were the only remedies produced on this machine. I have not been able to find the identity of those five remedies, although one certainly was *Lachesis*, since a record of a Boericke MM is reported by Dr. Berridge in the journal *The Organon*.

The machine was first pictured in Volume I of *The Organon* (1878, page 420), in an article by Thomas Skinner, MD.

With each turn of the crank, water is drawn into the glass cylinder and then pushed into the vial on the left. The vial is then given five shakes, and the next amount of water pushes the remaining water out the bottom of the vial.

Dr. Skinner, recounting how he became ill when he prepared high potencies of *Cinchona* and *Kali carbonicum*, suggested that Dr. Boericke's poor health might have been related to overexposure to very high potencies during their preparation.

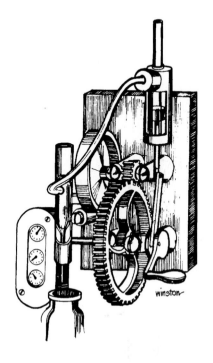

The Boericke Potentizer. Drawn from the picture in *The Organon*. A 1915 photo of the machine (seen on the cover), shows the machine in a horizontal position. It is not known what happened to the machine. It was not found when the Boericke and Tafel premises at 1011 Arch Street, Philadelphia, were cleaned out in 1992.

"It seems to me that the only legitimate way to prepare high potencies is to follow Hahnemann's method; or if anyone wishes to prepare high potencies according to his personal notions, he ought to abstain from giving his preparations the same numbers or designations as those prepared by the master's rule. I have, myself, carried many remedies to the 200th and my neighbor in business [A. J. Tafel] even to the 1000th potency. It is, of course, a very laborious process."

— *F. E. Boericke*

I found this picture in the attic at Boericke and Tafel. It was identified, in a pencilled scrawl on the back, as "Uncle Frank." There was no other identification. I finally found the same picture in Bradford's *Scrapbook*. It was labeled, "Francis E. Boericke, in retirement." I guess if you were a Boericke, he was "Uncle Frank!"

No need to go into the entire family lineage! This information was provided by Gretchen Worden whose mother, Mildred, was the daughter of Gideon Boericke.

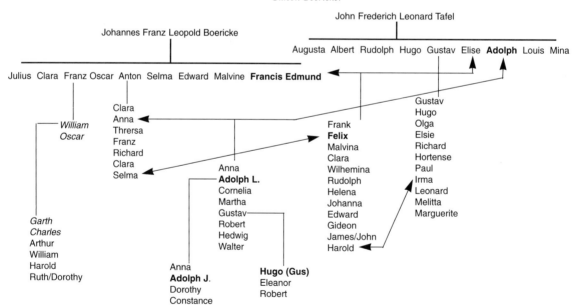

Those connected with the pharmacy are in **bold.** Those who were doctors are in *italics.*

Fincke's high potencies

Bernhardt Maximillian Fincke, MD
January 7, 1821 — October 21, 1906

Born in Saxony, Germany, one of eight children, Fincke left school aged 15 to work as an accountant. In Frankfurt, at 25, he contracted typhoid fever. While in hospital he met the Reverend William Taube, a follower of Hahnemann, and was introduced to homœopathy.

In 1851 he attended a meeting of the Central Society of Homœopathic Physicians in Leipzig, and met Von Boenninghausen, who convinced him to go to America—the "promised land" of homœopathy. Arriving in New York in 1852, he entered the University Medical College of the City of New York, receiving his MD degree in 1854.

Upon graduating he settled in Brooklyn and began a long friendship with Drs. P. P. Wells and Carroll Dunham. His relationship with Dunham became strained after Dunham's 1870 "Freedom of Medical Opinion and Action" address to the American Institute, and "…aroused differences of opinion which led to his partial estrangement from Dr. Fincke as well as from other staunch Hahnemannians of the day, who foresaw it as a tendency to break down the barriers between the schools at the expense of homœopathic integrity."

In 1865 Fincke wrote a text, *On High Potencies*. Three years later he married Maria Catherine Ficht. In 1896 he was elected president of the International Hahnemannian Association. In 1897 Fincke, with the help of the Brooklyn Hahnemannian Union, did the first proving of *X-ray*.

He began producing high-potency remedies in the late 1860s, and his remedies are still used today.

According to Stuart Close, Fincke was "reclusive" and "little known to the members of the profession in his own city… He was of a very sensitive, retiring disposition, and slow to give his confidence, but once bestowed, his friendship never wavered."

A naturalized American citizen, he kept portraits of Washington and Lincoln over his mantelpiece. Politically

Bernhardt Fincke, circa 1870

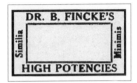

The unique label found on all Fincke remedies

he was a staunch Republican; in religion he was a lifelong member of the German Evangelical Lutheran Church.

Close relates that Fincke flew the American flag over his summer home at Bella Sylvia in Pennsylvania, raising it every morning and taking it in every evening.

Fincke was an accomplished musician on the piano and the French horn.

His death, relates Close, was peaceful. Several days before the end he began to have visions of all the bottles in his office becoming two feet high. "Most peculiar," he said. "Bottles with heads, all in a row, bending forward, and all going in one direction— toward the west— toward the setting sun."

This picture of a young Dr. Fincke was found in Hering's Scrapbook. It was identified as "Dr. B.F."

"Dr. Bernhardt Fincke, one of the greatest philosophers of homœopathy, had in one corner of his office a very old square piano. It was my privilege, about 1890, to sit by his side and play duets with him. But let me give you this incident in the words of Dr. Close, a bit of writing that I found the other day in a memoir of Dr. Fincke, still in manuscript:

'My wife and I spent delightful evenings with Dr. and Mrs. Fincke, in conversation and with music. Dr. Fincke got out his music, and he and Mrs. Close played Mozart duets together on a little tinkling old square piano, much like a spinet, one of the early pianofortes, sounding doubtless very like the instrument used in Mozart's time. It was interesting and touching, almost pathetic, to see the old man with his gnarled fingers, very intent upon the score, playing away for dear life to keep up with the nimble fingers of his young friend sitting beside him, and growing very warm and enthusiastic about it too. He played remarkably well, entering into the spirit of the music and the occasion. Dr. Fincke came of a noted musical family and was himself a good piano player in his younger days. He was a lover of good music, and regularly attended the orchestral concerts given each season in Brooklyn.'"

—Mrs. Stuart Close in *The Homœopathic Survey*, July 1930

The Fincke fluxion potencies

The International Congress in 1876 brought together several physicians who had been experimenting with methodologies of preparing homœopathic potencies. The group were Fincke and Swan from the United States, and Thomas Skinner from England. They were convinced the remedy's power, once it became sub-molecular, lay in the dilution of the material, and not in the succussion, although Swan and Skinner credit Fincke with being the first to demonstrate the effectiveness of fluxion alone without succussion.

Although Hering was critical of Fincke for being secretive about his process ("I am minded to try to find out the secret of Fincke's method by experimentation," said Hering), the method was not at all secret, having been patented in 1869.

The Fincke method used a one dram vial with a "neck" and a glass tube, called the "regulator." It was Fincke's belief that the potency was raised by one for every dram of water that would pass through the vial. To make a 200th potency from a 30th, you simply ran 170 drams of water through the vial. The water was pre-measured and siphoned through the vial (as in the patent pictured here).

The water source was attached (by tubing) to the regulator. The regulator was placed in the vial, with its tip resting on the bottom of the vial, and the water was regulated to flow at a rate of 500 drams an hour. The water would flow from the bottom of the vial and, because the vial was necked, there would be a slight back-pressure in the vial.

When the calculated potency reached one under its desired value (i.e., when the 199th was reached on the way to the 200th), the vial was emptied by a strong downward jerk of the arm. The vial was then filled with alcohol, corked, and succussed in a dactylus rhythm (ONE two three, ONE two three) 180 times. The vial was then labeled and used to medicate granules.

Fincke stated clearly that these potencies were not the same as Hahnemannian ones (those that had been prepared by serial dilution in the ratio of 1:100 with succussion) and

The Fincke potencies in the original vials, shown here full size.

Believe it or not!

I've told this story time and again:
In 1882 Bernhardt Fincke prepared some Belladonna tincture from the fresh plant, and then he worked it up to the 30th potency by Hahnemannian dilution and succussion.

He then took one drop of the 30th, placed it in a one-dram vial, placed the regulator in the vial and proceeded to make a very high potency. He ran several hundred gallons of water through the vial, for all intents and purposes, washing it thoroughly. He then took this very well washed vial, shook the water out of it, added alcohol, succussed it, placed a few drops on some sugar granules, and labeled it: "Belladonna MM(F)." He gave the vial to a friend.

Over the years, the vial went from doctor to doctor until it came to rest in the high-potency cabinet in the office of Dr. Maesimund Panos in Tipp City, Ohio.

One hundred years after Fincke "washed the bottle," Dr. David Wember phoned Dr. Panos and asked if she had any "very-high Belladonna." She put a few granules of the Fincke preparation into a vial, filled the vial with more blank #10 granules (thus making a "dry" graft), and mailed it to Dr. Wember.

Dr. Wember gave three of the granules to a patient of his and all her symptoms were relieved.

Can we believe it?

were to be clearly labeled as "fluxion" potencies.

The diluent was water from a Brooklyn tap— direct from the Croton, NY reservoir.

The intermediate potencies were saved in even hundreds to the 1M, in even thousands to the 10M, and then even five and ten thousands to the CM.

Upon his death, the entire collection of Fincke potencies was passed to Fincke's son-in-law, William Kaercher, MD of Philadelphia, who continued to sell them. When Kaercher died in 1934, his daughter kept the remedies and eventually gave them to John A. Borneman. As of June 1996, they were stored in the Boiron facility outside of Philadelphia.

From Fincke to Bradford

When T. L. Bradford, MD was compiling his Homœopathic Bibliography *(published in 1892), he wrote to all the pharmacies he knew to obtain the latest information. It appears that he wrote to Fincke to ask about his remedies. Fincke's curt answer is found in Bradford's* Scrapbook.

T. L. Bradford, MD
Philadelphia
Nov. 21, 1889

Dear Doctor
In answer to your kind enquiry, I am glad to correct a mis-apprehension on your part.
I do not keep a pharmacy. If I let the professionals and the people have my high potencies it is as a privilege, but I do not business as an apothecary.
Yours,

B. Fincke

Bernhardt Fincke, circa 1900

Letter from B. Fincke to Edmund Carleton dated Dec. 23, 1901

Dear Doctor:
The ebullient method was one of the claims for the patent and was rejected by me after it was given and before Skinner appeared.
My method of continued fluxion is described by the patent.
Wishing you a merry Christmas and a Happy New Year, I remain yours faithfully

B. Fincke

Dunham's 200s

Carroll Dunham was also interested in making high potencies. He made a stock of 200th potencies, some of which are still being used today. An article in the Spring 1997 issue of *Homœopathic Links* discusses their use.

The making of the potencies was discussed in an article written by Samuel A. Jones, MD, in the *American Observer Medical Monthly*, Vol. 16 June 1879:

"During his training, Dunham apprehended the 'potency' question in the true spirit of Baconian induction. He had witnessed Boenninghausen's administration of the two-hundredths, and had noted the results. On his return to America, ready for work, he proposed to try the two-hundredths. And first he must know that he is using two-hundredths. By making them himself he will disarm incredulity as to them; he will also obey the Hahnemannian injunction that every homœopathic physician should prepare his own medicines. Yankee–like he sought to lighten this labor, and at the same time do the work effectively."

As Dunham related it in a letter to Lippe:

"Determined to use machinery for succussion, and to use a force far exceeding the brachial power of any man, I availed myself of an abandoned oil-mill, in which, by waterpower, four stampers, consisting of large oak timbers, eight inches square and eighteen feet long, were, by a cam movement, lifted and let fall a distance of eighteen inches. By means of strong oaken receptacles, firmly bolted to the stampers, 120 vials (more or less) were succussed at one time, and thus that number of medicines was, by a single operation, advanced one degree in the scale of potentization

Several of us were invited to help Dr. Maesimund Panos clean her basement. There was a full set of remedies from Charles Dixon, MD, and another set from Elizabeth Wright-Hubbard. There was one set where all the labels on the corks had been worn off, so there was no way of knowing what the bottles contained. And there was a set of beautiful bottles from Smith's Pharmacy labeled as 200D. I (in my ignorance) thought they were "decimal" potencies. Bill Kirtsos thought they were handsome bottles, as did I. So he took the box and I took five representative bottles for my collection.

About a year later Bill was informed by André Saine that they were Dunham potencies. Shortly thereafter, Bill had a bad toothache and took a 200 Chamomilla from the set— the only 200 he had. He said the effect was almost instantaneous. Still good after all these years!

— a great economy of time. The force with which the succussions were made was considerably more than that of a half-ton falling eighteen inches; greater therefore, (by a rough computation) than that of six Jenichens (or ten Finckes) falling bodily, bottle and all, through a space of an arm shake. One hundred and twenty–five such succussions were given to each potency."

"So for his written statement as given in the letter to Dr. Lippe, and now for a bit of 'inside history' which he once gave me in an after-dinner talk while I smoked one of his cigars so that he could 'smell it.'

"His father assisted him in making these potencies. The 'bottlewashing' took them a whole week. They got done on the middle of a Saturday afternoon. Said he; 'The stampers had fallen for the last time. After an arduous week's work, countless bottle-emptyings and bottle fillings, there were the two-hundredths' before us. It was all silence in the old mill. We neither spake a word; we looked up into each others face, burst out into simultaneous laughter, peal upon peal, and laughing rolled upon the floor.'

"Have you ever made a 30th; felt the conviction creep into you deeper, and deeper, and deeper that you must have washed away all the 'medicine'? If so, you know why they laughed.

"But where was the laughter when those 'bottle-washings' were tried; when his fellow physicians were writing to him: 'Will you send me a little of the very same potency with which you cured so and so?' Where was the laughter when he was 'compelled as a matter of convenience, to request the Messrs. Smith, of New York, to take charge of them, and to furnish applicants at as low a rate as would compensate themselves for time, trouble and stock?'"

X, c, Q, LM, and K

When Hahnemann first began to serially dilute the remedies he used the centesimal scale— 1 part of remedy in 99 parts of diluent to give a ratio of 1:100. These potencies are designated by a "c." A capital "C" should not be used because, in Roman numerals, it indicates a "100." Many old prescribers labeled their 200c potencies as a "2C."

In the Hahnemannian method, a new bottle is used at each step of dilution. While there is no problem storing 30 bottles for the first 30 potencies of any one remedy, going to the next step of a 200th would require 200 bottles.

In 1828, Iseman Korsakoff proposed that after the 30th is reached, the same bottle be used for further potencies by simply discarding the contents of the bottle and, using that which is left adhering to the wall of the bottles as one part, adding 99 times that amount of diluent to the bottle. This method is now used by most pharmacies in preparing any potency over a 30th, and is often indicated on the label by a "K."

In 1833, Hering began to experiment with dilutions in the ratio of 1:10. By the late 1830s, both Samuel Dubs in the USA and Vehsemeyer in Germany began making remedies using that scale. The American potencies were indicated by an "X"— the Roman numeral for "10," while the European potencies were generally marked as a "D" for "decimal"— 3X or D3.

Another scale, the "50-millesimal" was developed by Hahnemann in his later practice. Produced by a fairly elaborate method, the ratio of remedy to diluent was 1:50,000. Often referred to as "LM" potencies ("L" for 50 and "M" for 1000), this designation is not accurate since, in Roman numerals "LM" is equal to 950. In Europe, the remedies are more correctly called "Q" potencies for quinquagenta millesimal.

Skinner's potencies

Thomas Skinner, MD
August 11, 1825 — October 11, 1906

Educated in medicine at Edinburgh University, Skinner was an outspoken critic of homœopathy. Becoming ill and giving up his practice to preserve his health, he was treated by Dr. Edward Berridge. After a dose of 10M *Sulphur,* he completely recovered. He became a devout homœopath.

Skinner attended the 1876 Philadelphia International Exposition, and upon returning to England he founded (with Adolph Lippe, Edward Berridge, and Samuel Swan) *The Organon*— sub-titled "An Anglo-American Journal of Homœopathic Medicine and Progressive Collateral Science." It ceased publication after the first issue of Volume IV in 1881.

His potentizer was developed after the 1876 meeting in Philadelphia where he met Fincke, Swan, Dunham, and others who were interested in the pharmacy process.

Skinner practiced in Liverpool, England.

The Skinner Centesimal Fluxion Potentizer was first described in an article by Skinner in *The Organon.*

The machine was designed to be used in a wash-basin in a doctor's office. The water supply was attached to the machine and provided the motive power. The vial had a spherical bottom and held just 100 minims of liquid. The water supply was adjusted (with the stop-cocks) so that the vial was filled with 100 minims of water before overturning quickly and forcibly ejecting the contents down the drain. In theory, one drop was left adhering to the wall of the vial. The vial was returned to the upright position, and the process repeated.

Skinner wrote that because of the many ways to adjust the machine's water flow, there was "no difficulty obtaining mathematical certainty" in the potencies.

The machine could make 50 potencies a minute, 8,000 an hour, 72,000 per day, and a 100,000 (CM) in about 33 hours. An MM (a 1,000,000) could be made in 330 hours or 14 days.

The original Skinner Machine is on display at the Library of the Faculty of Homœopathy in London

In 1903, James Tyler Kent wrote a letter to Dr. Royal E. S. Hayes, singing the praises of the Skinner potencies made by Boericke and Tafel.
Although the question asked by Dr. Hayes which occasioned this response is unknown, the reply from Dr. Kent is known. The original letter remains with Dr. Hayes' grand-daughter.

Chicago, Ill. July 30, 1903

Dear Doctor Hayes:
This is the first time I have had this matter brought to my find. I am astonished at such a report. I am perfectly familiar with the entire process of making Skinner potencies. I am the one who urged the firm of Boericke & Tafel to put in a Skinner Potentizer and make the potencies. If the small glass is weighed dry and then weighed again after it has been emptied the precise centesimal potency remains. Go to the Grand St. House in New York and see for yourself. The fact remains. It is the only cent. potentizer in the world that makes accurate potencies. Fincke's potencies are absolutely unknown in their making. They are made in secret. Swan's potencies were a fraud of the worst sort. I saw Swan make some and I discarded all I had. I have a full set of Skinner's potencies— they work well— I know how they are made. I know all about them and expect to continue using them. The story must be gotten up in the interest of someone! Go to New York and see the thing work and you will see for yourself.
Yours truly,
J. T. Kent

I had looked for a likeness of Swan for years. Bradford's Scrapbooks *yielded only a letter from him. I had given up. One day I was with André Saine at the Hahnemann Archives and while he was looking for items about Lippe, I decided to browse Bradford's* Scrapbooks. *I pulled out the "G" volume, because it was the only one I could pull free without moving anything else on the shelf. I was looking at the entry for "Gentry" and found a number of articles about Gentry (the author of the* Concordance Repertory*) and how he became a faith-healer and decreed that Christ speaks through him alone. And then, on the next page, was an article that Gentry wrote about the tuberculin vaccine and how Swan had done the same thing 20 years earlier. And there was this likeness of Swan! Got it!*

The work of Swan

Samuel Swan, MD
July 4, 1814 — October 17, 1893

Swan was born in Medford, Massachusetts, to a family full of homœopathic supporters; the name "Swan" being well known in New England homœopathy. His uncle was one of the area's first homœopaths. Swan worked in the mercantile trade for most of his life, until entering medical school at 55, graduating from the Homœopathic Medical College of Pennsylvania in 1867.

Swan began practice in New York City as an associate of Edward Bayard. Especially interested in both pharmacy and the use of morbific products as remedies, he was the first to manufacture and prove *Medorrhinum* (the gonorrhea nosode), *Syphilinum* (made from the syphilis chancre) and he discovered the value of *Tuberculinum* (made from tubercular tissue) 20 years before Koch.

He died from complications of a poisoning he received while triturating a preparation of a Japanese varnish.

"I shall not urge the proving of morbific products. These powerful agents must be proved by those willing to sacrifice health and comfort, and though humanity will be the gainer, the services of the provers will not be appreciated, and there will be little sympathy for their sufferings.

"Great care should be taken to record conditions, aggravations and ameliorations, the sides of the body in which symptoms appear, in fact every circumstance connected with the action of the drug.

"It would be a great help if some Journal would devote as much space as is needed to provings, so that all the profession would know where to look for them, and to where to send those they have made. Fragmentary provings are of great value if they consist of but one symptom. There may be some one looking for that very symptom."

— *IHA Transactions 1885* (page 38). "On the Proving of Remedies" by Samuel Swan

"Morbific products, nosodes, and other assorted remedies"

When Samuel Swan died, his widow gave his collection of remedies to Boericke and Tafel in New York. The remedies were for sale, and the potencies were 1M (1,000C), 50M (50,000), CM (100,000), MM (1,000,000), CMM (100,000,000), and DMM (500,000,000). The eventual fate of these remedies is unknown.

About 1,000 remedies are listed in the catalog. Some are fairly common. Some have identifying names beside them, or a short paragraph about the use. It tells us a lot about how Swan thought and gives us a glimpse into one of the most original minds in the history of homœopathy. Here is a sampling of what was offered:

Achrocordon Chococ. : *South American Serpent. Inveterate ulcers and sores; pain in scrofulous patients*

Bellpul: *Belladonna and Pulsatilla; where each is indicated but do not cure.*

Butyraceum: *Buttermilk; Valvular disease of the heart*

Carchardon rondeletti: *Chinese shark oil; Chinese remedy for deafness*

Caguil columbiana: *Uncontrollable desire for coitus*

Cerulea irides: *(Blue ray of the spectrum)*

Coagulum lac vaccininum: *Nausea and vomiting when nothing else would have any effect*

Colostrum: *Constipation of newborn infants*

Fel gryllus americana: *Brazilian cricket. Suppression of urine with or without pain. A boy who had fever and chills swallowed a live cricket and never had a chill afterwards.*

Franciscea uniflora: *From the Amazon and Orinoco.; holds same relation to rheumatism as Cinchona does to chills and fever.*

Fuligo splendens: *Chimney soot where hard wood is burned.*

Helios: *The sun*

Lachryma filia: *Tears of a young girl in great grief and suffering.*

Melito ursea: *Diabetic sugar*

Neurine: *Mixture of Ether phos, Glonoine, Cactus grand.*

Pediculus corporis (from Boston): *bed-bug*

Rakoczy: *Spring water, rich in sulphate of magnesia and sulphate of sodium*

Sal cerebri: *Salt secreted profusely from a gentleman's scalp with the perspiration, and on drying it was crystallized so heavily his head looked frosted.*

Scomber scomber: *Mackerel*

Seriaca barlowii: *From a silk handkerchief eaten by a cow, and taken from the stomach in a hard ball. During the three years she never had a calf.*

Syzygium jambolatum: *For diabetes mellitus. Verified.*

Verucca menstruo: *Menstrual blood from a woman who had warts, and with which many have been cured. Skinner.*

Vipera pseudochis major: *Atrocious pains of the whole body. Rheumatic pains at the full moon, continuing for years. Hemorrhage of bright red blood from nose and mouth. Scanty, seldom, or entirely suppressed urine.*

Vomito: *Blood from a yellow fever patient while moribund.*

Williams-Quella: *A Cronthal water; causes pain in all the teeth and gums.*

From Samuel Swan to T. L. Bradford:

Nov. 20, 1889

Dear Doctor:

I have no pharmacy and never had one— I am a practicing physician, who nearly 20 years ago, began making high potencies for my own use— from time to time physicians would try them, and finding high potencies so superior to low began to call for them so much I was compelled to put a price upon them, and as potencies as high and as effective are not elsewhere to be had, the demand continues. This is all there is to it and is not worth noting in your book.

very respectfully
Samuel Swan

The Santee/Nash potencies

In *Leaders in Homœopathic Therapeutics,* E. B. Nash writes:
"I habitually prescribe the 55M made by myself upon the gravity potentizer, so that I know exactly what it is. So often are we confronted with the question when we reported cures with the high potencies, where do we get them, and are you sure they are what they purport to be? Now let me say right here, if I have not done so before, that we have potencies as high as the MM made by ourselves upon this accurately self-registering potentizer, that are marvelous for their curing powers. We (Dr. Santee and myself) invented the machine for our own individual use and have never yet offered the potencies for sale. So we can hardly be accused of mercenary motives in reporting cures, from them."

The Santee Gravity Potentizer

Ellis M. Santee graduated from St. Louis Homœopathic in 1890. As such, he undoubtedly had Kent as a teacher. He was studying with E. B. Nash in the summer of 1888, and they were discussing potentization. As Nash said, "I always try to satisfy a student upon this point… before I let him fall into the error of the American Institute of Homœopathy— the error that there is no efficacy in anything above the 12th, because they cannot discover any substance of the drug with a microscope."

That year Santee developed the gravity potentizer. It is calibrated for centesimal on one side of the tipping tray, and decimal on the other. Once the water begins to run, the side fills up, tips and the water continues filling the other side until the weight tips it back. The water tube is attached to any ordinary faucet, and the apparatus head contains 30 fine holes, allowing the water to run with some pressure. It will potentize about 2M per hour.

Nash said in the February 1889 *Homœopathic Physician,* "I had thought that when this potentizer was perfect, and we should bring it to the notice of the profession, I would publish cases cured by the remedies prepared by it."

The Kent potencies

Little is known about the history of the Kent Potentizer. Kent himself did not mention it. However, it is mentioned in an early catalog of Ehrhart and Karl as being the machine on which they make the potencies between 10M and CM. The machine is now at Luyties Pharmacal in St. Louis.

The operation is simple, with all mechanisms being driven by a single motor. Two remedies can be made at once. The bottom of the glass tube holding the liquid curves inward and has a hole in it. The hole is sealed with a leather pad. The glass tube is filled with a liquid potency and it is shaken 10 times. A cam then lifts the platform holding the vials away from the square cam which has been applying the successive action. A second cam then opens the stopper at the bottom of the vial, and the entire content is drained— except the little liquid remaining in the re-curved bottom of the vial. The bottom is then capped, more diluent is added, and the cycle repeats.

The one missing part is the mechanism which filled the vials. Forrest Murphy, who had owned Luyties, was under the impression that the water ran continuously through the vials. Knowing how Kent was not happy with the continuous fluxion of Swan, it is likely that there was another mechanism that metered an accurate amount of water into the tubes at the moment the plug at the bottom closed.

Unfortunately, no one who saw the machine operating is still alive to tell about it. The machine was reported to be in use through the 1950s.

Ehrhart and Karl offered a range of potencies and remedies made on the Kent Potentizer. 900 remedies were available, and they all started from a 1000th [1M] that was hand-made by Urban Ehrhart. The Kent range of potencies were available in 10M, 50M, and CM.

Above that range, E&K used a fluxion machine designed by H. C. Allen. Starting with a CM Kent, they produced DM (500,000) MM (1,000,000), CMM (100,000,000), DMM (500,000,000) and MMM (1,000,000,000). These ultra-high potencies were available in 250 polychrest remedies.

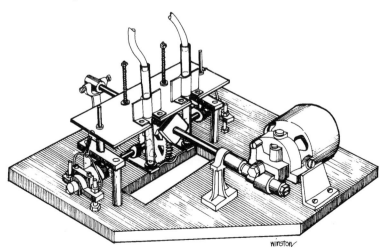

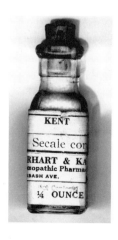

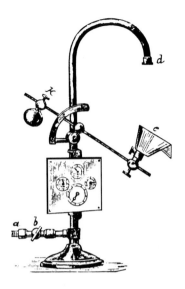

The S. P. Burdick Potentizer (top)
The Boericke and Tafel Skinner Machine (bottom)

The potency in the machine

W. W. Robinson, in an article on high potencies in the February 1941 *Homœopathic Recorder*, described the time when these machines were developed as "...an era when the physical and chemical sciences were beginning to take a more definite form, the concept of high potency thrived in what might be termed an atmosphere of 'gentle philosophy.'"

In 1829, Hahnemann said of the higher potencies, "there must be an end to this thing. It cannot go on indefinitely." Yet within 40 years Hering was urging the pharmacists to, "Go higher, ever higher."

As these people explored the "edges of the envelope" of potentization, the rhetoric to justify the methods flowed thick and heavy. The experimenters believed they were following the works of Hahnemann to the letter, and developed elaborate justifications to bolster their thinking. Thomas Skinner wrote of his machine, "...Hahnemann himself, if he could witness them, would highly approve." Each swore they were the ones "doing it right."

The potentizer of S. P. Burdick was discussed in an article in the May 1879 *North American Journal of Homœopathy*. The author, Martin Deschere, claims the Burdick machine is the "first correct and truly centesimal potentizer," and goes on to question Skinner's claim to the same for his machine.

In the end, the proof was in the use— did the potencies prepared on these various machines actually work in the clinical setting? Judging from the cases presented in the old journals, most of them did work.

A Boericke and Tafel catalog of the turn of the century was offering potencies made by Jenichen, Skinner, and Swan— along with their hand-made "Tafel's 200 and 1000" potencies. Ehrhart and Karl, in Chicago, were offering "Ehrhart's hand-made 200 and 1000" as well as higher potencies by Kent and even higher ones by Allen.

The Second Generation

The authors
The historians
The move west

The authors

Although by 1880 it was clear the homœopathic educational system was lacking integrity, the second generation (those who knew and were trained by the greats like Hering, Farrington, Dunham, Fincke, and Wells) were attempting to hold on to the purity of the Hahnemannian method. Many were well-known by their colleagues and are spoken of with admiration in the Society Transactions and journals of the day, yet they were simply good practitioners and never authored books. The ones we do know best are those who left their mark through their writings. It would be a Herculean task to name all the homœopaths of that grand era. What follows are glimpses of some of that era's major and minor figures.

Edwin Moses Hale, MD
February 2, 1829 — January 15, 1899

As a young man, Hale was treated for pneumonia by Dr. A. O. Blair of Newark, Ohio. His recovery was so successful he decided to become a physician. He studied under Blair and then attended the Cleveland Homœopathic College. Settling in Jonesville, Michigan in 1852, he established a large practice.

Hale authored the first edition of *New Remedies* in 1862, one of the first books discussing the new indigenous remedies of the USA— *Phytolacca, Gelsemium, Urtica urens, Chelone glabra* and others. One of his early books (1866) was *A Systematic Treatise on Abortion* which, writes Bradford, "On account of some obscure wording on page 319 of this work, Dr. Hale was accused by some of the profession, of advising, under certain circumstances, the induction of abortion. To make his meaning clear, printed slips were issued, to be pasted over the obnoxious words."

In 1884 he wrote a short essay on *The Cat and its Diseases*. In 1864, Hale was invited to be chair of materia medica at the Hahnemann College in Chicago. A prodigious author, he has 55 entries in Bradford's *Bibliography*. He served as editor of the *North American Journal of Homœopathy* from 1860-1869, and as editor of the *Homœopathic Observer* from 1867-1874.

Edwin M. Hale.

Reuben Ludlam, MD
October 7, 1831 — April 29, 1899

Graduating from the University of Pennsylvania Medical School in 1852, Ludlam settled in Chicago and turned to homœopathy within a year, after seeing its successes during a cholera epidemic. He was one of the organizers of the Hahnemann Medical College (1860) where he held the chair of obstetrics and diseases of women and children.

He was one of the earliest to speak out on behalf of women, urging them to become professionals. He was one of the first, in Victorian times, to advocate internal exams in gynecological cases, saying: "We should respect the delicacy of sex... but to allow any squeamish scruples to be in the way of patient recovery... argues both a criminal and crazy neglect on the part of the physician in attendance."

"His lectures are purely extemporaneous— no notes before him— and are remarkable for their systematic and practical character." Bradford's *Bibliography* lists 35 works by Ludlam, including his *Lectures on the Diseases of Women*, published in 1888. He was co-editor of the *North American Journal of Homœopathy*, and the *Medical Investigator*.

While getting ready to perform an operation, he said, "I feel weak." He sank into a chair, and died.

Timothy Field Allen, MD
April 24, 1837 — December 5, 1902

Timothy Allen was born in Westminster, Vermont and gained his undergraduate education at Amherst College. He gained his medical degree from New York University, and served as a surgeon in the Civil War. Returning to New York, he entered partnership with Dr. Carroll Dunham, and studied homœopathy with Dr. P. P. Wells in Brooklyn, New York.

He was professor of Materia Medica at the New York Homœopathic Medical College and later became its president. He was responsible for getting the half-million dollar grant from Roswell P. Flower, used to build an addition to the college which became the Flower Fifth Avenue Hospital. As professor and surgeon at New York Ophthalmic Hospital, he was responsible for converting it to a homœopathic institution.

Allen's two other interests were music and botany. Allen served as organist in several churches until his other duties forced him to retire. He was on the Board of Directors of the New York Botanical Gardens.

CINA.

Artemisia maritima, var. Stechmanniana, Besser; (A. Lecheana, Karel et Kiril; A. maritima, var. pauciflora, Weber.)

Nat. order, Compositæ; *Common names*, Flores Cinæ (Semen Cinæ), Wormseed, Wurmsamen.

Preparation. Tincture of the flower heads (commonly called seeds).

Authorities. 1, Hahnemann, R. A. M. L.; 2, Ahner, ibid.; 3, Gross, ibid.; 4, Langhammer, ibid.; 5, Ruckert, ibid.; 6, Stapf, ibid.; 7, Andry, De gener. vermin. observ., ibid.; 8, Bergius, Mat. Med. Observations, ibid.; 9, Pelargus, Obs. I, 8, 31, 279, obs. of overdosing, ibid.; 10, Noack, effects of a teaspoonful of the powder in a boy of $2\frac{1}{2}$, Hygeia, 16, 81; 11, Schmid, a boy of 5 took several large doses of the seeds, Deutsche Klin., 1852; 12, Archive für Hom., 16, 2, 206, effects of powder on children; 13, von Linstow, effects of 10 grammes of seeds on a girl of 10, apparently suffering from worms, Vjhrsch. f. Ger. Med., xxi, 1, 80, 1874 (S. J., 165, 21).

Mind.—Emotional. *Delirium,[9].—*Delirium, and crying out,[12].—* *Cries piteously if one takes hold of it or carries it* (after three hours),[1].— **The child is whining and complaining,[6].*—Moaning and groaning (in the afternoon),[1].—Great anxiety and apprehension, while walking in the open

Allen compiled the *Encyclopedia of Pure Materia Medica* over 10 years. It was a complete record of all provings done with homœopathic drugs. A partial page is reproduced here. The 10 volumes were published between 1874 and 1879. A fire in 1879 destroyed all stock of Vols. 2, 4, and 9. They were re-printed immediately.

The volumes were offered by subscription; 500 subscriptions were pre-paid to insure each volume's publication.

Allen had input on the work from Hering, Dunham, and Lippe, as well as from Richard Hughes in England.

The symptoms of each remedy are prefaced by a listing of the provers and the doses they took, or the other sources of information (such as accidental poisonings). So the symptom we read here of "Moaning and groaning (in the afternoon)" was reported by Hahnemann, using several provers, in his *Materia Medica Pura*.

The joy of using Allen's work is that you can find the entire symptom "constellation" in the prover's words and not pushed into the language of the *Repertory*. For example, in the proving of *Clematis*, Dr. Schück, aged 41, took 10 to 30 drops of the tincture daily, and reported: "Must go to bed earlier than usual; fell asleep only after long restless tossing about, with increased internal heat and violent headache; sleep disturbed by confused dreams, lasting till only 3 a.m., when he awoke with sudden starting and could not fall asleep again."

Charles F. Millspaugh, MD
June 20, 1854 — September 15, 1923

A graduate of Cornell University, Millspaugh received his medical degree from New York Homœopathic Medical College in 1881. He was a childhood friend of the Swiss naturalist Louis Agassiz.

American Medicinal Plants was first published in 1884. While practicing in Binghamton, New York he wrote a small *Repertory of Eczema* in 1885. He edited the *Homœopathic Recorder* from 1888-1890, and published many botanical papers between 1890 and 1915.

Millspaugh moved to Chicago to become curator of the Field Museum of Natural History. He was professor of botany at the University of Chicago and professor of medical botany at the Chicago Homœopathic Medical College. He was also a member of the IHA.

The Gold lettering on the leather cover of an original Millspaugh's *American Medicinal Plants*, with his drawing of *Hypericum*.

American Medicinal Plants *went through several printings after its introduction in 1884. A full "quarto" size, it was published in six folios, available as a subscription. A second printing in 1887 combined all the works into a single, large volume, with a gold imprint of the above pictured title on the black leather cover. Millspaugh dedicated the work to his artist father, "to whom I am indebted for whatever I may possess of art in drawing and coloring," and to T. F. Allen, "my honored professor and preceptor."*

Although the reviews of the time were somewhat "picky" about the work ("he should have shown this portion of the leaf instead of that") the colored plates are a wonder to behold. The volume was reprinted in the 1980s by Dover Books in a smaller size without the color plates. Original volumes are now selling for over $1,000.

William Tod Helmuth, MD, LLD
October 30, 1833 — May 15, 1902

Born in Philadelphia, he studied under his uncle, William Sheaff Helmuth, who taught at the Homœopathic Medical College of Pennsylvania. Helmuth obtained his medical degree from the school in 1853, and served as chair of anatomy until 1858 when he moved to Missouri. In 1859 he was one of the founders of the Homœopathic Medical College of Missouri, and in 1869 he organized the St. Louis College of Physicians and Surgeons. He accepted the position of chair of surgery at New York Homœopathic in 1870, and in 1893 he became dean. In the world of homœopathy he was renowned as a surgeon, and wrote several texts on the subject. He received an Honorary Law Degree from Yale University in 1888.

Described as, "A man of so genial and congenial nature, so affable, so approachable, so reasonable and so gentlemanly, none could be offended with him, but were constrained to aid him, and soon found him and his surgical art to be a contingent that they could not well succeed without," Helmuth was a prolific writer and among the 36 works listed in Bradford's, two are collections of poetry: The Scratches of a Surgeon and With the "Pousse Café;" being a Collection of Post-Prandial Verses.

Helmuth was the orator at the dedication of the Hahnemann Monument in Washington, DC in June, 1900.

HOW I BECAME A SURGEON

In the year eighteen hundred and fifty-three,
A few months after I took my degree
(Which styles me a "regular " H. M. D.),
On the Institute books I enrolled my name.
Being young in years and unknown to fame,
(The inference here I hope you'll excuse);
But I borrowed the money and paid my dues,
Which, as far as my recollection can get,
I think that I have not repaid as yet.

Be that as it may, without more delay
I went to the Institute that very day,
to hear what the old fellows all had to say.

Williamson, Hempel and Kirby and Gray,
Bayard and Joslin, McManus and Small,
Dake, Hering and Pulte, I heard them all.

Throughout that meeting I could not but feel
That the spirit which ruled those men was— zeal
Zeal for the system and zeal for the dose;
Zeal for applying similia close;
Zeal for the proving of medicine pure;
Zeal in proclaiming each wonderful cure.

My friends, 'twas this zeal, right be it or wrong,
That laid the foundation so broad and so strong
Of this Institute young— as it was in those days—
Now crowns it with glory and honor and praise.

Excuse the digression, the moments are fleeting,
And let me get back to that Institute meeting.

My nature's susceptible— very, I own it,
And years and gray hairs suffice not to tone it.
So the zeal of the rest inflated my breast;
And as nothing but symptoms and provings would stand
At the meetings in those days, I too took a hand;
And to show to the members for science my love,
I asked the committee for something to prove.

After some months' delay, on one beautiful day
(And if I remember a right 'twas in May),
There came to my office a nice little box,
With a nice little letter from J. Redman Coxe.
"Dear Doctor," he wrote, "I enclose you a vial
Of wondrous secretion; pray give it a trial.
As the bottle is small, in unpacking don't break it;
The liquid is viscid; before you can take it,
Heat gently, then wipe off the vial and shake it.
Then pour out exactly ten drops in a spoon,
And swallow it quickly, and if very soon
Queer symptoms develop, please write them to me,
As ever of old, your friend, JRC."

"P. S.— If you knew all the trouble I had
in procuring a dog undoubtedly MAD,
You'd drink the solution with infinite pleasure
Regarding each drop as a wonderful treasure."

"Good gracious!" I said to myself— then a pause—
A stiffening sensation surrounded my jaws
I seemed to be looking at things in a fog
And the atmosphere round me smelled strongly of dog.
And just at that moment I felt that my zeal
Was ebbing quite rapidly out at my heel.

But I plucked up my courage and worked at my chin,
Its suppleness seemed as it ever had been,
And the thought flashed across me 'twere better that I
Should ask a few doctors this virus to try,
If bad opisthotonos came with each breath,
To end in convulsions and coma and death,
With meekness the pleasure to them I would give,
Enroll THEM as martyrs— and I myself live.

The difficult question was, who should I ask
To enter upon such a dangerous task ?
Who would assist me to prove? was the topic;
Who would engage in the act philanthropic?
I picked out ten fellows all brim full of knowledge,
All eager for glory and just out of college.

Then I made a dilution as Boericke makes,
And gave to each vial just two hundred shakes,
Increasing succussion as Jenichen did,
By pounding the vials on pads made of kid.
Then I sat down and wrote to each of my friends:
"Dr. Helmuth's kind greetings. This vial he sends
For a proving, and trusts that with infinite care
Each prover will give it a trial most fair."

"Must take it when fasting," I finally wrote.
"And as it develops each new symptom note.
'Tis slow in its action, as often appeals.
For the virus is known to be latent for years,
But when the zymosis you once can detect
The prover will never know what to expect.
Be careful in using." In closing I said,
"No more is obtainable— Doggy is dead."

My letters were posted and day after day,
I waited to hear what the provers would say.
Not a line, not a symptom, however, appeared.
My reason was staggered; I really feared

109

The Faces of Homœopathy

That though I was acting as sly as a fox,
That I might be victimized sadly by Coxe.
The virus most certainly taken they had,
But nobody yet seem inclined to go mad.
So I musingly muttered, "These provers won't die,
They took it— I alter my mind— so will I,"
And immediately swallowed a dose of the same
As my friends who were patiently waiting for fame,
Yet tortures terrific we had to endure—
Incubation was slow— zymosis was sure.

Remorse consumes my soul to-night,
When I, in guilt arrayed,
Behold, oh, dreadful, dreadful sight!
Those wrecks that I have made.

Those lovely youths, so fair and true,
Great gifts of promise had;
No matter how they seem to you
They are all raving mad.
The briny tears course down my face;
The deed, indeed I rue it;
And though a melancholy case,
I did not mean to do it.

But listen, my friends, how it acted on me:
I went into fits, and then— went on a spree,
And when I recovered I scarcely could see.
From that very moment my pretty left eye
Close up to the internal canthus did lie,
And there it remains by day and by night,
Impairing my beauty and marring my sight.
Strabismus convergent if but in one eye,
Is a source of most constant discomfort, and I,
Beholding the wreck of those beautiful boys,
Saw them losing their reason, deprived of the joys
Of exuberant manhood, and shrieking with pain,
Said "damn it" (Excuse me) I never again

For friendship, or science, or money or love,
Will ask your committee for something to prove.
I did my whole duty, have had quite enough;
Give somebody else all your poisonous stuff.

Then, then it was, fellows, I first saw the light,
And surgery beautiful dawned on my sight.
I studied its present, I delved in its past,
And found what my spirit had yearned for, at last.

Found science and art in proportion so grand,
The effort of mind with the dexterous hand,
Combining themselves with such exquisite care,
And yielding results so remarkably fair,
That I bowed down in silence and bended my knees
And claimed the department belonging to me.

I saw what I thought was my pathway in life,
discarded all provings and stuck to the knife.
And though I've been fairly successful, 'tis true,
There's one thing in cutting I never can do.

I may cut out a bone or extirpate tumors,
I may amputate limbs and evacuate humors,
Kill every bacillus and aspirate sacs,
Apply plaster jackets to carious backs,
Make beautiful noses by art rhinoplastic.
Cure pulsating tumors with bandage elastic.

I may stretch every nerve, perform herniotomy.
And advocate still supra-pubic lithotomy,
I may do all this cutting with ecstacy— but
I never will dear old acquaintances cut.
And I hope in return that wherever I be
No dear old acquaintance will ever cut me.

Thomas Cation Duncan, MD
1840 — July 16, 1902

Duncan was born in Kinross, Scotland, emigrated to the United States, and gained his medical degree at Hahnemann Chicago in 1866.

He was the editor of *Medical Investigator/ United States Medical Investigator* from 1866-1888.

With his brother, he formed a publishing house, Duncan Brothers, which specialized in homœopathic literature.

He has 14 entries in Bradford's *Bibliography*, most of the books dealing with the treatment of children: *Diseases of Infants and Children; Domestic Homœopathic Treatment of Children*, and others.

Cultural standards in 1878

How to be Plump, by Duncan, was published in 1878. In the preface, Duncan says:

"'How shall I get fleshy? I would give anything to be as plump as Miss —!' 'Poor child; it is nothing but skin and bone! What shall I feed it that it will fat up?' 'I would give a dollar a pound for more fat!' 'I flesh up in the winter, and then I feel so much better!' 'This climate agrees with me nicely; I never was so well and fleshy in my life.' 'Since I became fleshy I am very well, indeed.' 'She was thin and sickly, but now is the very picture of health.' 'When in Europe I was so fleshy, and had such an appetite.' 'While drinking water at— I felt so much better and fleshed up.' 'The hot baths did me so much good; but cold baths make me sick.' 'I have fleshed up remarkably this year (a wet year) and feel, oh, so much better!' 'When I weighed one hundred and forty pounds I felt well; now I weigh only one hundred and ten pounds, and feel so miserable!' 'What has fifteen or twenty pounds of fat to do with health?'

"Such are a few of the problems that cluster around *How To Be Plump*, the solution of which, this work attempts.

"Why cannot 'the picture of health' be painted in all faces? Why is plumpness associated with health and leanness with disease? Why are "Americans proverbially lean?' These are vital questions, that touch the philanthropic, interest the statesman, and arouse scientific investigation.

"The rules for healthy feeding are very simple, when once understood. The following pages have been prepared, so as to give the widest dissemination with the hope that they may prove as valuable to every lean person, as their personal and professional application has to."

The chapters:

- How I Became Plump
- Leanness As A Disease
- The Healthy Or Physiological Standard
- The Importance Of Water
- The Value Of Fat
- The Necessity For Starchy Foods And Sweets
- How To Become Plump

Rollin R. Gregg

Rollin R. Gregg, MD
August 19, 1828— August 4, 1886

Gregg attended Cleveland Homœopathic College for one year and then transferred to Philadelphia, receiving his degree from the Homœopathic Medical College of Pennsylvania in 1853. He practiced in Buffalo, New York.

An obituary noted he was "Plain and unassuming in manner... An enthusiast in his profession, he exercised it conscientiously with less regard to his own comfort than to the good of his patients." Despite a busy practice, he devoted one afternoon a week to seeing the poor with no fee charged. He died after a lingering illness.

His *Illustrated Repertory* is one of the unique books in the literature.

The Illustrated Repertory of Pains of the Chest, Sides, and Back by Rollin R. Gregg, MD, was published in 1879.

The arrow tail points to where the pain arises, and the head to where the pain terminates. A two-headed arrow indicates a darting or stitching pain in both directions. A hook indicates a drawing stitch. A heart placed on an arrow indicates a throbbing stitch. Short lines or bars indicate a tearing stitch. A pincers is a pinching pain, a half-globe is a pressing pain, and a crooked line indicates a contractive stitch.

As an example, Agaricus *has a "pinching pain in the left side of the chest down to the umbilicus," while* Chin. sulph. *has "stitches in the chest from the right side to the pit of the stomach."*

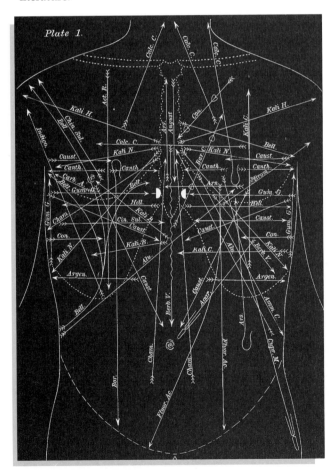

112

William A. Yingling, MD
January 12, 1851 — April 3, 1933

Yingling was born in Westminster, Maryland. He took his A.B. from Western Maryland College, and his medical degree at the University of Maryland, intending to become a medical missionary in India. He then studied for the ministry at Northwestern University in Illinois, but poor health prevented him from going to Bombay.

For seven years he was a minister in Findlay, Ohio. He went to Kansas for his health, settling near Dodge City. He was involved in the cattle business, but when the Indian Territory was closed to grazing, he went broke, losing about $75,000. The town of Nonchalanta, Kansas was named such on his suggestion in 1886.

"He reluctantly returned to the practice of medicine to relieve the suffering in the sparsely populated country north of Dodge City… He was known as a homœopathic physician." He practiced in Emporia, Kansas.

He wrote the still–published *Accoucheur's Emergency Manual*, first published in 1895.

He died at 82, having been "sick with paralysis for six months." He was buried at Memorial Lawn Cemetery in Emporia, Kansas.

A son, J. Max Yingling was the designer of the suspension bridge over the Mississippi river between Marquette, Iowa and Prairie du Chien, Wisconsin.

No mention has been found in any sources to indicate how Yingling became interested in homœopathy.

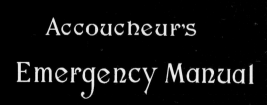

The gold embossing on the original printing of Yingling's book by Boericke and Tafel in 1895.

Eugene Beauharis Nash, MD
March 8, 1838 — November 6, 1917

Nash studied medicine with Dr. T. L. Brown in Binghamton, New York, and graduated from Cleveland Homœopathic in 1874. He practiced in Cortland, New York. For seven years he was professor of materia medica at the New York Homœopathic Medical College. He was the president of the International Hahnemannian Association in 1903. In 1905 he gave a course of lectures at the Homœopathic Hospital in London.

He was a "devoted Sunday School worker" and was reported to have "a fine tenor voice." In 1913, upon the printing of the 4th edition of his *Leaders* he wrote: "To my good wife, who has done the clerical work under my dictation, is due much praise. This on account of my blindness. As I draw near the end of my earthly career I hope to leave an influence for good that will live many years."

Eugene Beauharis Nash was the author of Leaders in Homœopathic Therapeutics. *This brief materia medica has been one of my favorites, if for no other reason than the remedies are presented, as Nash says, "following the bent of my inclinations," rather than in alphabetical order.*

E. P. Anshutz relates how a manuscript from Dr. Nash came to Boericke and Tafel in 1893, and was returned with a note telling him how to make it more readable. In 1897, B&T printed Leaders in Homœopathic Therapeutics *which went through four editions by 1913. Says Anshutz:* "Dr. Nash visited Philadelphia and his publisher tendered him dinner. Everything that a fine restaurant had was at his call, but his food and drink was of the simplest, water, a cup of tea, a bit of some meat, and a few vegetables. His talk was interesting— wish we could recall it. But there comes a memory of his saying that in his start in practice he feared he would lose his eyesight, and came to Philadelphia to consult Dr. Ad. Lippe. That old homœopath prescribed for him and the trouble vanished. Perhaps it was this that confirmed in him the truth of homœopathy from which he never deviated.

"At the dinner he took the occasion to thank the publishers for returning his first manuscript, saying that he could see now that it would have never achieved its present success under the original form."

Samuel A. Jones, MD
June 11, 1834 — March 9, 1911

Born in Manchester, England, Jones' family moved to the United States and he grew up in Utica, New York. He served as a surgeon in the Civil War. Jones was the dean of the homœopathic department at the University of Michigan in Ann Arbor in 1880. Described as "a live wire," he was a most outspoken proponent of homœopathy. He authored a little book published in 1880 called *The Grounds of a Homœopath's Faith*. It is the transcript of three lectures he gave in 1879 to the students of the "regular" medical school at Ann Arbor.

Dr. James C. Wood, one of his students, said, "All who knew him dreaded his caustic pen and still more caustic tongue." Small in stature, he was known at Ann Arbor as "little pill Jones."

Upon being called a "damn liar" by a prominent physician, Jones quietly said, "You are a gentleman, sir; now we have both lied."

Jones, in an argument with an administrator of the school at Ann Arbor, wrote: "You have not enough calcium in your backbone to whiten your pate."

His adversarial nature appeared at an early age. He enrolled at the Homœopathic Medical College of Pennsylvania, took some courses, and then left. When he decided to return, the administration could not find his record of attendance. Expressing disgust with the school's incompetence, he enrolled in the Homœopathic Medical College of Missouri in St. Louis, graduating in 1860. He then returned to Philadelphia, with his medical degree, attended one year at the school which had previously denied him admission, and received his MD from there in 1861.

As a hobby, Jones collected the writings of Thoreau, Hawthorne, and Melville. The University of Illinois at Champaign-Urbana has a number of original editions of these works belonging to Jones.

Dr. Wood tell the story: "Jones had been called into consultation the week before to see a farmer's wife, living six miles in the country, desperately ill with a colic of some sort. On this particular morning the farmer came in to pay him. His report was that Jones had relieved his wife almost instantly with the medicine he had prescribed and she had

Samuel A. Jones.

remained well since. Jones' fee for the consultation was thirty dollars, at least twenty-eight more than the farmer had ever paid his regular physician for the same trip. With great deliberation he extracted from his wallet three ten-dollar bills and grudgingly handed them over, saying as he did so, 'Dr. Jones, thirty dollars would hire me two good men on the farm for a month. I think your bill is robbery.' Jones replied, 'Well, damn it, the next time your wife gets a bellyache, hire two good men for a month!'"

Jones' legacy remains with us to this day. In 1985 Jones' grand-daughter, Carol Jane Prescott, established a $75,000 fund through the National Center for Homeopathy for the "education of physicians in homœopathy." The "Samuel A. Jones Scholarship" has provided several physicians their homœopathic education.

"Science studies the phenomenon of poisoning; Art runs for the stomach pump."

"…Science is apt to be puffed up with a vain conceit of itself. But it resembles the Irishman's pig, of which, he declared, after he had killed, cleaned, and put it upon the scales, 'My pig doesn't weigh as I thought it would, and I knew it wouldn't!' The living, grunting pigs of science are always over-weight; but the progress of science is to be traced by the slaughtered pigs along the wayside that have been killed, cleaned, weighed, and found wanting. They didn't weigh as much as they thought they would; but, ah, they didn't 'know that they wouldn't'— the more's the pity of it! These slaughtered pigs are known as theories; and they have such pretty curly tails, and after the manner of all pigs when scratched by an admiring hand, they give the grunt of piggly satisfaction; like all pigs they are most beautiful in death… Oh ye students, weigh the pig before you buy it…

"…These creations, or should I say fictions, are like the wooden guns that are sometimes made to play a part in warfare. Looked at from afar, they seem to be capable of making havoc, and they sorely afright the timorous, deterring them from going boldly up to them and finding out they are only impositions.

"They are called Quaker guns because they will never do duty in a fight. Science has whole parks of these Quaker guns, and, would you believe it? There are scores of physicians calling themselves homœopathic, whom a display of these wooden imbecilities has frightened until they actually ran out of camp… Some few years ago a Quaker gun was brought to bear upon another wooden gun known as the dynamization theory, and then you should have seen these homœopaths, so called, run. They dropped their knap-sacks, cartridge boxes, guns and made for the woods, and there some of them are until this day. Others went over to the enemy, body, boots, and breeches, and others are under cover in the American Institute of Homœopathy. The incident lives in history as the 'Retreat of the Feeble Minded,' and will be read by their children with becoming pride."

When Jones died many of his books remained at the libraries of the schools at which he had taught, but his personal papers went to the library of the University of Illinois at Champaign-Urbana, and it was there, in 1982, that I perused them and gained an appreciation of this wonderful man.

Jones' "caustic pen" can be viewed (at right) in an article he wrote, titled "Science and Art in Medicine," where he speaks, in no uncertain terms about the American Institute and "The Milwaukee Test."

Erastus Ely Case, MD
May 28, 1847 — October 27, 1918

Case graduated from Yale in 1872 and from the New York Homœopathic Medical College in 1874. He practiced medicine in Hartford, Connecticut for 44 years. He was president of the International Hahnemannian Association in 1901. His *Clinical Experiences*, a collection of cases and papers he presented, is an amazing testimony to the materia medica knowledge and the skill of this grand prescriber. Recently re-published, original copies of Case's little book are "homœopathic gold."

T. G. Sloan, MD, who learned homœopathy from Case said:

"Dr. Case was not brilliant, but was a tremendously hard worker, the most industrious man I ever knew. Years ago he copied long-hand *Boenninghausen's Pocket Book*, from cover to cover, as it was out of print and he could not get a copy.

"He was a thorough repertory student. Some of our men depend more than Dr. Case on their knowledge of materia medica, but he used his repertories and went through to his *Guiding Symptoms* or other materia medica. He was very thorough and painstaking.

"He was never idle. He was one of the very few really happy and contented men I have known.

"After a patient had told his story he usually asked, 'what other troubles have you?'"

Of Dr. Case, Royal E. S. Hayes said:
"Apparently he used all repertories using one or another according to some reason of his own, not accepting the belief that Kent's swallowed all the others. He dropped remarks to me about them at various times. Of Gentry's he said, 'I use it sometimes but you do not need to buy it.' Of Boenninghausen's, 'I use Kent's every day at my desk but for hard chronic cases I always go to Boenninghausen.' He knew repertories; and he had such a faculty for apprehending the individuality of the patient that the repertory was to him not merely a machine to work along through but a quick conveyance to, or almost to, the certain remedy. He was not only a master in collating essential symptoms but he appeared to know exactly what to do with them in the way of tracking down a remedy. He was full of what might be called 'a knowing wisdom.'"

I had been reprinting some of Case's "Drills in Prescribing" in the National Center of Homeopathy's newsletter. I received a letter from a reader asking me to ask Dr. Case if it was possible for him to include the repertory rubrics he used to find the remedy, since the reader was struggling to find out how Case had determined the remedy from the scant information given. I informed the reader that not only had Dr. Case been dead since 1918, but those who knew him when he was alive had asked the same question! He certainly was a master of the remedies and their symptoms.

Stuart Close, circa 1925

Stuart M. Close, MD
November 24, 1860 — June 26, 1929

Close intended to study law, but his father died in 1879 and his mother remarried a homœopathic physician, turning Close's mind to medicine. He studied the *Organon* with his step-father, attended medical school in California for two years, completing his studies at New York Homœopathic, graduating in 1885. After finishing school he preceptored with P. P. Wells and Bernhardt Fincke, and set up practice in Brooklyn, New York. In 1897 Close founded the Brooklyn Homœopathic Union, a group devoted to the study of the principles of pure Hahnemannian homœopathy. He was elected president of the International Hahnemannian Association in 1905. From 1909 to 1913 he was professor of homœopathic philosophy at New York Homœopathic. His lectures were published in the *Homœopathic Recorder*. They, in turn, became his book, *The Genius of Homœopathy*, one of the most concise books on homœopathic philosophy ever written.

It is reported he had one of the finest homœopathic libraries in the country. He was deeply interested in genealogy. In the words of Julia M. Green, MD, "I think he did not know himself. He seemed to wear a gentle armor of protection, and look out on the world from behind it."

Close relates a case of a 45-year-old woman whom he was called to see. The woman was confined to her bed. She gradually grew weaker and weaker until she was pronounced to be dying. Close was called when there was no hope left. He arrived to have the family say, "It's too late, doctor, she's gone." He did a rapid examination and found her limbs cold and rigid, but the body still warm. There was no pulse, and no visible respiration. Her eyes were fixed, the lids slightly open, and her features had the expression of death. "But the thought of death was not in my mind in spite of the evidence. I drew down her lower lip and shook a few pellets of Arsenic 45m (Fincke) upon the exposed mucous membrane and rubbed her lips against the gum. Then, following a peculiar, but impelling impulse, I talked to her and rubbed her stiffened arms and legs. Presently she opened her eyes and looked at me as I bent over her, and whispered to me 'I'm coming back.'"

Ten minutes later the woman told Close that although unconscious of her surroundings, she was "alive in her mind." Her father and mother (who had been dead many years) came for her to take her away with them. "She had left her body and was just about to leave the room with them when she heard me call her to come back. She felt that she could not disobey me and regretfully left her father and mother and came back. The next she remembered was opening her eyes and seeing me, and talking to me. She went on to make an uneventful recovery and has led a healthy life for these 20 years past."

Edward Pollock Anshutz
March 23, 1846 — January 31, 1918

Anshutz came to Philadelphia from Ohio in 1872. He was editor of *The New Church Life*, a Swedenborgian magazine. In 1885 he joined Boericke and Tafel as literary editor and manager, a position he held until his death. He was also editor of *The Homœopathic Recorder* and the *Homœopathic Envoy*. As editor of several homœopathic journals, Edward Pollock Anshutz preserved, in the printed word, the art and science of homœopathy.

In 1909, the Hering College in Chicago conferred upon him an honorary Doctorate of Medicine.

Said T. L. Bradford, in a memorial: "The desk is there and the office chair. The desk is still littered with the papers of a literary man. Over the chair back lies the well-worn office coat. The pigeon holes of the desk are full of treasures of the pen, waiting to be passed upon and maybe to be printed and given to the world of doctors... It is as though the busy editor had stepped for a moment into the next room, and would be back shortly with the usual kindly greeting, 'How are you Doctor?'"

Andrew Leight Monroe, MD
April 4, 1856 — c. 1935

Born and raised in Louisville, Kentucky, Monroe gained his medical degree from the Hahnemann Medical College in Philadelphia in 1879. He practiced in Birmingham, Alabama, until 1885, when he returned to Louisville. He was chair of materia medica at Pulte College in Cincinnati for three years after which he moved to the Southwestern Homœopathic College in Louisville serving as professor of materia medica and the school's dean. He wrote a wonderful primer called *Monroe's Materia Medica Memorizer*.

P roud as a queen, yet greatest depression,
L arge things seem small, distrust and suspicion.
A head as to menses, much dark clotted blood
T hus often for women Hysterical good;
I ndurated and fallen the womb we do find,
N euralgias and pains that are cramping in kind,
A nd "putty–like" stools serving bowels to bind.

— *Monroe's Materia Medica Memorizer*, 1882

The historians

Homœopathic history's records were kept alive by William Harvey King in New York and Thomas Lindsley Bradford in Philadelphia.

William Harvey King, MD, LLD
February 21, 1861 — July 24, 1942

King graduated from New York Homœopathic in 1882, and received his doctor of laws from Central University of Iowa in 1902.

In 1884 he devoted himself to investigating electro-therapeutics, and in 1901 published *Electricity in Medicine and Surgery*. For 10 years he was the editor of the *Journal of Electro-Therapeutics*. From 1894 on he held the chair of electro-therapeutics at New York Homœopathic. He was the first to demonstrate the use of x-ray in a college of medicine.

His four–volume *History of Homœopathy in America* was published in 1905 and remains a landmark work on the subject.

Thomas Lindsley Bradford, MD
June 6, 1847 — December 13, 1918

Born in New Hampshire, Bradford gained his medical education at Harvard Medical School and the Homœopathic Medical College of Pennsylvania, receiving his degree in 1869. He practiced medicine in Skowhegan, Maine until 1877, when he moved to Philadelphia.

He soon joined the faculty of Hahnemann Medical College, and in 1894 became the curator of the college's library.

His literary works were many: *Homœopathic Bibliography of the United States; History of Hahnemann Medical College and Hospital; Index to Homœopathic Provings; Life and Letters of Hahnemann; The Pioneers of Homœopathy; The Logic of Figures;* and *A Characteristic Materia Medica,* as well as contributing many of the articles in King's four-volume *History of Homœopathy*.

While library curator he established the collection known as Bradford's *Scrapbook,* 35 volumes, alphabetically arranged, filled with letters, photos, and other ephemera relating to homœopaths.

The move west

While Chicago and St. Louis had been the "western homœopathic centers" during the 1840s, homœopathy reached out to California in the aftermath of the 1849 Gold Rush.

Samuel Lilienthal, MD
December 5, 1815 — Oct. 3, 1891

Born in Munich, Germany, Lilienthal was granted his doctorate of medicine from the University of Munich in 1838. He immigrated to America in 1839. In 1847, in Lockport, New York, he was introduced to homœopathy. After living in Haverstraw, New York he moved to New York City in 1857. He joined the faculty of the New York Homœopathic Medical College in 1869, as chair of clinical medicine. On the recommendation of Dr. Hering, Lilienthal became the editor of the *North American Journal of Homœopathy* from 1872 to 1885. He also proved several remedies including *Carbolic acid* and *Physostigma*.

Lilienthal's brother Max followed him to the United States, where he founded the Hebrew Union School and became an influential rabbi in the American Jewish community. Samuel and Max married sisters; Sam married Caroline (Rachel) Nettre in 1843, and Max married Babette Nettre in 1845.

In 1887, Samuel moved to San Francisco to join his son, James, who was teaching at the Homœopathic Medical College of the Pacific. He retired after a year. The Lilienthal family, through Samuel's children, became influential merchants in the San Francisco community.

Martin Deschere, MD, said of him: "One of his most notable characteristics was his punctuality. He retired every night at 10 p.m. and rose at 6. From this hour on until 9 he wrote or studied. Then came the business of the day. After dinner he generally studied until 9. In this way he was enabled to do the enormous amount of literary work he did."

In a memorial service, Dr. Brinkman said: "Dr. Lilienthal always entertained the most friendly feeling toward the ladies in the profession. Twenty years ago the popular feeling was entirely different from what it is at present, and he was largely instrumental in bringing about the change. He

"I thought I should see a young man before me, and now that hard-working Lilienthal is as grey as I am."
—*Hering upon meeting Lilienthal*

Samuel Lilienthal as a young boy

constantly endeavored to persuade them to join the various societies, county, state, and national, and endeavored to bring them forward in every legitimate way."

An obituary, penned by Dr. Samuel A. Jones, appeared in the *Homœopathic Recorder* in November 1891. It provides a rare glimpse of the man by one who knew him as a friend and colleague:

"It is nearly a quarter of a century since I first met him who was Samuel Lilienthal. A series of introductory lectures were being delivered at the mother college in Philadelphia, and I preceded him by one night. I was the guest of Dr. Hering, who easily persuaded me to prolong my visit so that I might attend Lilienthal's lecture… I did not agree with him; but the sincerity of his convictions disarmed criticism. How racy, too, his German-English pronunciation, for he religiously avoided our anserine 'th' sound. It was always 'Homeopatic,' 'Terapeutic,' with him to the last… On the morrow we journeyed together from Philadelphia to New York, and thus began one of the pleasantest friendships that death has ever broken…

"A few years later that restlessness which so often disturbs the country physician when he is deceived by the glamour of a 'city practice,' seized me, and I looked with longing towards Gotham. No sooner did 'Old Sam' hear of my desire than he pressed me to come to New York, and to share his office,— and this, mind you, without paying a stiver of rent. He made it the more easy for a poor and proud spirit to become his almsman by urging that I should assist him in his literary work, revising his Teutonic English, discussing medical papers in the journals, and talking with him, 'for the two of us can talk like the * * *, you know!'

"I not only shared his office; I was also welcomed to a home circle which, though lacking a mother, had a gentle warmth that would melt the shyest…

"But let me not forget the divine nights, for 'Old Sam' was an ardent lover of music, and between the opera and Thomas's Garden we had our noctes in which we forgot every care. After the opera, or one of Thomas's concerts, came the late lunch, the 'Pilsener'— for they had 'Pilsener' in those days— and then home (even I had learned to call it 'home'), and the soothing cigar, and the talk late into the night, and finally the sudden, 'By tunder, Sam Jones, we must go to bed !'

"No. 230 West Twenty-fifth street,— I am again sitting by the office window, and the perfume of the ailanthus tree is wafted in, and I have turned from my book and am waiting, not for the 'patient,' but to hear the well-known sharp staccato footsteps that tell me 'Old Sam' has finished his morning round of visits, and then his cheery greeting, and then the paper for the *North American* that must be read and criticized— and, I must add, accepted in spite of all criticisms: his heart continually running away with his head…

"From an intimate acquaintance… I can truly declare that

Samuel Lilienthal spent more on medical literature in a single year than did the late Dr. Croesus in his whole lifetime…

"Lilienthal was also an indefatigable reader. Many suppose that this implies a limited practice; the inference is not valid in his case. He was indeed a busy practitioner. How did he find time to read? By utilizing the spare minutes. No sooner had he laid aside his visiting case than he picked up the journal that had been read up to the very minute of his starting upon his round of visits. Or if he did not begin reading the moment he entered his office, he took the unfinished manuscript from his portfolio, and with his nose close to the paper, for he was shortsighted, began writing at once. I have always detested interruptions when writing; but he husbanded the few minutes before dinner would be ready, and this will explain his productiveness. To his earnestness he added industry. I wish it could be computed for how many years of his life he had a pen in his faithful hand. It was a matter of surprise to me how much his pen could put upon a page. He wrote as small a hand as Hahnemann; and perhaps both learned that economy in the early days when writing paper was much dearer. Dear old soul! He actually prided himself upon his chirography, which often looked as if it had been done by a choreic spider on roller skates.

"Only for Dr. Lilienthal the *North American Journal of Homœopathy* would have perished of inanition long ago. How chivalrously he came to the rescue; he felt as if fealty to those who had inaugurated that magazine demanded that he should put on his armor and leap into the gulf… And how incessantly he translated, and translated, and translated for it! O, the drudgery of translating! No glow of composition to warm one; a mere hewing of wood and carrying of water for another.

"My only objection to his excerpts was that, like Hering, all was fish that came to his net. It mattered not who vouched for the printed statement, he accepted all without a challenge because he thought all as earnest and as truthful as himself.

"As an editor, I think he was lacking in the critical faculty, and I doubt if his editorial work will prove anything other than ephemeral. I do not think that any of his utterances on any of the questions that have arisen within the last twenty-five years, have, in any degree, molded the opinions of his readers. He could be steadfast to his own convictions— no one more so— but he could not follow his convictions with fire and sword when 'the heathen raged and the people imagined a vain things.' When the fiery Lippe would fulminate his anathemas like a pistareen Pope, I recollect that Lilienthal would write him letters of such stern rebuke that I used to wish one of them might be published in the *North American*, if only to assure its readers of the sex of the editor…

"I remember a portrait that hung in his bedroom; it was that of his Rachel who, long years ago, left him lonely, but with a love in his heart that time could not change. I have often wondered if it was not this unquenchable love for his dead wife that made his manner so charmingly tender and winning to all women.

"There was a blending of knightly courtesy with a fatherly fondness, and wherever he came he conquered."

"Once I was young, but now I am old. Take this third edition as the old man's testament to his many students and younger colleagues, for your success rejuvenates your old teachers."
— *Lilienthal's introduction to the Third Edition of* Homœopathic Therapeutics *(1890)*

William Boericke, MD
November 26, 1849 — April 1, 1929

Born in Austria, Boericke immigrated to the United States as a child and settled in Ohio. He went to California to manage the Boericke and Tafel pharmacy in San Francisco in 1870. He returned east to attend medical school and graduated from Hahnemann Medical College in Philadelphia in 1880. He moved back to California where he had a successful practice in San Francisco. He was one of the founders of the Homœopathic Medical College of San Francisco in 1884. In 1901 he authored *Boericke's Materia Medica.* It went through nine editions in his lifetime. His brother, Oscar (a graduate of Hahnemann Medical College, 1898) added a repertory to the book in 1906.

Boericke was editor of the *California Homœopath* and served on the faculty of Hahnemann Medical College in San Francisco.

His granddaughter, Jean Barnard, remembers he "used to call all us kids 'Dove' and he would always kiss and hug us, he was a very loving man."

"Our family belonged to the high society in San Francisco at the time because Granddad was the physician of choice in the area between 1880 and 1920. People came from all over the world to be treated homœopathically by him. My parents used to always say 'Poor Papa' because he worked so hard, and the thing I remember the strongest is them saying 'don't bother Papa.' My family was very devoted to him, whatever he said was the law. Although he emigrated from Austria, he had no accent and there was no German spoken in our house. He and I used to go on walks together down Tamalpais Avenue. I remember he took such long steps, I would scurry along next to him as he engaged me in conversation."

He died of a massive heart attack. Jean recalls, "Many months before, he had developed angina symptoms after racing my father down Tamalpais Avenue. He was about 5'9" and fairly fast on his feet for a man in his late 70s."

Two months after he died, his house burned to the ground. Everything was turned to ash except the stone fireplace and, oddly enough, all of his homœopathic books.

Willis A. Dewey, MD
October 25, 1858 — April 1, 1938

A native of Middlebury, Vermont, Dewey graduated in 1880 from the New York Homœopathic Medical College. He was an intern at Ward's Island Homœopathic Hospital, and then spent two years abroad. In 1884 he moved to California where he was professor of anatomy and then chair of materia medica at the Homœopathic Medical College of San Francisco. From 1888 until 1892 he was the editor of *The California Homœopath*. He returned to teach in New York in 1894 and in 1896 assumed the chair of materia medica at the University of Michigan at Ann Arbor.

He authored *Essentials of Homœopathic Materia Medica, Essentials of Homœopathic Therapeutics,* and *Practical Homœopathic Therapeutics,* as well as collaborating with William Boericke on *The Twelve Tissue Salts.*

176   ESSENTIALS OF

What are the mental symptoms of Coffea?

It produces an ecstatic state of mind; unusual activity of mind and body; full of fancies; acuteness of all senses; great flow of thought.

What drug has the symptom that children wake at night unnaturally bright and playful, evincing no desire to go to sleep again?

Cypripedium.

What are the mental conditions of Glonoine?

There is forgetfulness; the patient loses her way in well-known streets; confusion of place.

A partial page from *Essentials of Homœopathic Therapeutics*

W. A. Dewey, circa 1925

The story is told that Ward's chauffeur, an elderly black gentlemen, told Ward how he could not wait to be able to drive over the magnificent bridge that was being constructed across the San Francisco harbor. The day before the bridge opened, the chauffeur died. Two days later, Ward, wearing the chauffeur's cap, and chomping a cigar, as the chauffeur had done, drove the hearse with the chauffeur's body across the Golden Gate Bridge and back again.

James William Ward, MD
March 14, 1861 — July 12, 1939

From 1885 until 1939, the driving force of homœopathy in the Bay Area was James William Ward. Born in Minneapolis, Minnesota, Ward received his medical degree from New York Homœopathic in 1883. Soon after the Hahnemann Hospital College of San Francisco was formed in 1884, Dr. Ward was hired as professor of physiology, and two years later he became professor of gynecology. He was school dean from 1899 until 1916.

In 1902 he was elected president of the San Francisco Board of Health, holding this position until 1907. As such, he was in charge of the relief efforts in the aftermath of the San Francisco earthquake in 1906. In 1922 he was re-appointed health commissioner.

In 1891, while visiting Germany in the company of William Boericke, Ward inquired of Dr. Haehl as to the whereabouts of the "mysterious" sixth edition of the *Organon.* Haehl said it was with the Boenninghausen family. Ward said he would pay $1000 for it at any time. On April 8, 1920, Ward received a cable from Haehl asking if the offer was still good. It was, and the sixth edition eventually came to San Francisco, California.

Ward was described as "short, energetic, and vital. To the end of his days he retained a well-earned reputation as a great ladies' man."

His final work, *The Unabridged Dictionary of Sensations "As if"* was completed just two weeks before his death. "Seven years of zealous research was required, entailing innumerable hours of unselfish toil long after the arduous duties of his professional day had closed. The compiling of this great work required the patience of a superman but it was done, and perhaps it was an indirect cause of undermining that marvelous physique that finally succumbed on July 12, 1939, just eight hours after he had finished a busy day at the office."

This inscription is contained in a small book titled The Principles and Scope of Homœopathy. *I received the book as a gift from Richard Moskowitz, MD, who has a good many books from Dr. Close's library.*
The following letter was found in the book:

January 10, 1926
My dear Dr. Close:

A few days ago I sent you the first copy from the press of my lectures delivered at the University of California. You will see much of your writings throughout. The preface tells the story. The book is purely for the young men and women at the University. They are not for sale but for gratuitous distribution.

In a condensed form they answer many questions that the young nurse or doctor needs to know, alike also the laity.

I am deeply indebted to you in it all. We can all work overtime to spread the tale of homœopathy.

With a wealth of good wishes to you always, believe me.

Faithfully yours,
James W. Ward

James William Ward, 1939.

Florence N. Ward, MD

The ladies' man

In 1895 James William Ward divorced his wife to marry Florence Nightingale Saltonstall, an 1887 graduate of Hahnemann Medical College of the Pacific. They immediately left for Europe to further study medicine. Returning to San Francisco they resumed their busy practices. They had three children, the last a little boy who died shortly after birth.

In 1906 they separated. It was reported that Ward was "most responsive to the ladies." They were divorced in 1908, and the newspaper .carried this statement by Dr. Ward:

> "My wife is an estimable woman. No one has a more fruitful future. But our separation was inevitable. She was too deeply immersed in her ambition to excel in her profession to give me the womanly love and affection that I craved.
>
> "Lack of wifely love was the cause of disruption in my home. I found I could not retain that peace of mind that it was essential I should have when I could not get at home the womanly love and affection for which I longed."

As soon as the divorce was final, James William Ward remarried, but it was reported there was an "embarrassing interlude" when another woman doctor made headlines by threatening to kill him for not marrying her.

Dr. Florence Ward went on to a successful career. In 1915, she was the first woman elected to the American College of Surgeons. She ran her own 59-bed sanitarium in San Francisco (pictured left). She was the vice–president of the American Institute of Homœopathy.

She died December 15, 1919 aged 59.

The Mental Hospitals

Middletown
Gowanda
Allentown
Patton
Norwich
Westboro
Fergus Falls
Talcott: the writer

Organon
Paragraph 228

Mental and emotional diseases that arise from somatic diseases can only be cured by homœopathic medicine directed against the internal miasm, in conjunction with carefully adapted living habits. It is also important that the patient's physician and relations observe a psychically fitting approach toward the patient as an assisting diet for the soul. To raging insanity they must oppose quiet fearlessness and cold-blooded [unemotional] firm will. To distressing, plaintive lamentation, they must oppose silent regret in their looks and gestures. To senseless chatter they must oppose a silence not wholly inattentive. Disgusting and atrocious behavior and chatter must be opposed with complete inattentiveness. They must safeguard against property damage without reproaching the patient for this, arranging everything so that corporeal punishments and torments are thoroughly abolished…

Organon
Paragraph 229

On the other hand, the following behaviors are entirely out of place: contradiction, eager agreements, violent reprimands and vituperations, as well as weak, timid compliance. These are equally detrimental treatments for the spirit and the emotional mind of the patient. Above all, these patients are embittered, and their disease is worsened through scorn, deceit, and noticeable deceptions. The physicians and attendants must always appear as if they credit such patients with reason.

The mental hospitals

Ever since Hahnemann treated Klockenbring at Georgenthal in 1792, the homœopath has always recognized "mental diseases" are treatable, and that asylums for the "insane" where inmates are beaten or neglected is not an acceptable standard of care.

In 1866, there was a call by the New York State Homœopathic Society for a state asylum in New York to be operated by homœopaths. By 1870 the legislation was approved, and in 1874 the State Homœopathic Asylum for the Insane opened at Middletown, New York.

In 1886 the Westboro State Homœopathic Hospital opened in Massachusetts and, shortly after, others opened in other states.

The *International Homœopathic Directory of 1931* presents information (reproduced below) concerning five of the hospitals, although all seven were listed as operational in the *1941 American Institute of Homeopathy Directory of Homeopathic Physicians*.

Middletown

Middletown State Hospital, Middletown, New York

3,092 beds. 17 homœopaths on staff. No allopaths. Drugs prescribed in order of frequency:
Belladonna, Hyoscyamus, Nux vomica, Bryonia.

Middletown treated 11,000 patients between its opening in 1874 and 1916 when it was described as "the finest Homœopathic Insane institution in the world of which the school may be justly proud, because since its establishment the treatment employed has ever been of the strictest homœopathicity and the results have been little short of marvellous."

The Middletown State Hospital
was the largest of the state mental
hospitals to be under homœopathic
control.

The elegant entrance (above) led
to the complex of 47 buildings
that included the patient facility
in the West buildings (middle).
The pharmacy (below), here seen
in a picture taken at its opening in
1874, boasted that no narcotic or
sleep-producing drug was to
found within.

Gowanda

Gowanda State Hospital, Helmuth, New York

1,288 beds. 8 homœopaths, 1 allopath. The following drugs are the commonest, in order of frequency:

Belladonna, Aconite, Nux vomica, Gelsemium, Arsenicum album, the Mercuries, Phosphorus, Glonoine, Bryonia, Rhus tox, Strychnine phosphoricum, Ignatia, Passiflora, Viburnum, Aurum, Hyoscyamus, Stramonium, Veratrum album.

Originally created in 1894 as the Collins State Homœopathic Hospital, the name was changed in 1899 to Gowanda State Homœopathic Hospital. The hospital also had a nursing training school. Said the 1916 report: "There is no drug restraint employed, but all cases are treated according to strict homœopathic principles."

Allentown

Homœopathic State Hospital, Allentown, Pennsylvania

1429 beds. 7 homœopaths, 2 allopaths.

Prescriptions made between June 1, 1928 to May 31, 1929:

Bryonia 301, *Belladonna* 297, *Nux vomica* 227, *Gelsemium* 225, *Causticum* 109, *Rhus tox* 107, *Allium cepa* 99, *Eupatorium perfoliatum* 85, *Arsenicum album* 83, *Merc sol* 81, *Phosphorus* 70, *Aconite* 59, *Hepar* 58, *Merc i-r* 57, *Colocynth* 53, *Arnica* 50, *China arsenicosum* 49, *Sulphur* 48, *Pulsatilla* 46, *Aloes* 38, *Drosera* 32, *Hydrastis* 32, *Phytolacca* 32, *Calcarea carbonica* 31, *Lycopodium* 29. 149 different remedies were used in the year.

Potencies prescribed, in the order of frequency were: 3X: 1922, 1X: 368, 6X: 339, 2X: 225, 13X: 111, 12X: 70.

The state hospital was "entirely homœopathic by legislative enactment." The Germantown Homœopathic Medical Society— a group of about 200 "influential physicians"— raised the necessarily preliminary funds. In 1903 the state government appropriated $250,000 and in 1904 the hospital opened.

As of 1997 the hospital was still operating as a psychiatric hospital. There is no record as to when the practice of homœopathy ceased.

Gowanda State Hospital (circa 1930)

Allentown State Hospital (circa 1915)

Patton

Southern California State Hospital, Patton, California
3,250 beds, 6 homœopaths, 5 allopaths.
Opened in 1893 the Southern California State Asylum for Insane and Inebriates, it also had a tuberculosis pavilion.

Started as the "Highland Insane Asylum" it was located in the wilds near San Bernadino. It grew its own food and had many acres of orange orchards. The rail-line ran nearby and old maps still show a stop called "Asylum." It is now the Patton State Hospital for the Criminally Insane.

Norwich

Norwich State Hospital, Norwich, Connecticut
2,652 beds. 6 homœopaths, 6 allopaths. Remedies used in order of frequency: *Agaricus, Anacardium, Aurum, Baptisia, Belladonna, Chamomilla, Aconite, Hyoscyamus, Ignatia, Nux vomica, Pulsatilla, Stramonium, Cantharis, Coffea, Sepia, Lycopodium, Argentum nitricum, Alumina, Zincum met, Phosphoric acid.*

The Norwich State Hospital for the Insane opened in 1904 under homœopathic control "with remarkable successful results in treatment." As with the others, it ceased using homœopathy in the late 1940s. It was a psychiatric hospital until the mid–1990s, when it was closed.

Westboro

Westboro State Homœopathic Hospital. Westboro, Massachusetts

With 1,235 beds, it opened in 1886 with a charter which stated that the hospital must have a "medical department in charge of homœopathic physicians." When it ceased using homœopathy is not known. It is still operating as the Westborough State Hospital.

Southern California State Hospital (circa 1915)

Norwich State Hospital (circa 1915)

Westboro State Hospital (circa 1915)

Chapter 147 of the laws of the State of Minnesota for the year 1887, provided: "That the superintendent and corps of physicians appointed for the Third Hospital for Insane, located at Fergus Falls, shall be the school of Homœopathy." A description of the hospital said, "This hospital is thus intended by law to offer to the victims of insanity the advantage of that method of medication which has proven by experience to be successful, and which has been adopted by a large number of the intelligent citizens of this country as the method they prefer in the treatment of themselves and their families. The law 'similia similbus curantur' shall therefore be rigidly enforced in prescribing for those committed to the care of this hospital. Every prescription must, in accordance therewith, be based upon a careful study of the subjective and objective symptoms presented by the patient, and the adaptation of the proper remedy thereto."

Fergus Falls

Fergus Falls State Homœopathic Hospital, Fergus Falls, Minnesota

Opened in 1890 with 1,700 beds, it still operates today as the Fergus Falls Regional Treatment Center for the mentally retarded, and those needing alcohol and drug rehabilitation.

Dr. William Leslie Patterson became the third superintendent of the hospital in 1927. He received a Masters degree at Yale and his MD from Boston University. Dr. Patterson started work at Fergus Falls in 1912 and served until 1968. It is probably under his direction the hospital ceased being homœopathic.

The writer

Selden Talcott, MD
July 7, 1842 — June 15, 1902

After serving in the American Civil War, Talcott graduated from Hamilton College in 1869 and from New York Homœopathic in 1872. From 1875 to 1877 he was chief of staff at Ward's Island Homœopathic Hospital in New York City. In April, 1877, he became superintendent of the Middletown Asylum which became the Middletown State Homœopathic Hospital.

It was said, "He was the first to fully demonstrate the successful application of homœopathy in the treatment of the insane."

His successes at Middletown were a described as, "a showcase to the nation and the world." He obtained results "that hitherto no superintendent in the country had ever attained."

He wrote one text, *Mental Diseases and their Modern Treatment,* but wrote many small pamphlets published by Middletown. Bradford lists 14 works under his name.

Selden H. Talcott

This poem was written by William Tod Helmuth in honor of Talcott's 25th year at Middletown. On May 15, 1902, the night of the commemoration dinner, Helmuth died in New York City. Talcott died a month later.

Look at my hair and see it silver gray;
Look at my eyes, behold the dangling glasses;
Look at my ears; you know full well that they
are not acute to every sound that passes.

You knew me when those same old locks were brown,
With ears responsive and eyes quick to see;
I recollect when you came up to town
With letters introductory to me.

A stripling then from dear old Munger's care,
Burning with Aesclepian flame,
With slender body and with flowing hair,
Up to your alma mater's courts you came.

Do you remember then, that I was teaching
The new suspension for a fractured thigh?
The old straight splint of Physic was impeaching
When you besought me Munger's splint to try.

Take down the worn old volumes from the shelves,
Turn to page five-hundred-ninety-five;
Ah! Memory then will tell us of ourselves,
Both you and I— Thank God we are alive!

As retrospection stealeth over the years,
To touch the men who lectured then to you,
Our hearts grow sad— our eyes o'erflow with tears,
So many gone— the remnants still so few.

But I must play your Ganymede tonight.
And give this cup all filled with ruby wine,
In friendships name from those who, with delight,
Have watched your progress since you fell in line.

Take it, old man, with all the love it offers;
Take it and keep it, for it tells a story;
Take it— 'tis better than o'erflowing coffers,
Take it, resplendent with true friendship's glory.

"Patients who are over sixty years of age, especially if their physical health is impaired, rarely recover; although they frequently become quiet and tractable, and often live to a good old age.
"Those who become insane before reaching the age of puberty are generally victims of profound heredity, or epilepsy, or traumatic injury to the brain, all of which conditions are unfavorable to recovery.
"From puberty to the age of twenty numerous cases of insanity are met with, the cause of which, in addition to those mentioned, are masturbation and irregularity in the performance of the menstrual function. Masturbators do not readily recover. Indeed, masturbatic insanity is one of the most intractable forms with which we have to deal. Insanity due to menstrual irregularity is often curable, providing the function can be established by the judicious use of appropriate remedies...
"From the ages of twenty to sixty the chances for recovery are most favorable; bearing in mind that the probabilities of recovery gradually decrease, especially in men after the age of forty-five. Women who have long been insane sometime recover after passing the forty-fifth year."

—Selden Talcott, "On Prognosis in Insanity."

A commentary...

In late 1997, a researcher was granted permission to review some Middletown Hospital case files. The few cases seen showed little use of homœopathic remedies. A few remedies were given, usually in a very low potency, apparently based on physical keynotes. Those operating the hospitals had a very limited understanding of mental illness (as we now know it). Much of the understanding was generated by preconceptions of the time and by the society in which they were functioning. Most of the work was before the major influences of Freud and Jung.

If the homœopathic hospital's results were so much better than those which came before, then the other hospitals must have been truly tragic places.

So what of these great cases? In retrospect, the remedies needed for the cases seem clear to us, and they might well have been clear to a well-versed Hahnemannian prescriber. Obviously, the hospitals were an outgrowth of the homœopathy of the time which was practiced without any understanding of homœopathic philosophy or the depth with which it can be used. Some cases from Middletown are presented in **Appendix A**, page 512.

326   STATE OF NEW YORK.

Total No. *4325*   No. for the year *77*

Name ███ *M. H* ███ Residence *Ronkonkoma, Suffolk,* Co.

Admitted *January 14,* 189*5*, by Dr. *Spencer Kinny* at *8* P. M.

Accompanied by *Dr Hrdlicka*

Order *Public*   Public Private

Medical certificate by Dr. *Adrian P. Van Deune* of *Sayville*   and Dr.

F. Chas Merritt of *Sayville*   approved by Judge *Wilmot M Smith*

of *Co Ct.*

Correspond with *F. J.* ███ *Ronkonkoma, Suff Co., NY*

The Women

The struggle for equality
The movers
Four women

The first woman practitioner, of course, was Hahnemann's second wife, Melanie who was trained by Hahnemann and awarded an honorary diploma from Allentown.
This painting of Melanie was commissioned by *The American Homeopath* in 1996 and painted by Susan Lowell of Antioch, California. It was derived from several known portraits of Melanie. It appeared, in full color, on the cover of the 1997 issue of *The American Homeopath*.

The struggle for equality

The women's suffrage movement began to change the fabric of American Society in the 1840s. Unable to enter male-dominated colleges, women established their own educational institutions in response to the growing demand that women be seen by doctors of their own sex. And many women, when given the choice, preferred homœopathic treatment.

The history of homœopathy is closely tied with the emancipation of women in the mid–1800s, both politically and spiritually. To sum it up in a page is almost an impossibility. That being said, here is a brief summary:

It was a time of Victorian morals. The body was not to be seen and there was a firm belief it was a woman's role to be unwell. We often see in literature of the time the "sickly woman." One doctor stated the common belief that "women had a fixed amount of natural energy" and if they worked too hard it would destroy their reproductive capacity. Not only were women taught by society to be sickly, but modesty was a virtue and Victorian standards didn't easily allow male physicians to examine female patients. The medical profession, a bastion of male-domination, began to define pregnancy and menstruation as pathological conditions.

Jacksonian democracy held the thread of anti-elitism, which, in some sense, denigrated the concept of "expert–knowledge" and led many into the self–help movement of which health–care reform was but just a part. The women were the ones who cared for the community when medical help was not available, and they were the ones who delivered the babies.

The legal system, as well, made women subject to male–domination. Women were not allowed to own property, and many women, upon their husband's death, found themselves destitute.

The temperance movement, stressing the evils of alcohol, was started by women who saw husbands spend the week's salary on drink, and then beat them when they complained.

All of these factors came together in the middle–1800s, when the country saw the rise of several movements, all connected by a common thread: the abolitionist movement to free the black slave, the suffrage movement, the temperance movement, and the binding political force of the newly–created Republican party.

To help themselves, women set up "Ladies Physiological Societies" to teach women hygiene principles. It was out of these groups the first medical colleges for women grew. There was, of course, great opposition from the medical establishment. Alfred Stillé, one of the founders of the American Medical Association, said that "women lacked rational judgment and were unfit to be 'scientific physicians.'"

Homœopathy, with its emphasis on detailed symptom pictures, the gentleness of the dose and response, and the emphasis on diet and hygiene, was an ideal candidate to fill the gap for those interested in a new medical model. Furthermore, many families were already treating themselves using "Domestic Manuals," the first of which was Hering's *Domestic Physician*, published in 1835.

As we, today, often find homœopathy after having unsatisfactory results from conventional medicine, so the men and women of the 1850s found their homœopaths in a similar manner. Once they found them, they generally stuck by them.

The homœopaths, by their very nature, were mavericks. Many of the original German practitioners had come to the United States because their politics were too radical in their homeland. Homœopaths, as a group, were less conservative than the regulars. After all, until the advent of homœopathic schools at the end of the 1840s, all the homœopaths were converts from "the old school."

It was a natural progression that those women who were interested in temperance, suffrage, and abolition, would embrace homœopathy. It was also apparent that the men in the profession would embrace the idea of women as physicians much more easily than their allopathic brethren.

With no state laws governing the practice of medicine, many women who learned homœopathy to care for their families became sources of health care for their communities. At the 1869 meeting of the AIH, it was observed: "Many a woman, armed with her little stack of remedies, had converted an entire community to homœopathy."

Nevertheless it was a struggle for many women. Some had come from families not supportive of the idea of their daughter being a doctor. Others entered the medical schools later in life, after they had raised a family. Many entered with a better general education than their male counterparts.

For the schools, it was not an easy transition. Although the Cleveland Homœopathic College became co-educational in 1852, it refused admission to women in 1853, and grudgingly admitted women again in 1854.

Between 1855 and 1857 we find women graduates only from the New England Female Medical College in Boston. In 1858 we find one more from Cleveland. Then, until 1870, all the female homœopathic graduates came from either the New England school or, after 1864, the New York Medical College for Women.

By 1872, New York Homœopathic, Hahnemann Chicago, St. Louis Homœopathic, Detroit Homœopathic, and Cleveland Homœopathic had opened their doors to women.

When the Pulte College in Cincinnati opened in 1872, it was a male-only institution. The faculty were severely divided over the question of admission to women and it was only when Dr. Pulte threatened to withhold endowment funds unless women were admitted, that the faculty of Pulte (over the objection of the trustees) opened its door to women in 1879.

The American Institute of Homœopathy opened its

The Cleveland
Homœopathic College

142

membership to women in 1870, five years before the American Medical Association took the same step.

Hahnemann Medical College in Philadelphia, the first of the homœopathic schools, finally opened its doors to women in 1941.

When charting women graduating from homœopathic schools, we find roughly 12% of the graduates each year were female (from a low of 7.65% in 1874 to a high of 21.78% in 1893).

And the women stayed in practice for a long time. For example, Theodocia Bennett Parker, from Peoria, Illinois, graduated in 1888 from the University of Iowa's Homœopathic Department. In 1941, 54 years later, she was still practicing in Peoria.

The New England Female Medical College

The Boston Female Medical School was established on November 1, 1848, through the efforts of Dr. Samuel Gregory. The school opened with two lecturers and 12 pupils. In 1852, it changed its name to the New England Female Medical College. 98 women graduated during its 25–year existence. Although it is credited in King's *History* as being a "homœopathic" college, there is no mention of homœopathy in any of the faculty minutes or school board meetings. However, two of its 98 graduates are found in Cleave's *Biographical Encyclopedia of Homœopathic Physicians*.

In 1870 a committee was formed in Boston to look into establishing a school to be known as the New England Homœopathic College. When the committee found another group was talking about forming a university in Boston, negotiations were begun to join the proposed medical school with the new university. In 1873 Boston University School of Medicine opened as a homœopathic school, and the New England Female Medical College was merged with the new institution.

Several years ago, a newspaper article quoted representatives of the Women's Medical College of Pennsylvania stating their institution (founded in 1851) was the first medical college for women. I wrote a letter questioning the statement and mentioned the NE Female Medical College formed in 1848. The reply was that the New England school "was not a 'regular' medical college." The animosity toward homœopathy raised its head once again.

The movers

In 1863, Clemence Sophia Lozier founded the New York Medical College for Women. She was also active in the suffrage movement, working with Elizabeth Cady Stanton, who was known as a fine lay homœopath in her community. Susan B. Anthony, a leader of the suffrage movement, was also a proponent of homœopathy and used Dr. Julia Holmes Smith in Chicago as her personal physician.

Clemence Sophia Lozier, MD
December 11, 1813 — April 26, 1888

Clemence Sophia Lozier, M.D.

Clemence Lozier was a cousin of Carroll Dunham. Her uncle was a physician and she studied medicine with him. Left an orphan at 11 years old, she married Abraham Lozier when she was 16. Her husband became an invalid shortly after their marriage, and she was widowed at 24. She had six children during their eight year marriage, with only one surviving. He became a homœopathic doctor. Of the others, two died in accidents and three died from medical treatment. It undoubtedly drove Lozier toward seeking a better mode of medical care. She introduced hygiene and physiology courses at an informal school she ran from her home.

Lozier moved to Albany, New York about 1844 and had "an unfortunate marriage" ending in divorce. The divorce was an important marker in her life. Inspired by a paper read by Elizabeth Cady Stanton in which Stanton proposed that a woman should have a right to divorce her husband on account of his drunkenness, Lozier later told Stanton: "...at a period when I was in the depths of despair, crippled in every effort for self–support or self–development by an unworthy husband. That letter came to me like a clarion call, to rise up, sunder such unholy ties, and walk forth to freedom. It filled me with the courage to do what I had long ago seen to be my duty."

In 1849 she attended lectures at the Eclectic College in Rochester, New York and graduated from the New York Central Medical College (an eclectic school) in 1853, since no regular medical school would admit women.

In 1860 she began a series of courses in her home for women. From these lectures, the New York Medical College and Hospital for Women opened in 1863.

Although started as a "wholly non-sectarian" school, within two years it came down solidly in the homœopathic camp, leading to the formation of a "regular" school for women by another early female medical graduate, Elizabeth Blackwell.

Lozier was prominent in the suffrage movement. During the New York 1862 race riots, she offered her home as refuge for "several colored people who fled from the violence of the mob." She was also president of the Moral Education Society of New York City and of the American Temperance League. It was reported her yearly income from her medical practice was more than $25,000 (this in 1870!) one of the highest incomes in New York City. She contributed $50 a week toward Susan B. Anthony's suffrage weekly, *Revolution.* Elizabeth Cady Stanton credited Lozier as one of the main financial sources for the suffrage movement. In all of Lozier's time serving as dean of the New York Medical College for Women, she never took a penny from the institution, but always put money in.

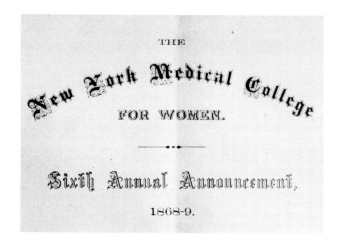

THE

New York Medical College

FOR WOMEN.

Sixth Annual Announcement,

1868-9.

Elizabeth Cady Stanton and her son, circa 1850

Elizabeth Cady Stanton
November 12, 1815 — October 26, 1902

Daughter of Judge Daniel Cady, young Elizabeth took notice of the discriminatory laws under which women lived. When she was about 10, she tried to tear out all the discriminatory laws from her father's law books, but Judge Cady, hearing of her plans, urged his daughter to work to change the laws instead.

In 1840, she married the abolitionist Henry Brewster Stanton. In 1848, she and Lucretia Mott were the leaders of the first women's rights convention in the United States. She joined forces with Susan B. Anthony in 1850 to work toward women's suffrage.

It is known that Stanton was a lay practitioner in upstate New York at the time the canals were being built in the area. But the story is deeper than that.

Judge Cady had a law assistant named Edward Bayard. Elizabeth was enamored with this young man, but with their age difference, Bayard undoubtedly saw Elizabeth as a child. Elizabeth was 12 when Bayard, then 21, married Elizabeth's older sister.

Bayard's health suffered in his busy law practice and he was advised by a reputable heart specialist to cease working. Bayard's wife suggested he consult a homœopath, Dr. Biegler in Albany, and Bayard was cured. He became a lay practitioner in upstate New York and was responsible for introducing homœopathy to the area.

In the early 1840s Bayard decided to become a physician and took his medical degree in New York, graduating in 1844. He was one of the first members of the American Institute of Homœopathy and was an active member of the International Hahnemannian Association. He lived until the age of 83. He was a close friend of Hering's. In 1841 he visited Hahnemann in Paris.

Elizabeth wrote about how, in later years in New York City, she and Bayard would stroll hand-in-hand and talk about how things might have been different had she been older. One gets the sense that although she respected and admired her husband, she always loved Bayard.

Edward Bayard, the shining knight

Edward Bayard, MD

"I once made a visit to Dr. Edward Bayard, in New York. As I entered the parlor, there, on the mantelpiece I saw an image of the Chevalier sans peur et sans reproche, in bronze, The French Knight of the Middle Ages, dubbed: 'without fear and without reproach.' The figure, to all appearances was a likeness of my friend Bayard, to the wart on his face. The knight was mounted on his horse, ready to join the Crusaders. I marveled, could a sensible man like my friend Edward, a descendant from the Bayards, have sent his portrait to Paris to have it reproduced in this form? This could hardly have been the case.

Mrs. Bayard came into the room to receive me and saw that I was puzzled while regarding the effigy. She told me that she and her mother, while traveling by themselves in Europe— the doctor having been too busy to leave home— had, while in Paris, entered a jeweler's shop, where, to their amazement, they beheld this bronze figure, mounted on a clock. Both of them observed at once that the image bore the very likeness of Dr. Bayard, even to the wart on his face. They decided to buy it and bring it home. The picture of the Knight 'without fear and without reproach' of more than a thousand years ago was the image of the man today. So much for family likenesses by heredity."

— Constantine Hering, MD June 20, 1869

Bayard, who preceptored Samuel Swan, was one of the first to prove and use Lac caninum. *Mrs. Bayard's dog, a cocker spaniel, was the original source for this remedy. The breed was chosen because "its affection for the human race is unusually strong."*

Susan B. Anthony   Elizabeth Cady Stanton

Suffrage meeting, circa 1890.

The trials of medical schooling

The following is an account, by Elizabeth Cady Stanton, of the first medical lecture to be attended by the students of the New York Women's Medical College at Bellevue Hospital. Stanton was attending, as a school trustee, in Lozier's place:

"Accordingly, at the appointed time with the class of thirty I entered the amphitheater. We were greeted by a thousand students with shouts of derisive laughter, and ever and anon during the lecture were pelted with chewed balls of paper. The professor selected the most offensive subject and disease for the day, thinking thereby to end the experiment. But the question how much we could, should, and would endure had been freely discussed and decided, and it was agreed by both trustees and students that, barring forcible expulsion, whatever was done or said we would maintain our ground for one season at least and vindicate the rights of our students to all the advantages of clinics and lectures in the hospital. Although the professor took especial pains to be as coarse as possible, and all his worst periods were vociferously applauded by the students, we quietly sat there through the entire lecture.

"One very touching episode for the credit of manhood occurred at the close of the lecture, that in a measure redeemed the occasion. Three young men sitting behind us on a bench quite alone, politely accosted me with many kind expressions of regret at our rude reception. One said, 'Pray do not judge all men by what you have witnessed today. There are many students here as shocked as you have been, who would be glad of some protection against the vulgarity seemingly inevitable to a medical education. We do hope you continue to bring your class; there must be enough chivalry and moral sense among so many students to prevent a recurrence of the disgraceful proceedings today...'

"As we left the building the students had formed themselves into a double line, through which we passed, mid jeers and groans, coarse jokes and shouts, pelted with bits of wood and gravel."

Four women

Susan Edson, MD
January 4, 1823 — November 12, 1897

Susan Edson was born in Aurelius, New York. She was one of the first women to be admitted to Cleveland Homœopathic College persevering against the sentiment of the times to graduate in 1854. During the Civil War she cared for soldiers at Fort Monroe in Virginia.

Edson was a long–time friend of President Garfield and was his family physician. Although it is now recognized that a surgeon botched an attempt to retrieve the bullet that wounded Garfield and created the septic wound from which Garfield died, Edson ministered to Garfield from the day he was shot, July 9, 1881, till the day he died on September 19th. Edson recounts she first heard of the assassination attempt shortly after returning home from tending to Mrs. Garfield through a long illness. Edson said she felt it was vital for her to remain with the President. She was paid $3,000 by Congress for the service.

With another homœopath, Carolyn Winslow (Ohio Eclectic, 1853; Cleveland Homœopathic, 1856), they chartered the Homœopathic Free Dispensary in Washington, DC. There they treated 2,000 patients a year— mostly women and 60% black. The clinic was merged with the clinic of the National Homœopathic Hospital in 1895. All the women homœopaths in the city gave some of their time to work at the Free Dispensary in some capacity.

I have two books in my library belonging to Susan Edson. One has only her stamp. The other has her signature— but it is in pencil on the dark brown paper of the flyleaf. No way of copying that!

Of the 98 graduates of the New England Female Medical College, only two are included in Cleave's *Biography*. Their stories are poles apart and are probably typical of the women seeking medical education in the mid-1800s.

Mercy Bisbe Jackson was born in Hardwick, Massachusetts in 1802. At 21 she married the Rev. John Bisbe of the First Unitarian Church in Hartford, Connecticut. He eventually became the pastor in Portland, Maine where he died, six years later, in 1829. They had three children.

Mercy "resorted to teaching, and opened a school for young ladies." After three years her "health failed under the arduous calling," and she opened a dry-goods store. Three years later, aged 33, she married Daniel Jackson of Plymouth, Massachusetts. In this marriage she had eight children, including twin boys and twin girls.

"The experiences of maternity… naturally acquainted her with the sickness of children and with the treatment of diseases there prevailing." She discussed her interest in medicine with her family physician, Dr. Capen (an allopath), and he allowed her to use his medical library. A friend introduced her to homœopathy, and she told Dr. Capen about it. He became interested and rode to Boston (a hefty journey in 1841) to procure books and medicines.

Mercy began practicing homœopathy in 1841 under Dr. Capen's study. Eventually deciding that she needed a degree, she attended the New England Female College, and graduated in 1860, aged 58.

In 1868 she applied for membership in the Massachusetts Homœopathic Medical Society and was turned down. She finally was allowed membership in 1874, becoming the first woman member. When Boston University was organized she was appointed professor of diseases of children.

The story of **Carolyn Eliza Hastings** is very different. Born in 1841 in Barre, Massachusetts, she taught for a summer before entering Mount Holyoke Seminary, and found it was not her calling. She had said that, if she were a man, she would be a doctor. When she was 20, she found there were medical schools for women, but her father "to whom the idea of a woman doctor was altogether new, and no less absurd, not to say revolting," prevented her from attending. Two years later he acquiesced and she began studying medicine with a local physician. She attended the New England Female Medical College in 1866, graduating in 1868. She settled in Boston and had a large practice. She was the Physician for the New England Moral Reform Society, "an institution for the reclaim of fallen girls."

"She became a disciple of Hahnemann from a clear and decided conviction of the truth… Thus she stands firmly and honorably in the midst of the growing ranks of homœopathy and the female physician."

Mary Florence Taft, MD
June 19,1853 — September 8, 1927

Mary Florence Taft was one of the Boston physicians whose life spanned the era from when women were just being accepted as physicians to the era which saw the beginning of the decline of homœopathy in the United States. Taft was a cousin of United States President William Howard Taft. She was born in Putney, Vermont. After high school she worked in the Harvard Library for four years. She took courses in education and established a private kindergarten in Newport, Rhode Island, where she implemented new educational reforms.

Taft graduated from Boston University School of Medicine in 1886, and interned at the Massachusetts Homœopathic Hospital. She worked closely with William P. Wesselhoeft in Boston, and developed a "decided interest in homœopathic materia medica." She had a private practice in Waterbury, Connecticut before accepting the position of professor of gynecology at Hering College in Chicago where she met Dr. Kent and Dr. H. C. Allen.

She eventually returned to Boston, where she practiced until retiring. It is said she made more converts to homœopathy and had been the preceptor to more students than any other homœopath in Boston.

When the American Foundation established its post–graduate course for physicians, Taft was the lecturer on materia medica. She was a member of the International Hahnemannian Association, having joined in 1889. Her name is often seen as a contributor to the journals and to articles found in the *Transactions of the International Hahnemannian Association*.

She traveled extensively abroad, and her last trip "though infirm in body" was to Switzerland to spend time with Dr. Pierre Schmidt.

She was a follower of Swedenborg, and her funeral services were held at the Church of the New Jerusalem in Cambridge, Massachusetts. Much of her extensive homœopathic library is now in the hands of Richard Moskowitz, MD, of Watertown, Massachusetts.

Her Bookplate. Close examination will reveal that the two books on the left are Swedenborg's *Celestial Arcana* and Hahnemann's *Organon*. The portrait, tucked in the top left, is of Swedenborg. The scrap of paper, behind the burning lamp in the top center, is the first page of Genesis. The woven ribbon reads, "Similia Similibus Curantur."

The Faces of Homœopathy

The Arrival of Kent

Kent's teacher
Kent's early work
The Post– Graduate School
The pupils
The Repertory
The Swedenborg connection

By the early 1880s, homœopathy was foundering without strong leadership, divided among many factions. As with other places and other times, a leader often emerges when needed. In this case, the masked-man rode in from the west.

About 1884 we suddenly see in the records of the societies, "Well what would Dr. Kent say about this?" He came, it seemed, from nowhere.

James Tyler Kent, MD
March 31, 1849 — June 5, 1916

Kent was born in Woodhull, New York, and reared as the son of Stephen Kent, town clerk, and Caroline Tyler. However, evidence strongly suggests he was the illegitimate son of his brother, Henry, and sister, Jane, since they were listed as "mother" and "father" on his death certificate. At the time of Kent's birth, Henry would have been 15 and Jane 13. The explanation that the "informant" for the information on the death certificate, his wife Clara Louise, was "senile" and confused the names, is a specious argument since Clara Louise lived until 1943 and was in fine enough mental health to re-edit the Kent *Repertory* several times.

A long article written about this subject by Hela Michot-Dietrich, PhD, appeared in the *Zeitschrift für Klassische Homöopathie*, November-December, 1985, and a condensed version appeared in *Homeopathy Today* in June, 1990.

None of the published biographies of Kent agree on his medical education. A biography in *The Medical Advance* of December 1884 gives his birth date as 1845. According to that biography he got his PhB at Madison College in 1864 ("when only 19 years of age") and received an MD from Bellevue in 1868.

His death certificate on June 5, 1916 gives his age as "67 years 2 months and 5 days" thus supporting his 1849 birthdate.

Most others biographies have Kent getting his PhB in 1868 (still at the age of 19) and an AM in 1870 at Madison College (now Colgate University) in Hamilton, New York. All biographies agree he studied medicine with Dr. Brown in Woodhull, and say he completed his medical degree in one semester at the Eclectic Medical Institute in Cincinnati, Ohio in 1871.

GUERIN Kent *St. Louis.*

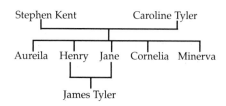

James Tyler Kent, St. Louis, 1882

Stephen Kent   Caroline Tyler

Aureila   Henry   Jane   Cornelia   Minerva

James Tyler

Another biography has him still attending courses at Bellevue, but when that could have been within this time frame is not known. We know he returned to Woodhull to practice. He was married at that time, since a grave in the Woodhull Cemetery adjacent to the graves of Stephen and Caroline Kent has the inscription: "Ellen L. Wife of J.T. Kent. Died Oct. 22, 1872 aged 19 years."

Kent moved to St. Louis, Missouri in 1874, began a medical practice and taught anatomy at the American Medical College (Eclectic) from 1877-78. He married a second time, to Lucia (last name unknown).

At some time between 1878 and 1879, Lucia fell ill and Kent was unable to help her. She urged him to call the local homœopathic physician, who cured her. Under the guidance of the physician, Richard Phelan, MD, Kent began to study homœopathy. He resigned his position at the Eclectic College and accepted a position of professor of anatomy at the Homœopathic Medical College of St. Louis in 1881, becoming professor of materia medica in 1883.

In 1887, Kent was elected president of the International Hahnemannian Association. In 1888, he accepted an invitation from the Women's Homœopathic Hospital in Philadelphia to take over the practice of the recently deceased Adolph Lippe. Shortly after he arrived in Philadelphia, he formed the "Organon and Materia Medica Society."

In 1890 he founded the Post–Graduate School of Homœopathics in Philadelphia. Most of the school's funding came from John Pitcairn, founder of Pittsburgh Plate Glass, a guiding figure in the Swedenborg Church in Philadelphia. Kent was slowly drawn to the works of "The New Church." John Pitcairn wrote to a friend in 1893: "I think you met Dr. Kent while you were here. If so you will be interested in the fact that he has been showing greater interest in our church than ever before and for the past few weeks has been attending the services on Sunday and also the Doctrinal Class on Friday evening."

The school and its free clinic flourished. By the time it closed in 1900, the school had seen over 40,000 patients and trained 30 physicians, all of whom became the leaders in the homœopathic movement and kept homœopathy alive in the United States and Great Britain through the first half of the 20th century.

James Tyler Kent, circa 1884

At the same time, Kent, with his pupils, was busy compiling his major work, the *Repertory of the Homœopathic Materia Medica*.

Lucia died on October 13, 1895. On July 2, 1896, Kent married Clara Louise Toby (October 12, 1855 — December 23, 1943).

In 1900, Kent accepted an offer to relocate the Post–Graduate School to Chicago, under the auspices of the Dunham Homœopathic College. He became dean of the Dunham College, then held a chair as professor of materia medica at the Hahnemann Medical College of Chicago, and taught at the Hering College. While in Chicago he also maintained a busy private practice and continued to edit his *Repertory*.

Kent was editor of the following journals: *The Homœopathic Courier* (St. Louis, 1881-82); *Journal of Homœopathics* (Philadelphia, 1897-99); *The Homœopathician* (Chicago, 1912-1916).

In the spring of 1916 he went to his vacation home in Stevensville, Montana, where he died after a brief illness. He is buried at the local cemetery.

His students published the transcriptions of the lectures on philosophy he delivered in Philadelphia, *Lectures on Homœopathic Philosophy* (1900), and the transcription of his extemporaneous materia medica lectures in Philadelphia and Chicago as *Lectures on Materia Medica* (1905). They also published, in 1926, a collection of his essays which had appeared in various homœopathic journals, under the title, *New Remedies, Clinical Cases, Lesser Writings, Aphorisms, and Precepts*. All four works are still in print.

W. W. Sherwood, MD, a pupil of Kent in Chicago, was the collector and editor of Kent's *Lesser Writings, Aphorisms, and Precepts*. The date on the desk-calendar in the picture is 1911. The open book is a Kent *Repertory*.

Homœopathy Myth and Fact

In his "Brief Biography of Kent," Pierre Schmidt writes of Kent being asked by his wife "to consult a homœopathic doctor who was quite old... Dr. Phelan with his white beard and black coat, came one afternoon in his carriage..."

An obituary of Dr. Phelan from 1902 shows a very fuzzy likeness of him but, clearly, there is no white beard— rather a dark goatee. Phelan died aged 66, so the meeting between Kent and Phelan happened when Kent was 29 and Phelan was 42.

Where did Schmidt get the information? From Kent's pupil Gladwin? It seems probable the "old doctor with the white beard" was in Gladwin's or Schmidt's imagination.

Richard A. Phelan, MD
1836 — November 14, 1902

Phelan was born in Ireland in 1836, and came to St. Paul, Minnesota, where he practiced law. He moved to St. Louis about 1860. He served with the Missouri volunteers during the Civil War, and afterwards attended the Homœopathic Medical College of Pennsylvania, graduating in 1867. In the graduate listings he is identified as "from St. Louis."

Phelan's death, on November 14, 1902, was attributed to "paralysis" in the *St. Louis Republic*, "senility" in the *St. Louis Post-Dispatch*, and listed in the *St. Louis Globe-Democrat* as "after a lingering illness." He is buried in Calvary Cemetery on West Florissant Avenue in St. Louis. Phelan is buried in Lot 96, section 14. 13 family members are also buried at the site, including his first wife and two daughters, all tuberculosis victims. All the graves are unmarked, as no head stones were ever placed on the plot.

The picture of Richard Phelan in the *St. Louis Post-Dispatch*

A new rectal applicator

This is a review written by Kent for the "Department of Electrology and Neurology" in 1881 for the Homœopathic Courier *of which he was editor.*

"In managing some forms of nervous affections, attention is drawn to induration and other structural changes of the anus and rectum, as a primary cause. Medication of the anal outlet has been more embarrassing than any other regions, and mechanical treatment has been found andrologeous. The following improved anal plug or Rectal Applicator, has served a valuable purpose in a two-fold way: It affords a means of dilation as well as a constant suppository. The screw plunger may be turned at will, constantly forcing out medicaments as are placed within the cavity of the applicator. Iodoform and cosmoline, or ergotine, extract of rhatany, with any convenient unguous substance, may be used. The instrument is presented to the profession as an improvement on the old anal plug."

Kent before homœopathy

Kent came into homœopathy from a background as an eclectic physician and a pupil of the leading "eclectic" teacher, John Scudder. Says Matthew Wood, the author of *The Magical Staff*:

"Kent's whole basic view of vitalism is completely that of an eclectic. For all he may have criticized the eclectics with their mongrel attitudes, he imbibed the philosophy of Scudder, and Scudder's influence can be felt on almost every page of Kent's *Philosophy* while, in my opinion, Swedenborg is much less evident.

"No one sounds more like Scudder than Kent. The influence of eclecticism in Kent is so pervasive, but also so subtle that nobody would know it was there— unless they read the textbooks through which Kent was educated at the Eclectic Medical Institute. Then they would find that he is a clone, almost, of Scudder, in his choice of words and his style of vitalism.

"Kent's emphasis on seeing the patient, the life of the patient, the 'wrong of life' (Scudder's phrase, copied by Kent), are eclectic ideas. Kent gave the philosophy, the feeling, the almost exotic quality of the ideas to his students, but he didn't spend four years teaching people to patiently observe patients as they did at the Eclectic Medical Institute. His interest is more philosophical, than practical— as are so many of his ideas. I think the eclecticism is as influential as the Swedenborgianism, but much more hidden and unknown."

In 1879, Kent wrote his first book, a small volume called *Sexual Neuroses*. At the time Kent was making his transition from eclectisism to homœopathy. Although the book is listed in Bradford's *Bibliography*, few have seen it. Happily, Chris Ellithorp has a copy and submitted a few snippets that will give us a sense of Kent in 1879.

Kent on "sexual neuroses"

"…animal life is not perpetuated except through sexual congress. Not life only, but good and evil of every degree; vice, folly, crime; love and hate; society, social evil and social good: all depend, largely, upon the sexual. It is the bond of our existence; it is the wheel of our fortune; it is our guiding star; and it may be our lodestone to crime and premature death. Passions leading to love, true and gentle, or jealousy, hate, revenge, murder and suicide, all hinge on circumstances connected, directly or indirectly, with the sexual."

"…The good people of the earth profit by the grand and noble sexual unity in the material existence, and by the pure, social relations, and chaste affections of the unmarried; but these are but a small part of human society. The masses express their worship for the sexual by debauch, dissipation, vice and crime. The common saying, whenever suicide or murder has been committed, that 'woman was at the bottom of it,' might just as well read, 'man was at the bottom of it;' as without the one, where would the other have been?

"It is the bad use of noble agencies that often constitutes vice. Nothing ignoble was intended by the Great Designer, should grow out of the sexual privileges, and when nobly appreciated, for moral beings a greater happiness or pleasure has not been instituted. But by long prostitution of these privileges, vices have originated; beliefs have been established; customs have been founded; even religions have been constituted and modified to suit the wishes of designing 'sexualists,' 'free-thinkers,' Mormons, etc. Occasionally, dissatisfied members of one sex will establish an innovation, or a revolutionary commotion, demanding rights which they claim have been usurped from them, and sometimes thirsting for prerogatives belonging to the opposite sex. They agitate their cause until their isolated followers establish societies and churches, effecting discord in families, and no good to the world in general, and for themselves an unenviable reputation. Such individuals are often advocating reforms; temperance, charity, etc.; but when good comes out of one, evil grows out of ten. They often take a decided stand against the opposite sex, and when their true history is known, it will be often found that they have been suffering from unrequited love, disappointment in matrimony, deception in society, misplaced confidence, illegitimate pregnancy, etc.; or, they are phlegmatic and passionless; or, hermaphrodites; or wanting in some of the sexual appendages necessary to constitute a perfect man or woman. Then, without the complete sexual system, harmoniously balanced, all is imperfect.

"...Among the aboriginal tribes, the sexual appetite is and has always been indulged *ad libitum*; not only in the natural manner, but in every conceivable way without noticeable harm to the organs themselves, or to the nervous system. In a lesser degree this is true of slaves, sailors and peasantry, and the lower orders of civilization. Sexual endurance diminishes in proportion to the advancement in civilization and intellectual culture. A long-cultured family can not sustain, in sexual indulgence, what to the uncivilized would be a matter of indifference."

On predisposition

"The innate or uncaused condition, which is so commonly found among the young, is quite likely congenital and constitutional. There is evidently structural malformation in the neuroglia, or nerve cells proper, which predisposes the child to sexual excitement. This may not be derived from the immediate parent, but far back. In the third or fourth generation, debauchers may be found. Licentious parents commonly predispose their children to morbid sexual desires; and what evidence have we that structural changes do not exist in or about the nerve centers that preside over the sexual functions, and that such changes are not constitutional? Then, with this structural change as a predisposition, the least cause will set the sexual centers into a blaze of excitement. They who are predisposed by many generations, show upon their faces the lines of coarse breeding; that they are the offspring of debauchers; congenital degradation; not but these conditions, under favorable circumstances, may be overcome, by rigidly cultivating opposite nerve centers but such opportunities are seldom presented and, when presented seldom embraced.

"...Copulation is the key to morality and society. So certain bonds of restriction and moral government of a social character exist, and they are made to restrain human beings and to control and limit copulation to a legitimate sphere; viz., man and wife. Any deviation from this legitimate course has long been denominated prostitution, which exists in public and private.

"The vice of changing partners has become so open and for such trivial causes that laws have been enacted, of the most rigid character, and then divorcing and remarrying are carried on to an alarming extent. These are only the attributes of copulation and erotic desire."

A case of nymphomania

Kent calls nymphomania "The most deplorable condition of all, to which the female is subject, is the uncontrollable, maniacal, erotic desire."

He has had "six cases under his observation." One case is of a 19 year-old girl who was refused by her "intended" after she attempted to have sex with him. She consulted Kent who, upon examination, found, "the clitoris and nymphae were red, dry, and hot; but as my digit came in contact with the soft parts... she became unmanageable for the time, until she had passed three or four orgasms... when she became more governable." When he examined her with a speculum she had more orgasms and "begged me not to withdraw the instrument." Said Kent, "Her modesty was gone when she was in the company of a male."

The treatment was two grain pills of monobromated camphor every four hours along with "formula number 1"; ice-water to the vulva at nights, and daily applications of Faradisation [light electric current] by placing a wetted sponge upon a chair with the patient seated on it, to which the negative pole is attached. The positive was used in his left hand, while the right hand massaged from the head to the spine.

The patient began "to improve immediately," and in "forty days she was quite herself again."

Kent arrives in Philadelphia

In the mid–1880s Mr. Charles Lee gave $40,000 to start a homœopathic hospital in Philadelphia. The Women's Homœopathic Hospital was to be run by the Women's Hospital Association, a ladies auxiliary of Hahnemann Medical College. The hospital opened on October 13, 1887, at the corner of 20th and Susquehanna Street (now an abandoned lot in a depressed neighborhood). Lippe, Alice Campbell, and William Wesselhoeft gave the opening addresses. Kent was invited but could not come. He sent an address to be read, but it arrived too late.

The hospital was "created and sustained" by women, based on pure Hahnemannian homœopathy. The charter forbade the use of drugs other than the potentized remedy.

The hospital had an on-going feud with Hahnemann Medical Hospital, which Lippe had condemned as "eclectic." The Women's Hospital board of directors complained that its physicians were using non-homœopathic treatments. In response, the eight employed physicians resigned and went to work at Hahnemann Hospital. It was a big furor in the newspapers at the time.

Meanwhile, the Women's Homœopathic Association was being urged by Lippe to start lectureships where homœopathic philosophy was taught. An editorial in the May 1888 *Medical Advance* asked for a postgraduate school. In the early spring of 1888, the Woman's Homœopathic Association started a fundraising program to establish a lectureship at the hospital. The fund was in memory of Lippe who had died in January.

By May of 1888, Kent was at 1419 Walnut Street in Philadelphia. The *Medical Advance* of July 1888 states that Kent began the postgraduate course and was the new hospital's consulting physician. Lectures on the *Organon* were advertised in the December 1888 *Medical Advance*.

The Post–Graduate School

While looking through some boxes of old papers in the Hahnemann Collection in Philadelphia, I came across a large ledger book, which upon inspection, I found to contain all the minutes of the Post-Graduate School of Homœopathics in Philadelphia. Little was known about the school. How the book arrived in the collection is unknown. The Post–Graduate School was in no way affiliated with the Hahnemann Medical College.

It is interesting to note that the president of the Post–Graduate School of Homœopathics was John Pitcairn, the founder of Pittsburgh Plate Glass, a devout Swedenborg follower. Pitcairn was responsible for building the New Church Cathedral at Bryn Athyn, Pennsylvania as well as his castle-like private residence.

William F. Kaercher, who served as the secretary of the organization, was the son-in-law of noted homœopath and pharmacist Bernhardt Fincke.

Kent's Post–Graduate School and Clinic occupied the two buildings at the left of the photo. The building on the right, with the steps, is the German Society of Philadelphia. The photo was taken just before the turn of the century.

The buildings at 613-15 were demolished sometime in the 1950s and were not replaced. The area next to the German Society is, today, a small, grassy park.

The grads

The 30 graduates of Kent's Philadelphia School with the Degree of Masters of Homœopathics:

June 6, 1892:
J. A. Tomhagen, Jennie Medley, William Johnson, Frederica E. Gladwin, J. Eugene Tremaine

April 27, 1893:
Allan S. Ironside, Frederick Scott Keith, S. L. Guild-Leggett

April 26, 1894:
Charles Louis Olds, Mary Augusta Johnson, Rosalie Stankowitch

April 25, 1895:
Clinton Enos, Maybelle M. Park, Helen Braddock Carpenter, A. Mary Ives, George Hover Thatcher

April 16, 1896:
Amelia Hess, Julia Loos, Mary K. Jackson, Lydia Webster Stokes, Henry Lincoln Houghton

March 18, 1897:
George H. Cooper, Hugh Cameron, Margaret Lewis, Josephine Howland

April 13, 1899:
Carrie Newton, Clyde Edwin Barton, Harvey Farrington, Alice Haley Bassett, Josephine Phelps

The school was formed on October 28, 1890. By January, 1891 suitable housing was found at 1317 Ridge Avenue, and in 1895 the school and clinic had moved to Spring Garden Street.

Each organization member signed a statement agreeing that the school shall teach homœopathy as promulgated in the *Organon* of 1833, and it shall teach "the employment of the single remedy, dynamized medicines, and the minimum dose, not singly but collectively," and that potentized medicines shall be used in the clinics.

This led to one case where a teacher, W. W. Baldwin, was accused of departing from the course and "teaching doctrine so opposed to those of the *Organon* that the members of the class and instructors protested to the Dean." Nothing more is known of the infraction, but Dr. Baldwin was removed as an instructor.

In the first four years the free clinic saw more than 36,500 patients. There were usually eight or so physicians on staff.

There was some internal dissension when, in 1896, Allen Ironside, a graduate, mentioned that Kent was infusing his lectures with "'New Church' doctrine to an extent that was giving the school a reputation as a Swedenborgian institution...."

A committee studied the matter and eventually decided the accusations were "vague, general, and indefinite" and did not contain any specifications. Dr. Ironside, who brought the charges, was asked to return his diploma.

The clinic continued until January, 1900 when Kent announced he had been approached by the Dunham College in Chicago to affiliate the school with their institution and he had decided to accept the offer. There were many factors involved in the decision. When the clinic started in 1890, most homœopathic colleges offered a three–year course of instruction. By 1900, they had expanded to four years. The Post–Graduate Clinic would be a fifth year of schooling and a greater expense to students. As an independent school it was subject to new restrictive state laws. Most of all, the Dunham College, unlike the Hahnemann College in Philadelphia, was dedicated to teaching pure homœopathic principles. Kent would be at home. The Post–Graduate Clinic closed in April.

In nine years, the clinic had seen over 40,000 people and

had trained 30 students, many of whom would become homœopathic leaders into the 20th century.

A more detailed view of the school is included in **Appendix B**, page 528.

The pupils

F. E. Gladwin, a pupil of Kent in St. Louis, followed him to Philadelphia where she assisted him at his Post-Graduate School.

In Philadelphia Kent trained Harvey Farrington, the son of E. A. Farrington. With the help of his students, he compiled the first edition of the classic *Repertory of the Homœopathic Materia Medica*.

Frederica Eugenie Gladwin, MD
February 18, 1856 — May 7, 1931

Born and raised in Connecticut, Gladwin taught high school in Chester, Pennsylvania, where she became interested in medicine and studied under Dr. Franklin Powel, a homœopath. She then attended the St. Louis Homœopathic Medical College. After graduating in 1890, she went to Philadelphia to set up practice and work closely with Kent, who had taught her in St. Louis.

H. A. Roberts called Gladwin, "one of the greatest teachers that our school of medicine has possessed... probably no one in the country had her knowledge of the *Repertory*, having worked with Dr. Kent in helping prepare it."

Said Dr. Julia M. Green: "She had a way of explaining things clearly, graphically; she could put herself in the pupil's place, see his difficulties and bring him back every time to the basic principles of homœopathic philosophy."

Gladwin was extremely deaf, enough so that ordinary conversation was lost to her. It was a life-long handicap that Roberts said, "would have spoiled the life of many a weaker individual."

Roberts tells the story that one summer, while teaching at the AFH Post-Graduate School, Gladwin found a one-cent piece on the sidewalk. She picked it up and remarked that she was going to "potentize it for homœopathy." She sought matching finds from all her students and patients in the form of "pocket change," and created an $800 scholarship fund from the single penny.

"Are you one who 'carries a chip on his shoulder' for those who do not see the homœopathic truth as you see it? Knock it off yourself immediately and forget it. Concentrate your thoughts on the truth of homœopathy as you have found it. Make it so vivid that all the world must get a vision but even then don't expect all to register it alike. When a ray of light is thrown upon a diamond it flashes back red or blue or gold, but the diamond remains steadfastly clear."

—F. E. Gladwin, 1928

Karvey Farrington [signature]

Harvey Farrington at the Hahnemann
Monument in Washington, DC, 1955;
Dr. Grimmer at the rear, holding his hat,
and Ray Seidel with the camera.

*When I met Lilly Spalding, the widow of Dr.
Ray Spalding, she asked me if I had ever met
Dr. Farrington. I said that he was, "a bit
before my time." She leaned over and said,
"He was a magnificent doctor, but what a
bore!"*

Harvey Farrington, MD
June 12, 1872 — June 9, 1957

Harvey Farrington graduated from Hahnemann Medical
College cum laude in 1895 with the degrees of Doctor of
Medicine and Doctor of Homœopathic Medicine.

In 1898, he graduated from Kent's Post–Graduate School
in Philadelphia. In 1900, Farrington followed Kent to
Chicago where he taught and practiced medicine for just
three months short of 57 years.

With W. A. Guild, MD, and Donald Gladish, MD, he
compiled the *Postgraduate Course in Homœopathy*, a book
still in print.

He died of pneumonia, just three days short of his 85th
birthday.

The development of the Repertory

Excerpts from the *Homœopathician*, July/August, 1914, by James
Tyler Kent, MD.

"I carried Lippe's *Repertory* with me for a number of years, until it
was not only interleaved but doubly and trebly interleaved, the
pages so closely written upon that it was impossible to find what
I had written into it, so that ended in confusion. But this was the
one upon which my earlier reliance rested.

"Then came the time, when I began to teach Materia Medica, in
1883, when I could readily see that we ought to have more.

[At this point Kent began to compile Allen's *Symptom-Register* and
Jahr's *Repertory* into the work— JW]

"Eventually I had a large manuscript of most of the repertory. I
talked with Lee, of Philadelphia, as Lippe's abridged form of a
new repertory was in his hands and Lippe desired me to enter
upon the work of helping or uniting with Lee to produce a complete
repertory.

"At that time I had completed a repertory of the Urinary Organs,
of Chill, Fever and Sweat, with other sections partly complete.

"Lee went to work and got out MIND, and later I helped him to
get out HEAD, but they were very incongruous.

"In a short time I saw that the plan started upon by Lee was not
what I had expected it to be; I told him so, and abandoned my

effort to help him improve the repertory. Then he became nearly blind, of both eyes, and said that his health was nearly ruined, that he could not go on with the work, and would have to give it up.

"Taking up what had been started, I then revised it thoroughly and formed it according to my own plan, which you now have in my *Repertory*.

"At one time Dr. Biegler, of Rochester, was in my office, looking over the pages, and some of the Boston doctors coming to me in Philadelphia wanted to look it over; they said: 'Why can't we have this *Repertory?*' I said, 'Because it will cost too much money. I have not made it for publication, but for myself, for my own use. It was made because of the demands of my business, and is the outgrowth simply of my own personal requirements. But I am willing that everybody should have it.'

"Then they insisted upon my making some plan for the publication of it, and Drs. Kimball, Thurston, and Biegler sent out circulars to see if they could secure enough subscribers to justify the publication... As I had talked it over with several other doctors, I did not believe there were more than three or four hundred, at the outside, who would have use for the work, or would want it.

"The circulars brought in a subscription list of between one hundred and ninety and two hundred, not more than two hundred, at $30 per copy. So I concluded that I would meet the rest of the expense and get it out, with hope that it might prove useful to the world.

"So it was issued, section by section. When the second section was out, I was notified by all except ninety of the original subscribers that, as the book was not what they expected to have, I might cancel their subscriptions. Ninety stuck to their pledges and their signatures and took the *Repertory*.

"It is, of course, a compilation; I did not manufacture the symptoms, but wrote them the best way I knew."

James Tyler Kent, circa 1900

"Many years ago before I studied medicine, I picked up a Lippe's Repertory. Before me was the symptom, 'Disposition to commit suicide by drowning.' Among the words following were Ant. and Bell. They were words I knew but I was sorely puzzled to know what an ant and a bell had to do with drowning. A little farther on I recognized Hell. and Puls. but they had left off the 'e' in the spelling of pulse. I wondered, but had a vague idea that the pulse and hell might bear some relation to 'wanting to drown oneself.' I tried to read more but found it no use. It was just words and words; most of them meaningless, so I gave up."

—Frederica E. Gladwin, 1927

Gibson Miller wrote, "For twenty years every spare hour was given to this book. The labor was immense, for every symptom had to be traced back to its original source, and only those who have undertaken such work can realize what it meant. But to him, it was a labor of love, and he grudged no time, trouble, or expense, if only he could, by means of this book, render the cure of disease more certain and quick... and it is little wonder that Kent's health several times broke down, but it was a labor of love, and nothing could alter his determination to complete the work."

The Swedenborg connection

Emmanuel Swedenborg (1688-1772) was a Swedish scientist, philosopher and theologian. Although the early work of Swedenborg was in the "hard sciences," Swedenborg is probably most known for his theological writings. He wrote the first work in Swedish on algebra, and wrote extensively on mining and minerals. In 1734 he published a work on natural principles where he introduced concepts through inductive logic that approach those of modern nuclear physicists. He suggested the nebular hypothesis for the formation of planets.

Beginning a study of anatomy and physiology, he was the first to understand the nature of cerebrospinal fluid. But his writings on anatomy and physiology led him to seek a deeper level, to try to understand human existence and the soul.

At 56 (the same age at which Hahnemann wrote the *Organon)* Swedenborg responded to a "divine vision and call." He described his spiritual senses as being opened so he could be in the spiritual world as consciously as in the material world. His writing, from this time on, was a revelation "from God" for a new age of truth and reason in religion.

The 18th century was described by Helen Keller (herself a follower of Swedenborg) as "The Cold Age of Reason." The influence of the writings of Rene Descartes and the interest in science were harbingers of the approaching Renaissance. Swedenborg's mastery of numerous diverse subjects made him the last of the multi-faceted "renaissance men." At debates among the theology students (Aristotelians) and the Cartesians at Upsula University, Swedenborg was a leading debater on the Cartesian side. Now Swedenborg was working on bringing Cartesian logic together with Christian theology.

His works outline the belief that all creation has its origin in divine love and wisdom, that all created things are but forms and effects of love and wisdom on the material plane and so "correspond" to spiritual realities. The material plane is one of effects whose causes are spiritual and whose purpose is divine. The Scriptures are written according to the principle of "correspondence" which, in turn, becomes the key to unlock their teachings.

He beheld in the Word of God a spiritual world in the world of phenomena. In effect, he wrote a commentary on the Bible, taking every sentence and describing the deeper meaning contained within. Through revealing this information, he believed that the Lord made his Second Coming.

As an example of this thinking, Wilson Van Dusen, in his book *The Presence of Other Worlds,* discusses The Book of Genesis. The sentence, "…And God created man in his own image," can be read as meaning that "[man] is given power of understanding…"

Says Van Dusen, "Swedenborg was looking for the God within. The whole of existence, all the worlds, may be understood. But the root understanding, the fundamental of all the rest, is how we relate to each other, what good we do, and what use we serve." Said Helen Keller, "He asked us to differentiate between life and existence."

Although Swedenborg neither preached nor founded a church, a small group familiar with his work, many of them clergy and physicians, founded the New Jerusalem Church in 1784.

Some of the clergy in England interested in the work of Swedenborg, believed that, in time, the doctrines of Swedenborg would be assimilated into the established Church.

The group that became the "New Church" included many artists, writers, doctors, and lawyers. It seemed to be "religion for the intelligentsia." Several of those who undertook to translate the works of Swedenborg from Latin to English were physicians.

While other Christian churches were interested in healing because Christ healed, the work of Swedenborg contributed a new level to the understanding of the relationship between man and the universe. In 1836, Luther Clark, MD, a prominent Boston allopathic physician, wrote in the *New Jerusalem Magazine:* "There is reason to hope and confidently expect that the heat and light descending with the New Church, will soon reach and reanimate the science of medicine."

The New Church seemed to attract those looking for a deeper and more personal way to define religion. It was as if a second layer of understanding had been added to the already accepted Christian theology.

At a time when the work of Ralph Waldo Emerson and the Trancendentalist movement in the USA was shaping people's thinking, the New Church offered the much sought–after hope of bringing true thinking back into religion.

It was not surprising that many physicians struggling to find answers to the "questions of life" found both homœopathy and the New Church.

Gram, a Swedenborg follower, successfully converted several prominent New York physicians to homœopathy and also introduced homœopathy to the members of the New Church. The periodicals of the New Church at the time were full of discussions of homœopathy and its relation to Swedenborg's teachings.

Although it is not known when the Lutheran-raised Hering took up the works of Swedenborg, he was known as a member of the New Church in Philadelphia. It was Hering who convinced young Rudolph Tafel to become his pharmacist. Tafel, in turn, came from a long line of Swedenborgians who had been involved in the translation of Swedenborg's work.

As interest in the New Church spread, so did interest in homœopathy. But one did not necessarily equate with the other.

In 1850, Constantine Hering said, "While there is good reason why Swedenborgians might prefer homœopathic treatment, there is none at all that all homœopaths be Swedenborgians."

The linking of homœopathy and Swedenborgism is very complex and certainly has been written about in much greater depth than the "surface look" presented here. For example, Garth Wilkinson, an allopathic physician in England, was so discouraged with his medical practice that he spent his time translating the works of Swedenborg from Latin to English. Wilkinson was a friend and correspondent with a number of the grand intellects of the time— Blake, Carlyle, Tennyson, Dickens, Emerson, Hawthorne. Wilkinson's work came to the attention of Henry James, a writer on theological and metaphysical subjects, and father of William (the psychologist and author of *The Varieties of Religious Experience*) and Henry (the author of *Daisy Miller, The Turn of the Screw*, and other novels). It was through the elder James that Wilkinson became interested in homœopathy. It was Wilkinson who gave us the remedy *Hecla lava*.

The centers of Swedenborgism in the late 1800s were Boston, Chicago, and Philadelphia. It was in Philadelphia that John Pitcairn, a wealthy industrialist, used his fortunes to buy land in Huntington Valley, a short distance from Philadelphia. He sold parcels of the land to other Swedenborgians and created the Swedenborgian community of Bryn Athyn, within which he built the monumental New Church Cathedral as well as his castle-like private residence, Glen Cairn.

Pitcairn's commitment to homœopathy was verified when he became the instrumental force in setting up the Post– Graduate School of Homœopathics with Kent at the helm.

It is with the work of Kent that we see the ultimate linking of the works of Swedenborg and Hahnemann, for both men thought of disease as a matter of the spirit— the *dynamis*.

Although it is unknown when Kent became interested in the works of Swedenborg, we do know that in 1893 he was attending "doctrinal" classes, and by 1896 he was infusing his lectures with Swedenborgian ideas. As Swedenborg's work was a commentary on the deeper meanings in the Bible, Kent's *Lectures on Homœopathic Philosophy* was a commentary on the *Organon*— dissecting each paragraph and telling us how to understand the deeper meaning within— but seen through a Swedenborgian filter.

In the work of Hahnemann, Kent saw a complete set of correspondences with the work of Swedenborg. We can see this clearly, time and again, in his lectures as he discussed "simple substance," "will and understanding," and "series and degrees," within homœopathic practice.

According to Kent (and Swedenborg), where there is a conflict between "will" and "understanding" or "wrong thinking" and "wrong willing"— the source of susceptibility to disease has been disturbed, causing weakening of the internals from which disease originates. In the spiritual world, heavenly spirits bring about health while diseases correspond with impurities— since "diseases are intrinsically impure." The idea, according to Kent, is to restore health by harmonizing "wrong willing" and "wrong thinking." In this sense, Kent regarded the prescriber as serving the spiritual condition of the patient.

Kent maintained that remedies cannot affect the Soul, which is the innermost part of a human— only man's *will* can influence the Soul. The "understanding" can be influenced by remedies. Kent wrote: "all medicines operate on the will and understanding …first upon affecting man in his ability to think or to will, and ultimately upon the tissues, the functions and sensations." By the medicine changing the "will and understanding" the patient "wills" rightly and then thinks rightly and thus overcomes his disease.

Stretching this line of thought further, since the high potencies are perceived as "finer energies" then they alone are capable of touching the will and intellect, and in turn affect the spirit through the mind. And when one begins to think in *this* manner, the giving of the high potency becomes the equal of a sacrament.

Since many of those who carried homœopathy into the 1930s were pupils of Kent, the quasi-mysticism of Kent's model was passed to his students, a number of whom also embraced Swedenborg's ideas .

It is this linking of Swedenborg and homœopathy that some believe is the reason that homœopathy failed so miserably in the early 20th century and continues not to be regarded as a true medical science.

Denis Demarque, a French homœopath critical of Kent's linking, says that if Kent had confined his interest in Swedenborg to his "internal life" (as had Gram, Hering, and others), then there would be little problem. But "…that which cannot be allowed is the transposition by Kent of the ideas of Hahnemann into the language of Swedenborg; the enlightenment of Kent has given homœopathy in the Anglo-Saxon world the allure of a religious sect."

This debate continues to this day.

The Faces of Homœopathy

In 1980, I purchased a used Homœopathic Pharmacopoeia from Henry Williams. It was the first old homœopathy book I purchased. When I finally looked through it, this letter fell out. It was certainly an omen of better times to come, as I uncovered more buried treasures! "Farley" is most likely Robert Farley, an 1886 graduate of Hahnemann Philadelphia.

Dear Farley:

I have put up Cenchris Cont and Sinapis for you. As I intend to make a copy of Cenchris for Preston I will send him vials of the potencies and with it Sinapis potencies.

You can copy the provings from it if you like. I want you to lend a hand in it. I shall make higher potencies of Sinapis alba and will send them to you.

Fraternally,

J. T. Kent

Homœopathy in Great Britain: I

Frederick Foster Hervey Quin
Robert Ellis Dudgeon
Richard Hughes
The Cooper Club
James Compton Burnett
John Henry Clarke
Edward Bach: A detour

The rise of homœopathy in Great Britain parallels the rise of homœopathy in the United States. Homœopaths in the two countries corresponded freely and the two communities were certainly entwined.

Many physicians who took up the homœopathic banner in Great Britain became authors whose writings became influential world wide— among them Dudgeon, Hughes, Burnett, and Clarke.

As in the United States, medicine in Great Britain in the 1830s was an entirely unregulated profession. But Great Britain retained its "class-ranked" society— one of the trappings that fell by the way in the populist United States. Within medicine in Great Britain there was an unspoken ranking, with medicine comprising three professions: physicians, surgeons and apothecaries— in that order of status— "physician is a profession, surgeon is an occupation and apothecary is a trade." These clearly demarcated roles, evolved over several centuries, were not supposed to overlap. But by the 1830s the roles' defining edges were blurring and thousands of unqualified practitioners were operating in what was an overcrowded medical marketplace.

In this early marketplace several "lay" homœopaths had learned of homœopathy direct from Hahnemann himself. In a time of anti-establishment movements in all segments of society, this group desired to take homœopathy to the masses in the same way the "botanical doctors" tried to do with their practices in the United States. They met with opposition from some physicians who wished to keep homœopathy the preserve of the medical aristocracy. It was a beginning which would eventually lead homœopathy in Great Britain along a very different path than that in the United States.

Frederick Foster Hervey Quin, MD
1799 — November 24, 1878

Frederick Foster Hervey Quin was to England what Hering was to the United States. Although Queen Adelaide had been treated by Dr. Stapf, it was not until Quin began practice that homœopathy gained a foothold in Great Britain.

Quin's heritage is a mystery. He was thought to have been the illegitimate son of the Duchess of Devonshire, formerly Lady Elizabeth Hervey, whose first marriage was to John Foster, though no evidence exists of the link.

Quin took his medical degree at Edinburgh in 1820 and was supposed to become Napoleon's physician at St. Helena. Before he could leave for the appointment, Napoleon died. Quin then became physician to the Duchess of Devonshire and accompanied her to the continent. While in Naples, he met Dr. Necker and learned of homœopathy. After the Duchess' death in 1824, Quin was appointed physician to Prince Leopold of Belgium, and upon returning to England in 1827 he was practicing homœopathy. He subsequently traveled to Köthen to meet Hahnemann, and studied with him for two years.

Were it not for his high social standing, his open adoption of homœopathy would have certainly caused him more grief than it did. Homœopathy was looked upon by the medical profession as quackery, but with Quin as a homœopath, the method took hold, as it were, from the "top down" in society.

No notice was paid to Quin's practice until 1833 when the Royal College of Physicians asked Quin to be examined or cease practicing medicine. When Quin did not reply, they sent a second note, to which Quin replied he had received the first note and was not aware that a reply was necessary, and thank you, etc. He was not bothered by them again. One of the College censors advised to "let Quin alone, as homœopathy cannot last more than two years."

At one point, Quin had been proposed as a member of the elite Athenaeum Club in London. When the nomination was announced, Dr. Paris, the President of the Royal College of Surgeons, said, "A pretty pass we have come to when quacks and adventurers are proposed as members of

The Young Quin. The portrait, at the Faculty of Homœopathy in London, shows his striking red hair.

171

This cartoon of Quin appeared in *Vanity Fair* magazine on January 20, 1872.

this club." The next day Paris was approached by a friend of Quin and was told to offer a written retraction and apology or to justify his language with pistols at 12 paces. The apology was written.

Quin established the British Homœopathic Society in 1844, and founded the London Homœopathic Hospital in 1850.

"Perhaps Dr. Quin will be remembered by a wider circle as an amusing companion and a wonderful story teller than as a homœopathic doctor; for to the last he was a welcome guest at tables of some of the highest personages in the land and, like Yorick, he invariable contrived to set their tables 'on a roar.'

"His perfect manners, his thorough knowledge of human nature, his wonderful powers of conversation, anecdote, wit and humor, made him the pet of Society, and no dinner party, from the Prince of Wales downward, was considered complete without the presence of Dr. Quin. But those who only saw him in the midst of rollicking fun, jokes, and laughter, knew but one side of his character. He was not merely an outsider who was invited in for the sake of his wit and conversation, but having mingled from his youth on the most intimate terms in the social circles of the highest in the land, he became their personal friend, was looked up to and referred to for his advice on the most delicate matters, and his opinion was always trusted for tact, sagacity, and truthfulness... In all his sallies of wit he was never known to say anything of, or to any one, which bore a sting, neither did his intimacy with the highest personages in the country, as is the case of men of smaller minds, ever lead him to give up his professional and other friends. He was always ready to dine with an old friend as with royalty, and his ear was ever open to any request for advice or help in difficulty, from what quarter soever it came."

"The story is told that he met the noted allopathic physician, Sir Charles Lococke, on the street one day. 'I have been treating a patient of yours,' said Sir Charles. 'Indeed?' replied Quin. 'Yes, and cured him on your own method, too.' 'Indeed,' rejoined Quin, 'what medicine did you give?' 'Nothing,' was Sir Charles' chuckling reply. 'Well it is curious,' adds Quin, 'that I have been treating a patient of yours too, and I used your method.' 'Well,' said Sir Charles, 'and what was the result?' 'Dead,' answered Quin in glee."

—From Bradford's *Pioneers of Homœopathy*

Robert Ellis Dudgeon, MD
March 17, 1820 — September 8, 1904

Dudgeon qualified in medicine at Edinburgh in 1841. In 1849, he translated the 5th edition of Hahnemann's *Organon* into English, a translation still used today. His contribution to homœopathic literature was massive: *Lectures on the Theory and Practice of Homœopathy, Hahnemann's Therapeutic Hints, The Homœopathic Treatment and Prevention of Asiatic Cholera, Hahnemann: The Founder of Scientific Therapeutics, The Influence of Homœopathy on General Medical Practice Since the Death of Hahnemann,* and *Hahnemann's Lesser Writings.* He worked closely with Richard Hughes on the *Cyclopedia of Drug Pathogenesy.*

He also developed a sphygmograph (blood-pressure apparatus) in 1878.

Dudgeon helped found the Hahnemann Hospital and the School of Homœopathy at Bloomsbury Square London in 1850.

At 26, he joined the editorial staff at *British Journal of Homœopathy.* He was still working there when it closed in 1884.

He called himself a foreigner in London because of his Scottish birth, and was at home conversing in English, French, and German.

Of all the homœopaths of the time his thinking was probably the closest to that of Hughes, but Dudgeon retained a flexibility that contrasted sharply with Hughes' dogmatism.

Said Clarke: "Dudgeon had the faculty of arrangement, a very rare faculty, which homœopaths above all needed on account of the enormous amount of detail which was involved in their work." It was this love of index-making which allowed him to compile the mind section of the *Cipher Repertory* with Drs. Drysdale and Russell.

At a memorial service, Dr. Blackley said: "If I were asked to sum up in a few words the characteristics of Dudgeon which impressed me, I would say: 1) his transparent honesty; 2) his thoroughness; 3) his indomitable industry; and 4) his breezy good temper."

Those who knew him thought he would live forever. At 84 he cheerfully came out one evening to deliver a lecture on homœopathy to the Ladies' Guild of the London Homœopathic Hospital.

R. E. Dudgeon, circa 1860

R. E. Dudgeon, circa 1885

Yet, with all his hard work, he liked to play as well. He had a passion for golf and set aside one afternoon a week for his game, and would let nothing come in its way.

Said Dr. E. A. Neatby: "Dr. Dudgeon was always ready to step in and fill up a gap, either by writing an article or translating something which was sent to him in a hurry or by throwing light on an obscure passage of translation."

A contemporary said: "At the bedside he did not perhaps shine as a consultant; he was no courtier; he was much too honest, in fact, to be a fashionable consultant; but from my experience of him in consultation I can say that one rarely failed to get substantial help in diagnosis and many valuable hints as to the choice of remedies."

The dynamic vs. the material

Richard Hughes, MD
1836 — April 9, 1902

Educated at Edinburgh, Scotland, Hughes practiced in Brighton, England until a year before his death when he moved to Albany, Guildsford, to become the Catholic Apostolic Church pastor.

He authored *Manual of Pharmacodynamics* in 1867 and the *Manual of Therapeutics* shortly thereafter. He was an officer of the British Homœopathic Society, and an editor of the *British Journal of Homœopathy*. He worked with T. F. Allen on the 10 volume *Encyclopedia* and, unsure of the accuracy of the proving reports contained in Allen's volumes, he edited, with Jabez Dake, MD in the United States, the six-volume *Cyclopedia of Drug Pathogenesy*.

Said Dr. Bushrod James: "His personality was extremely winning; his voice rich, clear, and steady; his eyes beautiful in youth with the merry twinkle of fun or the soft glow of sympathy as occasion required, and always pure and true. He was tall and rather slender in figure, and as age drew on he leaned forward slightly, not as with years, however, but as though his tender ministrations to human sufferers had drawn him down to listen... He was handsome, with no shade of vanity; genial and gleefully able to either give

or take a joke, without a gleam of undue levity... He advanced his ideas with force, yet showed graceful respect to those who disagreed with his views, and his knowledge, gained by the utmost concentration and research, has been accepted as correct even by those who combated some of his theories."

In later years, British homœopathy (and homœopathy in general) was to be divided into those "Hughesian" and those not. In compiling the *Cyclopedia*, Hughes decided to eliminate all the proving symptoms that were gained from drugs taken at potencies above the 6c. He was, above all, a materialist. He saw a need to understand the pathology the remedies created on the organic level and it was this "pathology level" that he saw as being treated.

Thomas Skinner, critical of Hughes' approach, said that his concept of low potencies was "ideal for those who did not wish to stray far from their allopathic training."

J. H. Clarke said of Hughes (in regard to his advocacy of low potencies), "If it were put forward on the grounds that it meets the requirements of those who have not acquired the necessary gifts to practice the higher grades and not being a scientific improvement on the Hahnemannian method, then little be said against it."

Those who battled with Hughes had a rough road. His contemporary, James Compton Burnett was often at odds with him, and Hughes, who was considerably older, finally achieved supreme authority in the homœopathic world managing thereafter to block all roads to power as long as he lived. In 1883, he had selected John Clarke, one of his own most promising medical students, as his assistant editor on the *British Journal of Homœopathy*. The appointment lasted two years before Hughes realized his mistake and it was the first and last office Clarke ever held. In 1890, Clarke "let his hair down and bared his teeth" in a paper, "The Two Paths in Homœopathy," intended as an outright challenge to Hughes. Burnett meanwhile had been obliged, whether by overwork or by hostile pressure from above, to resign his own official appointments and to concentrate, as Clarke was forced to do for the rest of his life, on private practice.

In a letter to Tyrell in Canada, Kent refers to "that skunk, Dicky Hughes," and says, "I will fight him for the rest of my days."

Yet Hughes' work, on its own, remains a valuable view of the materia medica. His *Pharmacodynamics* was immensely influential when published in 1868. Said Burnett, "We all fed on it."

George Royal, MD, said his preceptor told him to read Hering's *Condensed Materia Medica*, and it made no sense to him. He met Dr. Erastus Case and asked his advice. Case said, "The foolish man! Why did he not give you Hughes' *Pharmacodynamics* first? Get that and read it through. Then you can appreciate Hering." Says Royal, "As a result when some allopathic physician asks me for advice about books I give him Case's advice and add Hughes and Farrington's *Clinical Materia Medica*. Both these books I read every year."

Robert Thomas Cooper, MD
June 2, 1844 — September 14, 1903

Robert T. Cooper M B

Cooper was a graduate of Trinity College, Dublin, gaining his MD in 1871 and his MA in 1882. He was an assistant physician and surgeon for ear diseases at the London Homœopathic Hospital. As with most homœopaths of this time, Cooper was a 'low potency man' who used mother tinctures and 3x potencies.

Cooper's mark on British homœopathy lay in his amazing work with cancer.

Cooper believed cancers to be the result of hidden 'growth forces' within the person very similar to the 'growth force' in trees and other plants. He believed a curative ability or action is inherent in all living plant material, and to access this curative nature the remedy need not be succussed or triturated— a single drop of the pure tincture will do.

Cooper writes that he discovered his system through some 30 years of careful observation. He declared there was "…existing in plant-remedies a force…which acted by virtue of a power in all respects similar to a germinating power in the human body… in the living plants we get a force which, if applied… to disease, will arrest its progress and even cause its dispersal."

Margaret Tyler, in her *Drug Pictures*, describes Cooper hunting in Kew Gardens for possible remedies. "Armed with a small bottle three parts filled with spirit of wine, he would secure his choice specimen and bottle it forthwith. He thus provided himself with the purest and most uncontaminated 'mother tincture' possible."

Cooper described the making of "arborivital" remedies thus:

"The preparation of remedies used are tinctures made on the spot from living plants, proof spirit being employed for the sake of preserving their inherent properties...by allowing the spirit to come into contact with the living plant— the branch, while still attached, being kept plunged in the spirit and exposed to sunlight while thus immersed— 'heliosthened,' as I term it."

Among the remedies he made in this "arborivital" manner were *Brassica rapa, Silphium perfoliatum, Scrophularia nodosa, Iris versicolor, Caltha palustris, Ornithogallum umbellata, Crocus vernalis, Crocus sativus, Matthiola annua, Thapsus bursa-pastoris, Juniperus and Spiraea ulmaria.*

Says Tyler, "Dr. Cooper had an uncanny genius for discovering unusual remedies; some of these he got, no doubt, from old herbals; but it has been said that he used to lie down before a flowering plant by the hour, dragging from it its virtues of healing. He made extraordinary play, in cancer, with some of his flowers, and one heard him called 'the man who can cure cancer.'"

The Cooper Club

Sometime along the way, Cooper, Burnett, and Clarke began meeting over dinner to discuss their cases. Tyler describes the group as "...Cooper with his genius for the discovery of useful remedies, Dr. James Compton Burnett, who had a genius for grasping their idiosyncrasies and possibilities and employing them with success for the patients that besieged him, and Dr. Clarke who noted them with the carefulness of genius and recorded them for the permanent help of humanity in his *Dictionary...*"

The group was eventually joined by Thomas Skinner. These dinner meetings became known as "The Cooper Club." After the death of Burnett and Cooper, Clarke and Skinner were joined by Charles E. Wheeler, Margaret Tyler, and John Weir. The meetings were held until about 1914.

James Compton Burnett, MD
July 10, 1840 — April 2, 1901

Burnett attended medical school in Vienna in 1865, and studied anatomy an extra two years. He was awarded the Gold Medal in Anatomy upon graduation: "Passing through a brilliant examination in anatomy, lasting one hour and a half, the professor shook hands with him, saying that he had never examined a student with so brilliant and thorough a knowledge of anatomy."

After graduation from Glasgow in 1872, he went to Barnhill Parochial Hospital and Asylum in Glasgow. He was converted to homœopathy there by a friend, Alfred Hawkes of the Royal Infirmary. In 1876 he took his MD degree.

Before his discovery of homœopathy, Burnett was in such despair over his medical results that he wrote of his "half determination to go to America and turn farmer." His love of the land was always strong, and he farmed his land in the country. Says Clarke, "It gave him infinite delight to see his nurslings grow."

Burnett was the one of the first to speak of the concept of "vaccinosis," that a vaccine could trigger illness. He outlined this in his small book, *Vaccinosis*, in 1884. He introduced the remedy *Baccillinum*, along with other nosodes. He was the editor of *Homœopathic World* from 1879 to 1885. When he left, the position was filled by J. H. Clarke.

As a member of "The Cooper Club," his observations are well noted in Clarke's three–volume *Dictionary of Materia Medica.*

He was the great–uncle of Marjorie Blackie, MD, who served as Physician to Queen Elizabeth II for many years, and he was the father of the British author, Ivy Compton-Burnett.

Says Clarke, "There was a directness about Burnett which led him to the centre of a situation more quickly than most; a fund of humor, a twinkle in his eye and a laugh that will long live in the memory of all who knew him."

His book *Fifty Reasons for Being a Homœopath* (1888) bears reading over and over.

His first wife died in childbirth. He met his second wife as a patient: "Dr. Burnett cured her in eight months with

Mercurius vivus, whereupon she got married, had 'several bouncing children and afterwards remained in excellent health… she was passionately devoted to her husband, as he was to her, but for most of their married life Dr. Burnett lived at a hotel in London, joining his family at weekends, seldom taking more than five days holiday together, and only towards the end of his life allowing himself one day at home in the middle of the week, which he allotted to writing."

It is said he had two sides, a family side and another, which was bellicose and litigious. This was uninhibitedly expressed throughout his career at the expense of "our friends, the enemy," his orthodox professional colleagues.

Burnett often compared the practice of homœopathy to gardening or chess, both favorite pastimes of his, both calculated to "appeal to a temperament which derived peculiar satisfaction from protracted, crafty and crabwise maneuvers."

Said his biographer, Clarke, "Burnett's shock tactics, his chatty tone and resolutely empirical attitude to clinical symptoms were anathema to Richard Hughes, who regularly gave him curt, dismissive reviews and a distinctly ungenerous obituary in the *Journal* when he died."

"It was Burnett's hope that he might 'die in harness, 'and it was a hope fulfilled; "He paid his last professional visit within a few hours of his death of heart failure at his hotel lodgings in London where he had been commuting to his clinic daily and returning twice weekly to his home in a large country house in Hove.

Said Hilary Spurling, "He was sixty. Twelve of his thirteen children survived him… of his twelve children, one died young of pneumonia; another was killed in the first war; three committed suicide. Two of his four sons made brief, childless marriages, his eight daughters remained unmarried so that, though he himself had ardently believed that 'the true source of national greatness is large families of healthy children,' his only legacy to posterity lies in the novels of his fourth daughter…"

And, may we add, in his magnificent literature and in the hearts of homœopaths, world-wide!

Burnett's Books

Gold as a Remedy In Disease
Diseases of Veins
Supersalinity of The Blood
Valvular Disease of The Heart
Diseases of The Skin
Diseases of The Spleen
Fevers
The Cure of Consumption
Enlarged Tonsils Cured by Medicine
Fifty Reasons For Being A Homeopath
Gold as a Remedy
Gout and Its Cure
Cataract Its Nature and Cure
Change of Life In Women
Curability of Tumours
Delicate, Backward, Puny and Stunted Children
Natrum Mur as a Test of The Doctrine of Drug Dynamization
On Fistula
On Neuralgia
Organ Diseases of Women
The Greater Diseases of the Liver
The New Cure of Consumption
Tumours of the Breast and Their Cure
Blood Poisoning and The Use of Pyrogenium.

Burnett at the start of his career

Burnett's conversion

Burnett left University with strictly orthodox medical views, "having been taught by good men and true that Homœopathy was therapeutic nihilism." This was the current view at the time, often expressed with a great deal more virulence. Homœopathy in Britain was confined to a more or less persecuted sect, actively ridiculed in the universities and widely despised outside them. Its followers were looked upon as quacks or cranks, its practice had narrowly escaped being declared illegal in the 1850s and the British Medical Association prohibited homœopaths from joining its ranks.

Burnett's immediate reaction, on resolving to try a first experiment in homœopathy, suggests the belligerent streak in his character which would later fully develop: "I would try the thing at the bedside, prove it to be a lying sham, and expose it to an admiring profession."

While working at a hospital, Burnett watched a little boy die of pleurisy. It affected him greatly. He confided his despondency to his friend Alfred Hawkes at the Royal Infirmary, who recommended homœopathy. Dr. Burnett purchased— "very much as if I were contemplating a crime"— Richard Hughes' two manuals, on pharmacodynamics and therapeutics, which at that time provided the standard introduction in English to "this dangerous ground."

Said Burnett, "I mastered their main points in a week or two, and came from a consideration of these to the conclusion either that Homœopathy was a very grand thing indeed, or this Dr. Hughes must be a very big —. No, the word is unparliamentary. You don't like the word? Well, I do, it expresses my meaning to a T; on such an important subject there is for me no middle way, it must be either good clear God's truth, or black lying."

Hughes had suggested *Aconite* as a remedy for simple fever and Dr. Burnett determined to test the advice on his children's fever ward, dosing all the patients down one side with *Aconite* and treating the others as usual. "Within twenty-four hours all the *Aconite* children were cured (save one who had measles) and smartly discharged, while the rest still languished in hospital. The experiment was repeated with the same startling results until a truculent nurse, impatient of the doctor's hard heart, dosed all the patients indiscriminately from 'Dr. Burnett's Fever Bottle' and emptied the ward."

Burnett said he was "simply dumbfounded." He spent his nights reading homœopathic literature and, "having suffered a conversion which he afterwards compared to St. Paul's on the road to Damascus, instantly resolved 'to fight the good fight of homœopathy with all the power I possess; were I to do less I should be afraid to die.'"

Burnett to a student

"'My dear fellow,' said Burnett over the dinner-table at which they met, to the young man whose insolent academicism had provoked the sleeping lion, 'Your mind is as full of scholastic conceit as an egg is full of meat, and you are therefore a doomed man, so far as scientific medicine is concerned; your cup of knowledge is full, but full of knowledge of the wrong sort; your knowledge is like those Neapolitan walnuts there, which have been dried in a kiln, and thereby rendered sterile; plant them and they will not germinate, and it is just thus with your scholastic learnings: all you know has been rendered sterile— incapable of germinating.

"Kiln-dried walnuts have a certain value as food, but they are dead; your knowledge has a certain value as mental food for other students if you like to turn teacher, but it is scholastically dried up and sterilized. You have no living faith in living physic— so far as the really direct healing of the sick is concerned, all your medicine is dead, as dead as a door nail...

"I shall also be pleased to introduce you to the physicians at the London Homœopathic Hospital, where you can watch the work done...

"Believe me, we homœopaths are not what you have been taught to think; we have no secrets; we aim all of us, each according to his ability and in his own way, to advance the true interests of our beneficent art, and our most earnest desire before God and man is to teach all we know to all knowledge-seeking lovers of truth...

"I will not mince matters with you: those who tell you that Hahnemann was an ignorant quack, that the homœopaths are quacks, are— well, they say the thing that is not. The word I should like to use would shock you, perhaps; be it so, you know what I mean. Tell it from the house-tops, and let it shock a callous, leech-ridden, stupid world...

"You claim to be 'regular'— but 'regular' what? You claim the right to ridicule and condemn cases reported by eminent

DELICATE, BACKWARD, PUNY AND STUNTED CHILDREN
BURNETT

homœopathic practitioners— on what principle or ground? Were you there? Did you see the cases? You know nothing of homœopathy, you have never tried it, and yet you claim the right of judgment upon homœopathic work. You live under a chronic delusion: when you say you do not believe this or that homœopathic cure, what you really say is this, 'I, with my regular practice cannot cure such cases; my professors cannot; we agree they cannot be cured at all, therefore these pretended cures of the homœopaths are not real.' In other words, you cannot cut a piece of cloth with a steel key, and it therefore follows that I cannot cut it with steel scissors, because both key and scissors are made of steel. You say steel cannot cut it, I say it can, and when we come to enquire into the matter it is found that you mean a steel key, whereas I mean steel scissors.

"If you want roasted pigeon for dinner you must procure the pigeon and roast it; it will not fall ready roasted into your mouth.

"What would you say if your gardener were to put in his seed without getting rid of the weeds and preparing the ground? So here: I want you to root out the weeds of scholastic prejudice and prepare your mental ground at least in some small measure, or I shall only sow good seed that either by reason of the unprepared soil will not spring up at all or else will struggle in vain with the weeds of conceit, ignorance, and prejudice.

"Come, friend, fair play, even for hated and despised homœopathy."

— Burnett in *Fifty Reasons for Being a Homœopath*

Curing the apple tree

"I had cured a lady of a tiny tumor of the nose; she was pleased and grateful, and subsequently brought to me her niece, on whom the doctors were about to operate for a small ovarian tumor; I cured this tumor also, but it occupied two years or thereabouts, and then aunt and niece both persuaded a friend to come to me. How long did I think it would take to cure her ovarian tumor? At least two years. I prefer the operation, said she; that will only take six weeks. But it took less. She died under or shortly after the operation… That same aunt and niece persuaded a lady from Chatham to come to me for a tumor of the breast; the lady's husband declined, as I thought it would take two years at the very least. She was successfully operated on, and thoroughly cured of her mammary tumor; nine months later she was again thoroughly cured of another tumor, by a perfectly successful operation; a few months thereafter she was again successfully operated on for another tumor, and just as she was getting well— she died… cutting off the apple does not cure an apple-tree of growing apples."

John Henry Clarke, MD
1853 — November 24, 1931

Clarke was educated at Edinburgh receiving his degree in 1877. He was a pupil of Richard Hughes, but found many "homœopathic doors" closed on him after he began to associate with "high-potency" prescribers in Liverpool like Thomas Skinner, and Edward Berridge.

Clarke served as editor of *Homœopathic World* for 29 years, from 1885 to 1898 and again from 1923 to his death in 1931.

Dr. Edgar Whittaker in *Homœopathic World*, January 1932, says of Clarke:

"Clarke… described the other leading members of the Cooper Club as 'the three most potent influences on the evolution of British Homœopathy today,' and wrote in 1901: 'It is not too much to say that during the last twenty years Burnett has been the most powerful, the most fruitful, the most original force in homœopathy.' Clarke was himself a physician to be reckoned with, and in time the author of a medical encyclopedia which rivaled Hughes."

For many years Clarke visited his patients in a horse–drawn carriage which was like an office inside, complete with a writing desk, as Clarke never lost an opportunity to work on his books. Noel Puddephatt knew Clarke well and told of Clarke's pet bulldog sitting in his consulting room, quietly watching what was going on.

Clarke said that all his work on his three–volume 'dictionary' was to save himself work. He wanted all the knowledge he had gleaned from a hundred sources in a place where he could lay his finger on it. His *Dictionary* is also invaluable for the drug-pictures and clinical experiences, written in his own lucid style, that precede each remedy all through the book. Clarke, however, did away with grading the symptoms by importance indicated by different type–faces. He said, "I have omitted the types, because all symptoms are of equal value." Keeping careful notes at the meetings of the Cooper Club, he wrote down everything said at dinner and the *Dictionary of Materia Medica* is full of symptoms with Burnett (B) and Robert T. Cooper (RTC) as sources. While it is difficult to glean much of Burnett's practice from Burnett's writing, Clarke's *Dictionary* gives much insight into the mind of Burnett. The three volumes of the *Dictionary* were completed in 1900. Criticized for

producing such a large work, he replied, "I have never found a dictionary that explained too many words." It remains one of homœopathy's standard works.

A prolific writer, Clarke was very supportive of the lay movement in homœopathy. It was his belief that as long as homœopathy was practiced it did not matter if the remedy came from a qualified prescriber or not. Many of his books were written for the untrained worker and domestic prescriber. "To Clarke the advantages of being given a remedy by a mature homœopath were far superior to being given something by someone who knew nothing about homœopathy at all."

While Clarke supported the lay homœopath, he berated the allopaths. Margaret Tyler said of Clarke: "A brilliant writer, he wielded a very caustic pen. But his influence for good might have been greater had he been less fierce, and made a little allowance for those whose real sin was ignorance. The old school was to be bullied and rated. Ignorance was 'cussedness' to be bludgeoned into knowledge— rather than tactfully helped and taught. He was so sure on his own ground, that he had no mercy on the man on the other side of the fence. 'Pandering to the allopaths' was his name for courtesy to men who are, after all, our brethren in the healing art. He set his fly-traps with vinegar."

Having been shunned by the British Homœopathic Society when Hughes held sway, he refused honors offered to him by the society at a later date. It was said in one obituary, "Things did not work out as he hoped and he lost touch with what was going on outside. The great sorrow was that he lived the last ten years of his life feeling far too much that his colleagues had let him down, that if they would have seen things his way, homœopathy would have progressed. He was constantly accusing homœopaths of 'placating' the allopaths."

A case from Clarke

Dr. Wheeler said he would never forget one case he had the honor to watch with Dr. Clarke. The case was a desperate one. The patient was a poor man, but Clarke was seeing him four times a day. Wheeler was called in for the chest condition and found the man had empyema which had ruptured into the lungs and pus was being discharged through the lung. The man was in a pretty desperate condition but even when Wheeler first saw him he was astonishingly well for his condition, which gave a certain amount of hope in the prognosis. Clarke pulled that man through and he got steadily well. The man was given six remedies a day. Every time Clarke saw him he would give something else. Wheeler said he saw the case six times, and sometimes he was having low potencies, and then the 30s, and after an hour or so he would be given a low potency. Said Wheeler, "Nothing could have been more satisfactory than the progress that that man made, and not long afterwards one would never have known that he had ever had empyema at all."

Dr. Clarke and Mr. Hyde: Clarke's other side

Clarke wrote on subjects other than homœopathy. He was an outspoken anti-vivisectionist. He also wrote a number of anti-Jewish and anti-German tracts.

Said Dr. Edgar Whittaker in *Homœopathic World*, January 1932, "In later years he was attracted by the poetry of William Blake, and wrote two small books on him. He was in fact in search of another battle ground, this time of a mystical and religious nature. He 'hated' all Germans pre-war, he 'loathed' all Jews post-war— they were against England. He failed in these last battles simply because he had made so many friends."

Clarke was treasurer and vice-president of a group called the "Britons," who later became the British Union of Fascists. He wrote five booklets during this time: *The Call of the Sword* (1917); *England under the Heel of the Jew* (1918); *Democracy and Shylocracy; White Labour versus Red* (1922); *A Patriotic Fund to Fight the Hidden Hand* (1923). In one of the books Clarke argued that Prussia and Germany were Judaic nations and the war was one of Jewish finance aimed at overthrowing the Christian civilization of England.

Noting that "Dr. Ruddock had been compelled to keep his publishing department in his own basement," Clarke established his own publishing house for his books— The Homeopathic Publishing Company— for no reputable publishing house wanted to touch "what was 'officially' anathema." Clarke's homeopathic output include the following works— most still available in print.

The Prescriber (1885) 9 editions
Revolution in Medicine (1886)
Odium Medicum and Homeopathy: The Times Correspondence (1887)
Indigestion: Its Causes and Cure (1888)
Dictionary of Domestic Medicine (1890)
Cholera Diarrhea and Dysentery (1893)
Therapeutics of Serpent Poisons (1893)
Homeopathy: All About It (1894)
Diseases of the Heart and Arteries (1895)
Catarrh Colds and Grippe (1899)
Dictionary of Practical Materia Medica, Three volumes (1900)
Clinical Repertory (1904)
Rheumatism and Sciatica (1904)
Life and works of James Compton Burnett (1904)
Homeopathy Explained (1905)
Thomas Skinner: A Biographical Sketch (1907)
Radium as an Internal Remedy (1908)
The Cure of Tumors by Medicine (1908)
Whooping Cough (1908)
Gunpowder as a War Remedy (1915)
Hahnemann & Paracelsus (1923)
Dr. Skinner's Grand Characteristics (1931)
Constitutional Medicine
Foundations of Materia Medica
Non-Surgical Diseases of the Glands

A detour

Edward Bach, MD
September 24, 1886 — November 27, 1936

Edward Bach (pronounced Batch) graduated from medical school in 1912. He became increasingly interested in the new science of immunology. In 1919 he was offered a position as bacteriologist and pathologist at the London Homœopathic Hospital, and remained there for three years.

He was introduced to homœopathy while at the hospital. He worked with Dr. Charles Wheeler on the development of the "bowel-nosodes," a series of seven different remedies made from intestinal flora. They were later joined by Dr. John Paterson. In 1926 Bach wrote, with Wheeler, *Chronic Disease; A Working Hypothesis.*

In the late 1920s he became interested in the possibility of using plant substances that would act in a similar manner to his seven bowel nosodes and in 1930 he left his London practice to wander the countryside looking for the flowers that would become healing agents.

The 38 "Flower Essences" he developed are often thought of as "homœopathic," but are neither homœopathic in their mode of manufacture nor homœopathic in their application. They differ from homœopathy in the most fundamental way possible, although they are a system in their own right with a good clinical record of efficacy.

Although Bach was a homœopathic student, his work rejected the cornerstone of homœopathy, the Law of Similars. Bach could not accept the notion of curing a natural disease by imposition on it of a similar artificial disease and he also rejected the concept of similarity in its own right. In a lecture he gave in 1931 called "Ye Suffer from Yourselves," he said, "It is obviously fundamentally wrong to say that 'like cures like.' Hahnemann had a conception of the truth right enough, but expressed it incompletely. Like may strengthen like, like may repel like, but in the true healing sense like cannot cure like… No doubt Hahnemann, by his method of potentisation, endeavored to turn wrong into right, poisons into virtues, but it is simpler to use the beauteous and virtuous remedies direct."

Bach could not understand how poisons, as used so readily in homœopathy (the venoms, the cyanides, the arsenics, etc.) could be of any healing value. He believed while they might be effective medicines that could conquer disease, genuine cures, what he called "true healing," would mean not fighting the disease with poisons but instead eliminating the faults that cause disease by promoting the opposing virtue. If illness is a "wrong" within, it cannot be driven out by a poison— another wrong. True healing, according to Bach, can happen only by "right replacing wrong, good replacing evil, light replacing darkness."

Said Bach of his remedies, "The action of these remedies [the Flowers] is to raise our vibrations and open up our channels for the reception of our Spiritual Self, to flood our natures with the particular virtue we need, and wash out from us the fault which is causing harm."

Between 1928 and 1930 Bach was making the first of the remedies by triturating the flowers for 21 minutes to (in his estimation) the 7c potency. He then succussed them up to an unspecified potency. In 1930 he wrote about the sun method where he claimed that exposure to sunlight for 3, 4 , or 7 hours became the 3rd, 4th, or 7th potency— certainly a move away from homœopathy. By 1934 he was using two methods— sun and boiling. In the sun method, the fresh–picked flower is placed on the surface of a dish of water and exposed to the sunlight. When the flowers wilt, they are picked from the surface of the water. An equal amount of brandy is added to the water and this becomes the "mother tincture." Two drops of this are diluted in 30mls of brandy to make the stock remedies. With the boiling method (which was used for tougher, woodier plants) the twigs were put in boiling water, simmered for an hour, then cooled, decanted and mixed with brandy as above.

Although he referred to these processes as "potentization," they are very different from the homœopath's potentization process.

In these later years Bach became extremely sensitive to the qualities of the flowers. The mysterious process by which he selected the flowers to test for his system was heavily intuitive. Somehow, he could sense within himself the powers of the remedies he was seeking. He returned to

Edward Bach, circa 1930

The Countess Katherine Wielopolska was the person who said to me, "You must go see my doctor," and sent me to Ray Seidel.

In the late 1920s she worked as a nurse at the London Homœopathic Hospital. She told me that one day she was standing with a group of nurses outside the hospital when a man came out, and stepped into a waiting car. Two doctors were standing nearby and she overheard one say to the other, "I wish I knew how he gets his patients better so quickly!"

She asked one of the nurses the identity of the man they commented about.

"Oh," they said, "That's Doctor Bach."

London on several occasions, but found the bustle and noise of the city too much to bear and went back to the countryside.

The reports of his cures while living in the English countryside are truly astounding, although several of the cures seemed simply to be the laying on of hands. He was certainly an amazing healer.

He published his new ideas in *Homœopathic World* through the early 1930s which was edited by J. H. Clarke until 1931. Clarke sensed the potential of what Bach was doing and urged him to "find what he was seeking."

Bach never cared much for his personal appearance and it was said his clothes were "well-worn." F. J. Wheeler tells the story of Bach being seen one day walking down a lane holding a new football. A passerby went to the store in town and asked if they lost a football because he had seen "a tramp walking along with a new one under his arm." "Why that is Dr. Bach," said the shopkeeper. "He just bought the ball to give to the village lads. He is always doing things like that."

Bach was described as "a friend to all." In his last years it is said that he went unshaven, although no likenesses of him from that period exist. He lived his last six years in the English countryside, working with his remedies and helping his neighbors. Always frail, he became increasingly worn and, being confined to bed for a month, he died in his sleep at the age of 50.

Kent in Chicago

Kent the teacher
Further divisions
The old Kent
Stevensville, Montana

The Dunham College in Chicago

In 1900, Kent moved to Chicago to teach at the Dunham Medical College and the Hahnemann Medical College of Chicago.

The Hering College in Chicago was started in 1892 by Henry C. Allen and a group of like-minded physicians who believed pure homœopathy needed to be taught, because all other homœopathic schools were teaching an eclectic blend of medicine with no philosophical background.

As with most institutions led by strong-minded people, there were differences in the faculty. By 1895 another "pure" college, the Dunham College had started.

Dunham college invited Kent, in 1900, to bring his Post-Graduate School from Philadelphia to Chicago. In 1903, the Dunham College merged with the Hering College, and the Post-Graduate program ceased.

Many of the faculty at Hering had been students of Kent's Post-Graduate School in Philadelphia.

Little is written to give us an image of Kent the man. Only a few likenesses of the man are known:
the 1882 photo (and line-cut from it), the 1884 line-cut of Kent with a beard, the oval photo that appears in the Repertory, *the photo that appeared in the Ehrhart and Karl Memorial Edition of his* Lectures on Homœopathic Philosophy, *and the photo of him with Clara Louise in their garden of their home in Evanston, Illinois. This last photo of Kent appeared in the* Homœopathician *in 1912.*

Kent the teacher

Kent delivered his lectures extemporaneously while referring to an interleaved copy of Hering's *Guiding Symptoms.* Those who studied with him said it took four years of lectures to cover 200 remedies. When Kent moved to Chicago, a number of letters of congratulation were printed in the *Dunham Medical College Journal.* The one below was from Maybelle M. Park, one of Kent's students.

"The true teacher is one who can give to others and show them how to get for themselves, and through this inherent ability, Dr. J. T. Kent has gained for himself a world-wide reputation. In lecturing on a remedy he makes it so walk and breathe and live that one cannot forget it. Heine said: 'All the world is a hospital, and all the men and women in it are merely patients.' So Dr. Kent peoples the world with remedies, making them so vital that as we walk on the street we say to ourselves there goes Mr. *Phosphorus*; Mr. *Sulphur* neglected his bath again this morning; Miss *Ignatia* is still grieving; Baby *Calcarea* is still chewing that pork-rind; how happy Miss *Pulsatilla* is out in the open air. This habit becomes fixed upon one as they grow familiar with the remedies. As a patient returned to the dispensary we frequently would look for his record under the index name of the remedy instead of his own name.

"Dr. Kent teaches materia medica by making it live, not by crowding the memory with keynotes, red tape, and worthless catch phrases, but by making each remedy an individual so real that when we meet the patient we recognize him by his photograph— as each detail of his aches and pains are detailed to us we recognize the finer lines and shadings of the photograph we have been holding in our mind. One who learns this system of prescribing will never have the slightest temptation to prescribe on keynotes, which is adapted only to the ignorant.

"Dr. Kent teaches homœopathic philosophy by making it a part of ourselves, by making it live in us. As we are a union of the material, mental, and spiritual, so everything has its grades of lower and higher being, and through these laws all the philosophy becomes clear and a new world opens before us as we interpret the old world in new light. Under Dr. Kent's teaching, Hahnemann's *Organon* becomes the life force of homœopathy, and the materia medica becomes the health force of humanity."

The last graduates

After moving to Chicago, the Post-Graduate School held only three sessions before the Dunham College was merged with the Hering College in 1903 and Kent became the head of homœopathics with H. C. Allen. The seven additional graduates of the Post-Graduate School were:

1901:
Harry Baker, Anna Doyen,
Frederick Lockwood

1902:
William Harrison, Peter McKenzie

1903:
Charles Becker, Joseph Huffman

Kent wrote little about himself and there is not much information about him from others. Therefore, finding any communication from him is of interest. This letter from Kent gives some idea of his teaching.

It is found on page 117 of the February 1929 *Homœopathic Recorder*, and was written sometime after 1903 when Kent began teaching at Hahnemann, but before the *Repertory* was printed as a single unit, since Kent discusses buying it as individual parts.

My dear Miss Sugden:

As you have paid $14.65 on the different parts of the repertory and as $15.00 pays for the whole repertory I sent you by express all the remaining parts. I am glad you are helped by my works. It is a dull time for pure homœopathy. The worst of the colleges sneer at it. I am glad I have a free choice at teaching. They are all very nice to me in our Hahnemann College of Chicago. I lecture twice each week to all of the four classes in the amphitheater. This gives the freshmen a chance to hear my entire course as it takes one 4 years to cover the Materia Medica. Ours is the only college in which a student is taught pure Hahn. Hom. It is true that much that is not true is taught by some other teachers. But I try to keep our students from observing the mongrelism.

Yours truly,
J. T. Kent

Further divisions

As the homœopathic colleges slipped deeper into "mongrelism"— the teaching of keynote prescribing, the use of conventional medicines, the lack of teaching of any philosophy— Kent and some members of the International Hahnemannian Association were working to keep the teaching and practice of homœopathy as close to Hahnemann's principles as could be. But for some, even those in the IHA were wavering too much.

This letter from Kent was found in Bradford's *Scrapbook*. Upon checking the *IHA Transactions,* we find that Kent was listed as an active member from 1885 until 1898. He does not appear on the register in 1899. Perhaps he "left in his mind" before his actual temporal leaving. Kent left the IHA in 1899, and rejoined in 1905. His thoughts were very clear in a letter to T. L. Bradford:

"Keynote" prescribing

The original "Keynote" system was introduced by Guernsey in 1868, who used it as a way of teaching the strongest characteristics of remedies to his students while stressing the need for the other characteristic symptoms in the case to fit the remedy as well. It was slowly degraded into a system where a remedy would be prescribed upon a single symptom— all cases of pneumonia would receive Phosphorus, all left-sided sore throats would receive Lachesis. It was this type of prescribing that Kent railed against and not the use of the "keynote" symptom in the older sense of "characteristic" as taught by Guernsey and Allen.

2133 Walnut Street, Philadelphia

Dear Dr. Bradford:
I quit the IHA in disgust 7 or 8 years ago and have none of the IHA Transactions. The IHA has not done any useful work for 10 years. And I don't think you will find any provings in their Transactions.
Fraternally,
J. T. Kent
2.8.1900

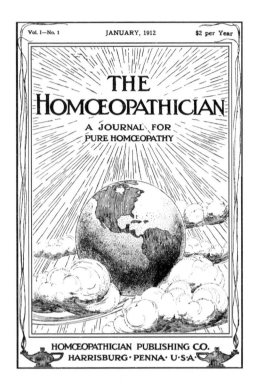

Vol. I—No. 1   JANUARY, 1912 $2 per Year

THE HOMŒOPATHICIAN

A JOURNAL FOR PURE HOMŒOPATHY

HOMŒOPATHICIAN PUBLISHING CO.
HARRISBURG · PENNA· U·S·A·

The Society of Homœopathicians

The divisions into Hahnemannian homœopathy and "mongrelism" reached an extreme in the mid–1890s with one group of "Hahnemannian" homœopaths deciding that the "Hahnemannians" of the International Hahnemannian Association were not following Hahnemann's word closely enough. The Society of Homœopathicians was formed by a group of extreme "purist" homœopaths in about 1895, and lasted about five years. About half the members were not members of the IHA. There were 18 founding members:

E. T. Adams (IHA), J. A. Biegler, Edmund Carleton, Stuart Close (IHA), F. S. Davis, G. B. Dinkerman, Olin Drake (IHA), S. Mills Fowler (IHA), J. R. Haynes (IHA), A. L. Kennedy, Samuel Kimball, Frank Wallace Patch, F. O. Pease (IHA), E. E. Reininger (IHA), E. W. Sawyer, J. W. Thompson, R. L. Thurston, J. A. Tomhagen (IHA).

In 1909, Kent formed a new Society of Homœopathicians, with his students as the main membership. In 1912 the Society issued its first journal, *The Homœopathician*, edited by Kent and Julia Loos, MD, of Harrisburg, Pennsylvania. The journal was published for four years, ceasing in 1916 after Kent's death.

Declaration of Principles of The Society of Homœopathicians

1. Disease, being a disturbance of the spirit-like force, is manifested by symptoms subjective and objective.
2. The healing powers of medicines is ascertained by proving them upon the healthy and by clinical experiences.
3. Disease is most effectively, safely, and rapidly cured by potentized remedies corresponding to the spirit-like force.
4. The curative relation of the medicines to the disturbed life force depends upon the similarity of the symptoms.

Rules of Practice

1. Only one remedy at a time is to be given.
2. Remedies are best given in potentiated form.
3. Surgical treatment is indicated only as stated by Hahnemann in section 186 of the Organon.
4. Suppression of symptoms by crude medicines, local treatment, or by any other means is unhomœopathic.

In Chicago, Kent had spent the years exhaustively editing his repertory, teaching at several schools, and maintaining a busy private practice. In his own words, he was "very tired." In the spring of 1916 Kent left for his vacation home in Stevensville, Montana. He died there on June 5, and was buried at the local cemetery.

The old Kent

The only description we have of Kent, the man, is by Julia M. Green, MD:

"The small man, shrunken and gray when I first saw him, but giving the impression of force and clearness; the keen eyes whose direct gaze through his glasses looked you through and through; the quiet strength of personality when talking of homœopathy which dominated him— there was no room for comment on his ill-fitting and ill-assorted clothes; he ignored his clothes and his dark office in his consuming enthusiasm for his work, and his listeners ignored them too. His health was very poor after I knew him; if vigorous in early manhood he must have been a tower of strength."

In 1910, in a letter to Margaret Tyler, Kent said that, "while I am only 61 years old, I am worn out." He continues, "I have been lecturing to classes on homœopathy and materia medica since 1883, and it has been a bitter fight continuously. Though I have enjoyed it, it has worn me out. For fifteen years I gained little but sneers; then, now and then, a pupil would try and do it. But not until I had put out the *Repertory* twelve or thirteen years ago could I feel that I had made any impression... There are 1,200 repertories now in use."

David Wember, MD, once interviewed Carl Junkerman, MD, (Hahnemann Philadelphia 1929) of Columbus, Ohio. Junkerman recalled visiting Kent with his father, Charles Junkerman, MD, and sitting on Kent's knee as Kent and his father talked. Carl recalls only that Kent wore a long, gray coat that he never removed, and that he sat close to the fire.

Bradford's *Bibliography* lists: "1889. Lectures on the *Organon*. Delivered at the Woman's Homœopathic Hospital, Philadelphia, and phonographically reported for the *Medical Advance* by Clarence Bartlett, MD."

Where are those recordings of Kent's voice now?

Kent, circa 1910

Why Stevensville?

Someone once asked me if I knew why Kent was in Stevensville. I didn't. I was then informed that many of the socially elite from Chicago vacationed in Stevensville. It was the last stop on the train from Chicago. You could get on the train in Chicago in the afternoon and by the next afternoon you were in Stevensville. "Frank Lloyd Wright built a big hotel there," said my informant. My curiosity was aroused.

Stevensville is about 30 miles south of Missoula, on the western edge of the state. It is far away from almost everywhere, especially from the east coast.

An obituary of Kent mentions that Kent went to "a family orchard property" in Stevensville, Montana.

Stevensville sits in the Bitterroot Valley, the Bitterroot mountains in the back and Idaho just on the other side. It had been a well-known source of apples. The Bitterroot orchards were among the world's largest.

In 1908, the Como Orchard Land Company began a "summer colony" project. It was a speculative proposal for the University of Chicago professors. Designed by Chicago's up-and-coming architect Frank Lloyd Wright, it was to be called "University Heights." It was located several miles south of Hamilton, in Darby. The success of the development led to the Bitterroot Irrigation District contracting with Frank Lloyd Wright to design a vacation inn and residential development to be located just outside Stevensville. It was to be called "Bitterroot Village." The Bitterroot Inn, a magnificent structure, was built in 1908 and served as a country retreat for many professionals from Chicago, until it was demolished by fire on July 28, 1924.

Frank Lloyd Wright's Bitterroot Inn at Stevensville.

The Kent Property

Among those who bought property from the investors was Kent and his wife, Clara Louise. The parcel, 40 acres, was purchased, in pieces, between 1911 and 1914. In 1912, a house was built on the property.

Kent's house bears little resemblance to the sketches that Wright did for the Como Orchard project, and certainly is not of the "prairie school" design, but is similar to a "Western Bungalow" style. It is not known if it was designed directly by Wright or was simply similar in style to others he designed in the area.

The Kent house is about a mile away from the Sunnyside Orchards Cemetery. The house is sitting out on the flat, although not as isolated today as it was in 1912 when it was the only house there. It is distinguished by two large trees in the front yard and two old apple trees at the side.

The house has been considerably modified since Kent lived there. The current occupants have built an addition on one side and enclosed the rear porch.

Greg Bedayn and I visited the house in 1995 and were treated to a wonderful dinner in the same dining room that Kent had sat in. Mrs. Leone Bass, who had grown up in the house, was able to fill in many details about it. It was Mrs. Bass' father who purchased the house from Mrs. Kent in 1920 when Leone was four years old.

The sink had been in a different location; the house had been wired for electricity, but no power lines were available, so lanterns were used until the electricity was hooked up in 1926. The beautiful window in the dining room, now clear glass, had been leaded glass, like the others surrounding it.

The Kent House, circa 1920

The Kent House, 1995

Kent's Grave

In an obituary of Kent in the June 9, 1916 *Western News*, we learn Kent had been bedridden since he arrived in Stevensville a month earlier. Arthur Grimmer, in a reminiscence of Kent, commented on Kent's "failing health." It appears Kent went to his property in Montana to gain strength. The obituary said he was suffering from bronchitis which developed into Bright's Disease.

The Sunnyside Orchards Cemetery is about five miles north of Stevensville, adjoining the land that was to be developed for the Bitterroot Irrigation District Project. Kent's grave has one of the largest head-stones in the small cemetery, and is in fair repair.

In 1995, The North American Society of Homeopaths became the gravesite custodians.

the
Kent
grave

Homœopathy in Great Britain: II

The influence of Kent
R. Gibson Miller
Margaret Tyler
Dorothy Shepherd
Sir John Weir
Douglas Borland
H. Fergie Woods
Margery Blackie

The first student from Great Britain to study with Kent was Robert Gibson Miller from Edinburgh. He spent a year with Kent and returned to Scotland.

Robert Gibson Miller, MD
1862 — May 10, 1919

While at Glasgow, Gibson Miller became interested in homœopathy. Upon gaining his degree, he went to the United States in 1884 to study with Kent at the Homœopathic Medical College of St. Louis. Returning to Glasgow he helped set up the Glasgow Homœopathic Hospital. His personal, annotated copy of Kent's *Repertory* now resides at the Glasgow Homœopathic Library.

A patient described him as "the finest human being I have ever known; a noble soul, selfless, and without a flaw."

Margaret Tyler said of him: "Of striking personality, tall, thin, forceful, earnest, Dr. Gibson Miller commanded universal respect and affection. If you once saw him, you would never forget him... Three times his personality stands out vividly to the mind's eye— as the tall, kindly, but authoritative President of one of the sessions of the World Congress in 1911— as the long, lean, gray-clad figure, darting about from flower to flower at Kew, full of enjoyment in the sunshine of a half-holiday, and manifestly in his element among the plants, trees, and shrubs— as the man who, so overwhelmed with work, yet found time when appealed to to come south and deliver his splendid paper on 'The Comparative Value of Symptoms in the Choice of a Remedy.'"

Gibson Miller is known for his comparison table, the "Relationship of Remedies," often found at the back of some repertories. Christopher Gordon, of Scotland, was once asked by Gibson Miller if he had found the last column, "Duration of Action," useful. Said Gordon, "Well, you give the duration of action of *Rhus tox* as from one to seven days. I have used it in a single dose as a constitutional and found its effect maintained for three or four months."

"Oh, yes," replied Gibson Miller, "I think that column is not right."

"It would be amusing, if one had endurance enough, to go over the list of tangents and trumpet calls in our hoary transactions of the AIH, but we forebear; let them rest in their cellars and attics in well-deserved and dusty peace. One ounce from Gibson Miller's pen is worth more than a wheelbarrow of these doings. But the old hope chest and wheelbarrow— the same ones— are still trundling along, ever and anon dumping their load of 'progress' and 'modern science' to pick up a newer burden."

"The Comparative Value of Symptoms" by Royal E. S. Hayes, MD in the Homœopathic Recorder, *December 1929*

Kent began a long correspondence with Margaret Tyler. He served as a major influence in her medical education.

Margaret Lucy Tyler, MD
1857 — June 21, 1943

A graduate of both Edinburgh and Brussels, Margaret Tyler was instrumental in using money given by her father, Sir Henry Tyler, to fund a physicians' scholarship to go to Chicago to study with Kent. Although she maintained a long correspondence with Dr. Kent, she never personally studied with him.

A close associate of J. H. Clarke, she worked at the Royal London Homœopathic Hospital for forty years. Her specialty was treating mentally backward children. Her *Homœopathic Drug Pictures*, published in 1942, remains a standard today. In it, she brings the idea of presenting the symptoms of a remedy as a personalized picture far beyond that of Kent in his materia medica lectures. She wrote *The Correspondence Course on Homœopathy*, designed for those who could not attend the lectures at the Faculty of Homœopathy in person. At 86, she was on duty at the hospital the day before she died.

The Tyler Card Repertory: Tyler and Kent

On August 27, 1912, Kent wrote a letter to Margaret Tyler. Tyler had sent Kent a "card repertory" that she devised, and Kent returned a critique. I have seen only one such Tyler Repertory. It is in the collection of William Kirtsos in Old Chatham, NY.
Below are some excerpts from Kent's letter which give some insight into his thinking:

Dear Dr. Tyler:

I am glad to get your letter. I know you want me to be frank with you or my advice would not be worth much. Your card system is like ready made shoes that must fit everybody, regardless of the misery they cause. The first and highest thought in Homœopathy is the individual. OUR WORK IS INDIVIDUALIZATION. Your cards will destroy the highest ideal of Hahnemann, and my teaching as it aims to fit and adjust remedies to the masses instead of to each one. The card system destroys growth and progress that must come from working out the case, every case, in the work of every beginner. Give a beginner a card system and that will be the end of him. He will not grow. He will not learn or master the materia medica. I once planned a similar scheme, but I soon saw

Pictures of Tyler are as rare as hen's teeth. The most common, a picture of her working from a book, is a poor picture indeed. I was thrilled when Mr. Ainsworth gave me a copy of a picture taken at a 1932 dinner to honor Pierre Schmidt. Present were Weir, Schmidt, Blackie... and Tyler!

Leaning on his elbow at the table behind Tyler is Dr. Charles Wheeler.

Wheeler (1868-1947) was the person who linked the "Cooper Club" of the 19th century with the homœopathy of Weir and Tyler in the 20th century. The author of The Principles and Practice of Homœopathy as well as works with Bach, he was loved and respected by all. In his obituary it was said, "Why he did not write his recollections of personalities or the history of homœopathy in England one cannot understand. Maybe because, one felt he was one of the immortals and would never die. Be that as it may, one always felt diffident in suggesting he write down anything lest it be forgotten for, how could one suggest that he could forget?"

His death was called "the most grievous loss of this generation."

Ray Seidel told me how, as a young medical student a few years out of school, he went to his first International Meeting in 1939 or 1940. The lecture room was very crowded and he managed to find a seat in the last row. Just as the presentation was starting a "distinguished elderly woman" approached him and asked if she could sit on his lap. He offered her the chair but she grinned and said that his lap was probably softer and more comfortable. It was the one and only time he met Margaret Tyler.

that I must work out every case, making use of the fullest repertory accessible; curtailing nothing less I miss something important, and this meant a life charged against my conscience…

When I worked in a clinic I prescribed for twenty five to forty patients in one and a half hours and never neglected anybody. This can be done with anybody I think, unless he works uphill with his cases. A doctor should know the generals, common and peculiars, so that he can use them quickly if he has a large business…

Your card system will make mediocres out of good men as it will pervert advancement, growth, maturity in our pupils… Prolonged and deep efforts only can make an artist in healing or music… You are doing as I used to do. You are hunting for labor saving machines. These machines are useful in everything but art. They are as ruinous to the art of prescribing as they are to music. I want to see my pupils in your country become more than mediocre in their old age. I want them to do what I do. I want them to become masters. Now, my dear friend, don't spoil the good work. I am saying these things with the FULLEST LOVE FOR ALL OF YOU, for our cause, for me, for you…

I know very well that some of our young men have not the capacity to grow into healing artists, such might not be dwarfed by the cards. Yet others have the ability and should be helped in every way to the highest development.

I fully appreciate your efforts, and am quite willing that you should attribute my failures to approve your cards to old age and stupidity.

Sincerely,
J. T. Kent

The first presentation

Of all of the concepts Kent introduced, "constitutional prescribing" was perhaps the most controversial at the time (and remains so in many quarters). The term "constitution" is often used but rarely defined, yet those who talk about it seem to have no doubt about what it is. In the Kentian context it has nothing to do with the older "constitutional types" of Von Grauvogl as "hydrogenoid" or "oxygenoid." Nor did it have to do with the concept of "temperaments" such as "sanguine, phlegmatic," and the like. In Kent's view (as influenced by Swedenborg) all disease process starts at the level of the "will and understanding." Since the mind is the deepest level in the hierarchy of the physical body, treating the symptoms expressed through the "will and understanding" will heal that level, and permit it, in turn, to heal the other levels. To treat "constitutionally" was to treat that level— the symptoms expressed as those of the whole being, the "general symptoms" as Kent called them— those expressed by the "I," as seen in the expressions, "I am tired at 3 p.m.," or "I have no appetite," etc. These expressions of the whole person would take precedence over expressions of a part, "My leg hurts," or "My nose is running." This is not to say that the particular symptom would not be considered in the case but, rather, that in a deep–seated chronic case, the "constitution" is what needs to be treated.

On January 8, 1903, Kentian constitutional prescribing was formally introduced to England at a meeting of the British Homœopathic Society. Octavia M. S. Lewin, MB, BS, London; MD, Chicago, presented five cases where she discussed "the possibility of curing a patient by studying the generals of a case and prescribing thereon, while the particulars, and the special symptoms which the patient complains of especially, may be practically ignored as far as the prescription is concerned."

Of the five cases, all were cured with high potencies— 1M, 81M, and CM being used.

She summed up, "…if we neglect the general condition and allow ourselves to be led away and blinded by one symptom, we must look for breakers ahead. It is the patient himself that gets ill, and the symptoms that appear are merely manifestations of that fact and are to be considered as such."

At a time when most of the prescribers in England were using tinctures and potencies up to a 6X, the talk of "high potencies" was truly revolutionary. Several speakers expressed amazement at the choice of potencies and confessed to going to a 30c now and then. Dudgeon spoke out against the use of high dilutions and quoted "…with approbation the Latin maxim, 'quod fieri potest per pauca, non debet fieri per plura,' which may be translated, 'if we can do with medicines made with few dilutions, we ought not to employ many dilutions'…"

On the other side, John Henry Clarke congratulated Lewin on "…the courage which she manifested in treating them with single doses. Very few homœopaths had courage for this, but it was a thing to be cultivated," and he was very glad to find "that somebody was doing it." He confessed having experience with the high potencies, and "…could entirely corroborate Dr. Lewin's results."

There was a long discussion about the meaning of "constitutional" and while one doctor thought "diathesis" might be a more appropriate word, Clarke suggested "constitution" covered the patient in the totality and "the patient's condition was not covered by one episode of illness only. The patient's condition was covered by his or her whole life. That is to say, a disease which might seem cured might manifest itself in 10, 20, or 30 years' time, so when they spoke of recovery they must mean a recovery from a particular condition described and not the cure of a particular disease."

Clarke, who was the only one who spoke favorably about the method, said, "A good deal of what Dr. Lewin had said in her paper would be rather a foreign language to some of the members. She had talked about 'generals' and 'particulars' in a way that he had never heard previously in that Society; but it was very necessary that the distinction between symptoms which belonged to a patient and symptoms which belonged to a particular manifestation of disease should be distinguished, because they were both important, and they had different degrees of importance in different cases. It was quite possible to be led astray, by superficial symptoms, from the real remedy which was required to correspond with the actual constitution of the patient himself. The necessity of constitutional treatment was one which was lost sight of by most medical men, including homœopaths."

Of Octavia Lewin, little else is known. She was the first woman to read a paper at a Society meeting. Her MD came from a homœopathic school in Chicago. She obviously studied with Kent. The only school in that time frame (1900-1902) was the Dunham college, yet she does not appear in any graduate listing from Dunham at that time. Clarke commented, "There is no place in the world where homœopathy was taught as perfectly as it was in Chicago."

The ideas presented at this talk were reinforced by Margaret Tyler, and eventually by those who went to Chicago, a few years later, to study with Kent. The concepts began to gain acceptance and within a few years, doctors at the London Homœopathic Hospital were repertorizing their cases and prescribing in the 30c potency.

Dorothy Shepherd, MD
c.1885 — November 15, 1952

The daughter of a missionary in South India, Shepherd studied at Heidelberg and other European medical schools, receiving her degree from Edinburgh.

As a child, she was raised with Hering's *Domestic Physician* and homœopathic medicine, but her medical training drew her further and further away from homœopathy.

She said, "Then by some good chance I heard about the Hering College in Chicago. The name Hering conjured up memories of a tattered old book, a long–legged child reaming over its contents. I must go and find out the truth which so long had evaded me." In 1906 she traveled to Chicago and studied at the Hering Medical College. Her teachers were Tomhagen and Dienst, both pupils of Kent. In none of her writing does she mention meeting Kent, although he certainly was in Chicago at the time.

"Since my return I have tried to apply the lessons. I must admit that homœopathy has never let me down; I have failed when I did not have sufficient facts. Homœopathy is a life–long study, it requires the burning of the midnight oil, but it is worthwhile."

A contemporary article said she was "one of the most valiant and incisive exponents of homœopathy. She always maintains that the true healer must be a scientist, and an artist, and the 'art of healing' was one of her favorite themes. She gave long and unselfish service in London's poor folks' dispensaries. She felt that homœopathy was for the people— not for a coterie."

An obituary mentions she established a homœopathic teaching center at Bramshott in the 1940's, but little else was said about it.

She was wrote several books about homœopathy, all filled with first-person experiences that are a delight to read: *Homœopathy for the 1st Aider* (1945); *Magic of the Minimum Dose* (1937); *More Magic of the Minimum Dose* (1949); *A Physician's Posy* (1951); and *Homœopathy in Epidemic Diseases* (posthumous 1967).

In 1908, the scholarship from Henry Tyler sent four students— John Weir, Douglas Borland, Fergie Woods, and Percy Purdom to Chicago. They spent a year, and returned to England to spread the word about Kent's way. Of the four, three became prominent beyond the borders of Great Britain. Of Percy Purdom little is known. He graduated in London in 1906, had a practice there upon his return, and died sometime in the mid–1940s.

Sir John Weir, MD
October 1879 — April 17, 1971

Weir received his medical degree from Glasgow in 1901. He learned of homœopathy from Gibson Miller who had treated him for boils. Upon returning to England after studying with Kent, he was appointed physician at the London Homœopathic Hospital and the Compton Burnett lecturer on materia medica in 1911. He was appointed Royal Physician in 1918 and served King George V (1918-23), King Edward VIII (1923-35), King George VI (1936-52), and the whole Royal Household of Queen Elizabeth II (1952-68).

At the funeral services for King George VI in 1952, he prescribed *Ignatia* for five kings and three queens— a feat he said few others could claim.

Weir was described as a "well-to-do Scottish gentleman clubman and golfer, a great teller of 'pawky-jokes' and 'wee-stories.' He was a thrifty scot but in little ways he was generous; he often gave boxes of Lindt chocolates to his colleagues' wives. A diplomat at heart, a confirmed bachelor, he was meticulously neat in his dress— and in his thinking. It is said that once, when he went to dinner at a friend's house, he got up between courses to straighten a picture that was slightly askew."

With his colleagues he restored a more liberal atmosphere and brought homœopathy back to more Hahnemannian ideas through Kent's influence, after the Hughes' school of thinking. Weir spoke on homœopathy before the Royal Society of Medicine in 1932 shortly after he was knighted. He authored many papers, among them: *Trend Of Modern Medicine*, (1923); *Science & Art Of Homœopathy* (1927); *Homœopathy: A System Of Therapeutics* (1928); *Homœopathy An Explanation Of Its Principles* (1932); *Samuel Hahnemann And His Influence On Medical Thought* (1934); *Hahnemann On Homœopathic Philosophy* (1935).

Raymond Seidel told me of stopping to talk with Sir John Weir during the Homœopathic Meeting in Washington, DC in 1955. As they were talking, Kent's pupil, Arthur Grimmer (who was 81 years old at the time) walked by. Weir threw his arms around Grimmer and said to Seidel, "This was my teacher in Chicago!" And Grimmer looked at Weir (who was 76 at the time) and said, "John! You've gotten old!"

Although he was spoken of as the "kindly father-figure"of British homœopathy, others found Weir autocratic; someone who "got his way too easily." Others questioned if he had the same deep understanding of homœopathy as did Wheeler, Clarke, and Borland.

When Margery Blackie offered some "doggerel verses lampooning well-known hospital personalities" at a hospital dinner in the 1930s, Weir was not amused. He did not forgive her for a long time.

Douglas M. Borland, MD
1885 — November 29, 1960

Undecided as to whether to go into the Church or medicine, Borland graduated from Glasgow and served in the medical corps in World War I. During World War II he was in charge of the Royal London Homœopathic Hospital.

Margery Blackie said of him: "He was a born doctor. He gave the impression of never being in a hurry and always having plenty of time to listen with sympathetic understanding to the many patients and colleagues who wanted help and advice."

Constance Babington Smith describes him: "At first meeting, Dr. Borland, who was a Scot from Glasgow, often gave an impression of aloofness. With his unhurried walk and impeccable suits, his amused drawl and what had been called 'the veiled touch of mild and kindly sarcasm' in his talk, he seemed to be an imperturbable man of the world. But all this was only a mask for his shyness; behind it there was an utterly charming, gentle, and generous personality. He was also, however, a man whose intensive dedication to his work took an inevitable toll— off duty he was a chain-smoker."

He was a prodigious author. His works included: *Children's Types* (1939); *Pneumonias* (1939); *Influenzas* (1939); *Digestive Drugs* (1940); *Some Emergencies Of General Practice* (1946); *Homœopathy For Mother And Infant* (1950); and a posthumous collection of essays, *Homœopathy In Practice* (1982).

Weir & Borland by Blackie

The first physician I met here
Was called, I fancy, Dr. Weir.
A large man with a rosy face,
He talked at an alarming pace,
Percussed my lungs, and banged my thighs
And told me stories thick as flies.
My heart went thump— my heart went hop,
I thought that he would never stop.

I came all over feeling queer
And tottered out from Dr. Weir
Replete with anecdotes galore.
But as to my pet maladie
No wiser than before…

And I was recommended then
To Dr. Borland— best of men.
He sat me down upon a chair
And stared with an absorbing stare.
I felt his eyes investigate
The deepest secrets of my state.
I almost heard him count my sins—
He knew them all, their outs and ins…

I almost melted on the mat
I simply rattled where I sat
Oh! What a power for a Physician
To know by force of intuition
His patient's scandalous condition…

Douglas Borland, c. 1940

Fergie Woods.

Harold Fergie Woods, MD
1884 — January 15, 1961

Woods completed his medical training in London in 1908. After studying with Kent, he joined the staff at the Royal London Homœopathic Hospital in 1909 as the Resident Medical Officer. He was the Physician at the Children's Homœopathic Dispensary in Shepherd's Bush, later amalgamated with the London Homœopathic Hospital in 1935. He was one of the International Homœopathic League's founders in 1925. The author of innumerable journal articles, he also wrote two books: *Essentials of Homœopathic Prescribing*, and *Homœopathic Treatment in the Nursery*.

The influence of Kent's ideas permeated through British homœopathy and were brought, almost to the present, by a group of physicians who had trained with Kent's pupils. Prominent in this group was Margery Blackie, whose book, *The Patient, Not the Cure*, presented many cases that showed her thinking along "constitutional" lines.

Margery Grace Blackie, MD
February 4, 1898 — August 24, 1981

The niece of James Compton Burnett, she was the youngest in a family of 10. She grew up with homœopathy and decided to be a doctor, entering the London School of Medicine for Women in 1917.

In 1924 she became a resident at the London Homœopathic Hospital where Clarke was the senior consultant, and her two "chiefs" were Douglas Borland and Charles Wheeler. She received her MB (Bachelor of Medicine) and BS (Bachelor of Surgery) in 1926, and received her MD in 1928.

Her acceptance and interest in "seeing remedies as pictures" can be seen when she tells of going to the play *Hedda Gabler* with her hospital contemporary, Frank Bodman. They spent the evening having fun identifying the characteristics of the various actors and actresses and "prescribing" for them, as well as for some of the audience. "We were quite amazed at the number of counterparts we had in practice as patients," she said.

Margery Blackie, c. 1920

Always of an evangelical faith and unquestioning dependence on the Bible, Blackie began to teach at the Missionary School of Medicine in 1925. The school was founded in 1903 to train students from Bible Colleges with an elementary knowledge of medicine.

She opened her private practice in 1926. The day after she opened she walked through the surrounding district. Wandering the streets, she noticed a small pharmacy with a very faded, almost illegible sign: "Homœopathic Dispensary, Monday, Wednesday, Friday." Upon inquiry, the pharmacist told her it had been closed for 12 years. She asked about re-opening it, and worked the weekend with the pharmacist getting the first–floor rooms ready. When she arrived on Monday, there were a dozen patients waiting!

She was still working at the Homœopathic Hospital as the clinical assistant to Borland. She also worked with Margaret Tyler on children's cases.

In 1949 she was elected president of the Faculty of Homœopathy, a title she retained for the next three years.

When Weir retired as physician to the royal family in 1968 at the age of 89, Blackie became the homœopathic physician to Her Majesty, Queen Elizabeth II.

She had edited the *British Homœopathic Journal* for a brief time, but was bothered by seeing more and more articles appearing about anthroposophical medicine and was greatly disturbed that classical homœopaths were withholding articles because of this trend.

In the early 1970s she was disheartened when the Faculty, under the leadership of Ralph Twentyman, swung toward anthroposophy, for she believed that anthroposophy was mystical and anti-Christian.

Some of her feelings might have been attributable to the suicide of two of Burnett's daughters while they were in a "mystic cult."

She wrote *The Patient, Not the Cure* in 1976. It was published again, a few years later, as *The Challenge of Homœopathy*.

Blackie retired as the Royal Physician in 1979.

In her retirement, there were always two books by her bedside: Kent's *Materia Medica* and the Bible.

Anthroposophy

"A religious system evolved by R. Steiner from neo-Indian theosophy, but placing man instead of God at its center. It aims at leading man by a certain discipline of 'concentration' and 'meditation' towards an 'intuition' in which the lower ego received the vision of the higher self. It teaches a highly elaborated and fantastic doctrine of the origin of the world and the various epochs of mankind, the 'sun-being' Christ, reincarnation, and 'karma.'"

— Oxford Dictionary of the Christian Church

Rudolph Steiner (1861-1925) developed a theosophy of the world, of which medicine was a part. Steiner saw the material/physical, the etheric (life-organization), the astral (the soul— through which we have desires, dreams and emotions), and the spiritual ego (the consciousness of self). Each of these levels, according to Steiner, focuses its energies in different physical organs. These are further defined into three systems: (Nerve-Sense (which supports the mind and thinking), Metabolic-Limb (digestion, elimination, movement), and Rhythmic (physical processes of a periodic nature— breathing, pulse, etc.). The treatment of the individual is dependent upon understanding the relationships in this "threefold nature of man" and determining which system is non-functional, and deciding upon a regime (based upon the theoretical construct) that will bring it back to center.

Although the remedies used are produced using the concepts of dilution and succussion, they are not applied using the law of similars, and therefore the system bears no relationship to homœopathy. It has been described by a homœopath as "an extension of allopathy by a spiritual science."

There are many communities, world–wide which are founded upon Steiner's concepts, as are Steiner–based schools ("Waldorf Schools") and Bio-Dynamic farms.

The Faces of Homœopathy

1900 –1925: The Decline

The legacy of Claude Bernard
The rise of the drug companies and the AMA
The closing of the schools
Homœopathy myth and fact
The "half–homœopaths"
The flu epidemic of 1918
Too little, too late

1900. All was not well. It was a new century. Pasteur's germ theory had become well established, Claude Bernard had described the body as a machine that responded to the laws of chemistry and physics, and medicine had begun to be driven by "science" and had moved into areas of increasing specialization.

Claude Bernard
July 12, 1813 — February 10, 1878

Bernard, at the age of 21, went to Paris as a playwright, but the critic who reviewed his works urged him to take up medicine. He worked under the physiologist Magendie and in 1855, succeeded him as full professor.

His work was the first to understand the nature of diabetes and liver function. His last work was the discovery of the vasomotor system. He was also very interested in the physiology of poisons.

He was accorded a public funeral, the first in France for a man of science.

Claude Bernard

Modern medicine: Bernard's legacy

Richard Moskowitz, MD, DHt, suggests that the concepts of conventional medicine all grow out of a statement made by Claude Bernard:

> "What we call immediate cause of a phenomenon is nothing but the physical and material conditions in which it exists or appears. The object of the experimental method and the limit of every scientific research is therefore the same for living as for inanimate bodies. It consists in finding the relations which connect every phenomenon with its immediate cause, or putting it differently, in defining the conditions necessary for the appearance of the phenomenon. When the experimenter succeeds in learning the necessary causes of a phenomenon, he is, in some sense, its master. He can predict its course and appearance; he can promote or prevent it at will…
>
> "As a corollary to the above, physicians do not imagine it is their task to seek the cause of life or essence of disease. The words 'life' and 'death' and 'health' and 'disease' have no objective reality. Only the vital phenomenon exists, with its material conditions. That is what they can study and know."

How does this statement "play out in reality?"

If we apply these ideas to human biology, we arrive at three elementary steps:

- We characterize the phenomenon to be studied.

- We identify its component parts and isolate the physio-mechanical causes.

- We develop technologies to manipulate them with as little disturbance as possible to the remainder of the organism.

The first casualty of this view becomes the "totality of symptoms" that is so important to the homœopath. We are no longer in need of looking at a totality but only at the isolated parts of the phenomenon.

A second casualty is symptoms that cannot be measured by objective criteria; things which a patient experiences but cannot be seen through testing of the systems.

Health then becomes a "norm" and illness becomes "abnormality." If this is the case, the goal of the physician is, therefore, not "to restore the sick to health— to cure" as Hahnemann described, but rather to correct the abnormality. And this is done by using drugs which can manipulate the phenomenon which is being studied and to bring it back into a normal activity range through destruction (antibiotics, radiation), substitution (thyroid extracts, etc.), or inhibition (MAO inhibitors, etc). In this view, there is either "normality" or "abnormality."

Said Moskowitz, "The work of Claude Bernard is a prophetic text. Modern medicine is living out the prophesy of Claude Bernard's vision."

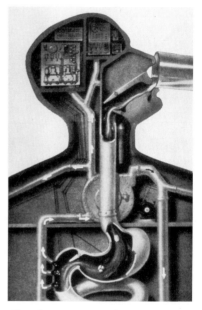

The ultimate view of the body as a machine. A Bayer aspirin ad from the early 1950s.

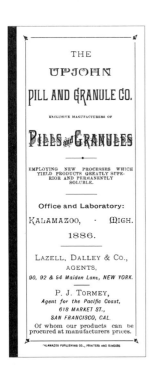

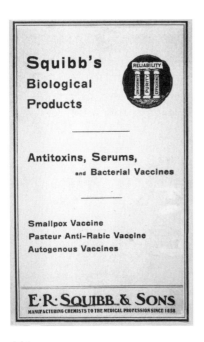

The Rise of the Drug Companies and the American Medical Association

Pharmaceutical companies like Sharpe and Dohme and E. R. Squibb started during the Civil War to supply the needed medical supplies. They were joined shortly after the war by Warner, Parke–Davis, Mallinckrodt, Lilly, Merck, Abbott, and others. They slowly moved from traditional medical products, usually derived from botanical sources similar to the homœopathic materia medica (although prescribed in different dosages), into the production and sale of "patent" medicines, compounds whose formulation was proprietary to the company.

The American Medical Association had an ethical ban against the use of such "secret nostrums," but the company of Frederick Stearns found a way around the ban by developing proprietary products where the ingredients were known, but the *name* of the product was copyright.

As Coulter writes: "The flooding of medical practice with these 'proprietaries' represented the final conquest of the medical profession by the patent-medicine industry… The proprietary craze was merely the newest avatar of the profession's unrelenting desire to simplify medical practice. The compounding of medicines were centralized, and the physician was spared the intellectual effort required to obtain knowledge of his principal means of cure. Instead of learning the powers and properties of medicinal drugs, he had only to memorize the names of series of specific compounds and prescribe them for the disease names of his patients."

Medical journals began advertising the products and physicians began prescribing them based upon the journals' authority rather than personal knowledge of the drug's pharmacology.

The local pharmacies were making better profits on the compounds than herbal remedies, and turned into "drug–stores" selling other products as well.

The drug companies began publishing their own medical journals, touting their own products.

Flooding the medical market with proprietary products paved the way for the acceptance of a new series of synthetic medicines developed in Germany. W. A. Dewey said in the *Journal of the American Institute of Homœopathy* (Vol. XI no. 9): "For twenty years or more the idea has prevailed in some medical or pharmaceutical circles that no drug or chemical possessed value unless 'Made in Germany.'"

The drugs were derived from the by-products of the coal-tar and aniline dye industries. These new medicines, developed as fever-reducing agents, found great acceptance since all disease states had elevated temperatures and pain, two things these new compounds seemed to allay.

The American Medical Association decided to accept advertising in its journal for products whose ingredients were stated although the actual formula need not be printed, and the advertisement could include therapeutic indications. Advertisers flocked to the *Journal of the American Medical Association* and, in effect, the drug companies became the largest source of income for the AMA.

The AMA opens to the homœopaths

The turning of the American Medical Association was directed by George H. Simmons, MD. A graduate from the Hahnemann Medical College in Chicago in 1882, he practiced homœopathy in Lincoln, Nebraska. For some reason, he changed his views about homœopathy and took his degree from Rush Medical College in Chicago in 1892. He returned to Nebraska and became an outspoken allopathic physician who was very involved in Nebraska State Medical Society politics.

In 1899 he became the AMA secretary and the editor of the *Journal of the American Medical Association*. Under his leadership the *Journal* grew from 13,000 subscribers in 1900 to more than 80,000 in 1924. Since the *Journal* was its chief income source, Simmons has been credited with completely reorganizing the AMA.

His first move was to remove the ethical ban on proprietary advertising, replacing it with a standard allowing the products to be advertised if the ingredients were listed.

At the time, physicians, generally, had very low incomes and were not highly considered in society. Simmons undertook to raise the standards of medical education to the extent that the public would respect doctors for their education and not think of them as quacks.

The homœopaths had become strong within the medical community and, as physician licensing began to be, once

"In consultation with old school practitioners all goes placidly until you speak of homœopathic methods. Immediately you lose caste. In place of interest being aroused towards you, or that which you represent, all is silence. Their approval lasts as long as you acquiesce in their methods."

—A homœopathic physician, 1910

A Vision of the Future

In 1904, W. H. King, the author of the four-volume History, *wrote a "fantasy" novel called* Medical Union Number Six.

The protagonist of the work was a doctor who returned home to New York in 1940, after having been shipwrecked for 35 years in Borneo. On his return he finds that the medical profession has been unionized (the doctors were the last to do so after the clergy).

Everyone had a specialty. If the "nose" specialist was attending a child with a cold in the nose and the child started to get a sore throat, then the "throat" specialist must be called.

The protagonist, who has joined "Medical Union Number Six," gets into difficulties when he finds that the specialist is not available and HE must treat outside of his union specialty if he wants to save the life of the patient.

again, state regulated, homœopaths were getting seats on medical boards and were responsible, with their allopathic counterparts, for determining who was qualified to be a physician in the state.

The homœopaths, purporting to be a "new school" of medicine, were always a thorn in the side of the conventional practitioner. In 1901 the American Medical Association changed its code of ethics to allow "every reputable and legally qualified physician who is practicing or who will agree to practice non-sectarian medicine," membership.

The state societies began to recruit physicians. Practicing homœopathy was allowed— as long as you did not state publicly that you were doing so. Those wishing membership had to sever all ties with "sectarian colleges, societies, and institutions." Several homœopaths pointed out the irony that, when you joined the local society, you went from being "the homœopath" to being just another of the town doctors.

As it became clear that the local medical societies and the AMA did not care what you did as long as you did not call yourself a homœopath, or try talking about it, one physician noted, "Looks as though the real thing at issue was the 'recognition of the union' rather than the 'welfare of the public.'"

Wrote one homœopath: "I thought there would be an opportunity to discuss homœopathic principles and homœopathic remedies if I joined the county and national societies of the old school, and so put some leavening into the lump. I found, however, that I was counting without my host. Such discussions were not permitted, so I am coming back."

Dr. J. N. McCormack, the brains behind the drive to bring the homœopath to the AMA noted in 1911, "We must admit that we have never fought the homœopath on matters of principle; we fought him because he came into our community and got the business."

The AMA began a concerted effort to bring homœopaths "into the fold" and to eliminate the homœopaths as a prominent and visible alternative to regular medicine which had its own organizational structure and social base.

The homœopathic schools came under attack. The AMA president, Charles Reed, stated that it was more important the student master the fundamental branches of "scientific medicine" than argue over therapeutic systems.

The poor quality of homœopathic instruction was another factor in the rise of "conventional" medicine. Those graduating from "homœopathic schools" often did not have a grounding in the basic principles of homœopathy and were taught a mish-mash of therapeutics which, when used, more often than not failed. So they fell back upon conventional methods and drifted to the allopathic camp.

We see this clearly in the case of Charles F. Menninger, the founder of the Menninger Clinic in Topeka, Kansas, who was an 1889 graduate of Hahnemann Medical College in Chicago.

Although he knew (at some level) that homœopathy was a viable system, he never learned the subtleties at his school where, according to his biography, he was taught that *Phosphorus was for pneumonia.* With this poor level of homœopathic teaching, it was easy to drift into conventional medicine after having little success with the homœopathic system.

The AMA, seeing this trend for those purporting to be "homœopaths" to resort to everything but homœopathy, saw it not as a lack in the homœopathic training but as a proof that the education in "scientific medicine" was worthwhile.

Said the *Journal of the American Medical Association:* "It is a favorable sign to find a faithful follower of Hahnemann who acknowledges the natural tendency of which most medical men are aware, and it causes us to renew our hope that the time is not so very distant when the believers in the efficacy of dilutions will cease to shut themselves up in a school and will become part of the regular medical profession, the members of which are ready and anxious to employ any and every means which can be scientifically shown to have a favorable influence on the course of disease."

The details of the rise and decline of homœopathy are fully documented in the book *Divided Legacy: Homœopathy in America 1825-1914*, by historian Harris Coulter. It is well worth reading.

Homœopathy is wholly capable of satisfying the therapeutic demands of this age better than any other system of medicine...

It is imperative that we exhaust the homœopathic healing art before resorting to any other mode of treatment, if we wish to accomplish the greatest success possible.

— *C. F. Menninger to the AIH, 1897.*

Harris Coulter, 1978

I was watching the TV news one night when Boris Yeltsin paid his first visit to the United States. At the press conference Yeltsin's "voice" sounded SO familiar. It was Harry, of course!

At another time, I phoned Harry just after he returned from a tour to Hollywood, California with Gorbachev. Sounding completely overwhelmed by the experience, he told me how he had dinner while sitting between Gorbachev and Annette Benning with Warren Beatty on the other side.

Harris Livermore Coulter, PhD
October 8, 1932 —

Coulter started out to be a Russian specialist. He was working on his PhD dissertation at Columbia University and was increasingly dissatisfied with the material he was finding for his subject.

Along the way, he discovered homœopathy when his wife consulted a homœopath while vacationing in France. He found homœopathy fascinating and decided to write more about it. He asked about changing his thesis topic, but not having to do with Russian material, the department would not accept it.

In 1963 Coulter moved to Washington, DC to work as a Federal Government translator, and looked up Dr. Panos who pointed him toward the National Library of Medicine in Bethesda, Maryland. Using the Library as his major resource, he wrote the manuscript that was to become the first installment of *Divided Legacy*.

In 1968 he visited his old department at Columbia University and told them of his work. They decided to grant him his PhD for, as he said, "my unsponsored dissertation on a topic entirely outside of my university studies."

The dissertation became Volume III of the *Divided Legacy* series, with Volume I and II being written shortly thereafter. Volume IV (*The Bacteriological Era*) was published in 1995.

All the while, Coulter had been working as a Russian interpreter, one of the top in the business. He has interpreted for Shevardnadze, Gorbachev, Solzhenitsyn, and Yeltsin.

When Coulter became interested in homœopathy, it was only a matter of time before he was asked to serve on the Board of Directors of the American Foundation for Homœopathy. "I was the only person involved in homœopathy who was born in the twentieth century at that point," he says jokingly. He remained with the organization through the early 1980s working in several capacities and editing the *Layman Speaks*, and the *Homeopathic Heartbeat*.

In the late 1970s Coulter became very interested in the issue of vaccinations, writing several books on the subject, including *DPT: A Shot in the Dark* (with Barbara Loe

Fisher), *AIDS and Syphilis: The Hidden Link; Vaccination, Social Violence, and Criminality.*

Coulter is currently working with a Russian physician, Valentine Ivanovitch Govallo, who has developed a therapeutic regimen for treating cancer. Coulter lives in Washington, DC.

In 1987 Tatanya Popova, MD, from the Ukraine, was invited to speak at the National Center for Homeopathy's conference in Boston. Harris served as the translator. It was magnificent watching and hearing him, as a professional Russian translator AND one involved in homœopathy, translate her presentation.

The closing of the schools

In 1910 the Carnegie Foundation, wishing to give money to medical schools but not having any standard by which to judge them, commissioned educator Abraham Flexner to conduct a study of American medical schools.

Although Flexner, in his final report, commented on the need for continued homœopathic education, he was extremely critical of the facilities of the 22 homœopathic colleges then operating. He considered many of them had inadequate facilities, generally, and those with adequate facilities had little clinical training for students.

Even at the prestigious Hahnemann College in Philadelphia, physicians controlling the hospital wards would not allow students in. The Flexner report resulted in many medical schools closing, including most of the homœopathic schools.

Abraham Flexner

The Flexner report

During 1909, Abraham Flexner visited all medical schools in the United States. His 846–page report, *Medical Education in the United States and Canada*, was then issued by the Carnegie Foundation.

In the report, Flexner proposed a specific model for medical schools to follow, based on the program at the Johns Hopkins School of Medicine. He also discussed the methodology of testing graduates of schools at the state board level and sought to have the state boards test competency in medicine rather than a test that could be passed by studying questions from previous exams.

While it is common to cite the Flexner report as a cause of the decline of homœopathy in the United States, very few have ever seen exactly what Flexner said about homœopathic education that was being offered.

So...here is an excerpt from the three pages of the Flexner Report dealing with the homœopathic schools.

From the Flexner report: Pages 159-161

"None of the fifteen homœopathic schools require more than a high-school education for entrance; only five require so much. The remaining eleven get less— how much less depending on their geographical locations rather than on the school's own definition. The Louisville, Kansas City, and Baltimore schools cannot be said to have admission standards in any strict sense at all...

On the laboratory side, though the homœopaths admit the soundness of the scientific position, they have taken no active part in its development. Nowhere in homœopathic institutions, with the exception of one or two departments at Boston University, is there any evidence of progressive scientific work. Even "drug proving" is rarely witnessed. The fundamental assumption of the sect is sacred; and scientific activity cannot proceed where any such interdict is responsible for the spirit of the institution. The homœopathic departments at Iowa and Michigan are in this respect only half-schools— clinical halves. For their students get their scientific instruction in pathology, anatomy, etc., in the only laboratories which the university devotes to those subjects, under men none of whom sympathizes with homœopathy...

Of complete homœopathic schools, Boston University, the New York Homœopathic College, and the Hahnemann of Philadelphia alone possess the equipment necessary for the effective routine teaching of the fundamental branches. None of them can employ full-time teachers to any considerable extent. But they possess fairly well-equipped laboratories in anatomy, pathology, bacteriology, and physiology, a museum showing care and intelligence, and a decent library. Boston University deserves especial commendation for what it has accomplished with its small annual income.

Of the remaining homœopathic schools, four are weak and uneven: the Hahnemann of San Francisco and the Hahnemann of Chicago have small, but not altogether inadequate, equipment for the teaching of chemistry, elementary pathology and bacteriology; the Cleveland school offers an active course in experimental physiology. Beyond ordinary dissection and elementary chemistry, they offer little else. There is, for example, no experimental physiology in the San Francisco Hahnemann: 'the instructor doesn't believe in it'; the Chicago Hahnemann contains a small outfit and a few animals for that subject; the Cleveland equipment for pathology and bacteriology is meager. The New York Homœopathic College for Women is well intentioned, but its means have permitted it to do but little in any direction.

Six schools remain— all utterly hopeless: Hering (Chicago), because it is without plant or resources; the other five (Kentucky, Pulte, Baltimore, Detroit, Kansas City), because in addition to having nothing, their condition indicates the total unfitness of their managers for any sort of educational responsibility. The buildings are filthy and neglected. At Louisville no branch is properly equipped; in one room, the outfit is limited to a dirty and tattered mannequin; in another, a single guinea pig awaits his fate in a cage. At Detroit the dean and secretary 'have their offices downtown;' the so-called laboratories are in utter confusion…

In respect to hospital facilities, the University of Michigan, Boston University, and the New York Homœopathic alone command an adequate supply of material, under proper control, though modern teaching methods are not thoroughly utilized even by them. The Iowa school controls a small, but inadequate, hospital. All the others are seriously handicapped by either lack of material or lack of control, and in most instances by both. The Hahnemann of San Francisco relies mainly on 80 beds supported by the city and county in a private hospital; the Detroit school is cordially welcome at the Grace Hospital, but less than 60 beds are available, and they are mostly surgical; the Woman's Homœopathic of New York controls a hospital of 35 available beds, mostly surgical; the Southwestern (Louisville) and the Cleveland school get one-fifth of the patients that enter the city hospitals of their respective towns, but these hospitals are not equipped or organized with a view to teaching. The Kansas City school holds clinics one day a week at the City Hospital; Pulte (Cincinnati) and the Atlantic (Baltimore) have, as nearly as one can gather, nothing definite at all. Several of the schools appear to be unnecessarily handicapped. The Chicago Hahnemann adjoins a hospital with 60 ward beds. But as the superintendent 'doesn't believe in admitting students to wards,' there is little or nothing beyond amphitheater teaching. A bridge connects Hering (Chicago) with a homœopathic hospital, but 'students are not admitted.' The Cleveland

school is next door to a hospital with which it was once intimate; their relations have been ruptured. An excellent hospital is connected with the building occupied by the Philadelphia Hahnemann, but there is no ward work…

Financially the two state university departments and the New York Homœopathic school are the only homœopathic schools whose strength is greater than their fee income. All the others are dependent on tuition. Their outlook for higher entrance standards or improved teaching is, therefore, distinctly unpromising. Only a few of them command tuition fees enough to do anything at all: the Chicago Hahnemann, Boston University, and the Philadelphia Hahnemann, with annual fees ranging between $12,000 and $18,000 [this is total income for the year— JW]. Nine of them are hopelessly poor: the San Francisco Hahnemann, Hering (Chicago), the Detroit Homœopathic, and the Atlantic Medical all operate on less than $4000 a year; the Southwestern (Louisville) and Pulte (Cincinnati) on less than $1500.

In the year 1900 there were twenty two homœopathic colleges in the United States; today there are fifteen; the total student enrollment has within the same period been cut almost in half, decreasing from 1909 to 1009; the graduating classes have fallen from 418 to 246. As the country is still poorly supplied with homœopathic physicians, these figures are ominous; for the rise of legal standard must inevitably affect homœopathic practitioners. In the financial weakness of their schools, the further shrinkage of the student body still inhibit first the expansion, then the keeping up, of the sect.

Logically, no other outcome is possible. The ebbing vitality of homœopathic schools is a striking demonstration of the incompatibility of science and dogma. One may begin with science and work through the entire medical curriculum consistently, espousing everything to the same sort of test; or one may begin with a dogmatic assertion and resolutely refuse to entertain anything at variance with it. But one cannot do both. One cannot simultaneously assert science and dogma; one cannot travel half the road under the former banner, in the hope of taking up the latter, too, at the middle of the march. Science, once embraced, will conquer the whole. Homœopathy has two options: one to withdraw into the isolation in which alone any peculiar tenet can maintain itself; the other to put that tenet into the melting-pot. Historically it undoubtedly played an important part in discrediting empirical allopathy…

It will be clear, then, why, when outlining a system of schools for the training of physicians on scientific lines, no specific provision is made for homœopathy. For everything of proved value in homœopathy belongs of right to scientific medicine and is at this moment incorporate in it; nothing else has any footing at all, whether it be of allopathic or homœopathic lineage."

The schools

In 1892, Bradford listed 23 homœopathic schools in his *Bibliography*. In 1905, King, in his four volumes, listed 22 homœopathic colleges with some in Bradford's list closing and others opening. By the time Flexner wrote his report in 1910 there were only 15. The colleges remaining at the time of the Flexner report are in **bold** type.

The schools were (with their dates of incorporation):

Hahnemann Medical College of the Pacific [San Francisco] (1881)
Hahnemann Medical College of Chicago (1855)
Chicago Homœopathic Medical College (1876) an offshoot of Chicago Hahnemann—United with Hahnemann in 1904
German-American Homœopathic Medical College of Chicago (1891-1900?)
Hering Medical College [Chicago] (1892)
Dunham Homœopathic College [Chicago] split from Hering 1895, united with Hering 1902
National Homœopathic Medical College [Chicago] (1891) became National Medical University and dropped its homeopathic affiliation
State University of Iowa, Homœopathic Dept. [Iowa City] (1877)
Denver Homœopathic Medical College (1894 closed by 1909)
Southwestern Homœopathic Medical College [Louisville] (1892)
Southern Homœopathic Medical College [Baltimore] (1890)
New England Female Medical College (1848) merged with Boston.

Chicago Hahnemann, below
New York Homœopathic, right

Boston University School of Medicine [Boston] (1873)
Detroit Homœopathic College (1872)
Homœopathic Medical College of the University of Michigan [Ann Arbor] (1873)
University of Minnesota, College of Homœopathic Medicine (1888)
Homœopathic Medical College of Missouri [St. Louis] (1864) closed by 1910.
Kansas City Homœopathic Medical College [Missouri] (1882)
Kansas City Hahnemann Medical College (1896) merged with Kansas City Homœopathic.
Homœopathic Department of the State University of Nebraska (1883-1887)
New York Homœopathic Medical College (1860)
New York Medical College for Women (1863)
Cleveland Homœopathic Hospital College (1849)
Cleveland Medical College (1890) split from Cleveland Homœopathic. Not in existence in 1905.
Pulte Medical College of Cincinnati (1872)
Hahnemann Medical College of Philadelphia (1848)
Philadelphia Post-Graduate School of Homœopathics (1890-1903)

At the time of the Flexner report, most schools were not teaching quality homœopathy. Many graduates, never fully trained in homœopathic methodology, saw little difference between homœopathy and conventional medicine and just "slipped into" a regular practice.

Southwestern Homœopathic Medical College, Louisville, Kentucky, left
Detroit Homœopathic Medical College, below

In June 1922, United States President Warren G. Harding, whose father was a homœopathic physician, hosted the member of the American Institute of Homœopathy on the White House lawn. But the public attention meant little as the schools had stopped teaching homœopathy.

The 1922 AIH Meeting. President Harding in the center (with hand in pocket). On his right is Brigadier General Charles E. Sawyer, MD, the President's physician.

Between 1911 and 1926 there was a steep drop in the number of homœopathic colleges operating. In Chicago, the Hering College merged with Hahnemann of Chicago, and then both closed by 1922. Louisville, Detroit, Kansas City, and Baltimore all closed before 1920.

The State University of Iowa merged the homœopathic school into the regular medical school and then dropped the homœopathic component. A similar fate was faced by the medical department at the University of Michigan at Ann Arbor.

The Hahnemann Medical College of the Pacific was taken under the wing of the University of California. After the death of James William Ward, in 1939, it ceased homœopathic instruction, although a chair for the subject was kept.

New York Homœopathic absorbed the New York Medical College for Women in 1918 and soon changed its name to New York Medical College and Flower Hospital.

The Pulte College in Cincinnati was absorbed by the Cleveland College in 1911, and, in turn the Cleveland College was absorbed by Ohio State University in 1913.

By 1940, the Hahnemann Medical College of Pennsylvania, alone, remained.

According to a memo written by James William Ward in 1926, Hahnemann in Philadelphia had 631 hours of homœopathic instruction in a department staffed by one professor, one assistant, and 19 part-time teachers.

The New York Medical College had a similar number of hours devoted to homœopathy and a similar number of teachers.

Boston College was still teaching some homœopathy, but did not report to Ward on its figures.

The University of California had 144 hours of instruction in homœopathy with no full time faculty and two assistants. According to the report, students wishing to take the course were not able to arrange their schedules to do so because required clinical classes were scheduled at the same time as homœopathic classes.

Charles Kettering and Homeopathy

In 1913, the Cleveland Homœopathic College, which had merged two years earlier with the Pulte College in Cincinnati, was merged with the Ohio State University at Columbus, Ohio, with the understanding that a College of Homœopathy was to be established. In 1916, the College received a gift of $2500 from Charles Kettering, a homœopathic supporter and President of General Motors. The following year, Kettering gave another $8,000 to the Department of materia medica and therapeutics. In 1920 Kettering gave 60 milligrams of radium (worth $7200), and later that year he gave 1000 shares of General Motors stock. The proviso was that the gift be administered and used by the College of Homœopathic Medicine.

In 1922 the board of trustees decided it was foolish to maintain two colleges of medicine at the same university, and the board mandated discontinuing the teaching of homœopathy as of August 15, 1922. All Kettering's gifts were returned to him. Two chairs of homœopathy were created within the college of medicine, but homœopathy was not taught in the school again. Unlike most other schools, the homœopathic library was not disposed of. The 900+ volumes still reside in the stacks at the Ohio State University at Columbus.

Kettering went on to fund the Sloan-Kettering Institute for Cancer Research.

Corporate homœopathy

While looking through the book Hospitals and Sanitariums of the Homœopathic School of Medicine *published by the Council of Medical Education of the American Institute of Homœopathy in 1916, I found an article on page 96 that mentioned the "welfare department" of the Montgomery Ward Company in Chicago was under homœopathic direction. All injured were sent to Hahnemann Hospital. In 1915, the medical office treated 49,034 employees, 1,095 accident cases, and had 1,767 calls.*

"The savings to the firm in the matter of drugs alone has been enormous, to say nothing of the great lessening of days of illness that always obtains when homœopathic treatment is followed."

Other firms listed in the Directory *as being under homœopathic direction were: National Cash Register, Dayton, Ohio; General Electric Company, Fort Wayne, Indiana; Continental Motors Company, Detroit, Michigan; Chalmers Motor Company, Detroit, Michigan; Studebaker Corporation, Detroit, Michigan.*

In 1902, the President of the American Institute of Homœopathy stated there were 15,000 homœopathic physicians in the United States. He did not say that only about 2,000 were Institute members. Less than 150 were members of the International Hahnemannian Association—the handful who were practicing "pure" homœopathy.

While the older generation of doctors had all been converts from allopathy, and had all the fervor which conversion entails, those who had been born and bred to homœopathy, in many cases, had no strong feelings about it. Few had the fortitude to stand before the onslaught of conventional medicine and remain unbowed. The AIH Transactions began to sound like a conventional medical meeting, with little homœopathy being discussed. Furthermore, those in positions of power did little to stop the steamroller of conventional medicine.

Homœopathy myth and fact: the decline of homœopathy

Dr. Daniel Cook, in a presentation at the 1995 Ohio homœopathic meeting, said, "If we don't identify what caused the problems and conditions that led to homœopathy's decline back then, we may overlook them if they happen in our time. And there are certainly a number of parallels between homœopathy in the end of this century and in homœopathy at the turn of the last century. So, it's more than just academic interest that should make us wonder about this question."

In thinking that the Flexner report eliminated homœopathy from the face of medical education, we presumed that homœopathy was going strong until 1910. It wasn't. It is part of the myth.

There is also mythology about dissension in the ranks of homœopaths. We have heard there were two camps, both practicing good homœopathy; those who used high potencies and those who used low potencies, and the fight between them destroyed homœopathy from within. A careful perusal of the literature shows this is not the case.

There was, in all of this, an underlying, uniquely American phenomenon—the proliferation of the commercial medical college. All that was needed to start a medical college was a charter from the state legislature. Medical colleges, both homœopathic and allopathic opened up on a grand scale. They were not required to have a clinic, a hospital, a laboratory, or any other facilities. The entrance requirements were no higher than a high school education or school diploma, and even that was waived in certain instances.

As an example, we can look at National Medical University in Chicago, originally a homœopathic school. Although it ceased having a homœopathic affiliation by the time Flexner visited them, its graduates were still appearing in a listing of homœopaths published by the AIH in 1941. What kind of education did these people have?

One look at the Flexner report tells all. National was the medical department of the "Chicago Night University." The school was "owned by the dean." It occupied "a badly lighted building containing nothing that can be dignified by the name of equipment." There was no dissecting— anatomy was didactically taught. The dissecting room contained "one putrid corpse" with several limbs missing. The chemistry lab had its equipment "locked up" and "about ten" oil immersion microscopes were said to be "locked up" as well. "There is not a pretense of anything else. Classes in session were all taking dictation." The school had been declared by the Illinois Board of Health to be "not in good standing" yet was still operating. It was from this school in that year of inspection that Royal Scudder of Fort Bragg, California, Nicholas Lyncker of Jacksonville, Florida, and Werner Farlander of Chicago all gained their medical degrees, and they were still in practice in 1941 and listed in the *American Institute of Homeopathy Directory.*

Cook points out many homœopathic medical colleges had faculties drawn from allopathic ranks, with the exception of one department, the department of homœopathic materia medica and practice. The departments of surgery, obstetrics, medicine, and everything else were generally taught by allopaths. As a result, largely allopathy was taught at these homœopathic medical colleges.

Instructors at New York Homœopathic College stated that gallstones or kidney stones could not be helped by homœopathy; that you had to give morphine injections. One homœopath said in the *Transactions of the AIH in 1901:*

> "…men who have been in the practice of medicine eight or ten years say, 'When you go out to a case of neuralgia, don't spend half an hour trying to find out what homœopathic medicines to give, but relieve the patient first; give morphine and then put the patient to sleep, and then you can study up the case, and in that way hold the patient'… Everybody in the profession does that, nearly; there are only an exceptional few who do not."

The students of these homœopathic medical colleges were learning that pain is a specific entity to be treated by specific measures; that it is not a part of a totality, which should be treated as a whole by a single remedy. They were taught infections were caused by specific entities and are not to be seen in a totality of symptoms.

This ideal of the totality of symptoms was completely abandoned in all the homœopathic medical schools by 1880. Instead, students were taught the most important symptoms were the symptoms identifying the class of disease, i.e., the pathological indications (the common symptoms of the disease) of the case were the most important.

Hahnemann Medical College in Philadelphia supposedly taught homœopathy, yet Robert Farley, MD, a graduate in 1886 (and later a pupil of Kent) cited an example of a teacher who was using homœopathy and giving crude doses of drugs at the same time. Said Farley (in reference to what he was taught):

> "This is a specimen of the teaching and practice of the faculty of the Hahnemann College of Philadelphia. This kind of seedsowing cannot fail to produce an abundant harvest of 'empirics' calling themselves homœopaths, and homœopathy must suffer accordingly."

How much homœopathic medical teaching were the students receiving? The sad answer is, hardly any at all. What was taught in these schools as early as the

1870s and certainly by the 1880s throughout the United States and practiced by their graduates, was the rejection of subjective symptoms, rejection of the totality of symptoms, rejection of the single remedy, rejection of the *Organon*, rejection of Hahnemann's three basic rules of homœopathic prescribing, and finally the rejection of the Law of Similars itself. It was taught that both *contraria* and *similia* are natural laws of healing. It was reported in the *Homœopathic Physician* in 1887 that if the practitioner could not select between four possible remedies in a given case that all four should be given at the same time— "the prescriber is criminal if he does not."

It was the rare person who could pull themselves past their teaching and find the real system.

One such person was S. W. Cohen, a graduate of Pulte College, who wrote to H. C. Allen in 1889:

I have only practiced homœopathy 12 years. Up to within two years my buggy case contained only liquids and triturations, the liquids were composed of tinctures, 1st, 2nd, and 3rd potencies, and the triturations of 2x, 3x, and 6x. Besides this I employed every new specific (?) upon the market. I wasn't a Homœopath, I wasn't an Eclectic, nor was I an Allopath; but I was, what are perhaps three-fourths of the homœopathic profession today, but what to call it I don't know. I hooted at the single remedy, and was sure as mortal man can be of anything, that all reported cases of cures by the so-called high potencies were the basest fabrication.

Through the earnest efforts of some of my confreres, I in a weak (?) moment promised to give the high potencies and the single remedy a trial, and I did so with a vengeance. I knew, as do ninety-five Homœopaths out of one hundred that intermittent fever cannot be cured without Quinine; so chills and fever was the chosen field for my work. I was advised to procure *Therapeutics of Intermittent Fever* by H. C. Allen, MD. I did it. I have in the past eighteen to twenty months, or perhaps a little longer, used no Quinine and have cured— yes, I call it cured— every case of chills and fever with the single remedy in high potency... Now let several thousand Homœopaths [of the 95% majority] get up on their hind legs and howl: "It's a ___ lie!" That does not alter the facts. This experience I repeat constantly.

By 1911, the AIH compiled a long list of diseases lying outside the operation of the Law of Similars. For all intents and purposes, the AIH abandoned homœopathy at that point. The students were taught to examine the patient allopathically, to make allopathic diagnosis, and to treat these allopathically.

One homœopathic faculty member in 1884, admitting as much said, "We do not pretend to make homœopathists of our students, we only make them doctors, and when they leave, if they wish for homœopathy, they can get it themselves."

The American Institute, unfortunately, allowed itself to be dominated and taken over by these partial homœopaths, and became their spokesman.

The decline in American homœopathy began in 1870 when Carroll Dunham permitted graduates who had never learned homœopathy to become Institute members, hoping they would "pick up" homœopathy from the members who understood and practiced it correctly.

By 1880, the AIH was completely overwhelmed by the numbers of these partial homœopaths. In 1880 it did away with the provision that mixtures should not be a part of homœopathy, and mixtures became welcomed. By 1882, it said that whenever the law of homœopathy did not really work, you could practice whatever you wanted. By 1889, it decided that, unlike the AMA, they should not exclude members of the other medical camp, but should welcome them. And so, anyone who practiced medicine, even the allopaths, could join.

Homœopathy had flourished because of the purity of the method practiced and because of the great success it had. But practitioners graduating from the homœopathic medical schools from the 1870s onward felt more in sympathy to allopathic medicine than to practice according to Hahnemann's doctrines. The graduates often urged students to go to an allopathic medical school rather than a homœopathic one.

Says Cook:

"To say that in 1900 there were 22 homœopathic

schools and 12,000 homœopathic physicians in America is to re-write the history of homœopathy. Students at American 'homœopathic' colleges were taught to examine the patient allopathically, and then treat these allopathic conceptions of disease with any and every homœopathic, allopathic, and herbal drug that had a reputation for getting rid of the pathological 'entity' they diagnosed. Homœopathic medicines, if they were included in the prescription, were given in crude form (in fact rarely higher in potency than 3X), mixed with several other medicines, and given with the same frequency as allopathic medications."

By the time the Flexner report was published, the number of homœopathic schools had declined from 22 to 15, and enrollment had already halved. In the next nine years, that number declined from 15 medical schools to seven. So, the rate of decline was exactly the same in the 10 years before Flexner's report as after.

As Cook said of the decline of the schools, "It was an inside job that rotted within; it was not due to Flexner." Cook pointed out that Flexner was in favor of five of the 15 homœopathic medical schools then in existence. If the Flexner report had been followed, five homœopathic medical schools would have been maintained.

The "real" homœopaths were managing with great difficulty. They were having a hard time maintaining themselves, maintaining any associations and journals where pure homœopathy could be discussed and having any school or hospital where homœopathy could be practiced. They were constantly opposed by the partial homœopaths who out–numbered them 100 to one.

At the turn of the century the International Hahnemannian Association had about 100 members, and at its high point (in the 1930s) about 200. The Association was not against "low potencies" and in the *Transactions of the Association* you can read of cases being cured by all potencies. What it was against was "partial-homœopaths" who happened to also use low potencies, but prescribed by "disease category" and often mixed with allopathic medication. The disagreement that led to the splitting of homœopathic groups from the existing societies was *not* the issue of potency— it was whether homœopathy consisted of rules and methods, or whether it was up to each individual prescriber to define homœopathy and to practice it any convenient way.

The notion of blaming the decline of homœopathy on the "fanatical" high-potency prescribers, lays the blame on the very people who were responsible for preserving homœopathy in the United States. While pseudo-homœopathy failed to work for the practitioner and the patient, those using real homœopathic care knew its value and, like a persecuted sect which survives through the centuries by passing information from generation to generation, those who understood homœopathy as the methodology outlined by Hahnemann, managed to keep it alive.

"Why did homœopathy decline after 1900?" asked Cook. "It did not decline— it never got off the ground."

What died after 1900 was not real homœopathy, but the false homœopathy which was really nothing more than empiricism and allopathy which just gave way to the allopathic medicine at the time.

An article, by Cook and Alain Naudé, outlining this mythology in depth, has appeared in the *Journal of the American Institute of Homeopathy* (Summer 1996) and in *The Homoeopath* (No. 64 Winter 1997).

An AIH Definition

In 1899, the American Institute of Homœopathy, under leadership of Eugene Porter, MD, offered a definition of a homœopath:

> "A Homœopathic physician is one who adds to his knowledge of medicine a special knowledge of Homœopathic Therapeutics and observes the law of similia. All that pertains to the great field of medical learning is his, by tradition, by inheritance, by right."

Upon which Kent commented in 1912:

> "'The homœopathic physician is one who prescribes the single remedy in the minimum dose in potentized form, selected according to the law of similars.'
>
> "The superficial observer would not criticize either form of definition. The astonishing part of the first formula is expressed in the first part: 'who adds to his knowledge of medicine.'
>
> "Of what does the knowledge consist? Is it what all tradition counts as up-to-date use of drugs, such as cathartics, ointments, depressants, compound tablets, coal-tar products, crude drugs in general, etc.? Does it mean that the homœopathic physician must know these so that he can have something to which to add the special knowledge of homœopathic therapeutics in order to be a homœopathic physician?
>
> "It would be supposed that the homœopathic physician had abandoned the first to become a physician of an advanced and scientific order. It must be acknowledged that all of this knowledge of medicine, to which he is to add his homœopathic therapeutics, is traditional ignorance and absurdities. Now to this ignorance he is to add a knowledge of homœopathic therapeutics. Would it not be better and wiser to say that a homœopathic physician is one who has abandoned traditional absurdities and adopted the science and philosophy of healing according to the law of similars? Men who depend upon the diagnosis, the laboratory findings, the pathology, the bacteriology, for selection of their remedies are expected to add to such knowledge (?) a special knowledge of homœopathic therapeutics!

"It has been our experience to meet a large number of these so-called homœopathic physicians, but we have never met one who had added any knowledge of materia medica or the art of prescribing to his so-called general knowledge of medicine.

"The astonishing part of the formula is that it frames into the definition just the part that prevents every man from becoming a homœopathic physician. So long as he holds onto the traditional absurdities, even when called modern scientific medicine, so long he is incapable of learning the true art of healing according to the law of similars. So long as he believes that these absurdities are valuable knowledge, so long he feels no need of going into real knowledge of homœopathic therapeutics. It is not sin to know these absurdities so long as he realizes that they are such, but the formula calls them 'knowledge of medicine.' It cannot refer to anatomy, physiology, chemistry, etc., because to these he does not add, as they are a part of doctors' rights and possessions."

The move, on the part of the American Institute of Homœopathy to embrace the "half-homeopaths" had its toll. As the years went on, fewer and fewer of the "old homœopaths" came to the meetings. The American Institute became an organization of those who embraced homœopathy in name only. Certainly, there were a few stalwarts who believed that because it had the "name" it deserved the support. We find a number of members of the International Hahnemannian Association still supporting the Institute with their membership, if nothing else, and we find some still presenting papers about the use of the single remedy as applied in homœopathic indications.

While the general membership drifted further and further from the main tenets of the system, the organization, because of its name, still maintained committees for the study of materia medica, and drug provings.

What passed as homœopathy…

In the Transactions of the American Institute of Homœopathy *of 1900, we find the following:*

- *much of the discussion on subjects surgical: extra-uterine pregnancy, fractures, detached retina.*
- *the use of aromatic spirits of ammonia followed by a hypodermic of strychnia.*
- *the use of morphine to keep the patient quiet.*
- *the packing of the uterus with carbide of calcium in cases of uterine cancer.*
- *the treatment of cystitis and urethritis in women: boric acid in 10 grain doses; half dram dose of fluid extract of corn silk; irrigation of the bladder with carbolic acid 1% and dilute bichloride of mercury; potassium permanganate flushes; silver nitrate flushes; and a list of possible homœopathic remedies was appended.*
- *the recommendation of the removal of enlarged tonsils by surgery (with one doctor speaking out against it, saying he has cured most cases with the indicated remedy).*

The 1907 Transactions *has an article about the use of X-ray as a pain sedative, with an example of subjecting a man with herpes zoster to 8 to 10 minutes of exposure to x-ray a day with "pain and local symptoms greatly relieved."*

An AIH Journal from the 1950s had an article about the treatment of nausea in pregnancy. The main recommendation was for the use of barbiturates supplemented with drinking Coca-Cola syrup.

Two "half-homœopaths"

James Craven Wood, MD
January 11, 1858 — August 29, 1948

James C. Wood

Wood was educated at Ohio Wesleyan University. Upon considering medicine as a vocation he found two schools of thinking. "I learned very early in life that truth was often found in minority groups… I first visited a representative of the majority and I think it was his vicious denunciation of homœopathy that finally decided me…" And Wood's mother had been cured of a long-standing illness by "the little pills." He began to read medicine with Dr. A. I. Sawyer, and attended the University of Michigan at Ann Arbor, graduating in 1879. He became a partner in Sawyer's practice. Five years later Wood was appointed to the chair of obstetrics and gynecology at Ann Arbor. After a year studying in England and on the Continent, he accepted the chair of gynecology at Cleveland Medical College. In 1894, he published his *Textbook of Gynecology* and joined the staff at Huron Road Hospital in Cleveland. He was the AIH president from 1901-1902. He ceased his surgical practice when he was 75, but kept his medical practice in Shaker Heights, Ohio, having his office in the Rose Building, of which he was one of the first tenants.

He wrote his autobiography, *An Old Doctor of the New School*, in 1942. It is filled with wonderful anecdotes, and gives a deep insight into a homœopath who really didn't believe in the method.

He says: "…as soon as the American Medical Association no longer required the renunciation of homœopathy… by its applicants, I immediately joined the great organization."

In an essay on homœopathy, Wood wrote: "There is not a surgeon or gynecologist in the homœopathic school who believes it is possible to cure an ovarian cyst of whatever size by internal medication alone." This was said at a time when many homœopaths *were* effecting such cures. Wood admitted in his autobiography that he did not have the faith in homœopathy that his teacher had.

In his presidential address to the AIH in 1902, he wonders why homœopathy has not been accepted by regular medicine and says: "If the law of similars is what we claim for it, should it not long ago have been accepted by progressive

Two "half-homœopaths" do not make one "whole-homœopath."
— JW

and scientifically inclined physicians of all schools?... The law of action and reaction asserted itself here as it has ever done. Hahnemann passed from the gross materialism of his day to the extreme infinitesimal, which has ever retarded the recognition which homœopathy long ago should have received."

Wood follows this, in his autobiography, with an exposition of homœopathy's history and of Hahnemann's *Cinchona* experiment, citing examples of how quinine was now being shown to kill malarial bacteria in the laboratory. He then discusses a new drug, sulfanilamide, which is also able to kill bacteria, but is dangerous to use in certain individuals. He suggests in "another five years it will be much less frequently used... because the required dose will be sufficiently small as to make it harmless"— a prophesy that did not come to pass. He states, "vaccines are homœopathic, and in vaccine therapy, too, we have the most striking example of the law of similars."

He admits that homœopathy is useful in "functional" diseases— those where the symptoms are present, but the pathology has not yet formed. But once the pathology has formed, he sees with surgeon's eyes.

He quotes Fielding H. Garrison: "Whenever many different remedies are proposed for a disease, it usually means that we know very little about treating the disease."

He finds drop doses of tincture up to the 4X "more dependable than extremely high potencies" but "I am compelled to nevertheless admit that I have seen wonderfully striking results following the administration of the high potencies. Their advocates are, as a rule, thorough students of materia medica and prescribe drugs with splendid precision."

So here we have a physician who is torn. He reads the *Organon*, believes Hahnemann will someday be recognized as a great medical reformer, but he is inexorably entwined in the model of the body as a cellular structure and the molecular action of the medicines.

James C. Wood, circa 1942

An excerpt from Doctor Copeland's Home Medical Book:

What treatment is suggested by Copeland for nasal catarrh?
"Spray the nose very gently night and morning with a solution of three grains of camphor, three grains of menthol, in one ounce of albolene." If this does not work, he says you should "stuff the nose with a tampon soaked in Argyrol [a proprietary product containing silver nitrate], and then rinse it out with a 5 percent solution of salt."

Where is the homœopath here? Did he not believe in homœopathy? — JW

Royal Samuel Copeland, MD
November 7, 1868 — June 17, 1938

Copeland was an 1889 graduate of the Homœopathic Medical College of the University of Michigan at Ann Arbor. He was professor of materia medica at Ann Arbor, and was mayor of Ann Arbor in 1901. He moved to New York City to become dean of the New York Homœopathic Medical College from 1908 to 1923. He served as health commissioner for the city of New York from 1918 to 1923. He was the president of the American Institute of Homœopathy in 1908. He was elected senator from New York in 1923, and served until his death in 1938.

He was responsible for writing the *Homœopathic Pharmacopoeia* into the Federal Legislation that created the Food, Drug, and Cosmetic Act of 1938. It is said his death was caused, in part, by the incredible strain of getting the legislation passed.

The National Council Against Health Fraud, in their position paper against homœopathy (1996), speaks of Copeland as "the most foremost homœopathic physician of his day." But this comes from those who know little about homœopathic physicians. Few of his contemporaries would have agreed with that evaluation of his status in the homœopathic community.

Although Copeland considered himself a "homœopath" he wrote a domestic care book— *Doctor Copeland's Home Medical Book* published by John C. Winston in 1934— that did not even mention homœopathy.

When he was approached by the mayor of New York to be health commissioner he said he did not want it. One of the reasons was that he was a homœopath and the appointment might be looked at askance by critics (as it was!). The mayor replied, "That argument does not go with me because I have had a homœopathic doctor in my family for thirty years, and I notice he is just as scientific and just as able as any other man in the community."

During the 1918 flu epidemic, the fatalities at the New York City hospital on Wards Island were lower than in any other city hospital in the country. All the cases were under Copeland's direction and were treated homœopathically.

A contemporary account of our "homœopathic" Senator is found in the book *Diet and Die* by Carl Malmberg, published in 1935:

"…Now these same interests are expressing grave concern over some provisions in another bill drawn up in part by the medico-politician, Senator Royal Copeland. It is difficult to believe that their concern in this case can be genuine, for the bill is practically worthless as far as safeguarding the public is concerned. Indeed, any bill sponsored by the affable senator from New York who has so long acted as a paid testimonial writer and ballyhoo artist for various commercial interests could hardly be anything else."

Homœopathy and expediency

One might understand Copeland a bit more after perusing a small pamphlet he wrote in 1909 titled *The Scientific Reasonableness of Homœopathy.*

The work discusses the development of homœopathy and moves quickly to understanding the remedies based on the selecting from the mass of provings the symptoms of "minimum practical value." He can readily see the study of *Belladonna* will give a mental picture that could point the way to the proper selection of the remedy, and it can be done by understanding the materia medica without resorting to the repertory.

"Those of us who have not made use of the repertory, or of a sufficient amount of midnight oil, have said, mentally at least, 'I do not know of any homœopathic remedy for this case and I am justified in resorting to expediency.' With most of us, expediency has meant palliative, certainly material treatment.

"But the repertorial advocate says nay to all this. He insists there is still a way to select from the bushels of chaff the grain of wheat which may be made into the loaf of healing. Without present discussion of the details of this system, I wish to give earnest testimony to what it has revealed to me of the possibilities and actualities of successfully prescribing in cases heretofore apparently hopeless of other methods of homœopathic practice. Personally, I regret the years of active practice without working knowledge of the repertory, and I have promised myself that I shall make future use of the system, limited and circumscribed as here indicated."

It seems Copeland was trained in the "name" homœopathy but not at all in the "practice" of it, other than keynote prescribing on pathological symptoms. Judging by his "domestic manual" he never kept the promise he made to himself to study the system, and slipped further and further into expediency.

Royal Copeland, circa 1889

Homœopathy and the flu epidemic of 1918

As homœopathy was being abandoned by the half-homœopaths, watching its schools close, and being assaulted by conventional medicine at every turn, the world was faced with a great epidemic crisis— the 1918 influenza pandemic.

Into the breach of this challenge went the homœopaths. Even those, like Copeland who resorted to "expediency" in more complex ailments could clearly see the homœopathic remedies needed during this epidemic. Their results were astounding— and few paid any attention.

It is hard to imagine the devastation caused by the flu epidemic of 1918-19. People who lived through it reported that someone who was up and well in the morning could be dead by evening.

It was about as deadly as the Black Death. 20 million people died world–wide. 12.5 million died in India alone— four percent of the population. In the United States, 548,000 people died in the epidemic.

The following is an extract from an article entitled "Homœopathy In Influenza— A Chorus Of Fifty In Harmony" by W. A. Dewey, MD from the *Journal of the American Institute of Homeopathy* in 1921.

- Dean W. A. Pearson of Philadelphia collected 26,795 cases of influenza treated by homœopathic physicians with a mortality of 1.05%, while the average old school mortality was 30%.

- Thirty physicians in Connecticut responded to my request for data. They reported 6,602 cases with 55 deaths, which is less than 1%. In the transport service I had 81 cases on the way over. All recovered and were landed. Every man received homœopathic treatment. One ship lost 31 on the way.
  — H. A. Roberts, MD, Derby, Connecticut

- In a plant of 8,000 workers we had only one death. The patients were not drugged to death. *Gelsemium* was practically the only remedy used. We used no aspirin and no vaccines.
  — Frank Wieland, MD, Chicago

An aside of the time…

Sometime between 1917 and 1918, the American Institute of Homœopathy ceased using the "œ" digraph ligature in its name and literature.

- I did not lose a single case of influenza; my death rate in the pneumonias was 2.1%. The salicylates, including aspirin and quinine, were almost the sole standbys of the old school and it was a common thing to hear them speaking of losing 60% of their pneumonias.
— Dudley A. Williams, MD, Providence, Rhode Island

- Fifteen hundred cases were reported at the Homœopathic Medical Society of the District of Columbia with but fifteen deaths. Recoveries in the National Homœopathic Hospital were 100%.
— E. F. Sappington, MD, Philadelphia.

- I have treated 1,000 cases of influenza. I have the records to show my work. I have no losses. Please give all credit to homœopathy and none to the Scotch-Irish-American!
— T. A. McCann, MD, Dayton, Ohio.

In "Homœopathy In Influenza— A Chorus Of Fifty In Harmony" we find the following comments:

- One physician in a Pittsburgh hospital asked a nurse if she knew anything better than what he was doing, because he was losing many cases. "Yes, Doctor, stop aspirin and go down to a homœopathic pharmacy, and get homœopathic remedies." The Doctor replied: "But that is homœopathy." "I know it, but the homœopathic doctors for whom I have nursed have not lost a single case."
— W. F. Edmundson, MD, Pittsburgh

- There is one drug which directly or indirectly was the cause of the loss of more lives than was influenza itself. You all know that drug. It claims to be salicylic acid. Aspirin's history has been printed. Today you don't know what the sedative action of salicylic acid is. It did harm in two ways. Its indirect action came through the fact that aspirin was taken until prostration resulted and the patient developed pneumonia.
— Frank L. Newton, MD, Somerville, Massachusetts

- Aspirin and the other coal tar products are condemned as causing great numbers of unnecessary deaths. The omnipresent aspirin is the most pernicious drug of all. It

In reading accounts of the epidemic it seems many deaths were caused by a virulent pneumonia that was especially devastating to those who depressed their system with analgesics, the most common being aspirin. Raymond Seidel told me he decided to become a homœopathic doctor when he was a 10 year old delivery boy for a local homœopath. He said, "I saw that the people who were taking aspirin were dying, about half those who were drinking a lot of whiskey were dying, and those that received homœopathic remedies were living."

beguiles by its quick action of relief of pain, a relief which is but meretricious. In several cases aspirin weakened the heart, depressed the vital forces, increased the mortality in mild cases and made convalescence slower. In all cases it masks the symptoms and renders immeasurably more difficult the selection of the curative remedy. Apparently aspirin bears no curative relation to any disease and it ought to be prohibited.
—Guy Beckley Stearns, MD, New York

• Three hundred and fifty cases and lost one, a neglected pneumonia that came to me after she had taken one hundred grains of aspirin in twenty-four hours.
— Cora Smith King, MD, Washington, DC

• I had a package handed to me containing 1,000 aspirin tablets, which was 994 too many. I think I gave about a half dozen. I could find no place for it. My remedies were few. I almost invariably gave *Gelsemium* or *Bryonia*. I hardly ever lost a case if I got there first, unless the patient had been sent to a drug store and bought aspirin, in which event I was likely to have a case of pneumonia on my hands.
— J. P. Huff, MD, Olive Branch, Kentucky.

A Summary: too little— too late

Edwin Lightner Nesbit, MD in the August, 1919 *Journal of the American Institute of Homeopathy* spoke about the inevitable the decline of homœopathy being brought about by "half-homœopathy." His words fell on deaf ears.

"When Copeland says, 'If homeopathy had strength enough, and vigor enough and old-time stamina enough to fight its battles now as it did in the pioneer days, it could accomplish enough in this generation,' etc. I say, 'Yep, attaboy, and me too,' meaning 'amen.' Only from this practitioner's viewpoint I would say, if our homeopathic leaders— like Copeland— had the vision enough ten years ago to see the inevitable trend of their truckling to non-homeopathic 'standards' and to stand for 'standards' of their own devising alone, the homeopathic branch of the medical profession would have had more and better colleges of its own today than our pioneers ever dreamed."

1900 – 1925: The Keeping
Julia M. Green
The American Foundation for Homœopathy
Pierre Schmidt
Other issues of the time
The Electronic Reaction of Abrams
Guy Beckley Stearns
Cyrus M. Boger

At the same time the homœopathic schools were closing and the "half-homœopath" drifted closer and closer to allopathic therapeutics, a small group of "Hahnemannians" were keeping the therapeutic method alive. Many of them were at the meeting of the International Hahnemannian Association in Swampscott, Massachusetts in 1912. We find elders like Erastus Case; those who were to leave their mark through their writings like Cyrus Boger and Herbert A. Roberts; the teachers, J. H. Allen and J. B. S. King; the experimenter, Guy Beckley Stearns; and the clinicians, Benjamin Woodbury, Royal E. S. Hayes, Margaret Lewis, Grace Stevens, Julia M. Green, and Mary Florence Taft.

While cleaning up the files at the National Center for Homeopathy office a few years ago, I came across an old photo. It was identified as "IHA Meeting, Swampscott, Massachusetts, June 1912." The handwriting was that of Dr. Julia M. Green. None of the people in the photo were identified.

I checked the attendance register in a copy of the *International Hahnemannian Association Transactions* from 1912. About 50 people attended the meeting— as with all group photos, not everyone shows up— so there are only 34 people in the photo. With some help, I have identified 19 of those present. All have been matched against likenesses that have appeared elsewhere. Others at the meeting, whose likenesses I have seen, do not seem to be in this group picture. And Chris Ellithorp and I are still arguing over the likeness of Margaret Lewis; he says it is Carrie Newton. I maintain that while it might bear a resemblance to Carrie Newton, Dr. Newton did not attend the 1912 meeting.

The moral of the story: always identify photographs!

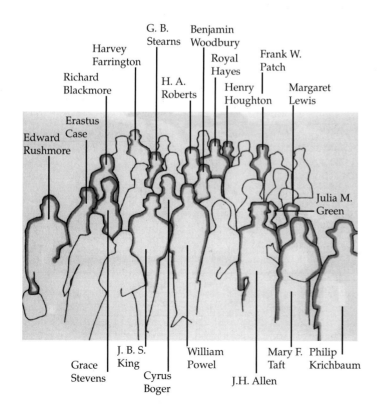

The Faces of Homœopathy

The other people attending the 1912 meeting were:

Alonzo E. Austin (New York City)
B. L. B. Baylies (Brooklyn, NY)
Daniel E. S. Coleman (New York City)
Horace B. Dean (Audubon, NJ)
W. H. Freeman (Brooklyn, NY)
Sarah L. Guild-Leggett (Syracuse, NY)
Amelia L. Hess (Philadelphia)
John Hutchinson (New York City)
Walter M. James (Philadelphia)
S. A. Kimball (Boston, MA)
Frances M. Morris (Boston, MA)
Mary Rees Mulliner (Boston)
Chas. H. Oakes (Livermore Falls, ME)
Edith M. Phelps (Milford, DE)
Franklin Powel (Chester, PA)
Carolyn Putnam (Kansas City, MO)
Hilmar C. Schmidt (Chicago)
T. G. Sloan (S. Manchester, CT)
S. H. Sparhawk (St.Johnsbury, VT)
Lawrence Stanton (New York City)
Edwin A. Taylor (Chicago, IL)
Richard True (Boston, MA)
Maurice W. Turner (Brookline, MA)
Frank C. Walker (Nantucket, MA)
Margaret B. Webster (Philadelphia)
Dudley A. Williams (Providence, RI)
Theo F. Winans (Mexico, MO)
W. A. Yingling (Emporia, KS)

The people in the photo on the previous page that have been identified are listed below. Many of them were identified through photos appearing in the *Homeopathic Recorder*. If they are not spoken of elsewhere in this work, a brief biography is included here:

Edward Rushmore May 18, 1845– November 24, 1925. (Plainfield, NJ) IHA president in 1893. A graduate of Jefferson Medical College in Philadelphia, he was introduced to homœopathy by Edward Bayard. Rushmore's notes were used by Kent to compile his *Repertory*.

Erastus E. Case (Hartford, CT)

Grace Stevens December 15, 1868– March 20, 1950 (Northampton, MA) A graduate of Boston 1901. IHA president in 1930.

John B. S. King February 12, 1855– August 28, 1929 (Chicago, IL) Graduate of Hahnemann Chicago in 1883. IHA president in 1913. Editor of the *Medical Advance*. I identified his likeness from a photo of the faculty at Hahnemann found in a Student Medical Fraternity Yearbook.

Cyrus M. Boger (Parkersburg, WV)

William R. Powel March 15, 1863– March 15, 1927 (Philadelphia, PA) Graduated Hahnemann Philadelphia in 1887. IHA president in 1925. Powel had bought a farm outside Philadelphia as a place to spend his weekends and eventually retire. While on the farm he was gored and trampled by his bull, dying two days later.

J. H. Allen 1854– August 1, 1925 (Chicago, IL) IHA president 1900. Author of *Chronic Diseases* and *Diseases of the Skin*. He taught at Hering College in Chicago.

Julia M. Green (Washington, DC)

Margaret C. Lewis October 13, 1868– July 13, 1953 (Philadelphia, PA) Graduate of the Women's Medical College of Pennsylvania in 1895, and Kent's Postgraduate School in 1897.

Mary Florence Taft (Newtonville, MA)

Philip E. Krichbaum d. July 17, 1928 (Montclair, NJ) Graduate of Hering College 1896. As per his wishes, his ashes were scattered over the Hahnemann Monument in Washington, DC.

Richard Blackmore 1872– 1933 (Farmington,CT) Graduate of Boston 1902. A picture of him in uniform appears in Dearborn's *Homeopathy in the Great War*. After the war he worked in the Veteran's Hospital in St. Cloud, Minnesota.

Harvey Farrington (Chicago, IL)

Guy Beckley Stearns (New York, NY)

Herbert A. Roberts (Derby, CT)

Benjamin Woodbury August 13, 1882– January 22, 1948 (Portsmouth, NH) Graduate of Boston 1906. IHA president in 1947. Wrote *A Materia Medica for Nurses* in 1916.

Royal E. S. Hayes (Farmington, CT)

Henry L. Houghton July 3, 1869– June 17, 1948 (Boston, MA) Graduate of Harvard Medical School 1894 and Kent's Post–Graduate School in 1896. IHA president 1917.

Frank Wallace Patch March 22, 1862– September 7, 1923 (Framingham, MA) Graduate of Boston 1888. IHA President 1907.

Knowing that with the closing of the homœopathic colleges all knowledge would be lost, Julia M. Green established the American Foundation for Homœopathy with a group of like–minded physicians. Although not a writer, and not known by the larger homœopathic community in the last decade of the 20th century, this diminutive woman and her iron will, served as the glue to bind homœopathy together in the United States for more than 40 years. In 1922, the AFH began a postgraduate training program for medical doctors. Held for six weeks each summer, it provided homœopathic training taught by the most experienced practitioners in the United States. Roberts, Boger, and Gladwin were among the first teachers.

Julia Minerva Green, MD
March 24, 1871 — December 11, 1963

Green's life spanned the time from the beginning of the decline of homœopathy almost through to its resurgence. Born in Malden, Massachusetts, she moved to Washington, DC, aged six. She graduated from Wellesley College in 1893 (she was the only one of her class attending the 70th reunion in 1963!) and Boston University in 1898.

Green began her medical practice in Washington, DC, in 1900, using a bicycle to make her rounds, with fishing weights sewn in the hem of her dress to keep it down while she pedaled. In 1907, she bought a car— the second one in Washington. The first was the President's!

Treated with homœopathy her whole life, she became interested in medicine but, "The only women doctors I knew were pseudo-masculine types and I could not face that." Falling ill, she was treated by a "woman doctor of the delightfully feminine type who showed me I need not be hesitant on account of the half-masculine picture I had seen." Green entered Boston University as one of 15 women in the 45–strong class.

The beginning years of practice were difficult for a woman. She says, "The doorbell rang and the maid answered. 'Is the doctor in?' 'Yes. I'll call her.' 'Oh. Is he a she?' 'Yes sir.' "Oh, I thought she was a he. You needn't call her.' And he fled as if the devil were after him!"

Green recalled: "In all this striving I had to deal with the greatest shyness one could imagine. It haunted me, held me back, made me appear tongue tied and very awkward.

The Faces of Homœopathy

That was my number one enemy, fought valiantly but very often without success until I was 50 when the American Foundation for Homœopathy was founded by one other woman doctor and myself (and several male doctors). The fight for that ever since has helped my morale wonderfully in fighting the timidity."

Green was barely five feet tall and soft-spoken. Asked once why she never married, she replied, "I didn't think I could do both jobs well."

Dr. Lucy Clark said Green, "learned to smell a disease from certain symptoms before any pathology showed or developed and thus kept her patients healthy and happy."

Green was the president of the IHA in 1933.

After 59 years of practice she slowed down a little after taking in Maesimund B. Panos as her student in 1959. Until her death she was still seeing patients a few days a week.

Sandra M. Chase remembers Green as wearing "funny custom made shoes"— the "Murray Space-Shoe" of the 1950s that were favorites of nurses, dentists, and other professionals who spent a lot of time on their feet.

Green lived in a beautiful house she had built in 1916 at 2726 Quebec St. in Washington, DC, when the area was barely settled and the roads were still unpaved. She slept outside on the side porch most of the year, exercised every joint in her body at least once a day, and walked 15 minutes every day.

The American Foundation for Homœopathy library and reading room, circa 1935

The American Foundation for Homœopathy

In 1921, 12 homœopathic physicians gathered to start a new organization. Those assembled were like a list of "who's who" in American homœopathy: Julia M. Green, Frederica Gladwin, Ida Virginia Reel, Eugene Underhill, Alonzo Austin, Guy Beckley Stearns, Stuart Close, Cyrus Boger, George Dienst, Frank Wallace Patch, Benjamin Woodbury, and Julia Loos. The group was temporarily called the International Foundation for Homœopathy.

One of the first orders of business was to establish a post-graduate training program in homœopathy for physicians. The first course, six weeks long, ran in 1922.

In 1924, the organization was officially incorporated under the name of the American Foundation for Homœopathy. The bylaws stipulated a 12–person trusteeship with seven physicians and five laymen. The original incorporators were Drs. Boger, Dienst, Gladwin, Green, Loos, Roberts, and lay persons Louise Ross, Edgar Speiden, Victor Esch, George Fleming and Charlotte Hallett.

The purpose of the organization was to "promote the art of healing according to the natural laws of cure from a strictly homœopathic standpoint; to establish and direct centers for the study and understanding of homœopathy, together with research work in any correlated subject; to diffuse knowledge among the laity concerning homœopathic principles; to serve as a reference center for all that relates to homœopathy and to serve as a repository for homœopathic literature and drugs."

To achieve that purpose, four bureaus were established: a bureau of investigation (changed in 1929 to bureau of instruction), a bureau of research, a bureau of publications, and a bureau of publicity. Under the bureau of publicity, a network of laymen's leagues were established. These were usually under the leadership of the wives of prominent physicians, and these groups helped to keep homœopathy alive at grass-root level.

In looking through the early minutes of the group, I was struck by how similar the issues were to those the National Center of Homœopathy faced 50 years later. I could summarize with the following conversation— the words are not quite exact, but the sentiment is!

"Where will we get the money?"
"I don't know. You have any rich patients?"
"No, but doctor so and so does."
"Maybe we can ask him."
"I don't think so. He had a falling out with doctor such and such and won't talk to us."

And this one:

"Who will contact all these doctors?"
"Miss so and so said she will."
"Can we pay her for it?"
"Not too much. She will charge by the hour."
"Do you think doctors would talk to a lay person?"
"I think some won't."
"Maybe we should get a doctor to do it?"
"No. Everyone is too busy."
"Maybe if we paid more?"
"Where do we get the money?"
"Who has rich patients?"

In 1922, armed with the names of Alonzo Austin and Frederica Gladwin, a young physician from Switzerland landed in New York City. The American Foundation for Homœopathy was just starting their course for doctors and Pierre Schmidt became the first course graduate. He went on to become one of Europe's most influential homœopaths.

Pierre Schmidt, MD
July 22, 1894 — October 15, 1987

Educated in Geneva, Schmidt first learned of homœopathy in London where he saw the results of homœopathic treatment during the 1918 flu epidemic. While in London he met both J. H. Clarke and John Weir. He came to the United States in 1922 and learned homœopathy from Austin and Gladwin who were working as the core faculty at the first session of the American Foundation school. Schmidt returned to Geneva where he established his practice. He was responsible for teaching "pure" homœopathy to several generations of physicians in Europe, as well as to those, like Elizabeth Wright Hubbard, who journeyed there to study with him. Gladwin always referred to Schmidt as "Sunshine."

Schmidt wrote several small pamphlets, helped edit the *Final General Repertory* of Kent, and translated the *Organon* into French. In 1925, he was instrumental in establishing the Liga Medicorum Homœopathic Internationalis (often shortened to just "Liga" or LMHI), an international organization of classical homœopathic physicians. He was a prominent figure at most homœopathic gatherings, and spoke at the Hahnemann Monument in Washington, DC, in 1955, on the 200th anniversary of Hahnemann's birth.

The 3000+ volume library of Schmidt is now in the possession of a trust in St. Gallien, Switzerland and is available for research purposes.

Robert Schore, MD, while studying with Dr. Kunzli in Europe paid a brief visit to Dr. Schmidt in 1979. He recalls:

"I was impressed with the grandeur of his office, a very large room containing hundreds of volumes of homœopathic texts and journals, many carefully bound in leather. His custom built wood remedy cabinets were magnificent. His examination room was a smaller adjacent room containing an exam table, an instrument table, and an acupuncture chart on the wall. I browsed around while I waited about twenty minutes for him to enter the room. I'll always remember the first thing he said to me (in a very abrupt manner): 'What questions do you have?' I had gone there just to meet him and chat about homœopathy in Europe, and I found myself intimidated as if I was in an audience with the Pope! I introduced myself as a student of his student, Dr. Jost Kunzli, who arranged for me to meet him. We had a very brief conversation. He said that it was very important to study everything about homœopathy and to have questions. He also mentioned that acupuncture could be an adjunct to homœopathy as long as the doctor was familiar with both systems of therapy."

Other issues of the time

Homœopathy and the Volstead Act

The Volstead Act of 1919 saw alcohol prohibited in the United States. While we may be familiar with pictures of "rum running" and the rise of people like Al Capone, who controlled the black-market alcohol trade, we forget that without quality alcohol, homœopathic pharmacy is impossible. During the time of the Volstead Act, the federal government allowed homœopathic physicians to regularly purchase small amounts of pure grain alcohol for their practice.

According to the information in *Jottings,* a small trade journal published by Boericke and Tafel, a physician could apply for a permit to let him purchase 15 gallons of pure alcohol a year. If he wanted more than that, a bond of $1000 had to be posted, and the physician could purchase up to 50 gallons a year. One had to complete five forms to get the permit.

By 1926, the law was changed to eliminate the need for a notarized (sworn) statement if less than 15 gallons were being purchased. As Boericke and Tafel said: "The government still protects the dear public from the possibility of becoming intoxicated on homœopathic dilutions."

The Power of the Small

Homœopaths, by the very nature of the science with which they work, see the world in a totally different way, often conflicting with conventional world-view models. In two arenas the homœopath, over the years, has come face to face with political and societal norms.

Vaccinations

The homœopathic opposition to the use of vaccines has its roots in the work of Dr. James Compton Burnett, who was the first to conceptualize that a vaccine (in his case the smallpox immunization) could cause a deep–seated illness, vaccinosis, and that the resultant illness is treatable by the use of homœopathic remedies. Furthermore, the "vaccinosis illness" is perceptible to the homœopath because the generalized symptoms it presents are often functional (rather than pathological) and are seen as pointers to a

The Twilight Sleep Movement: The homœopathic connection

The Twilight Sleep Movement (1914-1916) was a particular method of anesthesia used during labor and childbirth that was considered dangerous to use because the drug doses had to be carefully monitored and tailored to the individual response of the patient. This "individualized response" was right in line with homœopathic thinking. The movement in Boston was led by two homœopathic physicians— Eliza Taylor Ransom (the founder of the movement in the US and graduate of Boston University) and Edward Smith, an obstetrician at Massachusetts Homœopathic Hospital. Between them, they delivered 500 babies by this method.

When Ransom died at the age of 92 in 1955, she was hailed as "a world-famous doctor."

Mary Ware Dennett, an active suffragette, was active in the Twilight Sleep Movement, and was a strong supporter of homœopathy. When the American Foundation for Homœopathy was formed in 1924, Dennett was hired as a special representative to the AFH. The files of the AFH contain 10 years worth of letters between Dennett and Dr. Julia M. Green.

homœopathic remedy, while the conventional medical practitioner will not find the symptom constellation "treatable." So the homœopath, since before the turn of the century, has viewed vaccines as inherently dangerous to the human economy.

Poisonings

The homœopath is aware of the smallness of the dosage needed to affect a person. Through provings of medicinal substances, the homœopath understands the symptomology of such poisonings. This awareness has led them to be outspoken in several areas, most in direct opposition to societal, medical, and governmental standards. We find this in four definite categories:

• Opposition to the use of amalgam fillings in dentistry. The first notice of amalgam poisonings appeared in homœopathic journals in the late 1890s. Cases were described with severe functional pathology which returned to normal when the amalgam fillings were removed.

• Opposition to the use of aluminum cookware. Again, the homœopath was aware of the number of symptoms produced by the ingestion of small amounts of aluminum through cookware, and was able to isolate the source based on the symptoms presented.

• Opposition to the addition of anything to drinking water. As with aluminum, the homœopath is well versed in the symptoms of *Calcium fluoride*, generated by the provings, as well as those produced by the other fluoride compounds. The fluoridation of water becomes a safety issue, as would be chlorination of drinking water. In 1926 Dr. Arthur Grimmer pointed out the city of Chicago puts 300 pound of chlorine into the water supply every day, "making the average dilution of the drinking water equivalent to about *Chlorine* 3C."

Furthermore, as is seen in the correspondence and articles in the homœopathic journals, many homœopaths, as people, were strongly in opposition to any governmental effort to interfere in the lives of citizens, and were outspoken on the issue for political and medical reasons.

• Opposition to chemical food additives for similar reasons to the three above.

The Electronic Reaction of Abrams

In the early 1920s a physician at Stamford University, Albert Abrams (1863–1924), noted a unique quality to the sound he heard when percussing the abdomen of a patient. After much experimentation he found a healthy person would percuss with the same "dullness" when a sample of diseased tissue from the other patient was held against them. Abrams concluded there was some kind of "radiation" from the tissue to which the healthy body reacted.

He believed if the phenomenon were electronic in nature (as he thought it was) it should be possible to measure the frequency of the "disease" by placing a variable resistor between the pathological sample and the "percussed" patient and observing at which frequency the note of percussion changed.

Abrams also experimented with determining a drug's "vibratory rate." When he attempted to show his students the worthlessness of potentized remedies, he found, to his surprise, that the 3X potency showed greater strength than the tincture, and the higher the potency (he tried a 6X and a 30), the stronger the reaction.

As reported in the January 1923 *Jottings:* "Dr. Abrams published the results of his experiments and acknowledged

2   J o t t i n g s

A Machine to Measure the Strength of Potencies

Dr. Albert Abrams has stirred up a veritable hornets' nest in the dominant school of medicine with his

Oscilloclast, as he calls the instrument by which he diagnoses disease by means of a drop of the patient's

An article about the Abrams "Oscilloclast" in Boericke and Tafel's *Jottings* of January, 1923

Radionics

A system formed into a loose body of knowledge by Albert Abrams. His basic discoveries were: 1) all matter radiates, 2) this radiation differs in accordance with the molecular or atomic composition of the specimen, and 3) whatever its nature, this radiation can affect the human nervous system. Thus radionics could be considered the science and study of subtle vibrations/ radiations which have effects on living systems.

Dowsing is a form of radionics in that these subtle energies can be tuned in upon and used to uncover information which otherwise is hidden. The dowser, after centering himself, uses one of a number of types of dowsing apparatus (rods, pendulums, etc.) to tune into and locate the subtle vibrations...

— *Yasgur's* Homeopathic Dictionary

After the work of Abrams, radionic devices were made by the Delawarr's in the UK and by Ruth Drown in the USA.

There are a number of radionic devices available. Most are available as both diagnostic and treatment devices.

his belief in the homœopathic law of cure, then and not until then the wrath of the dominant school enveloped him. He has been denounced as a charlatan and fakir."

The Abrams' device was tested by *Scientific American* in a test reminiscent of that *Nature Magazine* conducted in the Benveniste Laboratory in France almost 60 years later (see page 461).

A report to the International Hahnemannian Association in 1925 said the investigation of *Scientific American* was undertaken "in a journalistic rather than scientific style," and publishing the article "killed off all chances of obtaining cooperation of those who could have shown it enough presumptive evidence to convince it that Abrams' claims had at least some basis in fact." According to the report, none but the negative evidence was reported; the efforts were directed toward disproving; there were false manipulations; and similar work overseas was ignored. The *Scientific American* article concluded:

> "...the claims advanced on behalf of the electronic reaction of Abrams and of electronic practice in general are not substantiated, and it is our belief that they have no basis in fact. It is our opinion that the so-called electronic treatments are without value."

Abrams resigned from the American Medical Association and the California Medical Society after the AMA printed an attack on him in its *Journal*.

The IHA Study

The IHA committee was headed by Guy Beckley Stearns, MD. In 1925, the committee published a paper of its findings.

The committee came up with more questions than answers. The sense was there is a measurable energy in people and in remedies, although the nature of the energy is unknown. The quality of the energy seemed to be affected by heat, light, and magnetism. It is also affected by the mental state of the patient *and* the operator. "It seems reasonable to deduce that there is a band of energy comparable to the spectrum of light and it can be called the 'energy of Abrams.' The outstanding difficulty in the practical use of the phenomenon is the necessity of a living subject for the detector."

The committee concluded:

"The phenomenon can be utilized for selecting curative measures, especially for remedies having a homœopathic relation to the patient. All the phenomena connected with the energy and the reactions are very delicate and labile and their control is difficult. Their importance, however, is sufficient to command the attention of the best minds in medicine."

Many people, some of them homœopaths, continued research in this area. Several homœopaths (one of the most prominent being Kent's pupil, Arthur Grimmer) used an Abrams-like device to determine the simillimum in difficult cases.

It should be mentioned that there was, in the minds of the committee, a great difference between the devices being used by experienced homœopaths and the devices being used primarily as a diagnostic tool without intimate knowledge of the homœopathic materia medica.

The difficulties and concerns expressed at that time are still with us.

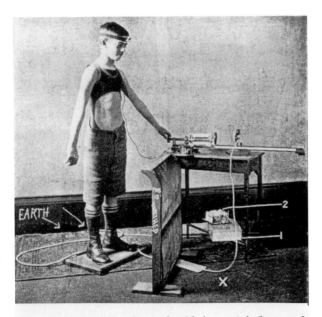

For actual practice there should be metal floor and surround earthed. 1—Tin box earthed ; 2—Sterilized envelopes with forceps ; X—Doctor sits here.

The work of Boyd

Dr. William E. Boyd of Glasgow, followed Abrams' lead and constructed a machine of his own which he called the Emanometer. As with the Abrams' device, the Emanometer used the abdominal reflexes of a human subject as a surrogate testing mechanism for the individual he was examining. But Boyd did countless studies and was very pragmatic and scientific in his approach.

Dr. Boyd's claims were investigated by a committee of orthodox medical men and scientists (the Horder Committee) and the findings were submitted to the British parliament. Boyd arranged a series of double blind tests capable of being evaluated on a statistical basis. In this manner the accidental success ratios could be compared with actual successes. The most rigorous of these trials, repeated at an interval of a few months, produced a 33,000,000 to 1 ratio in favor of the reality of the phenomenon. The controls were carefully kept by the investigating committee. The scientists concluded that while they did not understand the mechanism involved in the Emanometer the results were consistent and dramatically self-evident. The group then turned their findings over to a parliamentary committee. Although little came of it, this "official recognition" is one of the reasons that further work along these lines (known as radionics) has not been suppressed in Britain as it has been in the United States.

The Boyd Emanometer

G. B. Stearns, M. D.

Guy Beckley Stearns, MD
September 16, 1870 — March 25, 1947

A graduate of New York Homœopathic in 1900, Stearns returned to his alma mater to teach materia medica. "His mind was a searching and curious one, always *rerum novarum cupidus,*" said an obituary in the *Homœopathic Recorder.*

Investigating the "Abrams' reaction" he realized the reactions were not electronic but must be reflex-reactions transmitted through the autonomic nervous system. As an outgrowth of his research, he formed the Foundation for Homœopathic Research to collect information regarding the autonomic reaction to homœopathic potencies in a systematic way.

He investigated Boyd's Emanometer and his paper, *A New Basis for Medical Science and Boyd's Drug Classification,* is the subject's standard.

In 1932 he presented a paper to the IHA concerning a testing methodology to find the simillimum by using autonomic testing measuring pupilary reflex or the pulse reflex.

In 1942, Stearns and Edgar D. Evia wrote a small book called *The Physical Basis of Homœopathy and a New Synthesis.* In the book Stearns outlined all the work done up to then concerning the "energetic" nature of homœopathic remedies and of people's diseased states.

Stearns was the first (1928) who tried to prove experimentally the effects of high potencies through animal experiments, using guinea pigs and fruit flies.

Stearns was the IHA president in 1919.

While cleaning up at the Arch Street premises of Boericke and Tafel, I found, dust-covered and buried on a top shelf in the trituration room, a series of bottles labeled "Dr. Stearns." The remedies, all in the 3X to the 6X potencies were:

Sargatta Modesta
Sea Urchin Shell
Sea Urchin Inside
Red Ramshorn Snail
Chimney Soot

The Sargatta Modesta *bore the date "10/23/44."*
What was he doing with them?

One of the era's grand homœopaths was C. M. Boger. Although Boger is not as well known as Kent, he was extremely influential in the United States' homœopathic history. His influence was felt mostly through his immediate contact with other homœopaths at the IHA yearly meetings from 1888 until 1935, and through the legacy of about 100 essays— all presentations at the IHA meetings, or articles in the journals. He was one of the first teachers at the AFH postgraduate course.

Cyrus Maxwell Boger, MD
May 13, 1861 — September 2, 1935

Born in western Pennsylvania, Boger graduated from the Philadelphia College of Pharmacy and then gained his medical degree from Hahnemann College in Philadelphia in 1888. He settled in Parkersburg, West Virginia where he spent the rest of his life.

He was a German scholar and brought *Boenninghausen's Characteristics and Repertory* into the English language in 1905.

His ability to see "the big picture" and to understand the center of a case had him writing the *Synoptic Key and Repertory* in 1915, and the ultimate distillation of the Boenninghausen method in 1931 with his *General Analysis and Card Index*— a very spare repertory proven of great use to those who have investigated it.

He also published a list of additions to Kent's *Repertory*, a table of times of amelioration and aggravation, and a proving of *Samarskite*.

Fortunately for the homœopathic community, Robert Bannan produced, in 1993, a collection of all of Boger's writings. Open it up to any page and you will see his brilliance immediately.

Boger served as the IHA president in 1904. He was on the faculty of the AFH postgraduate course from 1924 until his death.

Always fond of home-canned foods, he died, aged 74, from food poisoning after eating a tin of home-preserved tomatoes. Upon being taken ill he drove himself to the hospital, but died shortly after arriving.

He is buried in the Lutheran Cemetery in Lebanon, Pennsylvania.

His granddaughter remember him as always working and not having much time to play with the children. He was "very Germanic and not very affectionate."

Yet he must have had an affectionate side. He was divorced after his wife found out he was having an affair with his secretary. He subsequently married the secretary.

COUGH,

51

CIST	CYC	FORM	HEP	KAL-M	LIL-T	MEN	NAT-C	PETR	PTEL	SAMB	SOU	TELL	VERB
CLEM	DIG	GAMB	HYDS	KAL-N	LITH	MEPH	NAT-M	PHEL	PUL	SANG	STAN	TERB	VIB-O
COCL	DIO	GEL	HYD-AC	KAL-P	LOB	MERC	NAT-P	PHO	PYRO	SANIC	STAP	THER	VIP

ACO	AM-C	ARG-N	BAP	CACT	CARB-A	CHEL	COC-C	DRO	GLO	HYO	KAL-S	LYC	MERC-C	NAT-S	PHO-AC	RAN-B	SARS	STIC	THU	XAN
ACT-AC	AM-M	ARN	BAR-C	CALC-C	CARB-AC	CHIN	COFF	DUL	GNAP	HYPR	KALM	LYCPS	MERC-CY	NIT-AC	PHYS	RAT	SEC-C	STRA	THYR	ZIN
AESC	AMY-N	ARS	BELL	CALC-F	CARB-V	CHI-S	COLCH	ELAP	GRAP	IGN	KOB	MAG-C	MERC-I-F	NUX-M	PHYT	RHE	SELE	STRO	?IL	
AETH	ANAC	ARS-IO	BEN-AC	CALC-P	CARD-M	CHIO	COLO	EUP-PER	GRAT	IOD	KRE	MAG-N	MERC-I-R	NUX-V	PIC-AC	RHO	SENEC	SUL	JB	
AGAR	ANT-C	ARU-T	BERB	CALC-S	CAUL	CHLO	CON	EUPHO	GRIN	IP	LAC-C	MAG-P	MEZ	ONOS	PLAN	RHS-T	SENEG	SUL-AC	URN-N	
AIL	ANT-T	ASAF	BORX	CAM	CAUS	CIC	CROC	EUPHR	GUAI	IRIS	LACH	MANC	MOS	OPI	PLAT	RUM	SEP	SUL-IO	URT-U	
ALO	AP	ASC-T	BOV	CAN	CED	CIMI	CROT-H	FER	HAM	KAL-B	LAUR	MANG	MURX	OSM	PLB	RUT	SIL	SYPH	VAL.	
ALU	ARAN	AUR	BRO	CANTH	CEPA	CINA	CROT-T	FER-P	HELL	AL-C	LED	MED	MUR-AC	OX-AC	POD	SABA	SPI	TAB	VER-A	
AMB	ARG-M	BAD	BRY	CAPS	CHAM	CINAB	CUP	FLU-AC	HELO	KAL-I	LEPT	MELIL	NAJ	PAL	PSOR	SABI	SPO	TARN-H	VER-V	
1	2	3	4	5	6	7	8	9	10	11	12	13	14	15	16	17	18	19	20	21

0 0
1 1
2 2 2
3 3 3
4 4 4
5 5
6 6 6
7 7 7
8 8 8
9 9 9

43 44 45

A Repertory face-off

In the July 1928 Homoeopathic Recorder, *Julia M. Green relates the following story:*
"I had great fun one evening giving these two teachers [Boger and Gladwin] a small group of symptoms of an acute case and watching them find the remedy by entirely different methods. Dr. Boger [using the Boenninghausen Repertory*] finished first and hit upon one remedy. Dr. Gladwin [using the* Kent Repertory*] came out with three remedies of which Dr. Boger's was one. She took these to the Materia Medica and decided on the same one Dr. Boger chose. Needless to say, it cured the patient promptly."*

The Boger *General Analysis and Card Repertory* was developed by Boger in 1931, and went through several editions. It consists of about 360 cards, usually furnished in a wooden box. Each card represents a rubric. If a remedy is indicated for the rubric, a hole is punched in the card in the appropriate place. To use it one simply pulls the cards for the rubrics in the case at hand, stacks them, and then look for the holes that go all the way through.

Since it is an eliminative repertory, the first card must be an accurate symptom of the case. Boger, in his book accompanying the cards, suggests the cards be used to find the general symptoms of the case, while the Kent *Repertory* be used to establish the case's specific symptoms.

One summer I brought my Boger *Card Repertory* with me to the NCH Summer School. Veterinarian Richard Pitcairn became very intrigued with it since, in animal practice, you are usually working with general symptoms. I made a copy of the booklet for him, and he converted it into a Hypercard stack for the Macintosh computer. Unfortunately, it is no longer available.

Boger's Electrical Potentizer

In the January 1929 *Homœopathic Survey* (a small journal published by the American Foundation for Homœopathy) mention was made of a method Boger used for changing a remedy's potency when it is still indicated, but no longer working:

"Electrical potencies made on a machine by Dr. Skiles of Chicago, constructed by Dr. Skiles' son. This is a machine making regular static discharges from positive to negative poles. At each pole, positive and negative, is a small cup of glass resting on a copper base— so thin it is really a film of copper, following the Leyden Jar idea. The copper cup holds the glass.

"Dr. Skiles uses the machine to make potencies of the patient's blood, carrying it to the 7th and 8th degree. I use it to extend the action of the high potencies; he has not used it in beginning potentization.

"When a patient continuously needs the same remedy and has gone through it in a series of potencies and then ceases to react to it, potentization of the higher potency is carried further by electrification in this static machine.

"The potentized remedy is placed in the positive cup and unmedicated sugar of milk is placed in the negative cup. Rotation is carried on to any number of electrical discharges desired. The potency from the positive pole is carried to the negative pole and stimulates the sugar of milk with the potency freshly activated through electrification. The remedy thus reactivated was *Rhus tox.* CM when the higher potency was exhausted, it was treated to 20 static electrical discharges. *Rhus* cm X20.

"When the desired number of strokes is made, the negative cup is emptied, washed, and exposed to sunlight.

"Dr. Boger has this machine in his office and personally operates it when in action so that he knows exactly what is being done…"

This is the only mention ever made of the machine. Its fate and whereabouts are unknown.

A visit to Boger

George H. Nitsche, MD, was a graduate of Hahnemann in Philadelphia in 1939. He told me how he, and two "older students" drove to Parkersburg, West Virginia to visit with Boger shortly before Boger's death. They had heard much about the man and wanted to meet him. They sat with Dr. Boger on his porch while Mrs. Boger served them lemonade. Nitsche didn't remember much of the time ("I was awed that I was really sitting with him!" he said). Boger urged them to continue their homœopathic studies.

Alas, when Nitsche graduated, he took his internship in Minnesota. There were few to discuss homœopathy with, and he felt like an outcast. Slowly he dropped homœopathy, and became a conventional practitioner.

When he sold me some of his old books in 1991, Dr. Nitsche expressed regret as to never making more of an effort to "use it." His "kit," a leather bag from B&T, contained 90 vials: 40 of the 30C, 40 of the 200C and ten others. He had used most of the Arnica, Arsenicum, Nux vomica, Phosphorus, Pulsatilla, *and* Silica. *The others remained unopened.*

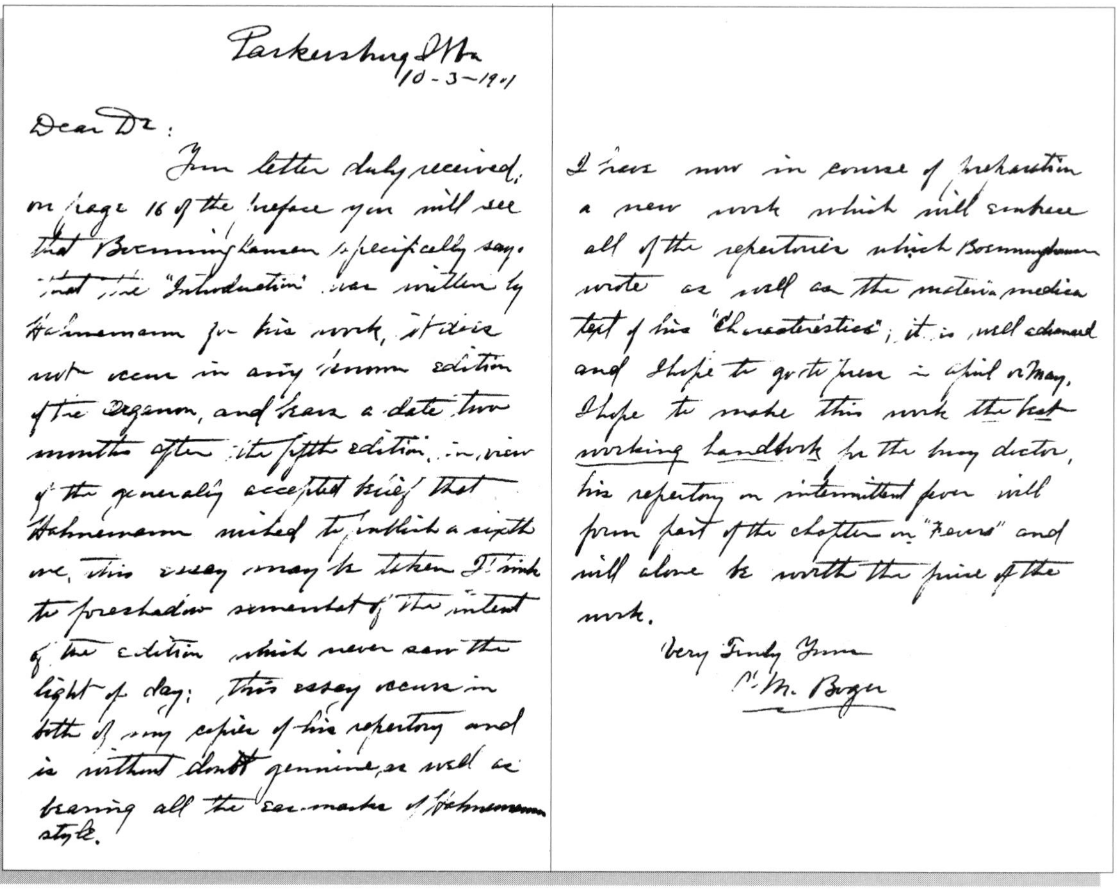

[Handwritten letter reproduced]

> Parkersburg W Va
> 10-3-1901
>
> Dear Dr:
>
> Your letter duly received, on page 16 of the preface you will see that Boenninghausen specifically says. that the "Introduction" was written by Hahnemann for his work, it did not occur in any known edition of the Organon, and has a date two months after its fifth edition. in view of the generally accepted belief that Hahnemann wished to publish a sixth one, this essay may be taken I think to foreshadow somewhat of the intent of the edition which never saw the light of day; this essay occurs in both of my copies of his repertory and is without doubt genuine, as well as bearing all the ear-marks of Hahnemann style.
>
> I have now in course of preparation a new work which will embrace all of the repertories which Boenninghausen wrote as well as the materia medica text of his "Characteristics"; it is well advanced and I hope to go to press in April or May, I hope to make this work the best working handbook for the busy doctor, his repertory on intermittent fever will form part of the chapter on "fevers" and will alone be worth the price of the work.
>
> Very Truly Yours
> C. M. Boger

Found in a book belonging to Edmund Carleton, of New York City:

10-3-1901
Dear Dr.
Your letter duly received. On page 16 of the preface you will see that Boenninghausen specifically says that the "Introduction" was written by Hahnemann for his work, it does not occur in any known edition of the Organon, and has a date two months after the 5th edition. In view of the generally accepted belief that Hahnemann wished to publish a sixth one, this essay may be taken I think to foreshadow somewhat of the intent of the edition which never saw the light of day; this essay occurs in both of my copies of his repertory and is without doubt genuine, as well as bearing the all the earmarks of Hahnemann style.
I have now in course of preparation a new book which will embrace all of the repertories which Boenninghausen wrote as well as the materia medica text of his "Characteristics;" it is well advanced and I hope to go to press in April or May. I hope to make this work the best working handbook for the busy doctor, his repertory on intermittent fever will form part of the chapter on "fevers" and will alone be worth the price of the work.
Very truly yours,
C. M. Boger

1925 –1940: The Final Blows

The move of the AMA in 1935
Strange bedfellows
The lack of clear vision

An Overview

By 1925 only two "homœopathic" schools remained. Some, like Boston University, convinced dropping enrollments were due to their "sectarian" nature, became allopathic in 1918. Others, like Iowa, and Michigan simply merged the allopathic and homœopathic departments into one.

Another factor in the schools' failures (both homœopathic and allopathic) was the severe money shortage. Between 1925 and 1929, even though schools were closing, several cities were trying to establish homœopathic hospitals. We read in the literature of planned homœopathic hospitals in Cleveland, Ohio, Portland, Oregon, and Chicago, Illinois. These efforts ceased with the financial crash that brought on the 1929 Great Depression. All schools were in financial dire straits, and the number of homœopaths in the United States was not sufficient to supply the funds for all that was needed.

Martin Kaufman, in his 1971 book, *Homeopathy in America: The Rise and Fall of a Medical Heresy*, suggested the difficulty in continuing the schools was caused by the internal dissension along the lines of the "high-low potency" split. He suggests that at the same time as the AIH was trying to increase the number of homœopathic schools, the Hahnemannians were "bitterly denouncing the quality of the education."

Kaufman says when the American Foundation started its course in 1922, it was "the first meaningful action intended to prevent the disappearance of the sect."

The Mid-West Homœopathic Hospital, Chicago. In February 1929, it was reported the building will cost $2 million and there was a "substantial sum in hand." There were no reports after that.

He then describes the program as a "total failure" unable to train enough practitioners to guarantee homœopathy's continued existence. He also sees the lack of AIH support for the Foundation's efforts a result of the Foundation being viewed as too conservative.

As we have seen, schools that the AIH were supporting were teaching little homœopathy, and the AIH was dominated by "half-homœopaths." Had the schools truly been teaching homœopathy and had their graduates been practicing homœopathy, then John B. Roberts, a president of the Philadelphia County Medical Society could not have said, in 1895, that there was so little difference between homœopathic and allopathic medicine that he regularly consulted with homœopaths. That he could not perceive the difference tells us a lot about the quality of the practice at the turn of the century.

As outlined in the next chapters, it was the American Foundation which maintained homœopathy in the United States. It was the few graduates of the AFH program who carried homœopathy into the future decades.

The move of the AMA in 1935

In 1935, the American Medical Association and the Council on Medical Education said they would not support "sectarian" institutions. New York Homœopathic Medical College became "New York Medical College" in order to maintain its "class A" rating as an AMA– approved medical school. Hospitals, whose titles included "homœopathic," dropped the word. Although the hospitals assured their homœopathic staff they would not be dropping homœopathy, it was gradually phased out and the hospitals fell under allopathic control.

A full list of homœopathic hospitals in each state can be found in **Appendix E** page 553.

In an editorial in the *Homœopathic Recorder*, January 1936, Herbert A. Roberts, MD, said:

"Since then [1900] one college after another has succumbed to the rigid requirements of a large paid all-time faculty, so that today there are but two colleges classed as homœopathic.

Camden Homœopathic Hospital, Camden, New Jersey

"These two have been rated by the American Medical Association as Class A, in that they meet all requirements of modern medical education. One of these colleges has an entrance class of 160 students, the other, 115 . These colleges have become so engrossed in teaching the fundamentals of medicine that they have failed to put their emphasis upon the teaching of homœopathic philosophy, materia medica and therapeutics, with the result that only a very small percentage of the graduates attempt to practice homœopathy at all; and soon, through association with hospitals and medical societies of the dominant school, they find it easier and more convenient to adopt that form of practice.

"The action of the Council on Medical Education and Hospitals of the dominant school of medicine, on September 15, is directed to putting an end to the teaching of any homœopathy in these two remaining colleges." [Hahnemann, Philadelphia and New York Homœopathic].

'According to the minutes, the survey of American medical schools so far revealed certain significant weaknesses; namely:

'There is a tendency for medical schools to enlarge their enrollment without a corresponding increase in personnel or instructional facilities;

'With a growing appreciation of the necessity for an intimate correlation between clinical and laboratory knowledge, it is evident that this can be obtained only by increasingly close contact between preclinical and clinical departments continuously maintained from the time the student first enters the medical school until he graduates;

'The advances of the medical sciences have been and should be independent of any sectarian point of view, and medical education should not be handicapped or directed by a dogmatic attitude toward disease;

'For these reasons, the Council took the following action:

'(a) Resolved, That in each medical school the number of students should not exceed the number that can be adequately taught with the laboratory library and clinical facilities available and for whom a sufficiently large and competent teaching staff is provided.

'(b) Resolved, That after July 1, 1938 the Council on Medical Education and Hospitals will no longer publish a list of approved two-year medical schools.

'(c) Resolved, That after July 1, 1938, the Council on Medical Education and Hospitals will no longer carry on its approved list schools of sectarian medicine.'

— *Journal of the American Medical Association,*
   October 5, 1935

Reading Homœopathic Hospital,
Reading, Pennsylvania

"This causes us to ponder if it be not better to let the vastly expensive teaching of medicine be done by the 'regular' colleges and we, as homœopaths, devote our time and energy to the study of homœopathy as a postgraduate course. With the vast sums these colleges have at their disposal thorough homœopathic training courses could be developed at a Master's degree given in homœopathic practice.

"In this country The American Foundation for Homœopathy has a summer training course of six weeks; this is the only place where homœopathy is taught so that a student becomes equipped to really practice homœopathy. It is the only place where a student learns how to practice homœopathy so that he is not almost forced to revert to ordinary medical procedures simply because he has not the basic knowledge or appreciation of the curative possibilities of homœopathic therapeutics...

"...The principles of homœopathy are indestructible, and will last; but it is our duty to preserve an active application of homœopathy in as pure a form as possible for those who come after us... So far, with the single exception of the Foundation work, the teaching of homœopathy in this country is a matter of individual contacts, for while modern medical education (even in the homœopathic colleges) has sought to eliminate preceptorships, they have offered no substitute, and homœopathy, the method of prescribing for the individual, is best taught by individual attention, in small groups."

Ann Arbor Homœopathic Hospital, Ann Arbor, Michigan

Strange bedfellows

When the Social Security Act was passed by the Roosevelt administration in 1935, the threat it might have been to the medical establishment was perceived by the American Medical Association as an imminent danger. The fear of "socialized medicine" was very real to the conservative medical profession who were wary of any incursion into traditional "American freedoms."

For all their differences, homœopathic physicians were as conservative as their conventional colleagues.

Lucy Stone Herzog, MD, an 1891 graduate of Cleveland, attempted to form a "united front" with the AMA, which she called the "saviour of American medicine." In an article in the *Journal of the American Institute of Homeopathy* in August, 1937, she said "organized medicine must hold control of medical work, not lay-reformers and politicians."

At the 1939 AIH general meeting, Daniel Ferguson, MD, said the moment medicine is socialized anything in our daily lives could be socialized.

A national committee was formed to liaise with the AMA to protect medical profession interests.

In the March 1940 *Journal of the AIH*, Herzog reported the "homœopathic school has joined the dominant school in a united front for the duration of the war against regimentation of the medical profession and to prevent socialized medicine." During this time almost every issue of the *Journal of the AIH* had a letter or article by Lucy Stone Herzog.

In retrospect, the fears were unfounded. Not much came of the joint committee, other than provisional acceptance by the AMA in recognizing homœopaths, and a desire of many homœopaths to forge links between the two schools.

The lack of clear vision

As I look through the editorials in all the homœopathic journals from 1890 on, I am struck by the sameness of the message and I am amazed those in the homœopathic movement had neither the slightest comprehension of the political power of conventional medicine and the drug companies, nor the understanding of the seductive nature of the conventional medical model.

When the German coal-tar pharmaceuticals and aspirin came along, the homœopaths saw the dangers and said, "Give them time, and the allopaths will see the dangers too." They didn't.

After the 1918 flu epidemic came and went the figures spoke for themselves. Allopathic death rates were often as high as 30%, while homœopathic rates were 1%. The homœopaths said, "They will see what we have." They didn't.

Then the vaccine therapies made their play. The homœopaths said, "They will see the folly of their ways and seek us out." They didn't.

Then Sulfanilamide comes along which kills enough people to become the impetus for stricter government drug regulation, as embodied in the FDA Legislation of 1938. The homœopaths said, "Well, now, they will finally understand." They didn't.

The February 1928 *Jottings* reported that medical investigators found a dose of botulinum toxoid equivalent to a 22X (or an 11c) was able to kill mice. "Homœopathy will soon be discovered by the AMA if they extend their medical investigations far enough." It wasn't.

A few months later a similar experiment was reported. Said the *Jottings'* editor, "Scientific medicine is most surely accepting the power of minute doses." They weren't.

In November 1929, *Jottings* reported a director in the New York Department of Health isolated eleven distinct pneumococcus that could cause pneumonia and suggested each needed a different medicine to treat it. "Again our friends the allopaths are catching up with homœopathy, and are blind to the fact that homœopathy blazed the trail they are following." They were.

We are still facing an amazingly frustrating scenario.

We show it to them and they don't see. A patient, given up as "terminal," comes back alive. "I used homœopathy," she says. "Spontaneous remission," says the physician. Another patient, cured of her allopathically "untreatable" illness, returns to the specialist. Re-doing tests and x-rays, the previous illness is gone. Says the specialist, "It must have been a mis–diagnosis. What you had was not curable."

In discussing this phenomenon with Harris Coulter, Harris re-stated what he clearly says in his Volume IV of *Divided Legacy*; The piece of homœopathy that is most threatening to the conventional model is neither the idea of similars nor the idea of infinitesimal but, rather, the idea that the therapy must be individualized for each case and the homœopaths have a *methodology* for doing this. "The idea that there are not a finite number of illnesses makes them crazy," said Coulter.

A physician once told me there are two kinds of folks in the world— those who experience and draw conclusions from the experiences, and those who draw conclusions and only experience that which supports those conclusions.

The rejection of homœopathy and the principle of similars is as old as homœopathy itself.

1930 –1940: Those Who Kept It Alive

Rudolph Rabe
H. A. Roberts
Royal E. S. Hayes
Alfred Pulford

While schools were closing, Hahnemann's homœopathy was kept alive by members of the IHA. The class of 1896 from New York Homœopathic College graduated both Rudolph Rabe and H. A. Roberts, who became master prescribers and leaders within the IHA. The IHA was blessed with men like Royal E. S. Hayes, of Connecticut, and Alfred Pulford, of Toledo, Ohio, both of whom were exceptional clinicians and wonderful writers. These people's words speak clearly and show us homœopathy's status during those dark years.

Rudolph F. Rabe, MD
January 18, 1872 — March 18, 1952

Rudolph Rabe received his education at Columbia College and his MD from New York Homœopathic in 1896. After graduation he spent a year at the University of Berlin. He taught materia medica at New York Homœopathic from 1904 to 1930.

Rabe practiced in New Jersey. "He was gifted with a marvelous memory; he seemed never to forget a remedy and its symptoms— an encyclopedia of materia medica… his skill in the use of remedies was astonishing, often seemingly miraculous. In listening to a patient's story he soon pounced upon the unusual, outstanding or peculiar aspects of the case, very quickly choosing the correct remedy."

Rabe served as IHA president in 1908, and was the editor of the *Homœopathic Recorder* after E. P. Anshutz.

He was a brilliant writer, with a sharp pen and mind that got to the heart of the issues. He was one of the last of the "old guard."

"Courting the Old School"

Rabe's eloquent essay is filled with images and metaphors. He clearly saw the demise of homœopathy, and placed the blame squarely on the shoulders of the homœopathic profession itself and to those who "fawn" and "curry favor" with the dominant school to the detriment of their own.

He was 44 years old when he penned this piece and lived to see his fears play out. Four years after he wrote this, his position as instructor of materia medica at New York Homœopathic was abolished.

"Homœopaths, early in their efforts to convince established medicine of the truth of their principles, were by the force of circumstances compelled to be sectarian. Sectarianism was not therefore, of our own choosing and its sin, if such it be, should not be laid at their door. Ostracism, both social and professional, was suffered by the pioneers, to a degree, be it said, which is quite unknown today, except in a few perhaps, of the English provinces. In America, all this bigoted persecution has happily long since passed away, but in its place has come a spirit of easy tolerance and fraternization which, though agreeable when superficially looked at, does not necessarily denote the acceptance by established medicine, of the principles of homœopathy.

"Organized homœopathy has, especially in the past, accomplished many things to its advantage and credit, such as for example, the control of certain state insane and other hospitals and the establishment of separate examining boards in various states in the Union; these boards however, have of late either disappeared altogether or have had their powers so curtailed by legislative or other enactments that, so far as homœopathy is concerned, their influence is practically negative.

"New York State is a glaring example of this nullification of all homœopathic interest and advantage, for although the licensing board contains one or two homœopaths among its members, these men have no opportunity to do anything constructive for homœopathy itself. The State Board of Regents does not require of candidates for license to practice medicine, an examination in materia medica, hence, so far as the board is concerned, or the State which it represents, it is a matter of indifference whether a candidate be from the colleges of the old school or of homœopathic persuasion. Sectarianism is thus broken down, in itself a good thing, but with its abolition comes the real danger of a loss of interest in the tenets of the homœopathic school. Hence it is, that in keeping with the spirit of catholicism in medicine, but two homœopathic colleges remain and numerous homœopathic hospitals have lost their pristine homœopathic characteristics. In its laudable desire to convince orthodox medicine of its right to exist and of its educational and professional equality, organized

Shortly before he died, I had a chance to visit with Joseph Kaplowe, MD, of New Haven, Connecticut. Kaplowe had been an active member of the IHA through the 1950s, and a perennial contributor to the Homœopathic Recorder. *After talking for a while, he said, "Can I ask you a question?" and asked, "Why did the schools close up?" I told him about the situation as I had understood it. He shook his head. "I just don't understand it," he said. "I went away for the summer and I came back to finish my fourth year at New York Homœopathic. When I got back, half the faculty were gone— all the people who had taught us homœopathy. I asked, 'Where are Dr. Stearns and Dr. Rabe?' And they said, 'We are not teaching that any more.' And that was the end of the homœopathic instruction."*

Kaplowe graduated in 1930— so it seems the last year for homœopathic instruction at New York Homœopathic was 1929. Yet, the school continued to advertise as a "homœopathic school" into the early 1940s.

homœopathy stands so erect, that it is in imminent danger of falling over backwards.

"We in these United States, dearly love noise and show and are given to hysterical fervor and exuberance, almost on a par with the old-time Methodist camp meeting; we are fond of fooling ourselves and of being fooled and thus exhibit a naiveté which for the foreigner at least, is difficult to understand. We invite to our national medical conclaves and banquets, men prominent in the professional and office life of the old school and then pat ourselves vigorously on the back, for the glory of our achievement.

"But do we really achieve anything worthwhile by these press-agent methods? Does all this diplomatic tomfoolery bring us anywhere? We doubt it and look in vain for evidence. Has any Old School college seriously taken up the study and investigation of homœopathy? If so, we have not heard of it. On the contrary, the juggernaut of established medicine continues to roll relentlessly on and to flatten out all doctrinal differences. In keeping with every other department of American national life, we are undergoing a process of standardization, which is killing all individuality.

"We have become 'good fellows,' who applaud vociferously every compliment thrown at us, but in our eager running after the glittering chariots of the old school, are divesting ourselves more and more of such shreds of principle as are left to us. The end is easy to foretell, unless we bestir ourselves at once and engage in a campaign, the object of which shall be the demonstration and acceptance of homœopathic principles.

"Organized homœopathy now represents itself, too often by means of the methods of the three-ringed circus; the tail is wagging the dog and the poor hybrid is threatened with an incurable palsy. Perhaps we would do well to study the progress of homœopathy in Germany, where chairs have been established in two universities; perhaps the German methods of thoroughness and devotion to principle, can be copied with advantage to ourselves. If so, by all means let us adopt them; but in any event, let us cast aside the ridiculous camouflage which deceives no one, not even the professional booster from the precincts of Babbitry.'

— R.F. Rabe, *The Homœopathic Recorder*, September, 1926

Herbert A. Roberts, MD
May 7, 1868 — October 13, 1950

After graduating from New York Homœopathic, Roberts practiced for a short time in Brattleboro, Vermont and then moved to Connecticut and established a practice in Derby.

He served as a first lieutenant in the United States Army during World War I, working as a medical officer on the troop ships. The story was told that another ship had so many casualties during the 1918 flu epidemic that it came alongside to take the extra coffins from Roberts' ship. Upon returning to port the medical examiner said to Roberts, "Used all your coffins?" To which Roberts replied, "Yes, and didn't lose a single man!"

Roberts was IHA president in 1923 and editor of the *Homœopathic Recorder* from 1927 to 1934.

He wrote *The Study of Remedies by Comparison, The Rheumatic Remedies,* and the classic *The Principles and Art of Cure by Homœopathy.* Within the *IHA Transactions* and *The Homœopathic Recorder,* he had penned 117 articles and 27 editorials.

When a patient said, "Doctor, I should think you doctors would get everlastingly tired of diagnosing cases and treating the same old diseases, day after day, year in and year out," Roberts responded by saying that no two cases are alike and "the individuality is part at least of the spice of medical life, which gives it variety enough to flavor it." He then summed it up in an article in the July 1926 *Homœopathic Recorder* called "Monotony," in which he presented a number of different cases— all of which needed the same remedy, and a number of similar cases— all of which needed different remedies.

Said his pupil, Allan Sutherland, "A completely modest man, no activity was ever undertaken with the thought of personal gain or self-aggrandizement. Long hours of research, writing, and teaching in the midst of a busy practice were cheerfully and unhesitatingly given to the end that homœopathy might be strengthened and its principles better understood… No homœopath of this generation was more greatly venerated and respected."

Was the eventual brilliance of Rabe and Roberts seen when they were students? We will never know. Did their classmates William Boies from Knoxville, Tennessee, or Frank Gale from Winchester, New Hampshire ever become quality homœopaths? Of the 30 in the class, 20 were listed in the 1925 Directory of Practitioners, and 14 were still listed in the 1941 Directory. William Boies is listed in both references. Frank Gale is in neither.

Royal Elmore Swift Hayes, MD
October 20, 1871 — July 20, 1952

Hayes graduated from the New York Eclectic Medical College in 1898. He was an early IHA member becoming president in 1926. He was a prolific writer, with a sharp wit, and a barbed pen. Although he never wrote any books, he contributed over 130 articles to the *Homœopathic Recorder* and the *Transactions of the IHA*. He also wrote for the *Journal of the AIH*. He was a prover of *Aduaxakah* and of *Erigeron*. Hayes was an uncompromising homœopath, as can be seen in his writing. He was one of the generation who was personally acquainted with Kent.

His grandson remembers how fast he drove his Pierce Arrow. Stopped by a policeman on a motorcycle, he was asked, "Doc, do you know how fast you were going?" He replied, "No faster than you were!"

He had a constant flow of patients. If they could not afford to pay cash, they gave him food or other items of barter. Said his grandson, "He never refused to treat anyone in need."

He insisted his family drink the spring water from the five gallon jug and not the chlorinated water from the tap. He peeled all fruit to avoid pesticides.

Hayes loved music to a degree that he almost became a musician rather than a physician. He owned three Mason and Hamlin pianos— an upright in the downstairs dining room, a large grand in the upstairs sitting room, and one which he gave his daughter— so he could play when he visited her. Often after visiting hours, he would play the piano; Chopin and Grieg were his favorites.

His daughter married a man of Italian descent. Hayes found he loved the language and learned it well enough to read Italian works.

He practiced in Waterbury, Connecticut.

The Pen of Royal E. S. Hayes

Homœopathy and materialism

"I would like to offer a little criticism concerning the status of homœopathy as an art and science in general and organized homœopathy in particular. There is an influential and able element in our school who seem to persist in trying to reduce homœopathy to a material science. They break out in a cold sweat whenever a little hole in the clouds of materialism appears and keep close to the consoling arms of medical science.

"Now I believe that we should not only perceive but admit that homœopathy is not a material science. No more than one would attempt to put a whole cow into a can for corned beef. The basis of homœopathy in so far as is material does, indeed, conform to the principles of science, but its theory is philosophical, and its practice is cognitive."

— R. E. S. Hayes, Presidential Address to the International Hahnemannian Association, 1926

Homœopathy and Science

"To come nearer home we fear that even homœopaths may be infected with a mild strain of the bacteria of 'approved' science. Even when some who need modern science least, who know without it what they are doing and how to do it show mild symptoms of the scientific tradition and it seems to disturb their self-evaluation centers… They seem to be always desiring to placate the terrible allopath; or they try so hard to be understood by him, to teach him our language by speaking his own or a mongrel language composed of the two; he must be convinced by imposing on the beautiful art of homœopathy the strictures of scientific method, as if the allopath were really scientific at all! The type of mind which homœopathy needs and which is susceptible to homœopathy is not the type which waits to be told by science or some authority what to do. The right minds for homœopathy will be attracted by the vision of it, by the spirit of adventure in the realm of principles and potentials. Trying to capture the modern scientist on his own level of practicality is a slippery enterprise. By lowering the price we are transferring an inferior grade of goods both ways.

"Solely as a means of demonstrating the truth of homœopathy the scientific method is superfluous. From the scientific viewpoint the procedure must be quite susceptible to both scientific and technical criticism; from an aesthetic viewpoint of homœopathy criticism is inevitable until science itself becomes aesthetic."

— R. E. S. Hayes, "Science" vs. Medical Sense, *Homœopathic Recorder*, July 1929

"Incompetent homœopathy is the millstone under which the school is staggering to its doom."
— R. E. S. Hayes, *Homœopathic Recorder*, April 1949

The Faces of Homœopathy

Will we get new homœopaths?

Hayes was 78 years old when he wrote this; a master homœopath, watching homœopathy wither.

"Other excellent criticisms of our brain-petrifying methods have appeared. About the most nail-on-the-head statement of the stultifying effect of these conditions of modern society is that of Dr. George S. Stevenson, President of The American Psychiatric Association. According to the Medical Times *for July, 1948, he says: 'Our public practices and other phases of our culture are too much guided by the capacity and requirements of the mentally deficient. The better elements of the community actually have imposed upon themselves regulations that are appropriate only to the mentally deficient. The social stage is wonderfully set for the purposes of politicians than for our worthwhile citizenry.'*

How then is homœopathy to gain many recruits? We should not expect them at present. The best we can do is to hold at all costs the little privilege that remains and cooperate with others who will support it and gain what little we can. When a more free and enlightened society can rear enough independent minds and wills they will raise homœopathy to its rightful office of cultivating sound minds and bodies.

"As to accounting or allocating these human shortcomings, we are not without a few interesting reservatories in our own camp. But that will be a captivating subject for a future writing— don't you think? It might reveal a little more about the downfall of homœopathy."

— R. E. S. Hayes
Homœopathic Recorder, 1949

In an address to the Connecticut Homœopathic Society in 1951, Hayes reviews his 50 years in practice, spanning the first half of the 20th century. He paints a clear picture of what "homœopathic" was at the turn of the century.

"When I joined this Society, in 1904 I think it was, only one member was able to cope with chronic disease, improve constitutions or deal homœopathically with severe crises. He was the only one, I believe, who was proficient in repertory work or possessed anything that could be assessed as a sufficient homœopathic library. There may have been one or two exceptions to this, members who did not appear at the meetings; and it will be a pleasure to be corrected on this point, if possible. Very few knew what it was all about at all. To be sure they knew there was such a thing as *Aconite* and *Belladonna*, to be given every fifteen minutes, together or alternately, and a few other procedures of like latitude. When a homœopathic remedy was used it was almost certain to be 1X to 6X. The 12th was high and the 30th had no medicine at all. But there were a lot of combination tablets, laxatives and sedatives to be seen on the shelves. Thanks to the rudimentary sanitation of those years, there was more acute disease so that a few remedies survived the dark years of homœopathic comprehension and eventually created an increasing demand for others.

"But at that time, not only was straight prescribing and the single remedy not adhered to, such supposed lunacy was tabooed and even booed. Once, when an orthodox member reported his remarkable cures, another member jumped to his feet and shouted out, 'He should be kicked out of the Society,' and the emphasis on 'kicked' was terrific!… Soon after I joined, another who understood homœopathy came into the Society, then a third who had pierced the fog. There was one very active member of the leadership type who had three stock questions which he always asked when a high potency hit was mentioned. They were: 1) 'Was there any medicine in the prescription?' 2) 'How do you know it was the medicine that cured,' and 3) 'Would not the patient have recovered without any medicine?' But the lady member was Scotch and she had a keen and lively sense of humor and appreciation of human nature. She metaphorically picked up his honor and sat him down plumb in a back seat. This act was repeated three times or so until it finally died a natural death. I am sorry that I cannot recall just what her answers were. But never was there in lady's eye a merrier, keener twinkle than whenever this particular gentleman would appear on the scene.

"There was a maxim current in those days that there was no matter in potencies above the 12th, the inference being, of course, that the attempt to use anything higher was fanatical. Some writers did recommend the 12th in certain cases, but apparently it was a demonstration of courage such as balancing oneself on the edge of a precipice. After a while, some genius had demonstrated a state of matter in the 30th. This was supposed to be proof that after all there was something in homœopathy. So, as the years rolled by, the more daring were coaxed into using the 200th and today even mention of the CM brings forth no audible snorts.

"While this was going on, perhaps to the lasting benefit of our art, our institutions were gradually 'fading away.' I mean really fading away. As you know, the external cause of this was pharmacal and medical monopoly in collusion with bureaucratic prerogatives. But ten times more ominous were the internal causes, that is, lack of understanding, fear of disapprobation, appeasement on the part of some, and the serenity and content of the purists. It was almost fatal. Many went over to the conventional caste and the ones tied to hospitals, asylums, clinics and colleges were too few to cope with the external pressure and infiltration. But the loss shocked the remnant into renewed efforts to improve their own therapy and homœopathic standing, so that now we have proportionately more real homœopathic practice with a minimal contingent than we had fifty years ago with a large one."

Royal E. S. Hayes in his office, circa 1945

Question:
When is it justifiable to prescribe for single symptoms or group of symptoms in homœopathy?
Answer:
a. When emergency demands the venture.
b. When the vital energy is past redemption.
c. When the symptom is a strong general as well as characteristic if no other considerations forbid.
d. When you expect never to see the patient again.

— R. E. S. Hayes, "Carriwitchets" *Homœopathic Recorder,* October 1929

One Hundred Emergency Shots

Through the years, Hayes wrote a series called "One Hundred Emergency Shots." Hailed as "examples of intuitive prescribing," Dr. Allen Sutherland compared them to E. E. Case's *Clinical Experiences.* The first series appeared in 1914, and was reprinted twice in the *Homœopathic Recorder*— once in 1933 and again in 1956. The few cases below are but samples.

By way of an introduction, Hayes says (in his best tongue in cheek style):

"While attending a homœopathic meeting some time ago I heard a group of members discuss the question, 'How do you give your morphine?' These reports illustrate the best way to give morphine and some other things."

Uremic Convulsions

Three weeks after parturition a woman has uremic convulsions and coma. No description was obtainable except than she screamed violently after each convulsion, then lapsed into several hours of coma. Cured in a half an hour after a dose of *Hyoscyamus* 1M.

Broncheopyra

A woman of 45 jumped suddenly from bed at night in terror with a dry barking cough that threatened to strangle her, she thought. Flushed face, hot perspiration, faintness, craved air, sat on bed acting as if strangling, though she was inhaling plenty of air. Improved at once with a dose of *Pulsatilla* CM.

Renal Colic

A physician with the name of Hayes laughed to himself as usual when he dropped into bed at night, but the smile was inverted when he became doubled up with a gravellous pain in the right groin. With some mechanical and visual difficulty the symptoms were located under *Natrum muriaticum* and a dose of the 1M provided a night's rest. Activity and exposure to cold weather prevented a complete cure, however, and a couple of days later the condition was as bad as first. Then a doctor friend called and in his tenderness of heart said, "Now doctor, you ought not to suffer this way, let me give you a little morphine." Said I, "Please go into my office and fetch out my remedy." In about three minutes he brought out *Hydrastis* 2M and I have had no return of the trouble from that day to this. The keynote was "Dull dragging in the right groin, with cutting sensation extending to the right testicle." That prescription alone was worth the price of Kent's *Repertory* and the *Guiding Symptoms.*

Alfred Pulford, MD
May 4, 1863 — August 4, 1948

Alfred Pulford was born in Bradford, England and went to the United States when he was 16. He graduated from Cleveland Homœopathic Medical College in 1885, serving his internship at Pittsburgh (Pennsylvania) Homœopathic Hospital.

He was a prolific writer, having more than 100 articles appearing in the *IHA Transactions* and *Homœopathic Recorder*. With his son, Dayton T. Pulford, he authored two books: *The Homœopathic Materia Medica of Graphic Drug Pictures and Clinical Comments*, and *Homœopathic Leaders in Pneumonia*. He joined the IHA in 1924, and practiced with his son in Toledo, Ohio.

The Pen of Alfred Pulford

"No musician ever became an expert by merely learning to play a simple tune, ignoring the rudiments of the art; no painter ever became a great artist who tried to paint without first learning the art of mixing paints and blending colors, and neither student nor doctor can ever hope to become a real homœopath who does not acquaint himself with the base and principles upon which homœopathy is built and stands— The *Organon*. This omission, by the majority of the homœopathic profession, is the reason that homœopathy is today largely represented by men who do not understand what homœopathy really means. After the *Organon* has been read thinkingly and intelligently, all those things not clearly understood will be brought to a clearer perception by reading a good work on homœopathic philosophy, of which Kent's stands out the most prominently. This intelligently read and understood, we are then in a position to take up the study of materia medica. As an introduction to the passageway of this vast subject Kent's *Lectures on Materia Medica* stands out most prominently, and gives the best exposition of how to study the remedy, elucidating its diverse actions, characteristics and comparisons. Next in importance, we would consider *Bell on Diarrhea*, etc., which will give a clear idea of how to select and apply the remedy. Once all those are mastered you have the beginning of how to gain a clear conception of homœopathy and how to select and apply the individual remedy, after which the rest will come comparatively easy.

"One can never truly enter the homœopathic field successfully who has not the desire and the will to divorce himself from modern medicine. Intelligence dwells in refinement; ignorance, in crudity. Homœopathy is the personification of refinement. Everyone who has studied homœopathy properly and practiced it strictly has been more than amply rewarded for his efforts, and swears by it. The rest swear at it."

— Alfred Pulford, editorial in *Homœopathic Recorder*, April 1930

Alfred Pulford, M.D.

"I have been accused of wielding a trenchant pen, of being dogmatic, and of being a grouch. If I appeared so, it is not because I love my fellow members less, but because I love homœopathy more. It is because homœopathy represents the truth, therefore does not need especial legislation to sustain it. My efforts have been spent in trying to have my fellow practitioners see the light, to goad them on to see the value of the most wonderful and most magnificent gem that was ever given to the medical world. I wanted you to see it and appreciate it; to know it as I know it."

—Alfred Pulford, last editorial
Homœopathic Recorder, June 1932

Potency selection

"The selection of the potency is even more of an art than the selection of the remedy. In truth only intelligent men should practice homœopathy; all others drift naturally into allopathy where brains and the ability to think, and think deeply, are not so much needed."

— Alfred Pulford, "Potency– its selection"
Homœopathic Recorder, August 1929

Reasons

"It is my steadfast opinion that the real raison d'être of medicine is the restoration of health or normal state to the sick. But most of us, especially our allopathic brethren seem to feel that the field of medicine is a mere playground; the sense of sacredness of human life seems to have been lost, or as if life was at such low ebb as to be of little value. The profession seems to be more concerned with theorization and dangerous experimentation even in some instances to the extent of satisfying a morbid or idle curiosity than either the restoration of health or in the perfecting of a definite plan to gain that end. To date homœopathy is the only method so far discovered that would lead us to that goal."

— Alfred Pulford, "Pointers"
Homœopathic Recorder, July 1928

Modern Homœopathy

Professor August Bier, of Berlin, presented a paper in 1925 called "What Shall Be Our Attitude about Homœopathy?" The paper was translated and printed in the *Homœopathic Recorder* in 1926. Professor Bier suggests homœopathy be investigated and then incorporated into regular medical education as a system of therapeutics. This is Pulford's response:

"In reviewing excerpts from the pen of Prof. Bier on homœopathy, I came across this: 'My advice is: If we come to an understanding with the scientific homœopaths, if we tolerate the honest fanatics among their ranks then homœopathy will be enabled to shake off its objectionable entourage.'

"As to just whom Dr. Bier considers 'scientific homœopaths,' and to just whom he applies the opprobrium 'honest fanatic,' he diplomatically leaves us in doubt. The so-called 'modern homœopath' in this country considers himself the only real 'scientific homœopath,' and the Hahnemannian the 'fanatic.' The truth of the matter is that the Hahnemannian is the only real scientific homœopath. There is positively no other. The truth is that the 'modern homœopath' knows very little, if anything, about homœopathy, which is fully attested by the fact that homœopathy's prestige in these United States has shrunken over 50% in the past 40 years. And furthermore, if he knew anything about it he would practice it, for it is more profitable to do so.

"If Dr. Bier classes the true Hahnemannian as, what they really are, the real scientific homœopath, then whom does he consider the 'honest fanatics?' If homœopathy should decide to cast off its 'objectionable entourage' it would have scarcely 100 adherents in these United States. I sincerely doubt if there are 100 doctors in America practicing homœopathy. The rest are all practicing a form of hybrid homœopathy tinctured more or less, principally more, with some phase of allopathy, as they firmly believe there is nothing scientific outside of allopathy.

"Just how much science there is in allopathy was well stated by a recent ex-President of the New York State Medical Society who is reported to have said in his presidential address: 'What we call the science of medicine is a most variable and unstable affair, constantly changing and constantly to change. Today we are justly proud of the body of scientific medicine. If we could live into the next generation, we should be ashamed of it.' It is natural that ignorance should follow ignorance, therefore ignorance of homœopathy follows the ever changing ignorance of allopathy."

— Alfred Pulford, Letter, *Homœopathic Recorder*, July 1932

The 1940s: The Final Closings

The last school

By the late 1940s, Hahnemann Medical College, the only school ostensibly teaching homœopathy after 1940, was in disarray. There were internal differences between the board of trustees and the faculty, with hard and heavy politics being played. The trustees, seeing an inadequate funding base, mandated more students be admitted. With more students, it became harder to teach at the levels required and scholastic standards fell. Some graduates were unable to pass their licensing exams.

In 1945, as soon as the pressure to supply physicians for the war eased, the American Association of Medical Colleges and the American Medical Association Council on Medical Education notified Hahnemann that it was being put on probation. Teaching of homœopathy did not help its probationary standing.

The 1947 yearbook of the Hahnemann Medical College in Philadelphia, *The Medic,* had on the first page a large picture of Samuel Hahnemann. At the back it had a four-page school history, including pictures of the founders—Constantine Hering, MD and Walter Williamson, MD. It was a last gasp. In 1947, the faculty and trustees voted to make homœopathy an elective course. It became a single course, taught by a single teacher, Garth Boericke.

The "Garth W. Boericke Society" was founded in 1936 as the organization for students who were specifically interested in homœopathy. In 1945 it was re-named the "Undergraduate Research Society."

In 1949, the probation was lifted, and Hahnemann Medical College divested itself of homœopathy. In 1949, the inside front cover of *The Medic* had a picture of Oliver Wendell Holmes, MD, reading his treatise on contagion of puerperal fever in 1843. A year earlier Holmes had written *Homœopathy and Kindred Delusions,* one of the major attacks on homœopathy that is still quoted today. The 1949 Yearbook is dedicated to "those men who have hewed from the surrounding forest of prejudice, superstition, medical and religious dogma, and the inertia of tradition a clear straight path of truth." And in a light type face are the

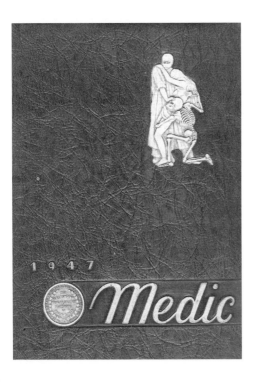

very names of those people: Aesclepius, Hippocrates, Herophyllus, Vesalius, Harvey, Van Leeuwenhoek, Hunter, Jenner, Holmes, Osler, Banting, Fleming. Who is missing? The very person the school is named after, Samuel Hahnemann.

Said one student, "Antibiotics came in and homœopathy went out." The school was completely reorganized with a heavy emphasis on research. Garth Boericke, certainly not a young man on the cutting edge of things, could not keep up with the language and modes of the research-oriented school, nor was *his* research viewed as valuable.

By 1950, the school, whose diplomas were granted for both an MD and an HMD, ceased offering the HMD degree. In 1958 the department of therapeutics, the only link left to homœopathy, was re-named the department of clinical pharmacology. The homœopathic pharmacy was "disposed of," along with almost all the homœopathic books remaining in the medical college library.

The new dean, Charles Cameron (a Hahnemann graduate of 1935), suggested the school name be changed because "Hahnemann" was too intimately connected with homœopathy and sectarian medicine. The name was eventually dropped in 1997.

All along there were those who thought, somehow, it might be possible to retain whatever vestige of homœopathy there was at Hahnemann, and by doing so retain some amount of legitimacy for the practice. By 1950 it was becoming clear that such a vision was indeed a chimera. When Boericke retired in 1959, homœopathy at the medical school in Philadelphia went with him.

An editorial in the *Journal of the American Institute of Homeopathy* in February 1957, speaks of the time:

> "Hahnemann was 'put on probation.' The resultant upheaval brought about a complete reorganization of its teaching program which eventually got Hahnemann 'off the hook,' but resulted disastrously for homœopathy... but homœopathy cannot exist without practitioners. In essence, homœopathy in this country received its death blow when Hahnemann 'got off the hook.'"

The early 1980s were a time of renewed interest in alternative medical therapies. Since Hahnemann had been the seat of the "original" alternative, the new president Bertram Brown (1983-1987) was curious to find out if any of the faculty were interested in homœopathy. Instead of asking directly, he simply placed some books on homœopathy on his desk and waited for comments when he had individual meetings with faculty and the department heads.

He reported that, to a person, everyone had looked at the books and expressed curiosity about why he was even looking at them and derision about the practice of homœopathy.

When the local homœopathic laymen's league was looking for a venue in the early 1980s for a two–day seminar, they approached Hahnemann. Although rooms were generally available for outside functions, the request was turned down and the group was told it would "not be appropriate" to have a homœopathic seminar at the school.

Garth Boericke and his father,
William Boericke, circa 1927

John A. Borneman, Jr. told me of cleaning out Boericke's office when the homœopathic program was finally closed at Hahnemann. "I found many bottles, all labeled 'tincture' but none had any color in them. He obviously topped them up with alcohol when they got low. Who knew what potency they were?"

Garth Wilkinson Boericke, MD
August 12, 1893 — January 8, 1968

Named for Garth Wilkinson, the British homœopath and Swedenborgian who introduced *Hecla Lava* into the materia medica, Boericke, a native of California, graduated from the University of Michigan at Ann Arbor in 1918. He taught at Michigan for two years, returned to California as an assistant clinical professor of homœopathy, then moved to Philadelphia, Pennsylvania, when he was appointed professor of materia medica and special therapeutics at the Hahnemann College. He held the position until he retired in 1959.

While at Hahnemann he worked in the Hering Research Laboratory with Rudolph Smith. He developed a lipid flocculation test (along the lines of that described by George Russell Henshaw, MD) and did the first work in observing liquid serial dilutions using magnetic nuclear resonance.

He was a president of the American Institute of Homeopathy, and taught materia medica at the American Foundation postgraduate school.

"Dr. Garth Boericke may well have been called the 'best known man on the faculty.' For four years he had lectured to us on the subjects of Homœopathy, Pharmacology, Materia Medica, and Therapeutics. Surely there is not an alumnus living who can forget his 'preambles' and his 'fourth class determinative symptoms.' 'Here is something to hang your hat on,' he would say, and again, 'This remedy is the hot stuff.' In his suave and sophisticated way he was a born humorist whose witticisms we feel sure would have made him an instant favorite in the most sedate royal courts. As a teacher he was ideal. It was his unhappy lot to present the driest and most difficult course on the Senior roster and yet we found ourselves listening eagerly to his drug pictures. None of us could appreciate the labor involved in preparing and delivering a lecture on Homœopathic Materia Medica, else we surely at the year's end, would have presented Doctor Boericke with an appropriate bouquet."

—1931 *The Medic* (Hahnemann Yearbook)

Teaching homœopathic pharmacy at Hahnemann was John A. Borneman, whose family is still in the business of homœopathic pharmaceuticals.

John A. Borneman
August 4, 1879 — April 8, 1955

Borneman came to the United States from Germany in 1890. He graduated from the Philadelphia College of Pharmacy in 1902, and worked as a pharmacist for Boericke and Tafel, along with another young pharmacist, Urban Ehrhart. By 1910 they had both left to form their own homœopathic pharmacies.

Borneman was the pharmacist for Hahnemann Medical College. He taught homœopathic pharmacy there almost until the time the school stopped teaching homœopathy.

Although the manufacturing facility was at Norwood, on the outskirts of Philadelphia, the Borneman Pharmacy opened a retail outlet next to the college and hospital in downtown Philadelphia in 1915. When the school stopped teaching homœopathy in the 1950s, the store was closed and the total operation was moved to Norwood.

John A Borneman, Jr.
May 16, 1904 — April 4, 1996

John A. Borneman Jr. took over operating the Borneman pharmacy in 1955. He began his career at H. K. Mulford and Company, a botanical medicine business that was the predecessor of Smith, Kline and French.

John A. Borneman III (Jack)
April 10, 1931 —

Jack Borneman received his pharmacy degree from the Philadelphia College of Pharmacy. He was managing the pharmacy until it was sold to Boiron in the mid–1980s. Jack is currently the president of the Homœopathic Pharmacopoeia Convention of the United States— the organization that acts as the interface between the pharmaceutical industry and the FDA. The HPCUS is responsible for writing the *Homœopathic Pharmacopoeia*.

John A. Borneman, circa 1935

John P. Borneman IV (Jay)
October 18, 1958 —

Jay grew up in the homœopathic pharmacy of his family. He holds a Chemistry degree and an MBA. When the family pharmacy was sold to Boiron, Jay became director of marketing for Standard Homeopathic in Los Angeles, California.

Elizabeth Ann Borneman
August 4, 1983 —

With four generations of homœopaths behind her, does she have a choice?

The Bornemans, Norwood, Pennsylvania, 1993. Jack, John, Elizabeth, and Jay.

Some Borneman Memories

An interview with John A. Borneman, Jr. 1983

Growing Belladonna

World War I came and the Department of Agriculture approached my father because they wanted someone to grow *Belladonna*. He already had the seeds— so he started a farm in Lawndale. *Belladonna* is quite a chore to grow. You have to start it in a cold frame over the winter. You sow the seeds in the fall and it comes up in the spring. Pot them up in two inch clay pots. They were quite successful. They grew it not only for homœopathic people, but also for Johnson and Johnson who needed it for the atropine. Then World War II came along and the Department of Agriculture wanted to know if we could grow *Belladonna* again. We organized a group of farmers in Lancaster, Pennsylvania. We had twenty three farms in Lancaster County growing *Belladonna*. They could only grow what they could dry. It has to be grown like tobacco.

The Hahnemann Cocktail

I remember the "Hahnemann Cocktail."It was a drink they gave to the drunks that were brought in to the hospital. It was *Nux vomica*, *Capsicum*, and aromatic spirits of ammonia. 10 drops of the tincture of each and a tablespoon of the aromatics. It did the trick. That was the "Hahnemann Cocktail."

Alcohol consumption

Since they used 50% ethyl alcohol as rubbing alcohol, it was a favorite drink of the orderlies and interns. When we noticed the level going down Dad would put about five or ten drops of *Croton* oil in it, and the culprits would be in the bathroom all the next day!

The students

The students would always drop by the store and talk to dad. They got more training at our store than they got at the college. There wasn't much homœopathy being taught by the late 1930s. There were the students who were interested in it and went to Boericke's lectures. I knew so many men who went to Hahnemann. We helped them get through and after five years they were no longer in homœopathy. They were good physicians but they didn't use homœopathy. They probably were never interested in the first place. They wanted a course in medicine and that is what they got. Those people that wanted to study it— maybe they got some good results in the very beginning so they stayed with it. Maybe there were four or five out of a class of 120 or so.

We had some of these men work for us while they were in school, and then they'd graduate and get started in a specialty like obstetrics and they never had any use for homœopathic medication— and Dad had put them through school! We had an office in Philadelphia across from the Nurse's Home, and we had students living on the second and third floor and Dad never charged them any rent. They roomed in our place for years! It seemed to me that they'd always get into some kind of specialty where they would never need our medication.

The salesmen

In the old days we had all these companies in Philadelphia, and then we had others coming in. Otis Clapp was in Boston and they had a representative down here to see the doctors once a month or every six weeks. Boericke and Runyon had a store in Philadelphia but they also had a salesman who would make the rounds. Dad had his men, and Boericke and Tafel always had salesmen making the rounds. But there were sufficient doctors in those days. I don't know how many there were in Philadelphia, but I'd say about one hundred. Chester had thirty or forty. Every large city had its homœopathic hospital. Hahnemann in Philadelphia, Crozier in Chester, Lee Memorial Hospital in Johnstown, Shadyside Hospital in Pittsburgh— every town had a homœopathic hospital. Later on they got restricted and they were no longer homœopathic hospitals. They changed their names, although homœopathic physicians worked there.

Potencies

Most of it was all low potencies. We didn't sell enough high potencies in a year to keep us in business one day. There was no demand for it so we didn't do it. They laughed at you. Doctors would come to me and say, "I want you to send me all the remedies this time in 3X but be sure to put some in!" "Why don't you buy the 2nd X or the tincture?," I'd ask them. "No I want the 3X but be sure you put some in!" It was unbelievable!

At the beginning we got some of our base high potencies from

"Bring me your tired, your poor…"

"They were never interested in the first place. They wanted a course in medicine and that is what they got," said John Borneman. So here's another perspective…

The United States has been a nation of immigrants. Each wave of immigration has engendered prejudice against the immigrants from the present inhabitants, even though they too were immigrants at one time.

At the turn of the century the United States received two major migrations— the Italians and the East European Jews. Soon, the children of the immigrants grew to college age, and those who wished to pursue medicine as a field of endeavor, often found their way blocked. The top medical schools were often closed to them— not because of finances but because of deep-seated prejudice— they were not places that Jews and Italians went.

The homœopathic schools which opened to women years earlier, were receptive to these first generation Americans. But most of the first generation had no undying love or interest for homœopathy. They wanted to be doctors, and the homœopathic schools gave them admission and a medical degree at the end.

A quick perusal of the names of those enrolled at New York Homeopathic Medical College during the 1920s and 30s will show this cultural bias very clearly:
Capobionco, Marchese, Angioletti, DeLucca, Romano, Borgia, D'Amato, Marone, Di Brizzi, Lombardi, Pizzi, Pellegrini… Rosenfeld, Goldstein, Pearlstein, Birnbaum, Horowitz, Shenker, Katz, Cohen, Kaufman, Gold.

B&T. In those days we didn't have any high potencies— 30X was the highest. We sort of scoffed at them. We didn't believe in high potencies. Now you see the results they're getting with them, it's a different story. In the old days, if we needed a high potency we sent down to B&T to get it. Every one knew that. The doctor would say to us, "The next time you're going down to B&T get me some…" whatever of a high potency. Later on when it became the thing, well, we had to do it ourselves. I did a lot of that myself. It's not that it was my business or anything, but I wanted to do it myself to make sure it was done right.

Combination remedies

Combinations were our salvation. As far as business was concerned, when you went into a doctor's office he would say, "Send me #14 for Catarrh, #52 for Headache," and so on. He bought very few single remedies. Later on that changed. Now, there are very few combinations sold. I often think about some doctors who were very conservative. They would say, "This patient needs *Nux vomica*, two tablets four times a day for a week." They would put just that amount in an envelope for the patient. The idea was to get the person back. These doctors lost their practice. The doctor down the street who gave them a whole bagful— four times as many as they could use— he had the practice. There were other men who bought the dilutions. They had a box full of dilutions in all sorts of potencies, but once they bought them they never bought them again. They'd fill the bottle up with 87% alcohol and keep using them.

The raw materials

There are all sorts of problems. We were looking for *Cactus grandiflorus* once and I called up a gardener who worked at the DuPont Estate. He said, "Come on over tomorrow. We're cleaning it all out. It's a dammed nuisance." So we got several hundred pounds then.
Some remedies are difficult to come by. Of course there's *Mephites*. For years every time we saw a dead skunk by the road we'd pick it up and put the glands in alcohol.
We had to go get the nitroglycerine to make *Glonoine*. We went over to DuPont [in Bridgeport, NJ] on the ferry— there were no bridges in those days. We ordered it ahead of time. We got 10% in alcohol— two five-gallon jars. When we went over there you had to take your shoes off and wear rubber soled moccasins. If people knew that I had five-gallon cans of nitroglycerine in the back of my car on the ferry, well, they would have died!

The decline of homœopathy

One of the problems with homœopathy was that it was too slow. It took too long to repertorize a case. A patient could come in to an "old school doctor" and say "I have a headache" and the doctor would give him some aspirin and send him home. The homœopathic doctor would want to find out what the cause was,

Glonoine

Nitroglycerine or Glonoine *(derived from G1=glycerine, O=Oxygen, N=nitrogen) was introduced into the homœopathic materia medica in 1847 by Hering. It was adopted by the allopaths for treating angina pain— one of the symptoms it can cause. It can also cause severe headaches. Jack Borneman told me that he dreaded the days when they were triturating nitroglycerine because he would have a headache all day from working the material.*

John Borneman told me that one day he received a phone call from Gus Tafel, telling him that they found a jar of Glonoine *in the basement. It looked like the alcohol had evaporated, and all that was left was a thick, jelly-like substance. Gus wanted to know what to do with it. John told him to phone the bomb-squad. It turned out to be enough nitroglycerine to completely destroy the five–story building!*

and it took a while. That was one of the drawbacks. If you go out into an area where a company owns a mining town, the Company or the union is paying for the health care. They can't take too long— give them two aspirin and they are on their way. They were never cured of anything. Just relieve them of their symptoms and get them on their way. The doctor didn't care, he was getting his money. He didn't want to get them well too soon anyway! That was very true of many of the towns that had a mine or a steel mill where the company paid the physician. Most of the conscientious doctors didn't make a lot of money.

Injectables and *Rhus toxicodendron*

Some of the things we put in tablet form we also put into injectables. We had a pretty good setup out here. We had automatic pipetting, and a good autoclave. We made a good product. There are doctors today that give B1 shots— they all have to have their shots. When they were getting their homœopathic remedies from us it was the thing to do. We thought they were pretty good products. We never had any complaints.

The main one we had was for ivy poisoning. It was the biggest one, and the most effective. "BOR-RHUS"— Borneman's *Rhus tox*. It was a high potency, a 200, in triple distilled water. In those days that was a high potency. It worked out pretty well.

I can gather *Rhus* with my bare hands and it doesn't effect me one bit, although it did when I was a boy. For a couple of years we had a number of boy scout troops who came to us when the season started. We'd give them all *Rhus tox*— I believe it was the 30X— four times a day for about six weeks. It seemed to immunize the whole troop.

I asked John A. Borneman, Jr. about using Anacardium *for treating poison ivy, and he told me that he would never think of prescribing* Anacardium *without also giving* Rhus tox. *Years later, while cleaning the lab, Jay came across the formula for the BOR-RHUS injectable. Although the label said it contained only distilled water and* Rhus tox 200C, *it appears that the old man put in one drop of* Anacardium *"to be sure!"*

The Borneman Labs at Norwood, PA, circa 1950

By the late 1940s, it appeared homœopathy was in its final decline. Many young doctors had served in the armed forces during World War II, and had learned the use of antibiotics and pain killers in the emergency work they were doing. When they returned, many of them were ready to apply this new found knowledge to the non-emergency practices of the general practitioner. In the view of Walter Kepler, MD, a 1948 graduate of Hahnemann, this factor was the biggest one that drove the physicians into the use of antibiotics and injections— they already knew how to do it. And the public was willing and ready to accept the "new and modern medicine."

As the Hahnemann Medical College was cutting its ties with homœopathy, the AFH postgraduate instruction continued under the leadership of a group of doctors who would teach the six-week course even if only one person enrolled.

The American Foundation course, 1952. The teachers (from the left) are Kenneth MacLaren, Eugene Underhill, and Julia M. Green. The pupils are Hans Kalm, MD (SC) (between Underhill and Green) Leroy Ryan, MD, (SC), Leandre Lacuna, MD, (Philippines) and William Wesner, MD (PA).

Anthony Shupis was a graduate of Hahnemann Medical College in 1938. He was one of the first to take the AFH postgraduate course after World War II. He was president of the Connecticut Homœopathic Medical Society, and delivered this address at the 1948 meeting of the Connecticut Society.

The state of homœopathy in 1948

"The precipitous drop in the popularity of homœopathy in contrast to its meteoric rise is to the present adherent a frightful phenomenon to behold. What has happened since the turn of this century to cause its undoing? Has time finally erased its utility? Has homœopathy finally proven to be just another passing fad to be regarded as just an 'historical curiosity' or will Hahnemann still refuse to lie quiet in some dusty corner of medical history like other 'centenarians'?

"Everywhere about us we see our numbers diminishing. Our undergraduate schools are no longer ours, old school physicians have been substituted on the teaching staffs and the control of our hospitals usurped by the surgical and mass drug clique of the dominant school.

"Although this is all too true, we are prone to accuse the old school of political skullduggery while whitewashing ourselves. Perhaps it would be better for us to turn about and view our collective selves as we are. In short, perhaps we have been too easily raped.

"Let us question ourselves. Are we homœopaths, or better still, are we 'fightin' homœopaths? Do we follow the teachings of Hahnemann or are we just graduates from where once homœopathy was only apologetically mentioned? How convincing were our teaching fathers? Have we pursued the study of homœopathy beyond our school borders? If so, how many have done so a whole week? These are but a few of the many questions we must ask ourselves.

"How many of us have ever studied The *Organon*, to say nothing of Hahnemann's *Chronic Diseases, Lesser Writings, Materia Medica Pura*, etc., etc.? Have we followed the study of these original teachings with the writings of subsequent workers? Can we honestly say we are really homœopaths? Have we in the treatment of our cases exhausted the possibilities in our search for curative remedies? Have we satisfied Hahnemann's definition of the highest and only calling of a physician?

"Returning again to self inspection, I wish to add an intelligent and highly informed layman's opinion respecting homœopathy's wane in popularity. Let us be candid and face facts. I quote you from Annie Riley Hale's *These Cults*, as follows:

"The Socialists have a dogma to which even non-socialists pretty generally will subscribe. If you can put your finger on the economic factor in any situation, you can count its life pulse. Every animal— including the human— like Napoleon's army, 'travels on its stomach,' and without food not even the most enthusiastic reformer can travel indefinitely. Brave, strong souls, like Samuel Hahnemann and the pioneer 'provers' of his therapeutic faith, could withstand the flames of persecution and survive. Their weaker brethren of later generations wearied of the unequal fight and finally surrendered to allopathic domination.

"In other words, homœopaths in America, during the past thirty years abandoned their own standards and conformed more and more to those of the older schools not, as Fishbein [Morris Fishbein, MD of the AMA] alleges, because they found their own inadequate and the allopathic remedies more efficacious, but because the allopaths being everywhere in control of the State, it was easier to earn a living by enlisting under allopathic banners.

"This is only one of a number of instances wherein the allopathic lion has shown itself willing to lie down with any therapeutic lamb which was willing to lie down inside the allopathic lion! The Fishbein allegation—'Homœopathy died from within—should be amended to read 'from within the allopathic system'— as it deserved to die. Sooner or later this is the fate of all systems which sacrifice truth for expediency."

"Again I return with more questions. These are all introspective and should be so. Is it not high time we stopped blaming our 'regular' school colleagues? Are not we, ourselves, to blame? Is not our blame the triple chronic state of ignorance, indolence and fear upon which breed the secondary factors to the detriment of our society and cause? It is time we followed Hahnemann's recognition of the outward manifestations alleviating internal ills and ceased suppressing our homœopathic feelings.

"Has so-called medical science advanced so far as to disprove homœopathy? To the contrary, all past and present day scientific discoveries are nothing more than revealing confirmation of the truth of homœopathy. Remember, no one yet has struck a death blow to homœopathy— and no one will. It is now one hundred fifty years that the most popularly (or fervently) hated branch of the healing art continues to survive. What is this heresy that the combined effects of indolence, ignorance, tradition, wealth and multitudinous majority cannot destroy? It is a truth and it shall never die.

"According to the Revised Constitution and By-Laws of the Connecticut Homœopathic Medical Society, 'The object of this Society shall be the advancement of medical science and the promulgation of the principles of homœopathy. Its objects shall be the same as those provided for in the constitution of the American Institute of Homœopathy, with which this Society is federated.' What have we done

287

Anthony Shupis
Hahnemann Yearbook photo, 1938

about the promulgation of the principles of homœopathy outside of homœopathic circles? Absolutely nothing.

"We are a society which slumbers all but two widely-separated days a year, then to awaken, peep at our waning shadow and again retire abashedly from our self-defamed Temple of Medical Truth.

"If our homœopathy is an asset to us and a boon to suffering humanity, then the world should know of it more fully. If, however, it is a chain enslaving us to the dominant school, it is one that can easily be broken and discarded.

"To members of the latter opinion, resignation from this society is the noble thing. We can all save face. Continued membership improves our lot not one bit. Let us not have in our midst, like the Philadelphia group, a society sprinkled with perfidious Iagos. Homœopathy's greatest curse is its band of shallow-minded camp followers whose only claim to homœopathy is exposure without take. So great is their assumed stigma that, instead of a sword, it becomes a crutch which leaves them in beggarly passivity to the utter contempt of both schools.

"If we can no longer recruit in our ranks the almost extinct homœopathically-minded graduates, then it falls upon us, as necessary, to attempt to educate our less fortunate regular school graduates. I am certain that there are among them many enlightened open-minded individuals who, given the opportunity, would avail themselves of it if it were offered. If we should attract only one, our purpose would be rewarded and our obligation fulfilled.

"Without action our boast is mere deflated egotism. Our Society needs succussion and dynamization to bring out its latent power, if any, towards a more respectful attitude by medicine in general. I, therefore, propose that an effort be made at this meeting to nominate a subcommittee to that on homœopathic enlightenment and, together, work out a plan for a postgraduate series of lectures for the profession in general, and to begin this fall.

"I also propose that the Committee on Homœopathic Enlightenment take a more active interest in enlightening the public on matters homœopathic. If these two elements would work in concert, we might have a double stimulating effect on both the public and the profession.

"I propose, further, that funds be made available out of our treasury for the furtherance of these aims. I propose, further, that efforts be made to procure assistance from our sister societies in the form of nationally recognized homœopathic lecturers.

"I am also of the belief that of necessity the lecturers shall be recruited from the so-called purists.

"Furthermore, I am convinced, and have history to prove it, that the meek shall not inherit the medical world of our generation. With frankness, that legacy, in its state of therapeutic chaos, is not for us homœopaths. We must build anew, like a homœopathic prescription, a structure composed of a minimum of material substance but a wealth of energy. It is only through our honest sincerity that we can will this. Any effort short of idealism is doomed. Without the will we shall find no way."

The ads

As Shupis was writing this, the "perfidious Iagos" were gaining strength and slipping further away from homœopathy and deeper into conventional practices.

We can see this in the *Directories* and *Journal of the American Institute of Homeopathy*. The advertisements appearing in these publications are instructive in understanding the kind of medicine that was being practiced by homœopaths.

This ad for local anesthetics appeared in the *1941 AIH Directory*. Others advertised rectal dilators for the treatment of constipation, portable x-ray units for x-ray therapy, and "Nitroscleran" for hypertension.

The advertisements in the journals are also instructive. The November 1945 *Journal of the AIH* contained ads for: Argyrol (a silver nitrate antiseptic), Camel cigarettes (with the doctor smoking), Sulmefrin (a nasal spray with sulfathiazole from Squibb), Dilantin (for epileptic therapy from Parke Davis), Semestrin (for menopausal symptoms by S. E. Massengill), Berocca tablets (B-complex from Roche), and Lactogen (an infant food product from Nestlé's.) Of interest is that particular issue contains both a cigarette ad and the third part of a three-part article by George Mackenzie, MD on the "Tobacco Habit."

It is interesting to note how many "homœopaths" were listed in the 1941 AIH Directory of Practitioners as "specialists." Some were general, but others very specific. For example: Carl Enstam advertised as a "gastro-enterologist," Franklin Cookingham (who was Kent's last living pupil) was listed under "Gynecology," Charles and Garth Boericke were both under "Internal Medicine," and A. Dwight Smith, was under "pediatrics." There was a section of specialty called "Homœopathic Prescribing" under which was found the names of Farrington, Grimmer, Hayes, Roberts, Rood, Stearns, and Sutherland. And under "Chronic Disease" we find J. S. Pugh, of Dallas, Texas— a pupil of Kent.

ALLERGY

Charles D. Miller, M. D.
407 S. Warren Street
By Appointment
Syracuse, New York

ANAESTHESIA

Everett A. Tyler, M. D.
1113 Medical Arts Bldg.
Philadelphia, Pa.

CARDIOLOGY

Carl A. Williams, M. D.
103 Fifth Street
St. Petersburg, Florida

A. B. Schneider, M. D.
Internal Medicine and Cardiology
9400 Euclid Avenue
Cleveland, Ohio

CHRONIC DISEASES

Ernest Risley Eaton, M. D.
53 West 83rd St.   New York, N. Y.
Chronic Arthritis and Allied Diseases

James M. Heimbach, M. D.
Proctology & Orificial Surgery
127 Greeves Street
Kane, Pa.

John Osenbaugh, M. D.
4632 Grace St.
Chicago, Illinois

CHRONIC DISEASES

J. S. Pugh, M. D.
510 Slaughter Bldg.
Dallas, Texas

DERMATOLOGY

James L. Church, M. D.
108 N. State St.
Chicago, Illinois

DIAGNOSIS

Howard M. Engle, M. D.
450 Sutter Street
San Francisco, California
Graduate of Hahnemann of Philadelphia, 1896

John C. Hubbard, M. D.
Diagnosis and Surgery
Hubbard Hospital
Oklahoma City, Okla.

F. C. E. Schneider, M. D.
1727 Fourth Street
Peru, Illinois
Diagnosing Chronic Diseases
Examinations & Ttreatments by Appointment

Lillian M. Thompson, M. D.
Diagnosis and Internal Medicine
30 N. Michigan Ave., Suite 1601
Chicago, Illinois
10 to 1. By Appointment
Except Wednesday

DIETETICS

F. Adele Schwartz, M. D.
11 S. La Grange Road
La Grange, Illinois

ENDOCRINOLOGY

John Duncan Wonder, M. D.
1020 Harries Building
Dayton, Ohio

EYE, EAR, NOSE & THROAT

W. L. Bywater, M. D.
120½ Washington Street
Iowa City, Iowa

1940 –1950: The Links with the Elders

Elizabeth Wright Hubbard
Charles Dixon
Arthur Grimmer
Musings of experience

While the 1930s had some second–generation practitioners who could say they knew Hering, Fincke, Wells, and other first generation homœopaths, the 1940s saw the rise of third–generation practitioners who would be instrumental in taking homœopathy into the 1950s. Among them were Elizabeth Wright Hubbard, Charles M. Dixon, and Arthur H. Grimmer.

Elizabeth Wright Hubbard, MD
February 18, 1896 — May 22, 1967

Elizabeth Wright was born in New York City. Educated at the Horace Mann School, she graduated *Summa cum Laude*. After graduating from Barnard College she went on several world travels where her interest in medicine was heightened by her introduction to homœopathy while in Europe.

She entered Columbia University's College of Physicians and Surgeons in 1917 in the first class to admit women and was one of the first three women to graduate in 1921. Wright was the first woman intern at New York's Bellevue Hospital, which at that time, served the entire East Side of New York City. There she volunteered to ride the night emergency ambulance, among other duties, certainly another first for a woman. Wright took further studies in homœopathy during two years in Geneva, Switzerland with Dr. Pierre Schmidt ("she was one of the most intelligent and gifted of my pupils,"said Schmidt). On returning to the United States, she opened her first practice in Boston. While living with her aunt, Mrs. Theodore Chickering Williams, a venerable Boston matron, Wright scandalized the staid community by making house calls in a 1913 Rolls Royce roadster she named "Rosalie."

On September 6, 1930, Wright married Benjamin Alldritt Hubbard of New York and began a private practice in New York which continued until her death.

In addition to her practice, Hubbard bore three children during the 1930s, Theodore Chickering, Elizabeth Wright II, and Merle, and also took the responsibility for raising two children, Benjamin and Isabel, from her husband's first marriage.

Hubbard's writings, lectures and teaching seminars on

homœopathy brought her international renown in medical circles. She was the first woman to be elected president of the American Institute of Homeopathy (1959), a post she held for two years. She traveled extensively throughout the world to bring the message of homœopathy to students and practitioners, and was one of homœopathy's most articulate advocates.

As well as her practice, her family and her teaching, Hubbard was deeply involved in the Anthroposophical Society of America. She was instrumental in bringing Rudolph Steiner's Waldorf School system from Europe to America, as well as the Christian Community, a religious organization based on the principles of Rudolf Steiner and Anthroposophy.

Some Memories of Wright Hubbard

Catherine Coulter described Hubbard as, "A very complex person, very brilliant. She was a 'large person' in the fullest sense. She had a large vision. She saw things in cosmic terms. I had a feeling that she was reading the person directly. If you didn't like her she really picked it up. She was physically large the way her spirit was large. Her voice was strong and deep, almost masculine, and she stood very erect so seemed even larger than she was.

"She had a very 'trenchant' mind. The kind of person that goes straight in, right to the heart of the matter. She made swift decisions, but she was human and when one has strong opinions they are not always accurate!

"At the time I knew her there was a lot of political squabbling within the homœopathic ranks. She tried to stay above it all, but couldn't resist getting involved. Then she would come down strongly on one side or another. She could cut through all the bickering.

"There certainly was genius there. I've heard she was an amazing teacher, although I never saw her teach. She liked getting involved with people, but she could be a bit arrogant and she could antagonize people, especially those whose minds she felt were narrow and needed stretching.

"Her writing style was terse, dense and highly quotable. There was much thought behind everything she wrote.

"She was very willing to talk about homœopathy to doctors but not to lay folks.

"She was very principled. She believed in giving one dose very high— and that was it. Her faith in homœopathy was absolute.

"Of course guessing someone's constitutional remedy is like guessing 'sun signs' in astrology, but I always thought she could have used a dose of *Lachesis!*"

Elizabeth Wright

Her Bookplate

Hubbard was a large woman. In one of her cases, she describes a patient as "...a little fat girl; oh, I am slender in comparison." The editor of the Homœopathic Recorder *in which the case was first published comments, "Dr. Hubbard considers herself fat. Actually, she is merely Junoesque."*

It was said that Hubbard used to keep baloney sandwiches in her desk so she didn't have to miss lunch during a long patient consultation.

Hubbard died "in harness." She was in the middle of a consultation, seeing the mother of Dr. Alexander Klein, a New York homœopath, when she had a stroke. Dr. Klein was present with his mother that day. Hubbard never regained consciousness and died two days later.

I remember hearing that Dr. Green did not like Dr. Hubbard because she liked to "frequent bars with men" and she "smoked cigars."

The Faces of Homœopathy

A choice of camps

A letter in the AFH files from Elizabeth Wright Hubbard to Julia M. Green. Dated May 5, 1948, the letter is discussing who to approach to serve on the AFH Board of Trustees. She says:

"… Dr. Whitmont who is so very brilliant in writing papers and eager and a hard worker, has poor judgment with what he connects himself with. He is extremely naturopathic and has done some chiropractic, I am told. Also, he is an officer of a semi-occult organization headed by Dr. George Haas, who knew Dr. Stearns. I feel we should use him but perhaps not elect him, until he is clearer just which camp he officially belongs in…"

In May of 1994, I sent a copy of the letter to Whitmont, asking if he ever figured out "which camp he belongs in." In a chuckling reply, he admitted that he still hadn't made up his mind!

Dr. Hubbard's Kit

Many physicians offered their patients "home kits" to be used upon instruction. Many kits had bottles marked only by numbers— so the patient had no idea of what the remedies were. They would phone the doctor, give their symptoms, and the doctor would say, "Take number 6 and call me in the morning."

Most kits were made for the physicians by Boericke and Tafel, and while cleaning their facility, I found the codes of many of the kits. I've reproduced them in the **Appendix**, page 508. They are a great study to see which remedies each doctor thought should be in their kit.

The Hubbard Kit, listed on the B & T file card (below) contained 46 remedies, all in the 200c potency. The kit also contained three different bottles of placebo:

"number 15: *Cubana:* Best general constitutional tonic. Give when in doubt about any other remedy and follow three doses of any other remedy with three to six doses of this, every four hours."

"number 25: *Essel:* Safe relief for mild pain, or if the symptoms are not specific."

"number 35: *Placebo:* for sleeping; nerve relaxer."

(Cubana is where the sugar is from and *Essel* is "S.L"— "sac lac"— saccharum lactose or milk sugar.)

Dr. Hubbard's Kit as of 5/8/59

1a Aloe	12 Chelidon	20 Kali bich	30 Psorinum
1 Ant tart	13 China	21a Kali carb	31 Pulsatil
2 Apis	14 Colocynth	21 Lachesis	32 Rhus tox
3 Arnica	15a Croton tig	22 Ledum	33a Rumex
4 Ars alb	15 Cubana	23 Lycopod	33 Sepia
5 Bellad	16a Drosera	24 Mag phos	34 Sil
6 Bryonia	16b Ferr phos	25 Essel	35 Placebo
7 Calc phos	16 Gelsem	26 Merc viv	36 Spigelia
8 Cantharis	17a Graphites	27 Natr mur	37 Spongia
9 Carbo veg	17 Hepar	28 Nux vom	38 Sulphur
10 Caustic	18 Ignatia	29 Phosph	39 Tuberc
11 Chamom	19 Ipecac	30a Podophyl	40 Verat alb

294

Charles A. Dixon, MD
1870 — October 1, 1959

Dixon practiced in Akron, Ohio upon graduating from the Cleveland Homœopathic Medical College in 1894. He served in the Medical Corps in World War I, and was one of the few survivors of a torpedoed troop ship. He joined the International Hahnemannian Association in 1920, and took the earliest American Foundation postgraduate course, when it was conducted at Julia Green's house. He came with his wife and little boy, and camped in a tent, which he erected in the nearby woods. He was elected president of the International Hahnemannian Association in 1940.

At the time of his death he was the honorary president of the American Institute of Homœopathy.

He practiced through the late 1950s and many of his patients are still seen by homœopaths in Ohio today.

He told his dear friend Celeste Beckwith Williams he could not bear to see people grow old and suffer the infirmities of life; loss of memory and bodily functions. He told her if he ever found himself in such a position he would rather kill himself than continue living. After a sudden decline in health, aged 89, he took his own life with a handgun.

Charles Dixon and Alcoholics Anonymous

In 1982 I met Celeste Beckwith Williams. Celeste was a long-time supporter of homœopathy and a close friend of Dixon. She told me the following story told to her by Dixon. I have told it many times over the years, and several people have taken exception to it, since the facts stated by Dixon were never corroborated by Dr. Smith, although I recently found someone who knew Dixon and told a similar tale.

Dixon had treated a pharmacist in Akron named Smith. Smith asked Dixon if he thought that homœopathy could be used to treat anxiety. Dixon assured him that it could. Smith then sent his physician brother, Robert, to Dixon as a patient. Robert was an alcoholic whose practice had been suffering because of his drinking. He was suffering from an "anxiety neurosis" which manifested as a tremor. He had been getting bromide salts from his brother. In the course of a few months, Dixon managed to clear the tremor and the anxiety with homœopathy. With the anxiety under control, Robert stopped his dependence on alcohol. The results were so dramatic that most people in town knew that Dr. Smith was no longer drinking.

One evening in May, 1935, a traveler came to Akron. Having just stopped drinking, he inquired of the desk-clerk at the hotel if there were any "old-topers" known to him, wishing to have some companionship for the evening, but not wishing to spend a night in a bar. The clerk, aware of Dr. Smith's change of habit, arranged for these two ex-drinkers to meet and spend the evening. Out of this meeting between Dr. Robert H. Smith and William G. Wilson grew the organization known as "Alcoholics Anonymous."

The writings of Dixon

Dixon was a frequent contributor to the journals and transactions. In his writing we find a "no-nonsense" prescriber who often sees things very simply— and is willing to share his processes with others.

"Many cases come to me for some sort of trouble completely dissociated from asthma, which they accept because they have been told by other doctors (some of them homœopaths) that it is incurable.

"That is really funny, because I have been curing asthma for many years. Now don't get me wrong; I don't cure every case that comes to me, probably not fifty percent of them, but that is the patients' fault, not mine. Some never come back the second time because I have failed to sell them a bill of goods; and some have been cured by that first dose of medicine, perhaps. Don't laugh at that statement! Just recently a lady looked me up after thirty-three years and told me that I did just that for her young daughter.

"There is no secret about these cures; it is just pure Hahnemannian Homœopathy. Lots depend on carefully taken case histories. The *Organon* tells you how to do it, and Kent's *Philosophy* makes the *Organon* easier. Don't overlook Kent's chapter on the second prescription; many cures are spoiled by that second prescription. Psora, Sycosis, Syphilis; Lots of homœopaths do not believe in these hereditary causes. I am sorry for them; they are the ones who miss the boat.

"I am talking about a lot of things that I never learned in college. Even back as far as my day [the early nineties] the college I attended didn't teach that kind of homœopathy. I learned it by independent study of the *Organon*, Hahnemann's *Chronic Diseases*, and finally the postgraduate summer school of the American Foundation. A first class knowledge of the Materia Medica is not enough (as many think) to do this kind of work. The repertory is essential, and I doubt if many are competent without postgraduate instruction; at least I didn't know until they taught me.

"This is just an outline of what is necessary for you to have or acquire to make it possible to cure the so-called incurable."

— Charles A. Dixon, *Homœopathic Recorder*, November 1948

Charles A. Dixon and friend.
St. Augustine, Florida 1953

This letter, typed on onion skin paper was found in the files at the National Center.

The First Fifty Years of Practice
by Charles Dixon
(dated May 8, 1944)

"Ho hum. I am sitting here wondering what the next fifty years will be like. For you see, I have finished my first fifty years of the practice of medicine, all of it in Akron, Ohio. Lots of water has gone over the dam (or should I say DAMN?) since my start as an MD. The changes that have come (and gone) in that time... I remember the first time I gave anti-toxin for diphtheria.

"When I was young in practice, I wasn't a very good homœopath. I hadn't been taught good homœopathy, so I gave anti-toxins, something that I stopped doing thirty years ago, for by that time I had taught myself the homœopathic law of cure, and since that time when I had learned that profound TRUTH, I have never given an opiate, cathartic, or vaccinated a patient.

"Neither have I taken out a tonsil since my conversion to the homœopathic law. For twenty years I alternated my remedies in low potencies, gave physics, used the hypodermic as well as combination remedies, and used all the samples the drug houses distributed so generously. As I look back on those days I realize that my ambition was to make money and be 'regular.' Of course, at that time a homœopath could not belong to the AMA or to the local allopathic societies, nor would the allopath consult with us; they refused us recognition, and now I refuse to consult with them.

"It is a significant fact that homœopathy has been on a steady decline since the AMA started their programs of benevolent assimilation, and the medical profession, at large (including the homœopath) broke into specialties. It has increased costs to the public enormously without giving them adequate returns in the pursuit of life and happiness.

"Oh! If I could only teach the public that surgery never cured anything; it deals with effects— and causes can not be removed by lopping off one effect after the other. When something goes wrong with an individual's tonsils, appendix, gallbladder, uterus, prostate, or what have you, we have a local manifestation of a constitutional trouble. In other words, it is in itself the effect which is still with the individual after the surgeon has removed the diseased organ. Surgery and surgeons will have an awful time squaring themselves with the ALMIGHTY when the final accounting takes place. The public has been so thoroughly sold to the idea of specialized medicine that they pay out their money, take the whole works— lock, stock, and barrel— and go home and die happy in the belief that they had the best that medical science can offer.

"This railroading of suffering humanity from one specialist to another is costing the medical profession dearly in prestige because it has bred a class of practitioners that can only be compared to the hijackers of the days of the Volstead Act. It gives me a pain

This picture of Dixon was given to Michael Garn, MD, in Ohio by an 80-year-old patient of his who had been delivered by Dixon. Those who knew Dixon say that the picture is very typical, with food stains on his shirt and vest. They say he was never fastidious about his appearance.

Tweedledum & Tweedledee

Dr. Maesimund Panos says some of her best memories of the Ohio State Homœopathic Society meetings in the 50s was the contrast of Charlie Dixon and T. K. Moore: the former was Tweedledum, short and plump, serious, and staid, while his friend T. K. was long and lean, always joking and needling Dixon mercilessly about whatever pronouncement he had just made. "Charlie was fairly dogmatic in his views, as you know, stating for example that in an acute case the indicated remedy should be given as a 10M in one dose only and never needs to be repeated; otherwise you had picked the wrong remedy. Of course, such statements left him wide open, and T. K. was always there to take advantage."

Thomas K. Moore, MD, 1945

(I won't say where) when I hear a homœopath excuse himself for giving non-homœopathic drugs and talk about the limits of the homœopathic remedy. Frankly, after fifty years of living with it I don't know what its limitations are, but I have come to the conclusion that its limits vary with the doctors who use it.

"Don't get the idea from my ranting that I think that every doctor that is using all these methods which I condemn is a fool or knave— they just don't know; they are only practicing what they have been taught, and are indifferent to the wonderful results that can be achieved by SIMON PURE HOMŒOPATHY.

"I am thoroughly convinced that if all of our homœopathic doctors were practicing PURE HOMŒOPATHY that our school would be the dominant school of medicine throughout the whole civilized world before many years.

"That would eliminate fully seventy-five percent of the surgeons and fully as large percentage of the specialized robbers, besides reducing the cost of medical treatment to the public at large by an even greater percentage.

"NOW, don't get the idea that I am curing everybody who comes to me. I lose plenty of them, but not to the undertaker. Most of them come to me because of friends who have boosted me instead of my homœopathy, and I am not able always to SELL them the homœopathic law— to keep them away from their aspirin, physics, salves, liniments, and numerous highly advertised nostrums. These failures don't disturb me in the least for I have come to the conclusion that a fairly good percentage of our citizenry don't deserve anything more than the specialists have to give them.

"The public at large is slowly becoming aware of the strangle-hold the AMA has on medicine and its practitioners until the medical profession has a well-developed case of jitters over the pending Wagner Act and what it is going to do to them. The trend for years back is toward socialized medicine and if it comes I am going to blame the AMA for it.

"My conviction is that we who are practicing true homœopathy have nothing to fear because our patients will still hunt us up, come HELL or high water."

The sheep in wolf's clothing

One of the gems I found in a box given to me by Henry Williams, was a small "pocket kit" owned by T. K. Moore.

It was made from a "doctor's sample," sent to Moore from Squibb. What drug capsules Squibb was marketing is unknown. The small, cardboard mailer contained 30 gelatin capsules of Squibb's latest product. Moore simply pulled open the capsules, poured out the contents, and then re-filled the capsules with remedies on number 10 granules, and labeled them on the cardboard insert. Just pull out the appropriate capsule, open it up, and dispense a granule.

Arthur Hill Grimmer, MD
August 29, 1874 — March 5, 1967

Grimmer was born in California, to a family who used homœopathic medicines. Young Grimmer grew up reading *Johnson's Family Guide*, and by the time he was seven, knew the indications of all 60 remedies by heart. By the time he was eight he had treated several people. Dr. Hoffman, in Healdsburg, California, urged young Arthur to attend medical school and study under Kent.

In 1902, Grimmer enrolled at the Hering Medical College in Chicago. Four years later he opened his medical office. Along the way, in his third year, he became the "quiz-master" assistant for Kent at his courses at the Hering College and at the Hahnemann College of Chicago. After graduating, Grimmer continued to assist Kent in his teaching and, in 1908, occupied the same offices as Kent. When Kent died, Grimmer assumed the practice.

Grimmer says this association with Kent not only helped in his homœopathic prescribing but, "it introduced me to the writings and philosophy of Emanuel Swedenborg, which changed my view of life from that of a doubting agnostic to the more appealing aspects of hope and faith, opening up vistas of beauty and use to better meet all the realities of life."

Grimmer became very interested in the Electronic Reaction of Abrams, wrote several papers on the subject, and was known to use a "box" often to verify remedy or potency choice.

Grimmer was also well–versed in astrology, and made regular reference to astrological aspects of remedies and patients.

Perhaps his best–known work was with the *Cadmium* salts and his reported cancer cures. He wrote 19 articles specifically about cancer treatment. Grimmer estimates he treated several thousand cancer cases during his career. He says between 1925 and 1929 about 150 biopsy–diagnosed cancers were cured by his treatment. During this same five–year period another 75 cases were palliated for 7-15 years with excellent quality of life. These 75 were cases in which extensive allopathic treatment had been administered.

Grimmer was president of the IHA in 1934 and then president of the AIH in 1953.

Arthur Grimmer, 1953

Among the many remedies I inherited from several sources, are vials of granules whose uses are completely unknown. One that has always been a mystery to me was a vial of "Congo red." A reference is found in the works of Grimmer:

"*Congo red* an aniline dye, has no homeopathic provings; its only therapeutic use was by Abrams, applied over cancerous growths to inhibit their growth.

"Clinically, in high potencies, this drug has cured several cases of breast cancer involving the whole breast which took on a stony hardness. The affected breast became much smaller than normal under the action of the drug. It acts best in warm-blooded patients and resembles iodine in the above effects. *Con, Carb an, Calc fl,* and *Silica* would be compared in stony hardness of the mammary glands."

Said Hubbard in his memorial: "He was one of the inner circle around Kent and was his secretary for some years. His knowledge of homœopathy was encyclopedic, and his interested extended into areas still under experimentation such as his version of the Abrams box. He was linked with names like Boyd and Stearns, Bryant, Morgan, etc. He was one of the most high–minded, tender–hearted, and sweet–souled men you could imagine, and probably among the very few most loved homœopaths, both by patients and confreres... Unfortunately he never published a book. Some people write it and others live it."

Grimmer, however, was a prolific writer. He published almost 200 articles and essays including 29 pieces on materia medica, 73 on therapeutics, and 19 on cancer— including a listing of 81 remedies he had found useful and their indications. In 1996 the Hahnemann International Institute for Homœopathic Documentation published the *Collected Writings of Arthur Hill Grimmer, MD*, edited by Ahmed Currim, MD. The homœopathy Grimmer lived was finally published.

Grimmer on Homœopathic Philosophy

"The aspect of our philosophy that deals with the life side of existence in its relation to the form side might be termed occult because it operates within the scope of the imponderable forces of nature.

"All energies of the cosmos are vibratory in character and are prior to and causative of all forms and ultimates in matter. Hence the 'Life Force' (Vital Force or Dynamis or Vital Principle of Hahnemann) constitutes one of the distinctive features of homœopathy, because it exists and operates in the sphere of the imponderables. Unless the physician can perceive and grasp the significance and importance of life processes, in the realm of health and disease his knowledge of the Law of Similars will avail him little in the realm of cure.

"Involved with this 'Life Force' of Hahnemann are a number of bodies or vehicles intermingling and ramifying throughout and in conjunction with the physical body of man and corresponding to the physical aspects of nature. These several bodies are classified by occult students and scientists as, first: the physical or chemical body which is subdivided into and made up of several subdivisions and variations of matter.

"We all know that the material world including the body of man is composed roughly of solids, water, gases and ethers. These solids, water and gases, make up the chemical band of nature, and from this division all the forms of mineral, plant, animal, including man, are derived. This is the physical body which corresponds to the crust of the earth.

"Intermingling with the physical body of nature and man, is the etheric body, comprising four aspects or divisions, each with its specific function to perform in the rhythmic march of nature. The etheric region of nature and man, while still physical, is invisible and intangible where our ordinary senses fail us, hence material science has no cognizance of this aspect of nature because no instrument has yet been devised to register the vibrations or energies flowing from this sphere. Likely some of the so-called electronic reactions of Abrams are vibrations from this plane. Only the trained clairvoyant can see the energies operating on this and other higher planes of life to be mentioned later on; he can see all the processes of life operating on all these planes of nature separately and in unison throughout all the vast intangible causative realms of nature."

— A. H. Grimmer "The Occult Side of Homœopathic Philosophy," *The Homœopathic Recorder,* January 1947

Grimmer's Writings: A Commentary

It is interesting to contrast the writings of Grimmer with those of Pulford and Hayes. Grimmer seemed to lack the deep sense of irony and trenchant observation his two colleagues had. His writing is very even and very literal. At a time when the homœopathic community was writing about the lack of practitioners and reasons for the homœopathic down-turn, Grimmer's essays all seem to be incredibly naive.

It is possible much of our current mythology about the reasons for homœopathy's decline has been derived from Grimmer's pen. In several essays, he lays the blame for the decline of homœopathy on the Flexner report and at the infighting between the "highs" and the "lows." He does not, at any time, acknowledge there was no real homœopathic education in the colleges and that which was taught was a mix of empiricism, eclectic, and allopathic practice with a dab of homœopathy thrown in. He sees the lack of homœopaths as the simple result of the schools closing, and *that* act the result of the Flexner report and AMA pressure.

It could be that his personal experience— being at Hering College in Chicago— was not an accurate reflection of what was happening in the rest of the world. After all, the Hering College was the only one teaching really pure

A deeper side

Several years ago, I finally met Dr. John Renner, after having a lengthy correspondence with him. He had been a pupil of Grimmer's at Chicago Hahnemann. Over the years he drifted further away from Grimmer's view of things, and finally, at the age of 92, had nothing good to say about Grimmer's work or the use of high potencies in general.

In his last years, Renner taught a number of physicians some of his skills in clinical diagnosis and body percussion. One of the students was Dr. Robert Milne.

After one National Center Annual Meeting, I was having dinner with Milne, and we fell to discussing Renner and Grimmer. It seems that, long ago, Renner sent some cases with which he was was having problems to Grimmer and Grimmer was unable to help them at all, returning them to Renner's care. Renner used this incident to discuss his low opinion of Grimmer, his machines, and his high potencies.

Milne asked, "Do you know why Grimmer had no success with these people?"

I opined that I didn't.

"Well," said Milne, "they weren't **his** *patients! They were still Renner's patients! If Renner had 'released' them, Grimmer might have been able to help them."*

Certainly, the "deeper" side of homœopathy!

homœopathy. Perhaps he never understood that his education was unique and that, all around him, the other schools were offering much less.

Did he choose not to see? Or did he not comprehend the enormity of it?

Musings of experience: 1948 –1950

While going through the American Foundation for Homœopathy files, I came across a folder of correspondences between Rudolph Rabe and Julia M. Green that took place between 1948 and 1951. In one, Rabe complained of being 78 years old and seeing no future in homœopathy in the United States. He was asking Green for her vision— if she really believed the American Foundation's work could "save" homœopathy and if the "postgraduate school" could really supply new homœopaths to the market. Despite Green's assurances, Rabe remained unconvinced.

These excerpts from Rabe's letters show well the homœopath's despair, the rise of "modern medicine" and the demise of the homœopathic medical societies.

"The IHA is now infiltrating the AIH more and more and is influencing those members who are still genuinely interested in homœopathy, but on the other hand, the majority of former AIH members have lost all interest in the organization. So where are the real homœopathic physicians to come from? Also, families which years ago employed loyal homœopathic doctors are now in the hands of the Old School or have gone over to osteopathy, chiropractic or Christian Science. Those who have gone over to the Old School have done so because they understand that school to be 'scientific and modern.' They want 'streamlined' medicine, even though many of them ultimately pay a high price for their folly. Unfortunately, they do not always associate the disasters with their abandonment of homœopathy. Our methods of practice are not theatrical, nor dramatic in the slightest degree, hence most of us who wish to attain reputation and financial success, take the popular, easiest way. That way is the road of powerful drug palliation, of unnecessary surgery, of organ tinkering and lastly, of sudden death to those who follow it. Witness the increasing number of deaths from coronary disease of prominent men who are the victims of 'scientific medicine.' Our well chosen, potentized remedies do not kill people. But we Americans are gullible people and 'fall' easily. We love to be humbugged, as old P. T. Barnum so many years ago observed."

— Rudolph Rabe, July 20, 1948

"This morning an old maiden lady of 87 years, very intelligent and possessed of a very keen mind, telephoned me from a town some twelve miles distant, asking me concerning her diet. I had prescribed for a diarrhea several weeks ago, giving a few doses of *Podophyllum* with prompt results; the 200th was used. This occasional patient formerly had a homœopathic physician, now long since dead and since her death there has been no one to take her place; she was an excellent prescriber. The old patient now calls upon a young, Italian-American physician whenever any simple ailment occurs and this man has persuaded her to have occasional 'shots' in the arm for a slight ankle edema. Over the telephone I gave her my opinion of this kind of treatment whereupon she remarked that I was criticizing another doctor's methods. I replied that I never criticize the therapy of another doctor, however much I may express my disagreement. I tell you this little and unimportant incident as another illustration of the increasing obstacles to the spread of homœopathy. Such incidents are becoming more and more frequent, because 'streamlined' medicine appeals to the majority of Americans, even to intelligent ones, as in this case."

— Rudolph Rabe, July 27, 1948

"A few days ago, Mr. George F. Humphreys of the Humphreys Medicine Company, Inc., called upon me and we had a lengthy conference on the status of homœopathy so far as this concerns this company in its sales of what were formerly known as Humphreys Specifics. Years ago, at the insistence of the late Royal S. Copeland who was dean of the old New York Homœopathic Medical College & Flower Hospital, I revised the literature of the Humphreys company, to make it conform to the requirements of the Health Department of the City of New York. Recently, the company had a survey made by the Research Consultants, Inc., New York who have revised the formulae of the various 'Humphreys Specifics.' This has been done to meet the constantly increasing pressure of State and Federal bureaucracies, a pressure which will one day suppress homœopathy completely as well as many other things, if continued. I need scarcely tell you that, for the most part, we have the late, unlamented Franklin D. Roosevelt and his left-wing stooges to thank for this. The New Deal has wrecked our country. Mr. Humphreys told me, without asking any pledge of secrecy, that where formerly 68 per cent of their business was done in this country, this now amounts to but 12 per cent and that 88 per cent is done with foreign countries, chiefly in South America. Their veterinary medicine business has been driven out entirely, due to Federal Government pressure and interdiction. Federal agents asked the representatives of the company whether any college of veterinary medicine in the United States teaches the use of homœopathic remedies. The answer of course, was 'No.' That answer was a death sentence to the further manufacture of veterinary remedies…

"I think that we make a great mistake in believing, as so many

Hahnemannians do, that the laity is hungering for homœopathy, for the laity is doing no such thing. Those of us who have, so to speak, been born into a homœopathic atmosphere, have an abounding faith in it, but the millions of people who think that homœopathy means 'home remedies' are very definitely a drawback to us. Average intelligence in our country is at a pretty low level, in spite of all the efforts at popular, so-called education; comparatively few people think; they prefer not to think and most of them have a 'newspaper' education via the tabloids. When sick, they demand instant relief, no matter whether such relief is harmful; it is constantly 'dope' and still more 'dope' for them. The Old School doctor gets his knowledge of therapeutics from the 'detail' men who call upon him each month; shots in the arm are his stock in trade and people call him Blessed; they do not want the little insignificant powders which the Hahnemannian gives them; they demand real medicine— something that will instantly take hold and which has a dramatic character. Then our liberal homœopaths say to me: 'Rabe, we don't doubt your honesty, But you can't prove your cures.' Also, 'we haven't the time to study the materia medica or to use the repertory.' Most of them would not know how to use the repertory anyway. Nor do they wish to learn. Of course, there are negligible exceptions, but these are few and far between."

— Rudolph Rabe, August 29, 1948

"With the death of homœopathy in our two medical colleges you realize that teachers of homœopathy will in a few years cease to exist. Those of us who have taught in the past are no longer able to do so, for various reasons, chiefly those of advanced years and of impaired health."

— Rudolph Rabe, May 2, 1950

"Yesterday, at the West Jersey Hospital in Camden, the annual meeting of the New Jersey State Homœopathic Medical Society was held, followed by the customary luncheon. Notices to the number of 220 had been sent to all homœopathic physicians in the state, of which number very few are members in good standing in the Society. Exactly 33 dues-paying members attended the meeting and but one address was made, on a surgical subject of a highly technical character, dealing with surgery of the mitral valve. This subject was presented by Associate Professor Dr. O. Henry Janton of Hahnemann Medical College and was graphically illustrated by lantern slides. There was no paper or address on homœopathy, as the latter is considered to be 'Poison' to any medical meeting. At the business session the question of the abandonment of our State Society was discussed and it was decided to send questionnaires to all dues-paying members in the state, before taking final action. Among the members present at the meeting were Dr. Henshaw of Montclair, with whom I drove down to

Camden and Dr. Arthur Weller from Orange. We were and are, the only members from the northern part of the state who ever attend. Homœopathy in New Jersey is definitely a dead issue. Practically all the members and non-members of the State Society are graduates of Hahnemann Medical College and frankly state that, they know little or nothing of homœopathy because they were never taught it. I know that Garth Boericke and Russell K. Mattern are doing their best to teach their students, but those men receive no cooperation or support from the rest of the faculty. Our New Jersey State Board has long since given up homœopathy as, one of the required examinations for license to practice in New Jersey, as no applicants wanted it."

— Rudolph Rabe, May 24, 1950

The others...

The decline of homœopathy in the 1930s and 1940s was gradual. The *1941 Directory of Homœopathic Physicians in the United States* listed more than 6,600 names. A number of those listed had been in practice for more than 50 years, some graduating as far back as 1878. The homœopathic schools had been teaching little homœopathy from 1900 on, and by 1930, most of the schools had closed. Few new graduates were coming into the marketplace while the old guard was rapidly dying off.

Yet the literature of the time is full of vitality. The International Hahnemannian Association was holding pure homœopathy together. Many of those writing and practicing had learned from the second generation— from masters like Wells, Boger, and Gladwin.

It was as if the essence of homœopathy, the real heart of it, drew in tighter to protect itself from the outside assault. Those holding it together should certainly not be forgotten. They held it together by example. They practiced real homœopathy with their patients. Their patients, in turn, recognized the special nature of the treatment and worked to keep the flame of homœopathy alive.

In 1944, the International Hahnemannian Association had only 147 members, 28 of whom were overseas— Drs. Das and Behram in Bombay, India; Drs. Fergie Woods and Weir in England; Drs. Gordon, Ross, and Poznansky in Scotland; Drs. Castro, Flores, Trevino, in Mexico; Dr. Dorothy A. Harris in Kaifeng, China; and Drs. Elwood David and Harry Jones in Africa.

Although a small group, the IHA was gaining new members at an increasing rate. While only 17 had joined between 1910 and 1920 (when homœopathy certainly had a larger presence), 42 joined in the 1920s, 37 joined in the 1930s, and between 1940 and 1944, 25 joined.

Many of these people would carry homœopathy into and through the 1950s: John Ames of Michigan, Lucy Clark of Ohio, Donald Davis of Connecticut, Howard Engle and Carl Enstam of California, Harriet Knott and Marion Belle Rood of Michigan, Charles Olds and Donald MacFarlan of Pennsylvania, Allen Sutherland of Vermont, and William Gutman in New York.

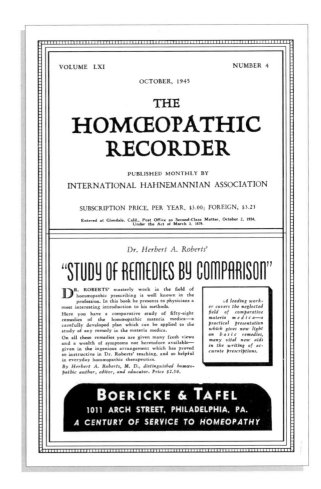

The 1950s: Drawing Together

The move for recognition
The merger

The move for recognition

In 1939, at the meeting of the American Institute of Homeopathy, Charles Boericke, MD, proposed to adopt a definition of homœopathy:

> "Homœopathy is a branch of the science and art of therapeutics. It deals with the investigation and application of the simile phenomenon, that phenomenon of similarity between symptoms (functional and structural) which a physiochemical agent produces in healthy organisms and for which it is applicable in diseased organisms."

This was the first step in getting homœopathy recognized as a specialty within conventional medicine.

The pulling together with the American Medical Association over the issue of socialized medicine, led several homœopaths to conclude that the "regulars" were ready to accept homœopathy— at least as a specialty in therapeutics rather than as an independent medical practice. In an article in the February 1944 *Journal of the American Institute of Homeopathy*, Rudolph Rabe suggested that the specter of "sectarianism" would disappear if such a change took place. Addressing the New Jersey State Homœopathic Medical Society in April 1945, Rabe said:

> "I feel our greatest sin of omission has been our failure to establish the exact sphere of homœopathy, to define its proper limitations; too often we entirely neglect the law of

The Trustees of the American Foundation for Homœopathy, October 4, 1952

(seated): Elizabeth Wright Hubbard, MD; Charles A. Dixon, MD; Julia M. Green, MD; Ray W. Spalding, MD; Marion V. Magruder (standing): Arthur B. Green; Edgar Speiden; John J. Lehey (general council); Kenneth A. MacLaren, MD; James Lavelle (treasurer); Henry T. Parrett

similars... homœopathy is, and ought to be, a definite therapeutic specialty to which those who wish to apply themselves exclusively, shall have that right. As such it should be honestly taught in all medical schools regardless of school or pathy; failing in this, homœopathy should be taught as a postgraduate study to those who are genuinely interested in it."

By 1946 a group within the American Institute sought a name change of the practice from "homœopathy" (which, they said, had unsatisfactory historic connotations) to "homœotherapy," while another group suggested homœopathy should become a medical specialty.

In 1950 the American Institute of Homeopathy began to consider the possibility of a specialty board. A committee was formed with members G. Kent Smith, Elizabeth Wright Hubbard, Julia M. Green, and Allen Neiswander.

Vigorous debate ensued. Louis P. Crutcher, MD, wrote a scathing article in the January 1951 *Journal of the American Institute of Homeopathy* where he called the attempt to gain recognition by the AMA "cowardly" and said there are but two schools of medicine: "homœopathic and hypodermic." The drive, he said, was like "asking Protestantism to become a 'specialty' under the control of the Roman Catholic Church."

The century of antagonism toward homœopathy by the AMA was hard to overcome. In November 1954, the general manager of the American Medical Association, George Lull, said, "Homœopathy is dead," a statement not well received by the American Institute or the International Hahnemannian Association.

In 1956, the American Foundation for Homœopathy bought table space at a Cincinnati Health Expo sponsored by the Academy of Medicine. Shortly before the expo took place the Foundation received a letter saying that "the committee feels there is not a place for the exhibit," and the money paid was returned. No explanation was given, but the sense was that it was rejected because it was "homœopathy."

Others within the American Institute were urging links with conventional medicine. Wyrth Post Baker, in a 1957 *JAIH* article called "The Place of Homœopathy in American Medicine," wrote: "It is time to divest ourselves about any paranoid delusions of persecution by the AMA."

Meanwhile the AIH committee studied quietly the

feasibility of a specialty board. No word of their deliberations appeared in the AIH *Journal* until an announcement in January 1960 by AIH president Elizabeth Wright Hubbard. She said the American Board of Homeotherapeutics had been legally incorporated in New York State, and it was accepting applications for the specialty designation— DHt— Diplomate of Homeotherapeutics. The person responsible for much of the "legwork" in getting the New York recognition was Henry Eisfelder, MD.

The AIH had understood that the American Medical Association would accept homœopathy as a specialty if 100 people registered with the American Board of Homeotherapeutics. When 100 members were finally granted Diplomate status, the AMA questioned the education of several applicants, and would not accept them. When others were granted the diplomate— raising the number to 100 again— the AMA again found exceptions. Even today the AMA has yet to grant the ABHT the status it requested.

In 1997, Allen Neiswander suggested that the AIH was not politically strong enough to wield much influence over the AMA.

The ABHT is still operational in 1998 and is still examining those with medical degrees (both Medical Doctors and Doctors of Osteopathy) for Diplomate status.

The merger

In the 1870s the American Institute opened its doors to all who wanted to be members, whether or not they subscribed to Hahnemann's doctrines. The International Hahnemannian Association was formed in 1880 due, in great part, to the fact the American Institute was generally formed of "half-homœopaths" and other eclectic prescribers. Most stalwart Hahnemannians sought refuge with the IHA, although there were also those who joined neither organization.

In the early 1950s the American Institute leadership began talking about bringing the International Hahnemannian Association under its direction. In an editorial in the October 1955 issue of the *Journal of the American Institute of*

Homeopathy, Donald Gladish, MD, said it clearly:

> "As the numbers of the Institute members have fallen, their degree of homeopathicity is increased, partly because nearly all the members of the IHA are also members of the Institute."

And it was clear that this was the case. In 1954, Arthur Grimmer was the the American Institute of Homeopathy president and the board of directors was composed of Wilbur Bond, Elizabeth Wright Hubbard, Allan Sutherland, Horace Reed— all folks who were practicing Hahnemannian homœopathy.

In 1957, AIH President H. W. Eikenberry replied to a group of inactive members threatening to resign from the organization en masse unless the American Institute abolished its journal or hid the name "homeopathy" somewhere in small print. Said Eikenberry:

> "We, the active members of the AIH are proud of our journal, proud of our organization, and proud of the principles for which we stand. And we have no intention of changing our policies.
>
> "They are ashamed at having their names associated with an organization whose members use *Lathyrus sativa* for the prevention of poliomyelitis, or *Sepia* for the cure of lupus erythematosus.
>
> "The basic reason for this self-inflicted shame: They Are Not Homeopaths!"

The AIH Board of Trustees Meeting 1955
(seated) Allan Sutherland, MD; Wilbur Bond, MD; Elizabeth Wright Hubbard, MD; Henry Eisfelder, MD; Arthur Records, MD; Carl Enstam, MD; Ralph Faris, MD; John Swartwout, MD; Paul Schantz, MD. (standing) Arthur Grimmer, MD; William Weaver, MD; H. W. Eikenberry, MD; Horace Reed, MD.

Ever since the late 1940s the AIH Annual Meetings and the IHA Annual Meetings had been held at the same place at the same time. It was only natural with the falling membership of both that the two organizations merge.

In December 1959, the *Homœopathic Recorder* ceased publication and was absorbed into the *Journal of the American Institute of Homeopathy*.

At the AIH/IHA meeting in 1960, the IHA disbanded. Said IHA President Ronald Troup, MD, in the May/June *Journal of the American Institute of Homeopathy:*

> "The spiritual essence of the International over the many years of its existence has lain in the maintenance of the best and truest tenets of homœopathic practice and an overall commendation is rightfully ours on the manner in which we have held to the line of our beliefs. Homœopathy is the gainer for our having lived."

Donald Gladish, MD
September 1899— June 30, 1967

Born in Indianapolis, Indiana, Gladish attended the Academy of the New Church in Bryn Athyn, Pennsylvania. After serving in the Marines during World War I, he worked for 10 years in the timber industry. He took pre-med courses in Chicago in 1928 and graduated from Hahnemann, Philadelphia in 1933. He worked with Harvey Farrington and established his own practice in Glenview, Illinois. He served in the Pacific in World War II and said, "The experience confirmed the outstanding benefits of homœopathic medicine in spite of the sulfas and penicillin."

Donald G. Gladish

Hugh Wilson Eikenberry, MD
January 2, 1908— December, 1969

Born in Peru, Indiana, Eikenberry's father was a homœopath. Eikenberry graduated from Hahnemann Philadelphia in 1934, and returned to Peru to practice. He served as a flight surgeon in World War II. A few lines under his picture in his yearbook tell it all:

"His wit and humor they never grow old,
And his 500th potency will knock you out cold."

A misreading of history

The merger between the AIH and the IHA has been completely misunderstood by one of the major historians in homœopathy, Martin Kaufman. In the book *Other Healers*, Kaufman writes:

"During the 1950s, homœopathic unity was finally achieved, with the merger of the 'pure' International Hahnemannian Association and the 'eclectic' American Institute of Homœopathy… Since the 'pure' group would be submerged in a larger 'eclectic' organization, the IHA polled its membership and discovered there was widespread support for a merger— an attitude which may have reflected the fact that 'pure' classical homœopathy was a thing of the past. There were only a small number of 'pure' homœopaths left, and as a result the IHA was no longer able to support its publication, the *Homœopathic Recorder*. As a result, in 1959 it was amalgamated with the *Journal of the American Institute of Homeopathy*, and the following year the IHA, which had been established in 1881, voted itself out of existence. In effect, the two factions had finally united."

This view is quite erroneous. As we can read in the records (and as we know by understanding the practice of those in the organization by looking at the cases they presented at conferences), the "eclectics" were leaving the AIH and those *remaining* were "pure" homœopaths. The two factions were not united— one of the factions— the "half-homœopaths"— had ceased to exist. As we follow the AIH from the 1950s to the present we see more and more influence by the "pure" homœopaths.

The 1950s: Keeping it Alive

Marion Belle Rood
Wyrth Post Baker
W. W. Young
William Boyson

The 1950s were dark times. The United States was experiencing a regressive turn under the influence of Senator Joseph McCarthy. Political and social suppression was rampant. All non-conventional ideas were looked upon with suspicion. It was a time when many "alternative" healers were prosecuted. Ruth Drown, a chiropractor in California involved in developmental work exploring the Electronic Reaction of Abrams, was sentenced to a jail-term for using the machines in her practice. Dr. Wilhelm Reich was jailed for his work on "Orgone energy" and his papers were destroyed.

There were a few who kept homœopathy alive during these dark times:

Dr. Marion Belle Rood, of Lapeer, Michigan, donated her life savings to fund the efforts to preserve the *Homœopathic Pharmacopoeia*. Wyrth Post Baker, through his testimony, preserved the place of the *Homœopathic Pharmacopoeia* in the Federal Medicare Legislation. The cantakerous W. W. Young, galvanized into action both those who agreed and disagreed with him, and William Boyson's "extraordinary personality and a flair for presenting educational material" endeared him to a generation of students who attended the AFH postgraduate course.

Marion Belle Rood, MD
1899 — December 22, 1995

Rood was the only woman in her physics masters program at the University of Michigan in Ann Arbor. She worked on the quantum theory during the 1920s. After two years of teaching mathematics in Tennessee, she attended New York Homœopathic Medical College as the only female student in her class, graduating in 1932.

Rood received her advanced training in homœopathy from her family physician, Dr. Harriet Knott, who in her later years, while blind, lived with Rood supervising her cases. Rood was invited by Grimmer to join his practice in Chicago, which had been Kent's practice. However, Rood wanted to stay in her rural home town of Lapeer, Michigan.

The stories of Rood are legendary. She lived in a house at the end of a dirt road outside of town. She had neither a telephone nor appointments. Her patients would drive up, sit on her porch, and wait. She began at 11 a.m., and would see the patients in the order they had arrived, taking as long as needed for each case. She worked until the last patient was treated, sometimes at 1 a.m. or later. Neighbors often brought snacks for the patients waiting on her porch.

Recalls Andrew Lange, ND: "In Dr. Rood's office in her living room, patients sat amidst piles of books, cats and dogs, dishes covered in lace, and wooden boxes filled with medicines. Records were kept on large file cards. She sat behind a small wooden side table with Kent and Knerr's *Repertories* guiding her. Busts of Hahnemann and Hyphatia watched over her. Hyphatia was a young woman mathematician and astronomer from Alexandria, and a the leading proponent of neo-platonic thought. Patients reported that she would leave them with an issue of *Scientific American* when she went to prepare their remedy, then quiz them about the articles when she returned. As a scientist, Dr. Rood kept a wide range of journals piled throughout the living room in which she saw her patients. She would regularly lecture her patients on the relationship between homœopathy and current developments in science, whether they could appreciate her insights or not."

Through Grimmer, she became interested in the Electronic Reaction of Abrams. She built a room with copper wire coils to block outside electromagnetic influences, in which she conducted tests. This method was the basis of a later study led by Guy Beckley Stearns and other members of the International Hahnemannian Association in the 1920s. Lange says: "Dr. Rood used this method for over 20 years in some of her most difficult cancer cases. In later years she no longer used the Abrams instrument, relying instead on her experience and the repertories to determine the remedy."

When a local reporter interviewed her after her retirement, he asked her what would her patients do without her to which she replied, "Well I hope they're all better. That's what is supposed to happen."

Along with Dr. Wyrth Post Baker, she testified before the Senate, to maintain the status of the *Pharmacopoeia*. Rood charged $10 for a visit, raising this to $20, when the *Pharmacopoeia* was again reviewed in the 1980s. She raised and contributed $50,000 which funded the updating of the *US Homœopathic Pharmacopoeia*.

Rood never married.

Marion Belle Rood, Maesimund Panos, and Rudolph Ballentine.

Dr. Ballentine worked with the Himalayan Institute in Honesdale, Pennsylvania. He was introduced to homœopathy by the founder of the Institute, Swami Rama. Ballentine taught David Anderson, MD, Dale Buegel, MD, and Dennis Chernin, MD, who authored the book Homœopathic Remedies *in 1978, one of the first new self-help manuals.*

Panos recalls spending time studying with Rood and seeing Ballentine standing on his head in the middle of the lawn, doing his morning yoga.

Wyrth Post Baker, MD, DHt
November 11, 1905 —

Born in Washington, DC, Baker did his medical degree at the Hahnemann Medical College, graduating in 1930 with both an MD and an HMD. He spent a year and a half in a preceptorship with Professor Harry Eberhard, head of the department of gastroenterology and internal medicine at Hahnemann. Returning to Washington, DC, in 1933, he acquired the practice of Dr. John Sharpe.

His picture in the 1930 yearbook identifies him as "Bugsy", a nick-name he said he brought with from from an unknown source in his childhood. The yearbook says of him: "We wish Baker every success in the years ahead, and feel certain that the Beacon of Homœopathy will burn brighter because of his sagacious championship."

And indeed homœopathy did burn brighter because of Baker, who became extremely active in the politics of homœopathy. He served as president of the Homœopathic Pharmacopoeia Convention of the United States, president of the American Foundation for Homœopathy, secretary and president of the American Institute of Homeopathy, president of the Southern Homeopathic Medical Association and a life member of the American Medical Association.

In 1965 when Medicare Legislation was moving through Congress, Dr. Baker was responsible for making sure the drugs listed in the legislation for reimbursement while under hospital care included those listed in the *Homœopathic Pharmacopoeia*.

Dr. Baker retired from active practice in 1993, at the age of 88.

Wyrth Post Baker
yearbook Photo, 1930

Clark Baker, the editor of the *Homœopathic Pharmacopœia* with his father, Wyrth Post Baker, 1997.

William W. Young, MD
December 5, 1900 — April 4, 1974

A graduate of Hahnemann Philadelphia in 1928, Young became president of the American Institute in 1968, elected, he said, by "the young rebels." He said: "No one was willing to say what was being felt and no one offered a way out. There was one exception— myself."

He pushed his "PPP"— Perpetuation and Propagation Program— whose goal was to teach homœopathy in all schools of medicine. But he was very much against "Homœopathy"— whose concepts he found vague, old fashioned, and worded in an ancient language. He wanted to teach "Homœotherapeutics." He questioned much of the language in the *Organon* of Hahnemann ("What are the 'irritable fibers'? Where do they exist? How can we find them?")

Wyrth Post Baker referred to him as "the Stormy Petrel." He possessed, as one said: "A brilliant intellect, keen judgment, and sharp criticism— none too diplomatic— that earned him the reputation of a bull in a china shop. He acted as a bulldozer, clearing the ruins of the past... His catalytic presence in meetings would dissipate at once the general apathy."

"He always spoke in exaggerations," said one old homœopath in 1997. "He was caustic and cynical. He was not one of my favorite people."

Young had an idea that the remedies were inert and the therapeutic effects were due to homeostasis. Said Harris Coulter in 1997: "In those years before homœopathy started to go up in the world, there were about six or seven old guys in the AIH who just kept trading places with one another. I thought they were all pretty pernicious, and Young was probably the worst. He had a theory that the homœopathic pills acted like glass beads, just by touching the nerves, without containing any energy. So all specificity of homœopathic prescribing was lost. He really believed this, and he would lecture on it at the drop of a hat. Thank God the FDA never heard of him, or I don't know where we would be. I took extreme pleasure in throwing boxes of his pamphlets into the dumpster during one of our moves."

In 1984 I was looking through the book Homeotherapeutics *written by Baker, Young, and Neiswander. An older physician, seeing the book, commented to me, "I'm not sure about that book. I just wouldn't trust Young. I met him. He wasn't smart enough to write that book."*

A friend tells this story:

He had just moved to Mechanicsburg, Pennsylvania. It was the weekend, and he got a bad case of poison ivy while cleaning his new yard. He recalled that as he was driving into town there was a house with a doctor's shingle. It was Sunday afternoon, and he was desperate. He drove to the house and rang the bell.

The doctor, an old man, was working in the garden. He led the young man to his office, asked him a few questions, and poured out some sugar granules on the man's tongue.

Never having had any experience like this in his life, the man asked about what had just transpired. "Oh," said the doctor, "that's a homœopathic medicine. Do you know anything about homœopathy?" My friend confided that he knew nothing about it at all.

"Well," said the old man, "homœopathy is what the smart guys do when they find out the other shit doesn't work!"

Who was this old homœopath? I asked Henry Williams. "That's Bill Boyson, all right!" he replied, "Always ready to get somebody rankled! Loved annoying people just to see the reaction!"

William Boyson, MD
1894 — April 23, 1972

Boyson worked as a mining engineer and then as the high school principal in a small Pennsylvania mining town before becoming a physician. He graduated from Hahnemann Medical College in 1930. After serving in World War II, he joined the AIH in 1948 and became president of the organization in 1963-64. From 1962 until his death he served as the dean of instruction at the American Foundation postgraduate course that was held at Millersville, Pennsylvania.

Harris Coulter says of Boyson, "A great guy who ran the NCH postgrad course for for a while. He was a tremendous character. But he was a very disorganized homœopath. I don't think he ever looked at a Kent *Repertory* in his life. He had a favorite book here and a favorite book there. He was a good family doctor and a good homœopath."

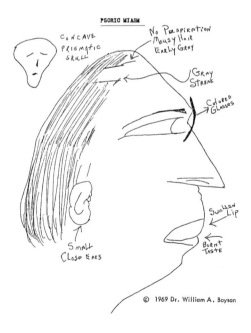

The "Psoric Miasm": a drawing by Boyson given to the classes at Millersville

1950 –1965: The New Leaders

Allen Neiswander
Henry Williams
James Stephenson
Maesimund B. Panos

The 1950s were a trying time for homœopathy. Hahnemann Medical College ceased teaching its one elective course. The senior practitioners were all well along in years, and membership of both the American Institute and the International Hahnemannian Association was decreasing as the elders died. The American Foundation's post-graduate course struggled along, with many of the students coming from India, but few Americans showing any interest.

The Laymen's Leagues were still functioning, but their membership, too, was getting older. Few younger people were showing any interest in homœopathy.

Many older physicians were leaving their libraries to the American Foundation, but few were interested in the old books. Many libraries were consigned to the rubbish-tip by relatives who had no interest in the preserving of homœopathy.

The state homœopathic examining boards were phased out because there were no homœopathic graduates to sit the exams. Said Allen Sutherland in 1959, "With no homœopaths being graduated from any medical school today, a homœopathic examining board is an anachronism."

The Illinois State
Homœopathic
Society, 1958.
There were no names
on the original photo.

In 1971, in his book, *Homeopathy in America: the Rise and Fall of a Medical Heresy*, Martin Kaufman wrote a grim summary:

> "By 1960, with few notable exceptions, the average homeopath was well over sixty years old. Every year, death further depletes the ranks. With only a few converts, the future looks grim, indeed. Unless this trend can be reversed, homeopathy will not survive for more than two or three decades."

The photo below, taken in 1961 at a dinner in Chicago honoring four grand homœopaths, cannot presage that these experienced homœopaths— Grimmer, Senseman, Wright Hubbard, and Garcia-Trevino— would all be gone within a few years.

But there were a few who kept the homœopathic light burning. They were from the next younger generation.

From the left, Eliud Garcia-Trevino, Elizabeth Wright Hubbard, Mary Senseman, Arthur Grimmer, Mrs. Grimmer

Allen Neiswander, 1950

Allen Neiswander, MD, DHt
January 31, 1914 —

Neiswander's father, Harry Allen Neiswander, graduated from Cleveland Pulte in 1912 and took the first formal American Foundation postgraduate course in Boston in 1924. The family camped for the six weeks on Boston Commons.

Neiswander graduated from Ohio State University at Columbus, Ohio, in 1942. The day of his graduation, he married Georgiana Rew, whom he had met at the school. He had to intern for a year before going into the service and he and Georgiana decided they might as well spend the year in a warm place. He applied for positions in Florida and California. As California replied first, the young couple moved to Los Angeles. Neiswander served with the Medical Corps in Europe and returned to California in 1946. He then attended the first six-week session of the American Foundation course held after World War II in Boston. It was taught by some of the grand masters: Elizabeth Wright Hubbard, Allan Sutherland, H. A. Roberts, Julia M. Green, Guy Beckley Stearns, Harvey Farrington, and Eugene Underhill.

Neiswander was very active in the American Institute of Homœopathy, serving as editor of the *Journal of the American Institute of Homœopathy* from 1968 until 1977, and then again from 1978 until 1982.

He has a limited practice in Alhambra, California.

Allen and Georgiana Neiswander, 1997

Henry Noyes Williams, MD DHt
September 24, 1915 —

Williams graduated with an MD from Columbia University in 1941. Williams originally heard of homœopathy from a health care provider who had treated Williams' wife. His curiosity piqued, he heard about the American Foundation postgraduate course, and took the 1950 session, taught by Wright Hubbard, Green, Sutherland, and MacLaren. Says Williams:

"On returning to my practice, I got an emergency call one evening to the home of a new patient. I found him in a dimly lit bedroom, sitting on the edge of his bed, his arms draped over a chair. He would not answer questions, only grunt. From the family I learned that he had a cold and had started to cough three days prior. He had just developed pains in his right side and refused all food. On examination, he had a dry fever, appeared short of breath, had difficult respiration with rales and dullness at the right base with severe pain on attempting deep inspiration. In spite of the lack of a friction rub, (he wouldn't attempt to breathe deeper) the diagnosis of lobar pneumonia with pleurisy was clear. What should I do?

"I took a throat swab (the patient wouldn't cough for me) which I later took to the hospital for culture and sensitivity. But which antibiotic would help control the infection and what medicine could I give to relieve his cough and pain? Too much could cause respiratory arrest and death. The picture suggested one of the homœopathic remedies that I had been studying. I took out the small homœopathic case that I bought at the course and put a few granules of *Bryonia alba* 200 on his tongue. As I went to replace the kit in my bag, I heard the patient take a deep breath. 'How do you feel?' I nervously asked. 'Doc,' he said, 'that's the first breath I've had in three days. As soon as that medicine touched my tongue I began to feel better.' I was now a convinced homœopath."

Williams was one of the incorporators of the National Center for Homœopathy in 1974. He was the dean of the educational program for the National Center for Homœopathy from 1980 till 1986. He retired in 1993 after 52 years of active practice in Lancaster, Pennsylvania.

Henry N. Williams, 1974

Henry N. Williams, Ohio, 1997

James Stephenson

James Hawley Stephenson, MD, DHt
March 29, 1919 — March 20, 1985

An intense desire to write had young Stephenson working as an executive trainee at Harpers Publishing from 1939-1941. With the advent of World War II, he enlisted in the Army, soon transferring to the Air Force. His bomber was shot down over Germany and he spent several years in a German prison camp.

Returning from the war, Stephenson enrolled in Cornell University, and received his medical degree in 1951. He then studied at the Raja Yoga Arcane School and with Ida Rolf.

Very interested in astrology, he read that the zodiac signs have a relationship to Schuessler's Cell Salts. He found the 12 Salts at the Boericke and Tafel pharmacy in New York, still open on 47th Street. They, in turn, referred him to Elizabeth Wright Hubbard. She cured him of a persistent pain he had had since being a prisoner of war, and she became his mentor.

Stephenson did postgraduate studies with the New York Society for Analytical Psychology, and studied cranial osteopathy with Howard Lippincott.

He was a trustee of the American Institute and served as its director of research. He belonged to the International Hahnemannian Association, and revived the organization in 1983. He was one of the first diplomates of the board of homeotherapeutics.

He authored *Hahnemannian Provings 1924-1959, The Index Medicus Homeopathicus Cumulativus 1958-65*, and, in 1976, *A Doctor's Guide to Helping Yourself With Homeopathic Remedies*. He also authored several poetry books.

He authored and co-authored many articles, from his first contribution ("Clinical Applications of Homeopathy in 100 Case Histories") in 1956, through his later work— "On the Possible Field Effects of the Solvent Phase of Succussed High Dilutions" (1966) and "First Evidence of a Bio-Physical Field" in 1969. He was one of the first to write about the measurement of homœopathic potencies with nuclear magnetic resonance.

He was described by Henry Williams as "a prodigious worker, an excellent prescriber, and a prince among men."

But there was another side. A homœopath who knew him said that he wouldn't share his vast knowledge. He kept things to himself. An aspiring writer, he was very disappointed his "self-help" book didn't get many people interested in homœopathy, while six years later, the book by Panos and Heimlich became a "homœopathic best seller."

Some say he had a permanent scar left by his prisoner of war experience. A female patient of his reported that while he was a good physician to her, his manner toward her was curt to the point of rudeness. Harris Coulter, speaking of Stephenson's wartime experiences, said it had "made him a terrible misanthrope— he hated everybody."

He died, aged 65, of a rapid developing pancreatic cancer.

Maesimund Banning Panos, MD, DHt
June 12, 1912 —

Panos comes from a long line of homœopaths, with both her father and grandfather homœopathic physicians. They developed the "Banning Brace," a mechanical support for spinal problems. Ads for the brace were often seen in the old homœopathic journals.

Dr. Banning, her father, took in a young preceptor, John Panos, a Greek immigrant who came to the United States to study medicine. John Panos finished medical school and, in 1939, married Maisie. Panos, by her own admission, didn't pay much attention to homœopathy; she was busy with her household and children.

In 1947, John Panos died, and Maisie found herself faced with all his patients asking for advice, as there were no homœopaths in the area.

The Homœopathic Recorder was still arriving in the mail, and Maisie was still reading it. Through the pages she became acquainted with Dr. Edward Whitmont in New York, with whom she visited and established a life-long friendship. Within a few years, at the age of 41, she decided to go to medical school and enrolled at Ohio State University.

After graduation she received an invitation to go to Washington, DC to work with Dr. Julia M. Green. She asked Whitmont, "Oh, she's so old, what can she teach me?" He replied, "You have no idea. She may forget your name, but she'll never forget her materia medica."

Panos moved with her family to Washington, DC, preceptored with Green, taking over Green's practice in 1959.

It was Panos who met George Vithoulkas in Greece in 1969 and introduced him to a whole new generation of homœopaths. It was Panos who understood where homœopathy in the United States needed to go, and helped take it there. It was mainly through her generosity that the National Center for Homeopathy survived into the 1980s. The mark Panos left in American homœopathy (and, in a way, homœopathy in Europe as well) is probably larger than anyone can estimate.

Maesimund B. Panos, 1982

Maisie (in the middle) with her father

Panos' father, Dr. Edmund Banning, Jr., graduated from the Cleveland Homœopathic College in 1892. He had fought in the Civil War; Panos has his commission, signed by Lincoln, hanging in her entry hall. "I was a child of his old age," she says.
I am amazed that I know someone whose father was in the American Civil War!

Through the years Panos became acquainted with the grand homœopaths of the time, including Elizabeth Wright Hubbard. Through Green, she became an integral part of the American Foundation for Homœopathy, and later, the National Center for Homeopathy.

In 1969 Panos attended the meeting of the International Homœopathic League (LMHI) in Athens, Greece. One evening while walking with a group of other attendees to view the sunset over the sea, she fell in beside a young homœopath and struck up a conversation. It was a chance meeting that would change the face of homœopathy in the United States. The young man "with the engaging personality" was George Vithoulkas. For the next few years she corresponded with Vithoulkas and returned to Greece a few times to visit. In 1974 she brought Vithoulkas to the United States for the joint American Foundation and LHMI meeting in Washington DC, introducing him to a whole new generation of homœopaths. The rest is history.

Panos married John Holtvoight in 1970, and relocated her practice to Tipp City, Ohio in 1972. In 1980, she was approached by Jane Heimlich (the wife of the "Maneuver" doctor) who was a writer interested in alternative medicine. As Panos said, "She would come up for two days at a time, scribble notes on those yellow legal pads and go home to organize it all, then come up again." The result was

Panos (far left) at the 90th birthday party for Julia M. Green (on the right)

Homeopathic Medicine at Home, which was published in 1980. It became one of the best selling "domestic manuals" and has been re–printed in several languages.

Panos and her daughter have published the *Cumulative Indices of The Homœopathic Recorder* and *The Proceedings of the International Association for the years 1881 to 1958.* They have also edited a collection of the writings of Dr. Elizabeth Wright Hubbard, *Homeopathy as Art and Science.*

Panos retired from active practice in 1992. Living in Florida, she is currently compiling an index of the *Journal of the American Institute of Homeopathy.*

Maesimund Panos, Edward Whitmont, and Henry Williams at the 150th Anniversary of the American Institute of Homœopathy, New York, 1994

An ad for the "Banning Brace," circa 1890.

names…

"How are they called?" When writing about times past, it is easy to refer to all the personages by the names we know them from their books. We have a single record of Kent referring to Richard Hughes as "Dicky," but, to his friends, was Kent "Jimmy"? Or was he "Ty" (for Tyler)? Was Nash "Gene"? We simply do not know.

Perhaps the 1970s became less formal or perhaps it is because I know many of these people on a personal level. To me Henry Williams has always been "Hal," Maesimund Panos always "Maisie," and Richard Moskowitz always "Dick."

It presented an interesting debate from the editor, indexer, and proof-reader, each in turn. In the end, I wrote it from my heart rather than from a place of intellectual "correctness."

A Letter to my Patients

All along the years it has been my constant hope that Washington and its environs might have continual service from sympathetic, warm-hearted Doctors willing to keep Homoeopathy in the Capital City of our Nation.

Now I may tell you that Dr. Maisie Panos is already in our midst with her two teen-age daughters, in the process of purchasing a home in this city near the right educational facilities for the girls.

My office is to have this wonderful helper in it, beginning September 1, 1959. You have been most understandingly kind to me during this long wait. Many of you have wanted to bring in friends and relatives as patients, but have refrained from doing it, knowing how overburdened I am. No longer need you hold back on sending in patients and spreading the word Homoeopathy as you have longed to do for several years. The new doctor needs to be very busy in order to support herself and her family in the proper way. It will be my pleasure to be right behind Dr. Panos for as long as necessary to have her thoroughly indoctrinated in the best of Homoeopathy.

Thank you, each one, for this.

God bless us all,

Julia Minerva Green

The letter from Julia M. Green to her patients, announcing Maesimund Panos.

The 1970s: The Resurgence

The new generation
The "Boston Ladies"

The resurgence happened so quickly, and on so many fronts, that it is almost impossible to construct a time-line picture of it. An event here triggered an event there. It was a time of the changing of the guard. However, it was not without strife.

One way to understand what happened is first to look at the people involved, and then to look at the "politics" of the time and observe the interactions. It was all very loose yet very deeply inter-related.

When Martin Kaufman was describing the demise of homœopathy in the 1960s, he could not have foreseen the revolution in consciousness that began to sweep the country in the late 60s and early 70s. When Timothy Leary urged a generation to "Turn on, tune in, and drop out," many of those hearing his message started their own self-evaluation, searching for ways to find self-fulfillment. Some were medical students searching within medicine for their own answers. A few found homœopathy.

The postgraduate classes held by the American Foundation (and subsequently administered by the National Center for Homeopathy) began to get more young physicians searching for better ways of healing—physicians like Bill Gray, Dean Crothers, Nick Nossaman, Karl Robinson, Sandra Chase, David Wember, and Richard Moskowitz— each of whom would play an important role in the homœopathic resurgence.

The 1972 Class at Millersville

(seated) Allan Sutherland, MD; Maisie Panos, MD; Lucy Clark, MD; Mrs. K. H. Rotermund (middle row) Dr. Upadhya; Dr. S. R. Wadia; L. Avery, DO; K. H. Rotermund, DO; David Wember, MD (back row) Dr. Maurice Soleillet; Jack Cooper, MD; Bill Gray, MD; Walter Telep, RN.

Bill Gray, MD, DHt
October 13, 1942 —

Gray graduated from Stanford Medical School in 1970. After serving his internship he re-evaluated his education—a process started in his junior year of medical school. He soon decided to drop out of medicine and "cast about for something to do." A self-confessed "rabble-rouser," he joined the War Resister's League (this was the height of the Vietnam War) and departed with a group on a bus travelling cross-country and stopping along the way to conduct anti-war rallies. His job was to talk about alternative medicine. "I was very interested in acupuncture," he said, "because of all the medicines it seemed to have a coherent system. But, at the time, it was hard to learn. There were no teachers in the United States and if you wanted to do it right you really had to go to China."

The bus trip ended somewhere in upstate New York, where one evening Gray found a magazine containing an interview with poet Theodore Enslin written by Richard Grossinger. In the interview there was a discussion of homœopathic philosophy. Homœopathy captured Gray immediately. At the end of the article was a list of "useful addresses." One of the addresses was that of Dr. William Gutman in New York City. Gray phoned Gutman and asked if he could apprentice with him. Gutman told him that he was too old to take on anyone, but if Bill wanted to learn more about homœopathy, he should attend the American Foundation program at Millersville.

In 1972 he went to the Millersville program. David Wember, who was also taking the course at that time, remembers Bill sitting, listening, and saying, "far out!" at regular intervals.

Gray returned to California and started a homœopathic practice.

In 1974 he attended the combination LHMI and AFH meeting in Washington, DC, where George Vithoulkas had been invited to speak. He learned from Vithoulkas that coffee was often an antidote to homœopathic remedies, and when he returned to California he asked his patients to cease their coffee intake. A good number of his cases improved from this alone. Recognizing how much he could learn from Vithoulkas, he arranged to spend a month in Greece at Vithoulkas' clinic. He went, returned to

California, then went back to Greece for another month.

It was not possible for him, as an American doctor, to legally practice in Greece. He saved his money, and supplemented his income by doing lectures about homœopathy, inspiring many people to study homœopathy. When he had saved enough to tide him over for two years, he left his practice and spent two years with Vithoulkas in Greece.

Gray then returned to the Bay area and by 1978, with the help of an un-named donor, formed the International Foundation for the Promotion of Homeopathy.

While in Greece he had begun work with Vithoulkas on a book. The work was completed in 1978, and the book, *The Science of Homeopathy*, became the first new philosophical text on the subject in almost 30 years. Since Vithoulkas' command of the English language at that time was not developed enough to write the full text, Gray wrote the book with Vithoulkas, based on Vithoulkas' ideas.

Gray was one of the organizers of the Hahnemann College and Clinic established in 1984. "My background really helped me set up organizations. I really know how to do that," he said, "but I don't work well within organizations. I do better on my own."

Gray is currently on the teaching staff at the Hahnemann College, and is in private practice in Davis, California.

Dean Crothers, MD, DHt
March 28, 1948 —

Crothers got his BS in psychology at Washington State University, and his MD degree from Washington School of Medicine in 1973. He started a family practice in July 1975.

Crothers had purchased Vithoulkas' first book, *Homeopathy: Medicine of the New Man*, during his second year in medical school. After reading it for the second time he wrote a letter to the Puget Sound Homeopathic Society asking for more information about homœopathy. This lay organization sent a delegate to his office. Says Crothers: "The man suffered from long-term multiple sclerosis and was nearly blind. He had studied homœopathy for years, using a magnifying glass to read the books. He was my first teacher, taking a bus from Seattle to Mount Vernon, 75 miles north, each Wednesday for several months. He

Dean Crothers

introduced me to many homœopathic books and to Kay Vargo of the National Center for Homeopathy. It was Kay Vargo, attending a meeting of the Puget Sound Homeopathic Society, who encouraged me to attend the Millersville course."

After attending Millersville in 1976, Crothers was still struggling to grasp the concepts and application of homœopathy in clinical practice. In 1978, Maisie Panos encouraged him to apply for a scholarship to attend Vithoulkas' school in Athens. Crothers mentioned to a loyal patient he would love to study with Vithoulkas, but even with a $1,000 scholarship it would be impossible. The patient asked for the names and addresses of some of Crothers' patients and within two weeks $1,000 arrived in the form of personal checks, none in excess of about $20.

After the experiences in Athens in 1978 and again in 1979, plus meeting Bill Gray at a meeting of the California State Homeopathic Society around that same time, Crothers decided to take the "Doctor's Course" in 1980. He became a course teacher in 1981. Jennifer Jacobs, MD, was a student in the 1981 class and, as Crothers said, "The rest is history." They were soon married.

In September 1980, during the Vithoulkas seminar at Esalen, Crothers attended his first American Institute of Homeopathy meeting. He described the AIH at the time as "nearly lifeless." On a trip to San Francisco in 1981, he visited Dr. Frederic Schmid and expressed an interest in participating on the Institute board of trustees. Schmid telephoned Wyrth Post Baker while Crothers was sitting in the office. Says Crothers: "I guess they were happy to see someone with some enthusiasm. I was elected president of the AIH in 1982, without the usual moving up through the ranks of second vice president, first vice president, president elect, then president. During my first (and only) term of office the AIH membership changed the by–laws so that my one–year term became a three-year term."

Crothers' presidency of the AIH marked the beginning of the resurgence of that organization. The "younger generation" were now in a leadership role.

Crothers and Jacobs have a private practice in Edmonds, Washington.

Nicholas Nossaman, MD, DHt
December 20, 1942 —

Nossaman graduated from the University of Colorado School of Medicine in 1968. He spent two years on a Navajo Reservation, in Crownpoint, New Mexico, running a 55-bed hospital and out–patient clinic with four other physicians. "I learned a lot about third world diseases and practical medicine and was fascinated by the respect and regard for nature inherent in Navajo healing rituals and medical beliefs."

After completing a postgraduate degree in health planning and administration, he was a primary care physician for three years in an urban community-oriented low-income neighborhood clinic. While there, he was introduced to homœopathy by a woman who had cured her headaches with the help of Dwight Smith, MD, in California, via a letter describing her symptoms.

Says Nossaman: "As so many of us have, she became rabid about it after her 'burning bush' experience, and had me interested after five minutes of conversation. Dick Moskowitz was in Santa Fe at the time, and became a major inspiration to me, as well as serving as a practical mentor in getting going. Along with Karl Robinson, Joya Schoen, Dean Crothers and others, I attended Millersville in 1976 and incorporated homœotherapeutics into my work at the community clinic, with the blessing of my medical director, financed by local and federal government grants.

"Taking a foray into leadership, I was on the National Center board in 1978, and elected president in that stormy period of the NCH transition. After resigning from the presidency, I turned my political interests to the American Institute of Homeopathy, running for the board and later becoming president of the AIH around 1985-1988 or so."

Nossaman is in private practice in Denver, Colorado.

Karl Robinson, MD, DHt
March 2, 1938 —

Robinson took his undergraduate degree in journalism at Yale, and worked as a newspaper reporter. In 1966 he took a year off and returned to Nigeria in West Africa where he had been a teacher several years earlier. Traveling by motorcycle to Gabon, he burned his leg on the motorcycle's manifold. The burn became infected and he was hospitalized at Lambarane, the hospital that Albert Schweitzer founded. Dr. Schweitzer had died the previous year and Schweitzer's daughter was the administrator of the hospital.

As Robinson was recovering he was given some books to read about Schweitzer. In reflecting on his own life, he decided to become a doctor. Returning to the United States he completed his pre-med studies and entered Hahnemann Medical College. His roommate's father had gone to Hahnemann in the 1930s and had trained in homœopathy.

After graduation Robinson became increasingly discouraged with conventional medicine. He attended the National Center course in 1976 with Dean Crothers and Nick Nossaman.

His intense interest in yoga had him visiting India in 1977 where he practiced homœopathy in the ashram clinic. He then took the "year course" in homœopathy at the Faculty of Homœopathy in London.

In 1978 he started his medical practice in Santa Fe, New Mexico. He did a three–week course in Greece with Vithoulkas that same year. He followed up with the "doctors" course with Bill Gray, and also attended the one month workshop with Vithoulkas at Esalen in 1980.

Always looking for new ideas, Robinson has studied with many homœopaths, and brought several to the United States as speakers. He has taught homœopathy in the south-west since the early 1980s.

From 1984 to 1990 Robinson was the editor of the *Journal of the American Institute of Homeopathy.*

He is in private practice in Albuquerque, New Mexico and in Houston, Texas.

Karl Robinson

When I took the job as Registrar for the NCH in 1981 I had to establish contact with the Faculty. Karl was the only person I hadn't met— and no one could tell me anything about him. I had been seeing his name in the literature for a while. He came from Albuquerque. He went to Hahnemann Medical College and then studied at the Faculty in London. Hmm... Karl... with a "K." I conjured visions of an old German doctor who had come to Hahnemann during the War years and then took refuge in the UK. He must have retired to the south-west for his health, I thought. Then I received a letter from him. Hmm... small, precise hand. It fit my picture.

And then we met. The voice said, "Hi. I'm Karl Robinson." I looked up and the elderly German gentleman faded rapidly!

Sandra M. Chase, MD, DHt
September 26, 1945 —

Chase's father had a childhood problem with tonsillitis not helped by orthodox medicine. His mother took him to Julia M. Green. The tonsils were cured and he became a firm believer in homœopathy. After he married, he and his wife continued their medical care with Dr. Green in Washington, DC.

Sandra Chase was born in the National Homœopathic Hospital in Washington, DC. The family physician was Dr. Green. Says Chase, "My next brother John Edward Chase, Jr., and I were delivered by Dr. J. E. B. Gregg Custis. By the time my youngest brother Geoffrey Lowell Chase was due, old Dr. Custis had retired and Dr. Green didn't trust the younger Dr. Custis and so she delivered Geoffrey herself. My father described her as coming out of the delivery room all disheveled from the experience. That was 1950 so she would have been about 79 years old!"

Upon Dr. Green's retirement, the Chase family was cared for by Maesimund Panos. Says Chase, "I believe that the early influence of my father, contact with these two outstanding physicians, and a long-held ambition of my own clearly pointed me in the direction of medicine."

Chase earned her medical degree at the Woman's Medical College of Pennsylvania in 1971. Says Chase, "I pursued a medical degree with the idea of becoming a homœopathic physician though I never mentioned that while I was in training."

While Chase was very much aware of homœopathy from early childhood, her effective homœopathic education really began at the postgraduate school of the National Center for Homeopathy in 1974. "I took the first of two courses," she notes. "I had the good fortune to learn from such great homœopaths as Maesimund Panos, Henry N. Williams, the late Lucy S. Clark, Ruth Rogers, and others. The next year the school offered follow-up courses which I took. As a result of my family connection with Dr. Panos, I also had the invaluable opportunity to do a preceptorship with her in 1974 and 1975."

Chase is very active in homœopathic politics, having served as president of the National Center for Homeopathy as well as the president of the Liga Homœopathica Medicorum Internationalis in 1994. She has also served as president of the American Institute of Homeopathy and as secretary of the Homœopathic Pharmacopoeia Convention of the United States, secretary of the American Board of Homœotherapeutics, secretary-treasurer of the Southern Homœopathic Association, and editor of *The Southern Letter.*

She is in practice in Fairfax, Virginia.

David G. Wember, MD, DHt
February 16, 1940 —

Wember graduated from Wayne State Medical School in 1965. After serving an internship in public health on Staten Island, New York, he joined the Peace Corps and spent time in West Africa. Upon returning he worked in a psychiatric residency at St. Elizabeth's Hospital in Washington, DC.

Disillusioned with medicine, he drifted slowly from it. His two young children were always sick with colds or earaches, and he was treating them with decongestants, which, he said, "I got by the bottle-full through my residency."

Somewhere along the way a friend suggested that he try homœopathy and gave him some remedies. "I used them on the children," he said, "and at the end of the year it seemed to me that they hadn't been as sick as they had in the past."

He found out Maisie Panos was practicing in Washington and went to see her. She convinced him to go to the Millersville Course in 1972. Panos was moving to Ohio that year, and the Washington Layman's League paid for Wember's tuition at Millersville, hoping he would be able to replace Panos as a homœopath in Washington. He returned to the course in 1973, and set up homœopathic practice in 1974.

He was one of the earliest pupils to go to Greece to study with Vithoulkas in 1976.

He was on the board of directors of the National Center for Homeopathy from 1981-1987, and dean of education from 1984-1987. His teaching of the Kent *Repertory* at the summer school initiated a generation of homœopaths into this arcane study. When the National Center split from the American Foundation in 1981, Wember was one of the principal players who held the National Center together.

He is in private practice in Rockville, Maryland.

Richard Moskowitz, MD, DHt
December 16, 1938 —

William Kirtsos (left), owner of Homœopathic Resources and Services, one of the finest private collections of homœopathic books and ephemera, with Richard Moskowitz, circa 1989

Richard Moskowitz M.D.

Moskowitz took his undergraduate degree from Harvard before entering New York University School of Medicine, obtaining his degree in 1963. He found both the training at the school and his clinical years at New York's Bellevue Hospital in New York a shattering personal experience.

"Nothing in my upbringing or education," he said, "prepared me for the reality in which disease was the basic condition and a vast nexus of goods and services had been created to manipulate and exploit it."

Having completed medical school, he took a hiatus from medicine with a two–year Fellowship in Philosophy at the University of Colorado. He then served a rotating internship at St. Anthony's Hospital in Denver, Colorado and subsequently became a staff physician at several hospitals and health clinics in Colorado.

"My evolution," said Moskowitz, "has been a long and tortuous one, but as soon as I discovered homœopathy, I knew that it was the prize I had been looking for."

In Colorado, fate put him in the path of a home birth experience. It was his first step to discovering a healing relationship that made sense and worked. Called to a home birth, he realized that it was his place to assist in the process and not to "be in charge"; that the woman who was delivering the baby had the situation well under control. "It was not like the hospital," said Moskowitz with his knack for understatement.

By 1974, Moskowitz was living in New Mexico, studying acupuncture. He had heard about homœopathy in the local health food store, and had read a book which he says, "didn't make much sense." He wrote to Dr. Sutherland in Vermont for some advice about a patient with a sensitivity to bee stings. Sutherland responded by saying: "Well, sonny boy, I think you'd better come to our summer school." He went to Millersville.

Describing the course, Moskowitz said: "At first glance, neither the sleepy state college campus where the course was given nor the rumpled clothes and advanced age of the homœopaths who taught it augured well for the future of the profession. Most of the faculty were quite old and semi-retired, and very few were actively earning their living from practicing the method they were teaching us. It was as if a whole generation of the most active, successful experienced practitioners who should have carried the main teaching load were missing. Equally upsetting was the fact that the course lasted only two weeks, after which we were simply turned loose to practice what we had learned on our patients. With no full-time schools, no teaching hospitals, and few retail pharmacies to send patients to, it was difficult to imagine that American homœopathy could survive much longer. Yet from the moment I began that course, I knew it was exactly what I had been looking for and that I could happily devote the rest of my professional life to studying and practicing it."

After the course, Moskowitz traveled to Greece several times to study with Vithoulkas.

Moskowitz has taught regularly for the National Center, and has conducted many homœopathic seminars for physicians and consumers. He has published extensively, writing articles and book reviews and providing homœopathic information for encyclopedias and resource publications. His two pamphlets, *Homeopathic Reasoning* and *The Case Against Immunizations,* are magnificently concise

Dick is, as I am, a collector. When he first started in homœopathic practice he phoned John A. Borneman & Sons and said that he wanted every remedy listed in the Kent Repertory in the 30th potency, on number 10 granules, in corked two dram vials. "I just wanted to be sure that if a patient needed it, I had it," he said.
After someone saw the picture below of his office in Santa Fe in 1982, they asked, "Well how many of those remedies does he use?" So I asked. And Dick replied, "Well, if you're looking at just remedies and not at assorted potencies, I'd say that over the years I've used, maybe, a hundred or so. But," he twinkled a grin, "I just had my first Stillingia case!"

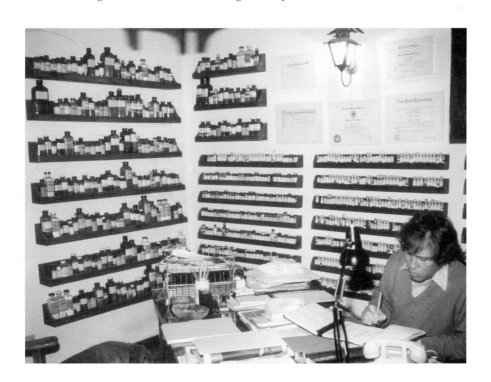

statements. His book, *Homeopathic Medicine in Pregnancy and Childbirth*, is based upon his years of experience of using homœopathy in over 600 births.

"I find that in addition to being of immediate and practical use to patients, homœopathy also provides me with an elegant and beautiful vantage point for the study of the natural world," Moskowitz says.

"Both the natural medicines of the earth and the illnesses needing their help are investigated in the same way, through what patients actually experience. Invasive laboratory tests and unconsenting animal subjects are seldom needed. Our knowledge of how each medicine acts and our patients' experience of illness thus run in parallel, each complementing and enriching the other as we put them together to obtain the best possible match."

Moskowitz is a past president and board member of the National Center for Homeopathy. A connoisseur of all fine things homœopathic, he maintains one of the finest private homœopathic libraries in the United States, as well as a grand collection of old, rare, and unusual homœopathic remedies.

He is also a wonderful opera singer! Moskowitz practices in Watertown, Massachusetts and is married to Linda Sklar, a practicing psychotherapist.

> I'm singing a lot these days, taking lessons with somebody who has sung at the Met, and performing regularly with the chorus I've sung with for the past four years, which is a real kick. Also I give out a few remedies from time to time, and even manage to help people occasionally. In short, not much has changed, and we're enjoying life for the most part.

An excerpt from a letter to me from Dick, January 4, 1997. When I first met Dick at Millersville in 1980, he showed me the notes he had taken at the course with Vithoulkas in Greece. They were all written in this beautiful, cursive hand.

The "Boston ladies"

Moskowitz, 1987, with the *grande dames* of Boston. From the left, Elinore Peebles, Dorothy Cornish (who had been Dr. Alonzo Shadman's secretary), Lilly Spalding (widow of Dr. Ray Spalding) and Ruth Green (the daughter of Arthur Green).

Boston, Massachusetts, was a major center of homœopathy for many years. In the 1940s the homœopathic community even funded its own hospital, a 15–bed facility in Brighton, that was staffed by IHA members.

But as the elder homœopaths died in the 1950s and 1960s, the hospital reverted to allopathic control, and the Boston community drew itself in. Those remaining held the treasure closely; the candle almost out but still flickering as those protecting it kept it glowing.

When Moskowitz moved to Boston in 1982, he was intensely scrutinized. The "Boston Ladies" sized him up and decided he was worthy.

Says Moskowitz: "I first met Elinore [Peebles] in 1982, within a few days of my arrival in Boston, incognito as I thought, on sabbatical, with no desire to start up a practice right away. At first I was a little taken back by this frail octogenarian quizzing me on Hahnemann and Kent in my own living room. When she told me, in a voice that brooked no contradiction, that there hadn't been a homœopath in Boston for 25 years, and that I'd better get busy, there was suddenly nowhere to hide."

Elinore C. Peebles
1897 — July 13, 1992

I had the good fortune to spend an afternoon with Elinore Peebles on two occasions— the first shortly after meeting her at the National Center meeting in Boston in 1987. It was Elinore who got me looking for the "story behind the story" and, in a way, started me on the history quest. She shook her finger as she talked. "I've read all the AIH Transactions," she told me, "and I know what happened to homœopathy. It was their own fault. They gave up following the principles, and it all withered. Thank God we had the IHA and the Kentians to keep it alive."

She was a veritable fount of information, and pulled no punches. She told me how, as a little girl, her doctor, Fred Keith, showed her the back gate to the house of Mary Baker Eddy, the founder of Christian Science. Dr. Keith told her he used that gate to come and go while he was doctoring Ms. Eddy, who still used homœopathy in her times of need. She told me how disappointed she was Dr. Wesselhoeft (the grandson of William Wesselhoeft) drifted away from homœopathy. "He was a good homœopath, and would use homœopathy if you asked for it, but otherwise he'd use conventional medicine," she told me. She did not understand how someone who had seen homœopathy work could drift back to conventional medicine. And she was still dismayed that Wesselhoeft convinced her son to be a conventional physician and not a homœopath.

She managed, through the force of her will, to keep the homœopathic heritage alive in the Boston area. She was an amazing woman!

Peebles' father, Charles Theodore Cutting, MD, graduated from the Hahnemann Medical College the year of her birth. Dr. Cutting set up his medical practice in Newtonville, Massachusetts, and young Elinore learned homœopathy directly from him, helping in his office when he saw patients, accompanying him on home and hospital visits, and eavesdropping on his case conferences with colleagues.

Elinore wanted to be a physician, but when she was 16, financial reverses abruptly put an end to both her dream and her childhood.

She soon married Waldo Peebles, an old friend of her childhood, and set herself to raising a daughter and two sons and a flock of grandchildren. She also became active in the Swedenborgian Church.

In later years Peebles loved to wear her favorite T-shirt, which announced "Here comes a Homeopath" on the front, and concluded "There goes a Swedenborgian" on the back.

In the 1940s and 50s, with homœopathy clearly on the decline and the Boston homœopaths beginning to die off without leaving replacements, Peebles devoted herself to homœopathic education and self-help with a zeal and ability that were an inspiration to all who knew her. She became active in the Boston Homœopathic Laymen's League and the Ladies' Auxiliary of Hahnemann Hospital in Brighton, the small homœopathic community hospital founded in the 1940s.

During the 1950s, with the help of James Stephenson and Dorothy Cornish, she organized the "Homeopathic Information Service" and published several splendid pamphlets about homœopathy for the general public. Some of these she wrote herself. During this period she was invited to speak to Harvard medical students, and helped organize a series of lectures at Boston University, which had been founded as a homœopathic medical school. For these labors she was awarded an honorary life membership to the AIH, whose professional meetings she regularly attended. The "Homeopathic Information Service" remained active until the mid–1970s.

The 1970s: The Revitalization

The fifth decade of the American Foundation
The formation of the National Center

Ralph Packman, 1970

The fifth decade of the American Foundation

In 1960, John Leahy, the legal council for the American Foundation for Homœopathy, read of a public relations effort in New Jersey which had helped the position of osteopathic physicians in that state. The person conducting the campaign was Ralph Packman, an advertising executive from Philadelphia. Packman was invited to meet several trustees of the American Foundation, and was soon appointed its public relations counsel.

Packman spent about a year studying homœopathy's position in the United States, and then made several recommendations, among them a closer alliance between the Foundation and the AIH, and the formation of a series of national "Laymen's Leagues." On the need for "fund-raising," Packman suggested this should not be undertaken until the organization had a base of at least 800 supporters.

In 1963 Kay Vargo, from Cincinnati, became the president of the "Leagues Federation," the person responsible for the running of the Laymen's Leagues. In the eyes of some trustees, the "Leagues" were often a problem, as the groups were often composed of people interested in using homœopathy but not having a homœopathic physician available to them. The issues formed the core of the continuing debate about homœopathic education and the question of lay practice.

Julia M. Green died in 1963 and the running of the American Foundation devolved, eventually, to her brother, Arthur Green (1884-1977). Dr. Green had left very specific instructions about disposing of her property and wanted to make sure the money would be used to maintain the Foundation as she saw it should be maintained. She had said, "I don't want to do it unless I am pretty sure the Foundation is going to succeed someday and amount to something."

The idea of using Dr. Green's house on Quebec Street as an office for the Foundation was quashed when the adjacent property owners opposed a variance that would have allowed more power into the building for the running of copying machines. The property, in possession of the AFH, was sold.

During the second year of Packman's tenure, money began to flow into the Foundation through a "gifts" program; physicians began asking for dental and veterinary courses to be conducted at the summer program, and support was offered for the magazine, *The Layman Speaks*, that had been published by the AFH since 1947. Packman pointed out that the "physician members of the board of directors were dragging their feet, letting the ball be carried as far as it could by the laymen." He also suggested establishing closer ties between the AFH and the American Association of Homeopathic Pharmacists, a trade organization.

The Layman Speaks had always been a bone of contention. Arthur Green's editorials were outspoken, opinionated, and often adversarial. As early as 1952 the subject of "controversial articles" was discussed by the trustees and

the pen of Arthur B. Green

... The physician who limits his view and his life to study what the "reputable" societies endorse will do the absurd without question and his patients will take the consequences. When one of the plainest things about humanity, that the most untechnical can discern, is that humanity is an aggregate of individuals, no two of whom are alike, at the same time one of the most prevalent absurdities is to suppose that any one medicine is right for all of them under any circumstance. But many doctors conform to the absurdity. Going along with the gang serves society in about the same way all through from adolescence to retirement, in medicine quite as much as out of it.

Editorial, The Layman Speaks, May 1958

[commenting upon a new arthritis drug, Meticorten]... Instead of individualizing their observations, they have made their test in the mass. Instead of testing on the healthy, they have tested the drug on the sick. Instead of delving to find the essential drug action, they have given it crude. All these mistakes have invariably given untrustworthy answers, results that always need revising, conclusions that always have to be modified if not wholly retracted. Let us put this new Meticorten by Schering Corporation in the little notebook and see.

Editorial, The Layman Speaks, April 1955

... Where is the doctor of ordinary medicine whose equipment would not improve by realizing that the man is never cured piece by piece but that man is an integrated unit? Where is the heart sufferer or heart worrier who will not welcome a word of hope and courage, to say nothing of rationality? Where is the layman, deluged by the hour with medical advertising and medical propaganda, to whom a fresh point of view would not be a beam of light?

Editorial, The Layman Speaks, April 1956

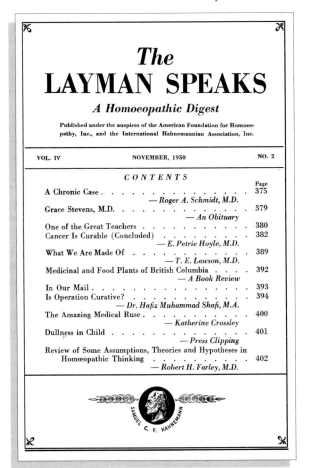

the pen of Arthur B. Green

[In reference to fund-drives]... Each one represents that it is the correct line of attack to "fight" such-and-such "disease." At solicitation time, victory is always in sight. Probably the drive to "fight" tuberculosis is old enough to antedate the bulk of American citizens. Therefore if it be true that every public campaign for research is set on the correct scientific line of attack, so that the "disease" in each case will be put out of action definitely, altogether, and permanently, why doesn't one of these drives for the big money make an announcement: "Thank you, we have succeeded. Our doors are closing. No more funds will be needed"?

Editorial, October 1955

several doctors said they refused to have copies of the magazine in their waiting rooms because they found some of the content— as well as the "unprofessional slurs"— objectionable, as Green was not kindly disposed to allopathic physicians and spoke out in a forthright manner. Dr. Lucy Clark, who was the AFH director of publications from 1957 to 1959 eventually resigned in frustration with Green's policies. She was replaced by Mollie Ray Carrol, who suggested those objecting to the articles should give examples of their objections to Green. But none stepped forward. By this time, Packman had conducted a survey showing the magazine's subscribers were satisfied with the content. Yet the magazine remained a source of contention. It was being produced at a loss, and in 1963 it was reported it would need five times its circulation to break even. Harris Coulter said (in 1995) that Green once asked the members of the board of trustees to attempt to sell "door–to–door" subscription to the magazine.

In 1967 the organization "restructured," and Coulter became director of publications. Green remained editor of *The Layman Speaks* until his 90th birthday in 1974. He was replaced by Richard Dykeman who served till July 1977, when Alain Naudé became editor.

In 1968, Packman suggested the American Foundation become a membership organization. It held its first meeting as such in 1969, but it was still a small organization. Of the 343 members in 1970, only 43 attended the membership meeting.

The American Foundation for Homœopathy managed to stay financially viable through a steady stream of income from grants and estates. In 1973 it received almost $250,000 from one estate. The Foundation's funds were invested and handled carefully, so they were on a solid footing.

The formation of the National Center for Homeopathy

In 1974, the AFH board of trustees received a legal recommendation that, because of current tax-laws, the organization's fund-raising and service aspects should be separated.

In retrospect, it was not an outside opinion that the separation should occur, but rather an inside opinion by a board member who was a lawyer.

Trustee Forrest Murphy (in 1997), offered the opinion that the reason for the separation was to distance the AFH from the lay-movement, since the Foundation's charter dealt specifically with educating physicians, and several of the board believed the organization could lose its foundation status if it considered educating laymen.

By creating the National Center for Homeopathy and having it responsible for the education, the AFH could go back to fulfilling its original charter. The re–organization was also a way to re–structure the organization's internal finances.

The entire Foundation's board of trustees resigned and

Kay Vargo, Arthur B. Green, Mollie Ray Carrol at a dinner honoring Arthur Green, 1970

two new boards constituted. Wyrth Post Baker, MD; Henry N. Williams, MD; and Forrest Murphy became trustees of the AFH, while Roger Ehrhart; Maesimund Panos, MD; Cranston Smith; Doris Waldstein; and Henry N. Williams, MD, became directors of the newly–formed National Center for Homeopathy. The articles of incorporation of the NCH were drawn, almost verbatim, from those of the AFH. The tradition of maintaining a balance of physicians and non–physician board members was continued.

The new organization was dedicated to the promoting of homœopathy in its most classical sense— the simillimum, the single remedy, the minimum dose.

The National Center became the umbrella organization, under which other homœopathic organizations functioned, while the American Foundation continued as the fund-raising entity. The National Center received its funding from the American Foundation.

The postgraduate school now fell under the aegis of the National Center, as did the publication of *The Layman Speaks,* which had a circulation of about 1,400 at the time. Kay Vargo remained the coordinator of the Laymen's Leagues.

The 1970s: The Bay Area

The early study groups
The arrival of Vithoulkas
Essences, seminars, and clinics
The unsung
The formation of the IFH

The early study groups

In the late 1960s and early 1970s, the San Francisco Bay area in California became the center for all things wild and wonderful. With so many people in the area exploring life-style alternatives it should come as no surprise that homœopathy would find fertile ground there.

Randall Neustaedter, OMD
November 9, 1949 —

The Bay area Homeopathic Study Group was started by Randall Neustaedter in February, 1972.

Says Neustaedter: "I personally became interested in homœopathy because I was cured of a lifelong ailment (colitis) by Roger Schmidt, MD, with a single remedy. I asked him for some information and he loaned me a few books. When I asked how I could study it he suggested I go to the Royal London Homœopathic Hospital, which I did. I told them I was a medical student, and I took their one–month course. I bought a box full of books at Nelson's pharmacy, including a copy of Kent's *Repertory*, Clarke's three–volume *Dictionary*, Fisher's *Pediatrics*, etc."

Neustaedter and Bill Gray started a "study group" and were soon joined by Dana Ullman, Corey Weinstein, Peggy Chipkin, Nancy Herrick, and David Warkentin. Later Lou Klein, Steve Cummings, and the rest of what was to become the Hering Clinic staff joined the study group.

"In 1974 I was 25 years old. I was sitting on my bed with my wife and said, 'Maybe we should start a homœopathic clinic.' We gathered a bunch of people and Corey took out a free loan for start-up businesses. The Hering Family Health Clinic opened in September 1975 in a medical building on Ward Street in Berkeley. The initial clinic staff included Corey Weinstein, MD, and Jack Guralnik, MD, myself, Chris Ciavarella, Marty Block, and Kathy Kallander as prescribers. We soon began a training program and Steve Cummings and Nancy Herrick signed on as students. They later became practitioners at the clinic. The clinic was structured as a state licensed health clinic, which required a doctor's presence at all times. During the early years, we hired allopaths who had an interest in homœopathy to do physical exams and diagnosis. One of those doctors was Jennifer Jacobs.

"The clinic was run as a collective which meant that all administrative decisions were made as a group at regular staff meetings and everyone received the same wage. Since we were all relatively new to homœopathy, our policy was that every prescription required approval from at least one other prescriber. After the initial visit, we would buzz another practitioner and hold a mini–case conference to discuss the patient's remedy. At the end of the day, the MD would sign all charts for the day.

"We had some training from the homœopathic old guard. Initially, a group of us (including Dana, Bill, Corey, and myself) would go for weekly lectures at Roger Schmidt's office in San Francisco. Schmidt had cancer at the time and wanted to pass on the knowledge he had acquired through his training with his brother, Pierre Schmidt, and his many years of clinical experience. He was probably the best homœopathic prescriber, meaning the most knowledgeable, in the United States at that time.

"We also brought in Maisie Panos in 1976 and Catherine Coulter in 1977 to see difficult cases at the clinic and share their expertise. Several of us would usually attend the San Francisco Homeopathic Medical Society meetings where Roger Schmidt, Franklin Cookingham (Kent's last surviving pupil), Ronald Troup, and Frederic Schmid would present papers after dinner at the old Hahnemann Hospital where those doctors had staff privileges and the pharmacy stocked homœopathic remedies. The hospital later changed its name to Marshall Hale Hospital and got rid of the homœopathy. The meetings were quite formal and we were not seriously acknowledged or allowed to participate.

"Jack Guralnik and I did a presentation about the clinic to the American Institute and the National Center in 1978. We got a lukewarm reception from everyone except Harry Coulter."

Neustaedter received his Acupuncture degree in 1983 and his Doctorate in Oriental Medicine in Hong Kong in 1988. He practices homœopathy in Palo Alto, California. He has written several books: *Homeopathic Pediatrics, Management of Otitis Media With Effusion in Homeopathic Practice, The Immunization Decision: A Guide for Parents*, and *The Vaccine Guide*.

In 1978, through Bill Gray's influence, George Vithoulkas came to the Bay area to deliver a series of lectures.

In 1980, Vithoulkas returned and delivered an intensive one–month seminar at the Esalen Institute in Big Sur. Bill Gray, Roger Morrison, George Guess, Peggy Chipkin, Nancy Herrick, Dean Crothers, David Warkentin, and Karl Robinson were present.

Meanwhile, in 1976, Dana Ullman was arrested for practicing medicine without a license. He had been working fairly openly as a homœopath, and prescribed for an undercover informant, which led to his arrest. The case was dismissed with the following requirements:

First, Ullman could not hold himself out to treat diseases or diagnose "disease" nor could he promise to do anything that would "improve a condition." Second, he had to enter into a formal contract with the client which defined his role as a non-medical health practitioner. Because these terms were stipulated in a settlement, rather than through a trial, the judgment did not constitute a legal precedent.

In the spring of 1978, Stephen Cummings and Randall Neustaedter published the first issue of the *Journal of Homeopathic Practice.* It came out quarterly and lasted for four issues.

The Hering Clinic closed in 1984 and was replaced, immediately, by the Hahnemann Clinic. Michael Quinn, a pharmacist with a strong interest in homœopathy, joined the clinic as the resident pharmacist and director of the Hahnemann Pharmacy.

Bill Gray, Nancy Herrick, Jonathan Shore, Roger Morrison at the The Hahnemann Clinic, Albany, California in 1994.

Roger Norman Morrison, MD, DHt
February 21, 1954 —

Born in Rochester, New York, Morrison graduated from the University of Tennessee Medical School in 1978. A friend found a magazine article about homœopathy written by Bill Gray and showed it to Morrison. Morrison recalls he read it and thought it a bunch of garbage and threw it out. Says Morrison, "That night I sat up in bed, recalled the article, and thought: 'but what if it is true?' And I fished it out of the trash and read it again." He phoned Vithoulkas and was invited to go to the "doctors' conference." Amazingly, his medical school gave him the two weeks off.

"I never met anyone interested in homœopathy until I walked into that conference," said Morrison.

He began studying Greek, and in 1982 went to Greece to work in the clinic with Vithoulkas. He returned to the United States in May of 1984, and with Jonathan Shore, Nancy Herrick, Peggy Chipkin, and Christine Ciavarella established the Hahnemann Clinic in Berkeley.

Morrison is married to Nancy Herrick and lives in the Bay Area. He practices at the Hahnemann Clinic in Albany, California.

Nancy Ann Herrick, PA
December 13, 1947 —

Growing up in Detroit, Herrick received her Masters degree in Child Psychology from Wayne State University in 1974. Shortly after graduation she attended a yoga seminar, where the yoga master discussed homœopathy at length. She remembers thinking to herself, "I've just finished my masters degree and now I'm going to have to take up a whole new study."

She took her Physician's Assistant degree from the University of California, Davis, in 1981. By then, she was firmly entrenched in the ripening homœopathic scene in the Bay area. She was one of the Hering Clinic's early members, and a founder of the Hahnemann Clinic.

Dana Ullman, MPH
December 22, 1951 —

"Although my father is a physician, I didn't think of medicine as a career when I entered college," says Ullman. Choosing his own major, something you could do as an honors student at the University of California at Berkeley, he graduated in 1975 with a degree in "Human Learning." In 1971, when Ullman was 19, a friend gave him a copy of Vithoulkas' book *Homeopathy: Medicine of the New Man*. Shortly after, while volunteering at the Berkeley Free Clinic doing "psych emergency" work, he saw an advertisement announcing the formation of the Bay Area Homeopathic Study Group. He joined.

He was giving lectures on homœopathy during his junior university year, and began selling books because there were no other sources for homœopathic literature.

He began publishing homœopathic books with Richard Grossinger of North Atlantic Books, partly in response to the poor physical quality of publications being brought in from India.

In May 1976, Ullman was arrested for practicing medicine without a license, and 10 months later the case was settled. Although it did not set a legal precedent, it did, said Ullman, "set a social precedent which suggests to other courts the possibility of a different way to look at health-care relationships."

After the case, Ullman decided not to resume practice because "I felt a deep compulsion to work to change how medicine and healing were perceived." He went back to school and in 1978 received his Masters in Public Health from University of California at Berkeley.

That same year he organized the first seminar on the west coast with Vithoulkas.

In 1984 he authored, with Stephen Cummings, *Everybody's Guide to Homeopathic Medicines*— one of the first new "domestic manuals." He also wrote *Discovering Homeopathy: Medicine for the 21st Century* (1988), *The One Minute (or so) Healer* (1991), *Homeopathic Medicine for Children and Infants* (1992), and *The Consumer's Guide to Homeopathy* (1996).

Ullman lives in Berkeley, California, where he operates Homeopathic Educational Services, publishes books, and works as a media liaison for homœopathy.

The arrival of George Vithoulkas

In 1974, Maisie Panos brought Vithoulkas from Greece to Washington, DC, for the concurrent meetings of the LMHI and the American Foundation for Homœopathy. At the Liga meeting Vithoulkas and Harris Coulter were honored at a banquet for authoring their respective homœopathic books.

The following day Vithoulkas spoke at the American Foundation meeting and met a number of young physicians. He impressed everyone who was there. It was the beginning of his unique influence on American homœopathy as well as homœopathy in most other countries.

George Vithoulkas, MIH
July 25, 1932 —

Trained as a civil engineer, Vithoulkas heard about homœopathy from Alain Naudé in 1960 while he was working in South Africa. As Vithoulkas tells it, "I had a car accident and although I was not hurt, the car was in need of repair. Without the car I was unable to visit friends in Pretoria. With nothing to do on weekends, I phoned Naudé and asked about the 'black book' on his desk— the one that looked like a Bible. I found it was Boericke's *Materia Medica,* and I rushed to Johannesburg to buy a copy. I began to read it on the bus on my way back and became completely absorbed. The next day I returned to the same pharmacy and bought all the major books they had on homœopathy."

Noel Puddephatt (who had studied with Clarke in the UK), was in South Africa and established a teaching class of 13 people, one of whom was a medical doctor. None, except the doctor, were practicing at the time. Also in the group was British homœopath Sheilagh Creasy.

Says Vithoulkas, "I went to meet Puddephatt in 1961, and we talked for a few hours. When Puddephatt realized my enthusiasm and the extent of my knowledge, he asked me to take over the teaching of the group as he was planning on going back to London. Shortly after, he left for London and I took over the teaching of the group for about one and a half years. I received the diploma of the school from Puddephatt in 1962. I left for India in 1963."

George Vithoulkas, San Francisco, 1986

Vithoulkas studied at the Homœopathic Medical College in Vile Parle West for two years, then he spent a year at the Calcutta Homœopathic Medical College with B. K. Bose, a direct pupil of Kent. Vithoulkas then moved to Madras where he completed his studies and was awarded the MIH (Member of the Institute of Homœopathy)— the initials we see after his name.

His first book (edited by Alain Naudé) *Homeopathy: Medicine of the New Man* was published in 1971 and re-published (edited by Bill Gray) in 1979. *The Science of Homeopathy* (also edited by Gray) was self-published in 1978 and published by Grove Press in 1979. *A New Model of Health and Disease* was published in 1991. He has also published eight volumes of *Materia Medica,* three of which have been translated into English.

Vithoulkas founded the Athenian School of Homeopathic Medicine in 1970 in Athens. He also started the Centre of Homeopathic Medicine in Athens, with 30 medical doctors on the staff.

In 1980 he began a series of seminars on the island of Alonissos, which eventually resulted in establishing the International Academy of Classical Homeopathy in Alonissos in 1995.

In December 1996 Vithoulkas was awarded the "Right Livelihood Award" in Stockholm, Sweden. Often referred to as "the alternative Nobel Prize," the award was created by Jocob Von Uexhull in 1980 to "honor and support those offering practical and exemplary answers to urgent problems facing the world today."

(NAME)

The Science of

Classical Homœopathy

AN INTRODUCTION

SPONSORED BY
THE BAY AREA HOMEOPATHIC ASSOCIATION
IN COOPERATION WITH NEW COLLEGE OF CALIFORNIA

1   2   3   4   5

The ticket for the first public lecture by Vithoulkas in the Bay Area. San Francisco, 1978

Vithoulkas and the LMHI

On a professional level, George Vithoulkas was dealt a blow from the international community in the mid-70s. The perennial conflict between the medically-trained homœopath and the non-medically trained homœopath played itself out one more time. This time it was between Vithoulkas and the LMHI. Vithoulkas had always been a part of the LMHI— the Liga Medicorum Homœopathic Internationalis— the international homœopathic league that was formed by Pierre Schmidt and some like–minded physicians in 1925. It was at the Liga meeting in Athens in 1969 that Maisie Panos first met Vithoulkas.

Although Vithoulkas was honored by the LMHI in 1974 for his contributions to homœopathy— specifically his book *Homeopathy: Medicine of the New Man*, Vithoulkas was not a medical doctor— and the LMHI was an organization of physicians.

In 1975, Vithoulkas, together with Alain Naudé, had thought of re-organizing the LMHI and forming two bureaus: the bureau of education and the bureau of promotion. He was very active in the group's workings. From 1970 to 1976 the LMHI executive committee made an exception for Vithoulkas— the only non-MD to be an LMHI member, but also the representative of his country as a vice-president for Greece.

In an undisguised effort to remove Vithoulkas from this position, the LMHI voted, in 1976, to limit the terms of the vice-presidents to only six years. Since Vithoulkas had already served for six years as a vice president, he was forced to resign from his post. He stayed as a full member of the LMHI until 1988, when a complaint about his status was voiced and he was forced to become an associate member of the LMHI. After 1977 Vithoulkas never again formally attended the annual LMHI meeting.

The Liga again honored Vithoulkas in Barcelona in 1989, but he never went to accept the award.

The conflict between medical and non-medical homœopaths within the LMHI continues to this day, often with great bitterness between the players.

Vithoulkas and Krishnamurti

One of the "legends" about Vithoulkas is that he "treated Krishnamurti."

Jiddu Krishnamurti was born in a southern province of India on May 12 1895. The eighth child of a Brahmin family, as a boy, he was identified by Madam Blavatsky, a leader of the Theosophical Society, as the potential vehicle for the reincarnation of the Lord Maytreya— The World Teacher, and the Avatar of the coming golden age. He was groomed for this role for many years. He then rejected all the adulation, denied that he was anything special, and developed a philosophy that the "master is not to be looked for without, but within." He maintained that all organized religions were barriers to truth. He continued for the rest of his life as a teacher with a philosophy of great subtlety. He attracted to him a number of eminent personages including such diverse people as Nehru, Bernard Shaw, David Bohm, Rupert Sheldrake, the Dali Lama, and Stephen Hawking.

The connection of Krishnamurti with homœopathy takes a few interesting turns. Alain Naudé was working as Krishnamurti's secretary, and convinced Krishnamurti to consult with Vithoulkas, who, at the time, was studying at the Calcutta Homœopathic Medical College.

Vithoulkas says, "I treated Krishnamurti back in 1965/67. Krishnamurti was extremely benefited by the homœopathic treatment at the time, in spite of the fact that he was in a very depleted state when I first met him in Benares in 1965."

After Vithoulkas, Krishnamurti continued homœopathic treatment with Pierre Schmidt.

Krishnamurti died at Ojai, California, on February 17, 1986, aged 91.

"Essences," seminars, and clinics

When I asked several people why Vithoulkas gained such prominence at a time when there were certainly other grand homœopaths around (Schmidt, Kunzli, Wadia, Chand spring to mind) most said Vithoulkas had charisma. He was charming and exciting to listen to. But there was more. "He knew something different," said Roger Morrison. "George Vithoulkas has an unparalleled understanding of homœopathy."

Bill Gray went to Greece to study with Vithoulkas in 1976, and when he returned, he began to teach those around him what he had learned. In retrospect, he hadn't learned as much as he thought. Said Gray:

"George would give me one to three cases from his clinic a day, to work on for homework. The next day he would look at them. If I was right, he'd say OK. If I was wrong, he'd hand it back to me and tell me to figure it out again. In the eight months I was there I never got one. It was very discouraging. When I was ready to leave I expressed my dismay that I had done so poorly. George then said, 'I'll give you a day at the clinic,' and gave me the 50 cases they had seen that day. I got most of them, so I guess all the failures had taught me something.

"But I guess that I still didn't get it. It's like doing math in grade school and doing calculus in college. The person doing calculus can certainly talk to the kid doing basic math— but he changes his perspective on things so he can talk at that level. If he talked at his 'calculus level' the poor kid wouldn't understand a word! I guess that's what George did with me. I left Greece thinking I knew a lot, but I really did not have a working concept of it yet.

"I came back and taught those around me everything I knew. I gave them everything, but I never suspected that I didn't know enough!"

When Vithoulkas came to the United States to do the Esalen Seminar in 1980, Gray told him that the group members were "experienced prescribers," Vithoulkas came with his most difficult cases. The first case, remembers Roger Morrison, was a case of *Corallium rubrum*. No one in the group had ever heard of the remedy. No one had read much materia medica. The group knew about 20 remedies, mostly the polychrests. "We were babes in the woods," said Morrison.

Recalls Gray, "As far as folks in the states went, these *were* experienced prescribers! The month at Esalen was a real eye-opener. Of all the cases George brought over I think that we got the remedy on only three of them— and that was over a period of a month!"

When Morrison, who spoke Greek, went to study with Vithoulkas, he was better able to understand how Vithoulkas was practicing, and it was much fuller than people were led to believe. And, he says, it took him six months to "get the picture."

Prescribing on only the "essence" of a case was a very seductive methodology— "any sign of cowardice, give *Lycopodium*." Although this was not how Vithoulkas

The "Doctors' Group"
Front: Ben Hole, Patricia Stribling, Karl Robinson, Harvey Powelson, Al Drucker, Dean Crothers. 2nd Row: David Guerring, Sandra Ross, Alan Levine, Joya Schoen, Laren Bays, Virginia Flanagan, Bill Fife. Back row: Bob Anderson, Dan Dixon, Roger Morrison, Bill Gray, George Guess, Don Rich.

The Faces of Homœopathy

An impression

"I visited the United States in 1981. It was my impression that Homeopathy in America was heading for oblivion unless a courageous reversal took place... The current membership of the AIH some 130 members; none of whom speaks up, or comes out of the closet to publicize homeopathy... Recently an impulse came from outside. A Greek civil engineer, and his student Bill Gray, MD, tried to propagate classical homeopathy... I note in the Vithoulkas courses where too much attention is paid to the symptoms of the mind, the emotions, the psychological approach. The students are trying hard to analyze the mentals... as though they were qualified psychologists. But the students usually come up with a weird hypothetical answer to the case... Vithoulkas leads his devoted disciples into a psychological labyrinth out of which only he himself is able to find the way out of the maze.

"In my opinion it is wrong to judge the success of homeopathic treatment mainly on the emotional state of the patient. The criteria of a real cure is the same for any other therapy; the whole patient should be improved... If I treat a case with hypertension... I am not impressed to hear how happy the patient is with my therapy. He may be feeling much better, but his blood pressure has not gone down. Vithoulkas considers this totally satisfactory and doesn't pursue the case any more... I dislike... giving each remedy "an essence." The use of such schematic drug pictures is very dangerous. This was warningly predicted by Constantine Hering because he felt it would lead to a decline for Homeopathy... The present day American Society is morally and physically so debauched that they urgently need good homeopathy... The spreading of so many malignant diseases among patients in all ages... The numerous young people searching for guidance, and groping for stability, and trying to find it in an alien far Eastern religion and drugs."

Jost Kunzli, in the Journal of the American Institute of Homeopathy, *March 1982. Pages 42-3.*

worked in his clinic, his outer persona and the force of his personality led a generation of homœopaths down the "essence" track. This mistake was compounded by the underground distribution of Vithoulkas' rough notes given out at one of his early seminars. Although he asked that the notes not be seen as complete in any way, the "stolen essences" were copied and distributed through the homœopathic community which, in turn, took them as gospel.

Amy Rothenberg, ND, described it as a situation where Vithoulkas assumed the people he was teaching understood the remedies in the same depth as he did. "He was giving them the 'cream' and they took it as 'whole milk.'" It took a number of years to understand the fullness of it.

Vithoulkas was persuaded by several students to work in the United States. Both the International Foundation for Homeopathy (in Seattle) and a group in the Bay Area were raising money for a Vithoulkas Clinic. Once, on the way to the United States, Vithoulkas stopped in London to give a lecture. He spoke to an audience of 2,000 people. His picture was on the front page of the *Times*. He then arrived in the United States and found a group of 52 doctors and health practitioners to teach. It was undoubtedly disappointing. Vithoulkas stayed for three months, and returned to Greece. The next three–month visit saw only 90 students. His last visit was in 1986, with 120 students in the class. In Vithoulkas' view, he felt that homœopathy could be better served in Europe than in the United States. "On my way back to Greece," he said, "I stopped in Holland and taught a seminar with 600 homœopaths." He returned to Greece and continued to teach in Europe.

Several people had invested in the formation of a clinic that would be centered around Vithoulkas. Over $200,000 had been collected— and used in three months. "His leaving," said Morrison, "was devastating to many people."

Vithoulkas will be discussing this era in more detail in a biography currently being written in Germany.

The Unsung

In every endeavor there are usually very influential people in the background. This is certainly true in the homœopathic movement.

There are those we know through their writing and personal influence, like Hering and Kent. There are those who wielded organizational power, like Royal Copeland who, while not a great homœopath, preserved the *Homœopathic Pharmacopoeia* in Federal Legislation through his power as a Senator, and there was Julia M. Green who held the factions of homœopathy together through the 1940s and 50s. There are others who go completely unrecognized except in passing. Gram is known as "the first homœopath in the US," but until one looks at the number of his pupils and their influence, one cannot see how important a figure Gram was. The same may be said of Alain Naudé.

Alain Naudé
October, 1927 —

Naudé was born in South Africa. He learned of homœopathy in Paris in 1950 and, as the old literature says, "became wholly convinced of the new system." He returned to South Africa, and while there introduced a young Greek engineer, George Vithoulkas, to homœopathy.

Naudé dedicated himself to studying homœopathy and in 1964 met Pierre Schmidt who became his teacher. Later, Naudé met Jost Kunzli, and studied with him. Naudé settled in the United States in 1970, studying with Roger Schmidt, Pierre's brother, who was in San Francisco.

In 1970, Vithoulkas showed Naudé the manuscript of a book he was writing. It was an introduction to the principles of homœopathy. Naudé worked with Vithoulkas on editing the text, re-arranging the order, and re-constructing the passages which were unclear in Vithoulkas' Greek/English. Naudé found a publisher for the book (Kouros Books) and, with an introduction by Naudé, the book was published in 1971. *Homeopathy: Medicine of the New Man* was the first "modern" introduction to homœopathy.

As homœopathy became better known, the book was

The 6th Edition from Kunzli

From Robert Schore, MD:

I guess it's time to set the record straight. After Alain read to me, in English from Pierre Schmidt's French translation of the Organon, a few paragraphs which I could not understand from the Boericke translation, so much came clear that I decided it was necessary to re-translate the Organon and I raised the money to get the job done. Alain had been told by Schmidt that it was his "duty" to create a decent English translation of the Organon. Naudé and Peter Pendleton literally slaved for two years creating the new translation. Peter (fluent in German) translated from both the German printing and from a copy I had made of the original document from the University of California San Francisco Medical School library. Alain translated at the same time from Pierre Schmidt's French translation of the German version. Sometimes they would spend all day on one sentence. Several times during the course of the translation, they would call Kunzli and consult. Kunzli read Peter and Alain's English version for accuracy while comparing it to the German version. On three separate occasions Alain traveled to Switzerland to spend intensive time reviewing the manuscripts with Kunzli. Originally our intention was not to list the translators, but we yielded to publisher pressure and listed the translators' names in alphabetical order. I managed to keep my name out of the text. Kunzli edited for accuracy and meaning. Naudé and Pendleton worked equally on the original translation.
It was a labor of love.

re-edited by Bill Gray in 1979. Naudé's introduction was dropped, and one by Gray was added. With the addition of a few materia medica "essence pictures," the book was re-published by Avon.

Naudé's major contribution to American homœopathy was his skillful editing of a number of homœopathic journals. In 1974, upon the retirement of Dr. Dwight Smith as editor of the *Pacific Coast Homeopathic Bulletin,* Naudé was persuaded to take over the editorship. The name of the journal was changed to *Homeotherapy.* Naudé continued as editor until 1980, when Robert Schore, MD, assumed editorship. The journal continued until February 1985.

Through his successful editorship of *Homeotherapy,* Naudé was persuaded ("dragged into it by my hair," as he put it) to assume the editorship of the *Journal of the American Institute of Homeopathy* from 1977 to 1979. He also served as editor of *The Layman Speaks* for the National Center for Homeopathy from 1977 to 1978.

Observing the intensification of politics within the NCH/AFH and desiring to "keep out of the whirlpool," Naudé quietly withdrew from his editorships of the two journals, and continued to edit *Homeotherapy* until 1980.

Between 1980 and 1982 he worked with Jost Kunzli and Peter Pendleton on a new translation of the 6th edition of Hahnemann's *Organon.*

Commenting that "you can't have the history of homœopathy unless you have homœopathy," Naudé has been quietly practicing homœopathy for the last 10 years in Dallas, Texas.

Bill Gray, Alain Naudé, and George Vithoulkas, Athens 1976

The International Foundation for Homeopathy (IFH)

The International Foundation for the Promotion of Homeopathy was founded in California in October 1978 by George Vithoulkas, Bill Gray, Don Gerrard, and others, with Vithoulkas as President. It was established shortly after Vithoulkas came to San Francisco to teach the first "professional" course.

The IFPH aimed to "elevate standards of practice to such a high degree that the results will open doors to governmental recognition and support." The first newsletter was published in June 1979.

In 1981, shortly after Vithoulkas returned to California to offer another course open to both "licensed and unlicensed" prescribers, the organization's name was shortened to the International Foundation for Homeopathy.

In the spring of 1982, the IFH, in conjunction with the American Center for Homeopathy and the Florida Institute of Technology, sponsored a one–day seminar with Vithoulkas. There was the hope that pending legislation to recognize the practice of homœopathy in Florida would lead to a school. But the legislation was not passed, and the whole idea came to a halt.

In the fall of 1982, the IFH executive director, Cynthia Lanahan, left to accept a position with the Boiron Research Foundation. Dean Crothers, now the executive committee chair, moved the operation to Seattle, Washington, where he was living and working.

In the fall of 1983, the IFH newsletter announced that Vithoulkas was going to move his base of operations to the United States and become a citizen. It was anticipated this would happen by fall of 1984. In September 1984, the

---

Aude Sapere — dare to taste and understand

IFPH NEWSLETTER

published by
the International Foundation for the Promotion of Homeopathy
4 Sherman Ave., Fairfax, California 94930

Spring 1981

foundation of the Hahnemann Clinic was announced in the newsletter. The Clinic was to serve as a base for Vithoulkas in the United States.

Then there was a gap. When the IFH newsletter, now re-titled *Resonance*, again appeared in August 1985, there was no explanation for the lack of contact, other than an apology for being out of touch during almost a year of restructuring. Vithoulkas' name is prominently missing from the magazine.

It appeared Vithoulkas had signed a contract to teach for the Hahnemann Clinic in Berkeley, and would not be teaching for the IFH. People who had donated funds to the IFH specifically to set up the teaching program with Vithoulkas, asked for their money back, and their request was honored, but the upheaval took almost a year to stabilize. The IFH continued as a non-profit organization, without Vithoulkas as president. Why didn't Vithoulkas come to the USA? It appears the announcement of his move might have been premature. For personal reasons, Vithoulkas decided to stay in his native Greece.

Between 1985 and 1995 the IFH continued to offer its professional six-session training program. In response to a desire for an advanced program for non-licensed people, the IFH taught a single "advanced acute care" program in 1993.

With the IFH located in Seattle, it was natural that a number of local naturopaths who had been board members of the IFH, would become more involved in the organization. During this decade there was a stronger influence from the naturopathic/homœopathic community in the persons of Stephen King, Judyth Reichenberg-Ullman, and Robert Ullman.

In January 1996, Dean Crothers, after devoting 13 years to the organization, stepped down from the board of directors and as editor of *Resonance*.

The IFH decided to completely re-structure their educational programs. The course offered in 1997 (which was opened to both licensed and unlicensed practitioners) was the last offered in the old format. The IFH decided to channel its energy into its annual case conference and into formal education, working, with Bastyr University, on a plan for a four-year homœopathic program.

In September 1998, citing a lack of continued operating funds, the IFH ceased operations.

Bill Gray on Education

"I read the cases in the old journals, and I read the cases of Kent. They were amazing. But in the cases I was treating I wasn't getting anywhere near those results. When I saw Vithoulkas I realized that he, in his genius, had understood homœopathy on that other level, and that's what was missing. I can't fault my instructors— Maisie Panos and Henry Williams— they were doing it as well as they could. But *their* instructors didn't understand that other dimension, or if they did, they didn't know how to communicate it.

"We were all learning just a piece of the thing, basically on our own, and struggling to keep it alive. And then George came along, and our practices changed immeasurably.

"I wanted to establish a school that would set a standard— an undiluted standard— that would say, 'this is what homœopathy should be.' We were going to pull the Phoenix from the ashes.

"How were we to save the world with homœopathy? I had been an organizer in med school and I knew some of the ropes. I knew that Americans had respect for foreign experts, they respond well to them. George was perfect as the great homœopath. I think we came up with the name

"You asked how this approach differs from ours. That is virtually impossible to describe. It's not a matter of procedure, or routine, or technique. Certainly, insight, his ability to throw out irrelevant data or perceptions while going to the heart of the issue— that is the most obvious difference. Here and there you can see some technical differences— underlinings, use of small rubrics, constant use of the repertory without detailed repertorization, the use of a much greater number of remedies, etc. But these are not important. The biggest difference is that we (despite our attempts to do otherwise) are basically dealing with data, which we match with data on remedies that we don't understand. Vithoulkas is dealing with essences. If we knew Materia Medica as deeply and broadly, we would tend to approach the whole process much more profoundly."

Letter from Bill Gray in The Layman Speaks, *April 1978, page 94*

'classical' homœopathy— it sounded right. And the whole idea just came together and blossomed.

"At the time (1976-78) the American Foundation and the National Center had their educational course. Maisie Panos, the president of the National Center for Homeopathy, was very interested in the training program we were thinking about. But she couldn't get the folks at the American Foundation for Homœopathy to support her in any way. It was a closed board and Maisie couldn't influence how the money was to be spent. And we couldn't wait. So we formed the International Foundation for the Promotion of Homeopathy as a group that would, basically, teach quality homœopathy.

"There were strategic issues, of course. I was quite convinced that the lay–people were going to be the important ones in the movement, and I wanted to teach them as well. The IFH Board eventually decided that they would instruct only licensed practitioners— but at the beginning we were teaching anyone who had the burning desire to learn."

1970 – 1985: The Naturopaths

Homœopathy and naturopathy
The schools
The practitioners

The rise in interest in natural therapies led to the growth of two colleges on the west coast that were training naturopaths; the National College of Naturopathic Medicine in Portland, Oregon, and the John Bastyr College of Naturopathic Medicine in Seattle, Washington.

Many graduates of these schools led the homœopathic resurgence throughout the 1980s.

Homœopathy and naturopathy

Both homœopathy and naturopathy share the basic concept of the body being a dynamic entity with the innate capacity to heal itself.

The name "naturopath" was coined in 1892 by John Scheele, a German homœopath, to describe the fusion of "nature care" and homœopathy into a unified system of natural therapeutics. In 1896, Benedict Lust, MD, brought naturopathy to the United States and established the first naturopathic school in New Jersey.

By the 1940s, a good number of states had passed naturopathic licensing legislation, but the schools that taught naturopathy were slowly closing. By the 1970s many of the states that had Naturopathic Boards decided to "sunset" them, since there was little need for a naturopathic board if no new graduates were coming on-line.

On the west coast, Western States Chiropractic, in Portland, was the last school to offer a naturopathic degree, with its final class graduating in 1956. In response to the closing of the school, a group of naturopaths led by John Bastyr, ND, formed the National College of Naturopathic Medicine in Portland, and began to offer naturopathic training. The Naturopathic State Boards in Oregon and Washington remained viable long enough for the new crop of graduates to become licensed. The school soon moved to Seattle and, eventually, back to Portland.

In the fall of 1982 the Homeopathic Academy of Naturopathic Physicians (HANP) was formed, "To establish standards in homœopathy within the naturopathic profession." An exam was written by eight homœopathic professionals in the fall of 1986. The writing of the exam was one of the first uses made of the new e-mail facility on *HomeoNet*. 46 people took the exam and only 26 passed, clearly establishing the exam's baseline.

It was such a thorough exam the American Board of Homeotherapeutics talked to the HANP about adapting the exam for its use. The result was that the HANP exam and the ABHT exam are now virtually the same, with each group offering its own oral exam.

The American Association of Naturopathic Physicians (AANP) was founded in 1986, replacing the National Association of Naturopathic Physicians, an organization plagued with unifying difficulties because it didn't have credible membership eligibility standards. The consensus was that the NANP would dissolve and the AANP would become the national professional body for naturopathic medicine.

Graduates of approved programs are eligible to sit the NPLEX— the exam used by all the states that license naturopathic physicians.

Although not all naturopaths are homœopaths, those that have pressed their homœopathic education and have taken the HANP exam, are, generally, good homœopaths and have the license to do it legally in eleven states.

The schools

The National College of Naturopathic Medicine (NCNM) was founded in 1956. In the early 1970s the school began an association with Kansas Newman College in Wichita, Kansas. Students would take basic science work in Kansas and then transfer to the Portland campus for their clinical training. By 1980, the Portland campus enlarged and was able to provide all training. In 1981 the school moved to a site in southeast Portland, a seven-acre campus which had housed an elementary school.

In 1996 it moved to southwest Portland. The school has a large library of more than 4,000 books, including a wonderful homœopathic collection, many of which were bought from the University of San Francisco when they were "cleaning their stacks of old books."

The John Bastyr College of Naturopathic Medicine was incorporated in 1978 by three naturopathic physicians in Seattle. It was approved by all states and provinces licensing naturopathic physicians in 1982— its first graduate year.

In 1994, with the school enlarging to include several new programs, including a masters program in acupuncture

NDs in 11 states

Naturopaths are licensed to practice as primary health care providers in 11 states: Alaska, Arizona, Connecticut, Hawaii, Maine, Montana, New Hampshire, Oregon, Utah, and Vermont. In Washington DC, a naturopath can practice if registered with the local government.

NCNM (above), Bastyr University (below)

The Southwest College

and oriental medicine, the school was granted university status.

In 1996 Bastyr University moved to a new campus, a 50-acre site on the northeast shore of Lake Washington, previously housing the St. Thomas the Apostle Seminary.

The 1990s saw two new naturopathic colleges established:

The Southwest College of Naturopathic Medicine in Scottsdale, Arizona, was formed in 1992, graduating its first class in 1996.

In 1997, the University of Bridgeport, in Bridgeport, Connecticut, began offering a program leading to an ND degree.

The practitioners

John Bartholomew Bastyr, DC, ND
1912 — June 29, 1995

Bastyr was born in New Prague, Minnesota. A graduate of the North West Drugless Institute with a degree in Sanipractic, he also had a chiropractic degree from the Seattle Chiropractic College. (Both schools are no longer in existence.) Bastyr learned homœopathy from Dr. Chal Bryant, of Seattle, who had been the president of the IHA in 1939.

Bastyr was a kind, humble man, and a great healer. He inspired a whole new generation of healers, whose lives he touched and changed immensely.

Said Melanie Grimes, in a memorial to Dr. Bastyr: "He and his peers carried the torch of alternative medicine for many years, when there were no students, and no new practitioners. They mortgaged their homes to buy a building in which to teach naturopathic medicine to the one or two students a year who would apply. In 1972, there was a ground swell of interest in alternative healing. Over 30 college–educated youth appeared to enter the class.

"He kept up to date on all the new, while carrying the knowledge of the old. He read voraciously, and never stopped learning and encouraging others to study. And most of all, he healed, practicing daily until his 80s. He delivered hundreds of babies, did underwater births decades ago, and during home births, would put newborns in shoe boxes in cooled wood stoves to keep them warm.

He practiced and taught classical homœopathy to hundreds.

"Dr. Bastyr was both grandfather and the father to students for the past 20 years, as there was no in-between generation to be our mentors. The Naturopathic College in Seattle, Bastyr University, carries on his name."

Melanie, who was tutored in homœopathy by Bastyr, relates the following: "One day, in his clinic, he asked me if I was pregnant. 'No,' I said. 'Well, it says here that you are going to be pregnant in July,' he said, looking at my chart. Later, I found out I had been pregnant at that visit, and I said to him, 'Dr. Bastyr, do you have a hot-line to God?' 'Well,' he said, 'well, yes I do.'"

It was said, at his memorial service, he was the last of an ancient species of tree, whose fruit had fallen far and wide, to propagate a new forest. He cast a large circle.

Stephen King, ND, DHANP
December 31, 1949 —

With a degree in English from Harvard in 1972, King was "always interested why well people became sick and why sick people got well." He became interested in macrobiotics and studied some acupuncture in the early 70s, but he was looking for a therapeutic system that included the mental sphere.

While working as a drug abuse counselor in Lincoln, Nebraska he came across Vithoulkas' book *Medicine of the New Man* in the local library. He read the book and said, "If this is true, then this is what I'd like to do." He found out the naturopathic schools taught homœopathy, and enrolled in NCNM, graduating in 1982.

King served as IFH president from 1987 until 1989. He organized the "Small Remedies and Interesting Cases" Conference in 1989 that has become an IFH staple.

He shares a full-time practice with his wife, Sheryl Kipnis, in Seattle, Washington.

373

I commented to Sheryl that there is an amazing variety of life experiences that have led people to homœopathy. She said, "I believe there is a core in each of us that knows where we belong and what we should be doing with our life. Everyone has it, but some are fortunate enough to manifest this core."

Sheryl Kipnis, ND, DHANP
January 18, 1954 —

"I was always interested in helping people," said Kipnis, "but when I considered going to medical school or becoming a psychotherapist, neither felt right." While at the University of Colorado in Boulder, Colorado, Kipnis came down with a viral infection. As with most viral illnesses, there was no conventional medical treatment. Someone suggested she consult a naturopath in town, which she did. While regaining her health, she sought more about the therapies with which her naturopath was treating her. She read Vithoulkas' *Medicine of the New Man* and felt it told a simple, yet deep truth about healing. She became interested in homœopathy, but had no idea where to learn about it. Shortly after, she found in the mail a catalog from NCNM that her roommate had sent for. She sent in her application, was accepted into the ND program, and graduated in 1982.

Stephen Messer, ND, DHANP
November 12, 1951 —

Born and raised in New York City, Messer took his masters at the University of Pennsylvania and worked as a high school biology teacher in Philadelphia. "I had left a long term relationship," he said. "I was meditating. I met the woman I was to marry. I looked at my life and I knew I wanted something different."

Reading a letter about a naturopathic college in *Prevention Magazine* put the idea in Messer's head. "I was thinking about the Peace Corps, " he said. "And then, one night, I sat bolt upright at 3 a.m. and realized that I wanted to be a 'natural doctor.'"

Messer applied to NCNM and was accepted in a special experimental class. It was a pilot program, separate from the regular program, with 15 people in it. The teachers, Robert Broadwell and Laren Bays were both very interested in homœopathy, and talked about it to the class. Messer's interest piqued, he read *Kent's Lectures on Homeopathic Philosophy*. "As soon as I read it I already knew it. A light went off in my head. I knew that this was what I was supposed to do."

Messer graduated from NCNM in 1979. By 1982 he was an HANP founder. He was elected to board of directors of the National Center for Homeopathy in 1987. He became dean of the National Center's instructional program in 1993, and in 1996 he was elected HANP president.

Messer lives in Eugene, Oregon where he maintains a private practice.

Robin Murphy, ND
August 15, 1950 —

Born and raised in Grand Rapids, Michigan, Murphy did his undergraduate work at the University of Michigan at Ann Arbor. The University of Michigan used to have a homœopathic department and all the homœopathic journals and books are still kept in the library's deep recesses. While doing research at the University library, Murphy stumbled across the homœopathic collection and became intrigued with the system it described. He continued visiting the collection until graduating in 1974, and then continued studying homœopathy. In 1976 he entered the National College of Naturopathic Medicine, on a Hahnemann Scholarship. He received his ND in 1980. While at the school he studied with Dr. Ravi Sahni and Dr. John Bastyr.

He directed the homœopathy program at NCNM from 1980-1984. He also taught at Bastyr University.

Murphy was one of the earliest "seminar" teachers, and is responsible for introducing many people to homœopathy. His teaching style has been described as "laid-back" and he brings a clarity to the interrelation between philosophy, materia medica, and repertory work.

He compiled the *Homœopathic Medical Repertory* in 1993, and the *Lotus Materia Medica* in 1996. He is the director of the Hahnemann Academy of North America which sponsors seminars on homœopathy and natural medicine.

His other interests include Egyptology, medical alchemy, and tai chi. He is presently writing and teaching in Pagosa Springs, Colorado.

Robin Murphy ND

Robert W. Ullman,
N.D., D.H.A.N.D.

Judyth Reichenberg-Ullman,
N.D., DHANP

Judyth Reichenberg-Ullman, ND, DHANP, MSW
February 10, 1948 —

Reichenberg grew up in suburban St. Louis. Her mother went to a chiropractor and wrote a letter to *Prevention Magazine* about her self-treatment discoveries, but Reichenberg thought it was all strange and unconventional.

"When I was 22, my spiritual journey began in the form of yoga and meditation. My lifestyle included herbs, fasting, cleansing, vegetarianism, and reflexology, in addition to a rigorous practice of yoga postures and long periods of meditation. Natural medicine was just one part of my yogic lifestyle. I never again took even an aspirin."

During her clinical preceptorships for her masters in social work she worked in a community mental health center and in a locked psychiatric ward, working primarily with people suffering from schizophrenia and manic depression.

"I was deeply impressed by a number of things: how these people subsisted on coffee, cigarettes, and junk food; how they lacked the peace and joy that I had found through my spiritual practices; how antipsychotics and lithium carbonate were the only options conventional medicine had for them; and, above all, how they were trapped in deep mental and emotional anguish, numbness, and hopelessness. I vowed then to find a natural, effective alternative to help these poor souls."

She first heard of homœopathy in 1976 when she consulted Dr. John Bastyr for a persistent bronchitis. He asked a question or two, and said, "This is a *Rumex* cough." She was well within a day or two. The cure left a lasting impression.

Seattle's Bastyr University opened in 1978, and Reichenberg decided to attend "five minutes after I heard about it." During her first year she read *Kent's Lectures on Homeopathic Philosophy,* and found it "rang true." Says Reichenberg, "It seemed like an integration of my personal and spiritual philosophy as well as my psychiatric experience. At that time no one had even heard of homœopathy and the philosophy seemed radical even compared to naturopathic medicine. I gained a reputation in school as a homœopathic fanatic and it never ended. I'm so glad."

Reichenberg describes herself as "hopelessly and happily

unconventional." She was president of the International Foundation for Homeopathy (1993–1998), past vice president of the Homeopathic Academy of Naturopathic Physicians, and co-author (with her husband) of *The Patient's Guide to Homeopathic Medicine; Ritalin-Free Kids,* and *Homeopathic Self-Care: The Quick and Easy Guide for the Whole Family.* She and her husband are in private practice in Edmonds, Washington.

Robert W. Ullman, ND, DHANP
May 17, 1951 —

Ullman grew up in suburban Philadelphia. Always interested in science, he decided to be a doctor. He says, "I followed my high school sweetheart (after we had broken up) to Ursinus College, a small church-related college in Collegeville, Pennsylvania in a futile attempt to rekindle my first disappointment in love. Ursinus was known for pre-med and women's phys. ed. The brains and jockettes made for an odd mix. I was stymied in my attempt to get into medical school by mediocre grades in calculus and organic chemistry, although I received honors in psychology. I went to graduate school in psychology at Bucknell University instead, hoping for another try at medical school later."

Ullman became interested in yoga and meditation and, as he says, "went through a somewhat ascetic yogi period."

While at graduate school he went to a health fair at a local college where a study group of the National Center for Homeopathy had set up a homœopathy booth. He found the little white pills and all the books fascinating. During a yoga retreat in Kansas he met John Collins, then a student at the National College of Naturopathic Medicine in Wichita, and learned naturopathic school was the best place to study homœopathy and become a natural doctor. He applied to NCNM and was accepted.

Taking the first part of the program in Wichita and looking forward to learning homœopathy, Ullman arrived in Portland in 1979. His teachers, Robin Murphy and Laren Bays were studying with Vithoulkas in California. Ullman got to use homœopathy in the naturopathic school clinic and found it very exciting to see it work on real people. He also had an additional 100 hours of training from Bill Gray, Peggy Chipkin and other Bay area homœopaths.

After graduation, he eventually moved to Seattle. As he says, "destiny was calling." He joined the homœopathic study group for practitioners in Seattle run by Stephen King and Sheryl Kipnis. Judyth Reichenberg also joined. Says Bob, "We had met briefly at the naturopathic board exams and I wandered into a class she was teaching, but no sparks flew, although I thought she was interesting. Right after a spiritual retreat where I had made a fervent prayer to meet my mate, Judyth called to ask me to study some cases with her, something we still do nearly every day. I am also very grateful for our loving partnership, practicing, writing, teaching, traveling and playing together.

"Our homœopathy practices have deepened and changed in exciting ways in the last three years with our study with the Bombay homœopaths, Rajan Sankaran, Jayesh Shah, Nandita Shah, Sujit Chatterjee and Sunil Anand. I feel my understanding of homœopathy keeps growing and I am continually challenged to do the best for my patients."

Ullman was the vice president of the International Foundation for Homeopathy (1995–1998), and past head of the homœopathy department at Bastyr University.

Paul Herscu, ND, DHANP
May 5, 1959 —

Born in Bucharest, Romania, Herscu and his family moved to Israel in 1961 and then to New York City in 1968.

While taking pre-med in college, Herscu became very ill after getting soaking wet on a long bicycle trip. A week after recovering from the cold-induced illness he woke up with "arthritis." The doctor told him it was a result of his recent illness and it would go away in about a year or so.

Herscu's girlfriend had just returned from England and suggested he try homœopathy. Within five minutes of the suggestion, Herscu's sister phoned and suggested he attend a lecture about homœopathy. Astounded by this "coincidence" he went to the lecture, and decided to give homœopathy a try. He saw a homœopath, and upon getting a remedy decided, "this was the flakiest thing I've ever seen."

Within two weeks, his pain ceased and he felt great. A follow–up visit resulted in a wrong remedy and a painful aggravation that finally cleared.

Said Herscu, "I noticed that my whole life was changing.

It was during that time that I decided to become a homœopath. Anything that can make me feel that good and that bad I wanted to do. Members of my family and friends at the time had mono, scoliosis, hypertension, and painful menstrual cramps. None could be treated with conventional medicine, but all could be treated with homœopathy. That began my interest in homœopathy."

In 1980 Herscu began studying homœopathy with Kent's *Materia Medica* followed by Roberts' *Art and Cure*, the *Organon*, and Boericke's *Materia Medica*. Herscu finally found Kent's *Repertory*. "It was like an ecstatic experience. I could not believe it. I did not know what some of it was but I got the gist of it and ate it up. I read it over and over, referenced it with materia medica study and it made things so much easier."

"In 1981 Bill Gray came to New York City and made the science of homœopathy live. He showed some videos of Vithoulkas doing materia medica and taking a case. It brought everything to life in living color. It was very influential at the time."

In 1982 Herscu attended the summer professional course in Millersville. He applied to NCNM that summer and flew out for an interview. "They asked if I wanted to see the library. I said 'yes' and when I saw the homœopathy books, the tour ended. I had found home. By the end of the second year I was helping to formulate the school homœopathy curriculum. By the third year I was teaching homœopathy. And by the fourth year I was helping out different practices around the country."

In 1985 Herscu met Vithoulkas. "I had been avoiding him on purpose. I wanted to meet him when I thought I would be able to follow everything he said— not just what he said but the reason behind it as well. I did not wish to miss anything."

Knowing of Herscu's knowledge of the literature, Vithoulkas asked him to "cull the literature for cured cases."

Over the next year Herscu compiled many cases from journals of "cured, one remedy cases," which Vithoulkas used as references in his *Materia Medica Viva*.

Herscu married fellow student Amy Rothenberg and they moved to Iowa on the request of several naturopaths who wanted them to work on getting naturopathic legislation passed in nearby Nebraska.

Herscu on learning

" I had no teacher of homœopathy as such, but I learned from the books. I took what I needed from them and built upon it. Hering spoke to me then and still does. I love his Guiding Symptoms. His materia medica is based upon provings loosely but more upon cured cases. And it is no strange coincidence that my materia medica and the total focus of my work has its roots in cured cases.

"In a way the fact that I had no living teacher was my saving grace at that time. I never had the mania to follow someone. I recall a discussion at NCNM about the repertory and how important it was and how we need to know it. Some people were stuck on what this or that teacher said and they did not use the repertory and so 'I was wrong.'

"Six months later Eizayaga came to lecture and these same homœopaths got so much into the repertory they repertorized their lunches. So I say, 'hey you are going too far— you are losing the patient for the rubric.' And they say, 'Oh no this is the way you do it.' I never had to get stuck like this because I did not have a teacher."

"It is during this time that Amy and I worked from 9 a.m. to 6 p.m. every day seeing many, many people, seeing what works and what doesn't, seeing how the materia medica information that was floating around at that time did not correlate very well with the practice, seeing how the day to day working models did not correspond very well to the actual practice. Soon we were treating whole communities— multi-generational stuff. It was great. We were the only people they could turn to. We got pretty close to passing the legislation, but we had our first child and decided to move east to be near our families."

In 1986, Herscu, with Durr Elmore and Ron Lamb, revived the Homeopathic Academy of Naturopathic Physicians— the organization that originally started in 1982 but never became active. Herscu's vision drove the revival, and resulted in the HANP exam, the first HANP Case Conference which served as a model for the IFH Case Conference and others, and the HANP journal, *Simillimum.*

In 1988, Herscu was invited to edit video cases that Vithoulkas was preparing for a series of video seminars. He had a chance to look at every case Vithoulkas ever taped. "I learned a lot— learned what GV said and what he did not say, what he did not know he did, I learned where his questions came from. It was a formative time for me."

Herscu moved to Amherst, Massachusetts in 1989, hoping for a break from the hectic Iowa schedule. But soon after his arrival, three local practitioners retired, and gave Herscu and Rothenberg their patients.

Herscu's book *Homeopathic Treatment of Children* was released in 1991. It was the first book about treating children that came from direct case studies. At the same time Herscu decided that a weekend seminar was a meaningless experience, akin to a "one-night-stand," and he began to teach a seminar that would serve as a model for many others— six three-day sessions, two months apart. In that format, what was learned in class one was used for two months in practice and then discussed in class two, etc. The idea worked well, and Herscu taught about 1,700 people using this format, in several locations in the USA and in Europe.

Herscu was also one of the first to teach to non-medically trained homœopaths, in his belief that the future of homœopathy is in the hands of both the medical and non-medical practitioner.

In the early 1990s Herscu started the *New England Journal of Homeopathy*— a peer-review journal that has become well respected in the community.

Says Herscu, "Even though I do so much in this field I also have a private life. I like to spend time with my wife and kids and like to read and fish and when I get the chance, play poker."

Herscu and Rothenberg have a private practice in Enfield, Connecticut.

Amy Rothenberg, ND, DHANP
March 14, 1960 —

Rothenberg attended Antioch College in Yellow Springs, Ohio which, she says, "encouraged a passion for learning, the importance of being able to express yourself verbally and in writing, the necessity for integration of any knowledge, and the essential nature of community."

She was always interested in some aspect of medicine, but she just didn't know which one. Taking six months' leave from Antioch to work at a co-op job in Oregon as a lab-technician at the University of Oregon Health Sciences Center, she hitchhiked cross country. The last ride dropped her in front of a health food restaurant in Portland. On the "roommate board" inside the restaurant she saw that two naturopathic students were looking for a house mate. "I thought naturopathic had to do with the great outdoors— trail maintenance and the like," said Amy. "As I was into nature and the price couldn't be beat, I went over and I guess they liked me, and there I was, all moved in."

The students advertising the room were Sheryl Kipnis and Joe Coletto from NCNM. "I caught the bug, and I decided this was for me." Upon graduation from Antioch, Amy returned to Oregon and started at the National College of Naturopathic Medicine in 1982.

Of her class, she says, "There was one fellow, I absolutely took a keen hatred to— Paul Herscu. I would pick fights with him all the time and I'm sure I really made him feel badly. But I could see from an early time, that he was really on to something, calm and organized in his thinking, confident and inspiring in his understanding of homœopathy— all of it: philosophy, materia medica,

"Amy has been my only living teacher. Her personality is such that people easily divulge their case to her. It is incredible to watch it— from the patients to friends, to strangers, to other homœopaths. Everyone just tells her everything. In that process I have watched the heart of homœopathy at work. While she does not know as much materia medica as others, she is definitely the best homœopath that I have ever met. Since most of the work is in getting what the real case is, she gets it on a silver platter over and again. Whenever I am stuck on a case, I refer them to Amy and invariably they get the simillimum."

—Paul Herscu, ND

381

repertory, application, predicting outcomes etc. And then one day after three and half years of school, Herscu asked me out. We went on a date and got engaged that night. We married the day after we graduated from NCNM.

"With the birth of our third child, I surrendered willingly and with pleasure into full time motherhood for a few years where the only thing I really did to promote the profession was continue to really love Paul with all my heart and all my soul— supporting him emotionally while he did his work, writing books, teaching all over, thinking, thinking, thinking of so many new ideas and ways to think homœopathically, starting the journal etc. You know what they say— behind every great man…"

Rothenberg was recently appointed to the Board of Health in Amherst, which, she says, "I hope will enable me to continue to bridge the gap amongst the different medical practitioners. I continue to work hard on legislative issues to gain licensure for NDs in Massachusetts."

"When I don't have my head wrapped up in homœopathy I do lots of other stuff: I'm one of the cantors at my synagogue, I love to do art, swim, garden, read, hang out with my husband and my kids and our circle of friends."

André Saine, DC, ND, DHANP
May 25, 1953 —

André Saine grew up in a medical family, with a father who, while a conventional physician, often didn't use conventional methods.

After being treated for a shoulder injury by a chiropractor, he decided to enter chiropractic school. Once there he found naturopathic medicine and homœopathy. Said Saine, "As soon as I discovered homœopathy I told myself, 'this is what I want to study.'"

Saine graduated from the Canadian Memorial Chiropractic College in 1980, and graduated from NCNM in Portland in 1982. He studied homœopathy with Robin Murphy, Bill Gray, George Vithoulkas, Francisco Eizayaga, and John Bastyr. But his real teachers, he says, are the masters from the past.

Possessed with a seemingly photographic memory, Saine spent months going through old homœopathic journals still stored in the stacks at the University of

Michigan Library at Ann Arbor. Spending a week every few months, he would arrive with his portable copying machine, and leave with copies of all the old journals.

Now living and practicing in Montreal, Canada, Saine is in great demand as both a teacher and practitioner.

The sequoia tree and homœopathy: An analogy

In a sequoia the branches never live as long as the trunk— the lower branches fall off and die and the new branches come out at the top. I compare these branches to the various "offshoots or parasites"— of homœopathy: Lux's isopathy, Griesselich's low dilutions and specific medicines, Hughes' pathological prescribing and physiologic materia medica, the polypharmacists, the complexists, the alternists, the organopathists, the eclectics, Schuesslerism, Kent's Swedenborgism and synthetic materia medica. Later we had Bach bowellism and flowerism, today we have the electrodiagnosticians, the materia medica fantasists and futurists, the grand elaboration of miasmatic follies, the very high dilutions only, and even the supra-Kentian Catholicism. All of these and more are but departures from the strict inductive method of Hahnemann. But like new branches at the top of the sequoia they attract many, and many become overly enthusiastic with these new approaches… As the tree continues to grow, these branches fall off and die to be eventually replaced by new ones. What remains always vital is the trunk, the foundation of homœopathy based on the strict inductive method of Hahnemann. That lasts, and will continue to grow forever.

— From an interview with André Saine in *Homeopathica: The Journal of the LMHI*, Autumn 1994

Learning from the masters

"Whenever I had spare time I would find myself in the library reading these old journals. That is when I really woke up to it. The more I read the more I realized that what I was being taught in class and what was written in modern textbooks presented a completely different perspective to the one I was reading in those old journals. Two different ways of proceeding, of practicing, one deductive, depleted of all scientific rigor, very often left to one's own fancies, while the other was essentially scientifically-based, inductive. The more I studied these old masters the more I realized that the modern homœopathic community had been almost completely cut off from its roots… I realized that the real masters of homœopathy had been very few. Even though most of them

A friend, having heard André espouse the wonders of the homœopathic collection at Ann Arbor, decided to visit the Medical School Library and search out some information.

When she informed the librarian she was interested in the homœopathic collection, the librarian drew closer and said, "You know, the collection has a patron! He comes here every month to research."

"Ah," said the visitor, "Yes. Dr. Saine."

Leaning closer, the librarian said, "You know him? Isn't he cute? And THAT accent… oohhh…"

had already been forgotten, we still had their writings to study. If we want to master a discipline, any discipline, we have to start from its roots.

"I had found in this old literature my best teacher, and, of the old masters, the one who taught me the most was Adolph Lippe. Lippe wrote extensively; he was probably the one who wrote the most for the journals. In almost fifty years of practice he published more than 600 articles. This means that Lippe would write one or more articles per month and some of them were 10 to 20 pages long. But if the sheer volume of his output was extraordinary, so was the quality of his work. I do not think there has been anybody else in the homœopathic literature whose quality of writing equals that of Lippe as far as the demonstration of the principles of homœopathy goes. He was probably the most faithful follower of Hahnemann. In his work, over a period of almost fifty years, he confirmed what Hahnemann had found fifty years earlier; through his writing, he demonstrated the great truth of the law of similars and validated Hahnemann's teaching day after day in his practice. Nobody in the history of homœopathy comes close to Lippe regarding success in treatment."

— From an interview with André Saine in *Homeopathica: The Journal of the LMHI*, Autumn 1994

1975 – 1990: Divisions and Healings

The "great unpleasantness"
The search for education
The seminars
The question of lay education
The last of the elders

The years from the mid–1970s to the mid–1980s were fraught with domestic difficulties in the United States. The military pulled out of Vietnam and Nixon resigned. The administrations of Reagan and Bush led to changes in the political and social fabric of the country. It was an equally trying time for homœopathy. The guard was changing and it took its toll, with every organization going through major re–evaluations.

"The great unpleasantness"

The American Foundation for Homœopathy and the National Center for Homœopathy
1978-1981

The business of American homœopathy between 1978 and 1981 has been referred to as "the great unpleasantness," but that title conveys little of what really happened. I believe it is important future generations have a full description of what did happen; the differences arising in policy, personalities, vision, and direction.

While the journals provide some information, one has to see the correspondence and to talk to those who were part of it to understand the full story.

In 1997, it is possible to look back on those times from a broader viewpoint. I have spoken to the "major players" of the time, and all have now mellowed and gained perspective on the situation. Hatchets have been buried. It was an "unpleasantness" because *everyone* was unpleasant. In retrospect, there were no good guys and bad guys (although it seemed so at the time). Of the time, Maesimund Panos told me, "I remember what happened. I remember when it happened. I have a hard time remembering *why* it happened."

It was a group of people behaving as people do; misjudging, over-emphasizing, over-reacting, under-reacting, striking-out, sulking, and exhibiting the "lower animal" behaviors we like to think we humans have risen above. In retrospect, it was as good as it can get in a kindergarten food fight.

Several people suggested that I not include the entire story in this book; that it is a boring litany of names and deeds. I offer here a brief summary of the events. Because of the possible interest to future generations, the fully detailed story can be found in **Appendix B** on page 522.

The background

The time was the late 1970s. It was "hippie time." Many of the (generally conservative) older homœopaths were having problems relating to young male physicians who sported long hair, beards, and an aversion to suits and ties. A social and generational rift was developing within the community.

The National Center for Homœopathy and the American Foundation for Homœopathy began experiencing a division over policy and vision. Believing a good part of the National Center's mission was education, Maeisimund Panos was looking for ways for several doctors to go to Greece to study with Vithoulkas. But the National Center was dependent upon financial support from the American Foundation for Homœopathy, and neither the Foundation nor the National Center's executive director, Ralph Packman, shared Panos' vision.

In 1979, at the National Center membership meeting, proxy votes were used for the first time. The election

An AFH dinner, circa 1976. In the foreground is Royal Rood (Dr. Rood's brother) and Madelene Leath. In the back (from the left) is Ralph Packman, Carol Vargo, and Harris Coulter.

resulted in a board change away from the vision of Panos and several of the younger board members.

Over the next year, friction within the board continued. At the next membership meeting in 1980 in Chicago, many proxy votes were cast, resulting in most of the board aligning with Panos and the younger members. Christine Zack DeZutel, who was being groomed for the position of NCH President, was voted off the board.

The new board looked at the "top-heavy administrative staff" and asked questions about the AFH's past policies, going back as far as the splitting of the National Center from the American Foundation. As the group asked these questions, it was cautioned by the American Foundation trustees to cease the inquiry. "This," said Richard Moskowitz, "made us even more suspicious that there was dirty-pool going on."

At a National Center board of directors' meeting in January 1981, the four older directors asked "the dissident majority" to resign. The six "young turks" rejected the proposal. As a result, the American Foundation ceased funding the National Center and directed the Center's staff to vacate the shared offices.

The aftermath: The unwinding

A group, led by Harris Coulter, formed a committee called "The Ad Hoc Committee for the Preservation of Homeopathy in the United States." It was approached by Wyrth Post Baker and Ralph Packman to form a new organization, and in early 1981 the American Center for Homeopathy was formed with Christine Zack DeZutel as president. The organization's goals were, essentially, the same as those of the National Center for Homœopathy.

Coulter organized an educational program for the American Center held in Melbourne, Florida, and timed to run concurrently with the National Center for Homœopathy course at Millersville, Pennsylvania.

Barbed rhetoric flew between Coulter, from the American Center for Homeopathy, and Moskowitz, from the National Center. The rancor was thick.

By August 1981, sensing the name was too close to that of the National Center, the American Center for Homeopathy renamed itself "The Homeopathic Headquarters of America." Their monthly magazine was

Christine Zack DeZutel

re-titled *American Homeopathy*. In the same building were the offices of the American Foundation for Homœopathy, the American Institute of Homeopathy, the American Board of Homeotherapeutics, and the Homœopathic Pharmacopoeia Convention.

In 1982, the Homeopathic Headquarters of America, in conjunction with the International Foundation for Homeopathy, sponsored a one–day introduction to homœopathy in Melbourne, Florida, taught by Vithoulkas.

The Florida course in Melbourne. From the left: Wyrth Post Baker, Joe DeZutel, Christine Zack DeZutel, Ron Jones (from the Florida Institute of Technology), George Vithoulkas, Cynthia Lanahan, Bill Gray.

In April 1983 the Homeopathic Headquarters of America again changed its name to the "United States Homeopathic Association" (an easy acronym: USHA).

In 1984, the USHA successfully marketed the *Homœopathic Pharmacopoeia of the United States*. Shortly after, it funded an *Arnica* study with animals at the University of Georgia.

In late 1985, the United States Homeopathic Association ceased as an entity, mainly due to lack of funding.

The aftermath:
The rise of the National Center

In the aftermath of the split from the American Foundation for Homœopathy, the National Center's board of directors decided that they must continue three things: the annual meeting, the newsletter, and the summer school.

The summer school continued with Dr. Henry N. Williams serving as Dean. Kay Vargo, who had been registrar, was ready for retirement. She had sided with the AFH in the recent split and resigned. I volunteered for the job and became the registrar.

Bernard Haviland, Kay Vargo,
and Maesimund Panos.
National Center Meeting,
Philadelphia, 1978

Williams asked Bernard Haviland and me to teach the lay introductory weekend. But a problem developed with the lay week. One of the teachers who had always taught the course had a car accident and could not make the session. Williams phoned Bill Gray (who had taught at Millersville in the past) to see if he could come, and Gray suggested he send an associate, Laren Bays, ND. It was a brilliant move and the start of a new life for the NCH summer program.

Bays simply knew he was going to teach homœopathy. He came armed with cases to discuss. He did not know it was a lay group.

Until that time, lay course members were taught neither materia medica nor therapeutics. They were taught homœopathic philosophy and the materia medica of the most basic remedies like *Arnica* and *Calendula.*

Bays quickly sized up the situation. He taught basic philosophy, and its relation to materia medica and therapeutics. He shared his cases and discussed why he chose the remedy he did. He taught homœopathy in its fullest. As one student said later, "We were always told to stay away from chronic cases, but no one ever told us what a chronic case was!"

The summer school in 1981 had almost twice the attendance it had in 1980. The National Center was back in business.

In the spring of 1982 the American Institute of Homeopathy decided to use the National Center as its contact address. In October the same year the American Board of Homeotherapeutics moved its address to the National Center.

A year later, in the spring of 1983, the American Foundation for Homœopathy vacated the premises it was sharing with the Homeopathic Headquarters of America and gave the National Center for Homeopathy, on perpetual loan, its library of more than 2,000 volumes. In 1986, the Homœopathic Pharmacopoeia Convention moved its address to the National Center. American homœopathy was, again, all under one roof.

The summer school continued to grow, with a dental course, veterinary course, and more advanced lay courses being added.

In July 1987, the NCH board of directors approved a pilot project, introduced by new board member Joe Lillard, to establish "Affiliated Study Groups." It was the re-formation of the "Laymen's Leagues," but without the strong central control. By March 1988 the National Center for Homeopathy had 2,750 members. A decade later, in 1997, this had risen to more than 7,000 members and almost 200 Affiliated Study Groups.

The newsletter, *Homeopathy Today* grew from a four–page sheet in 1981 to a 32–page (and sometimes 36–page) two color magazine by 1996.

In January 1991, the National Center for Homeopathy relocated to a spacious new office in Alexandria, Virginia. The library (now named the Maesimund Banning Panos Library) finally had a worthy home.

Joe Lillard, who first attended the summer school class with Laren Bays back in 1981, was elected president of the board of directors in 1994, becoming the first non–medical person to hold the position.

The mastheads from 1981, 1982, 1990 (the "œ" was dropped in 1986)

Joe Lillard, with a bag of *Arnica* flowers, outside his pharmacy, Washington Homeopathic Products

The search for education

Vithoulkas' charismatic personality, combined with his encyclopedic knowledge and accessibility, certainly were factors that drew students.

However there were others in the world practicing and teaching homeopathy. Pierre Schmidt was still working in Geneva, and many of his pupils were practicing in Europe. Jost Kunzli was one of Schmidt's students and a teacher for a new generation in Europe.

One of those who travelled from the United States to Switzerland to learn from Kunzli was Robert Schore.

Robert Schore, MD, DHt
July 13, 1943 —

Schore was raised in Detroit, Michigan, and received his medical degree from the University of Michigan Medical School in 1969. He was in regular general practice until 1974. He says:

"A friend who knew I was interested in nutrition sent me a copy of *Homeopathy: Medicine of the New Man*. He was walking past Standard Homeopathic Company in Los Angeles, saw the book in the window, thought it may be a nutrition book I would like to read, and mailed it to me. Funny how so many people still think that homeopathy is some part of nutritional therapy! I read the book and found it captivating. In the back was the address of the NCH. I called to find out about courses. For reasons I still can't explain, Group Health Cooperative, Olympia, Washington (my employer at the time) allowed me to arrange postgraduate leave time without a lot of notice. I went to Millersville in 1974, met doctors who talked about curing patients, not about malpractice, football, and women. I returned to Olympia, treated patients with homœopathy in the evening for free, enough to learn that it worked for problems I was told had no cure. Group Health became increasingly more intolerant of my ideas, so I quit, lowered my income by 2/3 and never looked back."

Schore was the editor of the journal *Homeotherapy* from 1980 to 1985, taking over from Alain Naudé who had been editor since 1974.

Schore is in private practice in Seattle, Washington.

R. N. Schore, MD

Kunzli and Schore, Washington DC, 1987

Kunzli by Schore

"I was introduced to Dr. Jost Kunzli in 1977. I traveled to Switzerland several times to study with Dr. Kunzli. He was a quiet, gentle, sensitive, unpretentious, and perceptive man. He insisted that the writings of Hahnemann and Kent were the most important, and that practice makes perfect; that it was more important to treat patients every day than to teach, write, or theorize homœopathically.

"He and I resonated well. So much so that during one, week-long, visit I arrived with 140 typed questions about my patients and about homœopathic theory and practice. I observed during patient consultations, dined with his family, and walked in the woods with Dr. Kunzli each afternoon. Each day I became more and more anxious about having my questions answered, but there were so many other things happening that there was no opportunity to take the list from my briefcase. On my last day there I planned to leave at 6 p.m. At 4 p.m. Dr. Kunzli said, 'Now, what questions do you have?' I hurriedly read my list for the most important questions only to find that I knew the answers to all but four questions which he answered by 4:30!"

The seminars

The concept of a "homœopathic seminar" was first seen in the early 1970s, as Bill Gray (in full evangelical mode) taught homœopathy to groups across the United States. As homœopathy became more known, people clamored for knowledge. While the National Center's postgraduate program for physicians remained one of the primary educational resources, the International Foundation began its courses on the west coast, and naturopath Robin Murphy began teaching a series of seminars freely discussing materia medica, case-taking, repertorial analysis, and posology with all who came— be they a licensed health care provider or not.

Experienced homœopaths from abroad, where homœopathy had continued to flourish, found fertile fields for their knowledge in the United States. One of the earliest lecturers in the United States was Francisco Eizayaga from Argentina, who brought with him a methodology which, on the surface, seemed very different from what Vithoulkas was teaching. It was a time where the students began to appreciate the fullness of homœopathic methodology.

Those who came to share their knowledge through the mid 1980s into the 1990s came in "all flavors." There were

Francisco Eizayaga, MD

medical doctors like Francisco Eizayaga, Jacques Imberechts from Belgium, and Vassilis Ghegas from Greece; doctors trained at homœopathic schools in India, like Rajan Sankaran; veterinarians like George MacLeod; and non-medical professional homœopaths like Sheilagh Creasy and Jeremy Sherr from England.

Top: Imberechts, Ghegas, Sankaran
Bottom: MacLeod, Creasy, Sherr

A commentary:
The dangers of the "guru mentality""

The 1960s saw many people starting on a quest for a spiritual path in a country that seemed to have lost its spirituality and was buried deep in the Vietnam War. The influences were many— the "tune in, turn on, drop out" of Timothy Leary, the music and lyrics of Bob Dylan, the Beatles, the Stones, the Dead, and the endless number of Indians ready to lead their followers to enlightenment— the Maharishi Mahesh Yogi, Rajneesh, Sai Baba, Swami Rama, Yogi Bhajan, Meher Baba, Swami Sachidananda, Baba Lethargee— to name a few.

In 1926, Rudolph Rabe, MD, described the American culture: "We in these United States, dearly love noise and show and are given to hysterical fervor and exuberance, almost on a par with the old-time Methodist camp meeting; we are fond of fooling ourselves and of being fooled and thus exhibit a naiveté which for the foreigner at least, is difficult to understand."

By the mid 1970s Rabe's description was playing out on the homœopathic field. We suddenly found a number of grand homœopaths "out there" and, with our full fervor, began to flock to them.

Homœopathy, whose greatest teachers had lived in the United States and had others flocking to them in the 1800s and early 1900s, had lost its greatness. Homœopathy in the United States was almost as it had been before Hering arrived in 1833— everyone knew a little but there were few who knew more.

While Americans were proud of their science and engineering marvels, those interested in homœopathy realized the living knowledge was often outside its borders.

Someone once asked George Vithoulkas: "Were Hahnemann, Hering, and Kent geniuses, or were they just hard workers?" Replied Vithoulkas: "Their genius lies in the capacity for hard work."

Yet, everyone was looking for homœopathic enlightenment; looking for that *one* thing that would let them "get it" with complete clarity, and little effort. They looked for the teacher who would give it to them.

The teachers came in waves— the Greeks (Vithoulkas and Ghegas), the Belgians (Imberechts, Geukens, Schroyens), the South Americans (Eizayaga, Candegabe), the Indians (Sankaran, Dixit, Banerjea, Shah), the English (Creasy, Sherr, Norland, Assilem)— as well as our continental home grown

guru
1. A personal religious teacher and spiritual guide
2. A person who acts as one's teacher and guide in matters of fundamental intellectual concern

—Webster's *3rd Unabridged International Dictionary*

crop (Herscu, Saine, Shore, Gray, Rozenberg, Klein, Murphy, Morrison, Zaren).

Most were fine teachers and had lots to offer to a group of people who were, as Roger Morrison said, "babes in the woods." But when you are an innocent, you think your first love is the best, and you tend to believe and idolize the first teacher you hear.

Some of the teachers were just interested in humbly sharing their knowledge while others seemed to become addicted to the "power and glory." And some, as their "fame" spread, priced themselves out of the market.

When I presented a slide show on the history of homœopathy for the Society of Homœopaths meeting in Nottingham in 1988, I apologized for not having a slide of one prominent homœopath by saying, "I couldn't afford them." It got a roar of approval.

"Many of these people were interested in astonishing us," said one homœopath who prefers to remain nameless. "They often practiced one way, but taught another way to make themselves look good and make us look stupid. I recall a case that I brought to a seminar early in my career. It was a case of scoliosis that I had little success in treating. The visiting homœopath showed the case to the 120 or so people assembled. Everyone was trying to prescribe on the 'essence' of the case. Suggestions were made of the remedies *Natrum muriaticum* and *Staphisagria*.

"Then the visiting lecturer pronounced the remedy. 'This is a case of *Calcarea fluorica*.' Everyone was astonished and amazed. But he never said, '*Calc fluor* is a keynote remedy in cases of scoliosis.' I felt as if that was something *he* knew, and he wasn't telling *us*."

Another type of incident happened over and over. The visiting grand prescriber would take a "live case" in front of the class and then announce, "This is a perfect case of *Stramonium*" (or whatever the remedy was). The audience would be astonished and amazed. They would leave with a clear picture in their minds of that being what a *Stramonium* case is like. But they never learned that the remedy *was* given and had *no* effect. So the "picture" they understood was not correct.

One student wrote on the internet of a follow-up visit of a case by the visiting teacher. The student said the teacher tried and tried to find *anything* that was better about the case and eventually found some minor symptom had been relieved, and announced that the remedy was working— while the class could see no improvement in the case at all.

In another instance a visiting lecturer presented a case and told the remedy that was given. The question was asked, "Did you see a follow-up?" And the reply, "No. She never came back. I'm assuming she got better."

When a student asked Roger Morrison at a seminar how sure he was of the prescription in a case he presented, he replied that he is *never* sure the remedy is the simillimum until the patient comes back and tells him that the remedy acted curatively.

In some cases, the miracles the students expected to receive in knowledge were sought by patients who expected the visiting homœopath to find the right remedy and to cure them overnight.

Several visiting homœopaths saw patients and were willing to follow them through their cure by keeping in touch by phone, letter, and the half-yearly visit— to become their practitioner as it were. When asked to handle a case, one visiting homœopath said he would accept only those who were committed to working together for a year. Yet, on the other side, there were those who were content with the one–shot prescription and not much effort expended on the follow-up— certainly an ethical question.

Said one old homœopath of the endless stream of teachers: "They are like a great preacher. You love listening to the sermon, even though what he's saying has been said before. You feel rejuvenated. And *they* love the audience."

One person wrote an enthusiastic report which discussed the methodology taught at a recent seminar, only to find the seminar presenter replying to the report by saying, in effect, "No, that's not what I said."

The easy access to these seminars is a knife which cuts both ways. They can be of immense value and can also lead one down a primrose path. It was all summed up well by an experienced homœopath describing a popular teacher:

"He has the simultaneous gift and liability of unmistakable charisma. He can hold a packed lecture hall in his palm from the first moment of silence to the lingering echoes. This is both wonderful and terrible. It's actually the piece I struggle with the most. I see understandably inspired students cling to the superficial trappings of his teaching without critical analysis or appreciation of the depth of roots or foundations they need to complete their education."

The ongoing question of lay education in the United States

From 1940 through the 1960s, homœopathy in the United States was in the hands of medically–trained homœopaths.

Then, during the 1970s homœopathy began to be openly practiced by people who were not medical doctors. This was given even more emphasis when those in the United States looked across to the United Kingdom and saw the development of training establishments, a professional register, and quality homœopathy being practiced by non-medically trained professionals. The contrast is one which bears looking at.

In the United States, the question of the lay practitioner has always been an issue not far from the surface. It concerned the American Foundation for Homœopathy when it was founded in 1924, and remains an ongoing issue through the 1990s.

Since 1835, homœopathy has been accessible to the non-medical person. That is the date when Hering published his first copy of *The Domestic Physician*. The books were sold with a kit of 40 remedies, and covered the treatment of a variety of domestic illnesses. Within a few years other "domestics" appeared— *Laurie's, Pulte's, Johnson's*— as well as a whole new industry of "combinations" intended for the self-treatment of ailments by the general public.

At a time of westward expansion in the United States, these domestic manuals and their accompanying kits were often the *only* medicine available along the trail. And because the medicine worked so well, there were many people who converted to homœopathy and sought out homœopathic physicians when they were available.

When Reuben Ludlam told the AIH in 1869 that many communities were "converted to homœopathy by a single woman with her domestic kit," he was not exaggerating.

Yet, with the rise of the homœopathic schools and the spread of homœopathic physicians, the practice of homœopathy by the lay populace after 1870 was, in the United States, not a great force to be reckoned with.

When the American Foundation for Homœopathy was established in 1924, it formed a bureau of publicity to bring to the public a greater interest in homœopathy. But the actual practice of homœopathy was kept in the hands of the physicians.

This was in sharp contrast to what was happening in Great Britain where, by common law, homœopathic practice was not limited to medically-trained physicians.

The involvement of laymen in the American Foundation was an issue that divided the organization through its history.

In 1928, Dr. Elizabeth Wright (Hubbard) said, "I am against it from A to Z. I have always thought from the first time I ever heard of the Foundation, that the laymen's end of it was a bad mistake."

Wright believed that lay involvement would negatively affect the relations of the Foundation with the AIH and the AMA. Dr. Green saw it as the Foundation's responsibility to find the "most intellectual people in this country to give them an idea of their own responsibility in selecting physicians and have it done upon some principle..."

The increasing attrition of homœopaths in the United States through old age, and the lack of homœopathic colleges, pushed the American Foundation into a double-bind. On one hand, it wanted to train physicians at the postgraduate level. On the other hand it wanted to educate the public to understand homœopathy and to demand access to quality homœopaths. The former was increasingly difficult with fewer physicians wanting to learn homœopathy. The American Foundation postgraduate course drew only two people in 1933 and three people in each year from 1934 to 1936.

In 1946 the American Foundation started a training program teaching the principles of homœopathy to lay people. They were to learn about palliation, suppression, cure, what is to be cured, individualization, the minimum dose, the principles of homœopathic pharmacy, and the principle of provings to establish the materia medica. They were *not* to be taught to use the remedies. *That* was the province of the physician.

The *Qualifying Course for Laymen* issued by the AFH in January 1946, makes the direction quite clear.

By 1961, there were a number of Laymen's Leagues operating. The American Foundation moved to have these independent leagues affiliate with the larger organization, to unite them and operate with a unified purpose. There were 11 leagues in 1963, rising to 16 leagues by 1974.

The *Qualifying Course for Laymen*: 1946

An excerpt from the 40-page booklet:

"When the principles have become familiar, the members of your group will be able to make for themselves intelligent selections of doctors who are qualified... They will know the importance of using remedies, if at all, under the guidance of their doctors, avoiding by that course the likelihood of delaying or confusing their own cases...

"Viewing Homœopathy in its true light, however, it is doubtful if any large endowed school was ever able for long to offer sound training in Homœopathy. Rather, from the first, it was necessary to take instruction from the few masters of homœopathic prescribing, after completing the usual courses in Medicine, even after, in many cases, years of actual practice as licensed physicians... Homœopathy is not so much a separate school of Medicine, but a post-graduate extension of medical training into the prescribing of the drugs for the sick.

"Since it requires this and no less for a competent homœopathic physician, Homœopathy is not something for the layman to play at. Under the guidance of a thorough homœopathic doctor, a layman may acquire a number of the more common remedies in moderate potency and hold them for taking under the physician's direction. The layman may even come to recognize a few of the remedies as he may see them indicated in those about him, and may be able to help frequently when prescribing is needed, but the layman must never expect to go far without complete medical training... Appreciating what comprises the proper training of the homœopathic physician, the layman is wise who makes use of it."

In retrospect...

In discussing his writings of 1976 with Alain Naudé in 1998, he says that within a few years of writing the editorials quoted here he began to change his views. Mentioning "maturity, retrospection, and a clearer vision" as factors behind the change, Naudé says that he began to understand that physicians, who are so steeped in the conventional medical model, could not, generally, have the deeper comprehension of the homœopathic model. "I began to realize that they were two different things," he said, "and to trust the preservation of homœopathy to conventional medicine would lead to either the demise of homœopathy or the development of using it in an allopathic way— either of which would have an adverse effect on homœopathy. In no way am I denying that the physician's knowledge is of value, but the majority would have a difficult time grasping homœopathy."

In December 1978 Naudé wrote an editorial in the Journal of the American Institute of Homeopathy *where he again suggested forming schools to teach homœopathy, and said:*

"If the AIH does not do this, it is inviting the laymen to start schools in which homœopathy will be removed from the profession forever. It is as simple as that: there will be schools and they will either be run by physicians or by laymen. Let us not forget that if Homœopathy is removed from the medical profession history will blame the physicians who caused the void in the first place, not those who tried to fill it in their own way."

It was a prophesy that would be fulfilled.

Although the leagues were told they had complete freedom to do as they wished and would have their own treasury and programs, as time went on they were subject to increasing control from the American Foundation (and later the National Center) central office. In a meeting with the Laymen's League of Dallas, Texas in 1982, I was told it chose to break away from the National Center because the Center's management wanted to approve every program it was planning before it was offered, and it felt the control was excessive.

The first formal "lay course" was offered at the National Center for Instruction at Millersville in 1966. The dean of the program, Dr. William Boyson, assured the AFH that, "The laymen were not being taught remedies nor therapeutics but just philosophy."

This view was emphasized by Alain Naudé in an lengthy editorial in *The Layman Speaks* where he said:

"Nobody could ever overestimate the importance of the lay homœopathic movement in America. If Homœopathy has not completely died out it is thanks to laymen; if it enters a great new period of its history it will be thanks to them— but only if they play the magnificent role which belongs to them, and which no one else can play: awakening and educating the public to Homœopathy, studying and understanding Homœopathy so as to demand the best medical treatment, representing the public medical conscience."

The "official" role of the lay person was to demand from the physicians more homœopathy. What they were to do if no one would listen to them was never discussed.

In 1972 it appeared that a legal case could possibly be instituted by the American Civil Liberties Union against the AFH on behalf of a health care provider (an osteopath) who was not considered a "physician" (read "MD degree") but wanted to be educated in homœopathy. The AFH had, until this time, a position that said, in effect, "if you were not an MD/physician you were a layman."

Because of this possible legal challenge the AFH decided on new criteria for eligibility standards for its educational programs. State practice and license laws were to be the measure of how much education could be provided.

The program changed from the "Postgraduate School for Physicians in Homœopathy" to "The Center for Instruction in Homœopathy and Homœotherapeutics."

The committee establishing the eligibility standards (Drs. Panos, Williams, Baker, and Forrest Murphy) stated, "At no time will the practice of medicine be taught to unqualified persons."

But even letting in non-MD health professionals was problematic. Dr. Lucy Clark, who was teaching at the school, questioned the wisdom of instructing chiropractors in homœopathy. In a memo of April 15, 1975, she says: "The full use of Homœopathy requires conventional medical training... I believe good homœopathy is safer to use, in safer hands, with fewer but able and sympathetic MDs and DOs than with 'the fringe'... The 'fringe' can bring into homœopathy more problems to be solved, than solutions to our lack of good homœopathic physicians and prescribers, at this time, without more unity."

Certainly, in the back of everyone's mind at this time was the open practice of homœopathy by a number of lay people, alongside physicians, at the Hering Clinic in Berkeley, California.

The problems created by the "lay prescriber" are outlined by Alain Naudé in his editorial:

"There is an unprecedented new demand for homœopathic treatment among the public. Because the great homœopaths of the past have not secured the preservation and transmission of Homœopathy within the profession, so that there are not nearly enough homœopathic physicians to meet the new demand, a great wave of lay homœopathic practice is sweeping across the country. Most lay prescribers started tentatively, at first practicing legitimate domestic Homœopathy in their families, treating the acute household ills for which every home medicine chest has always been intended, and then gradually tackling wider horizons, greater challenges, chronic conditions— thus sliding imperceptibly into the practice of medicine.

"Unfortunately there are some who go a different way. They argue that if there is no place for Homœopathy within the profession it should be allowed to flourish outside of it. But unfortunately it does not flourish in this way. If an orthodox medical education does not guarantee any homœopathic proficiency, nor does its absence. People who dispense with all credentials, standards, and controls become a law unto themselves, and need fulfil no requirements beyond those of their own integrity, conscience, and understanding. Even if lay prescribers are motivated by the highest integrity, and exact of themselves the highest standards of homœopathic practice, they cannot possibly fulfil those standards without a medical training...

The Ullman Case: 1976

Alain Naudé, the Editor of The Layman Speaks, *commented upon the arrest and release of Dana Ullman in California on charges of practicing medicine without a license:*

"But a recent ruling in a California court has allowed a layman to practice Homœopathy, under certain conditions. He explained to the judge (and afterwards to the press and the whole nation) that Homœopathy is a part of 'holistic health-care,' and not medicine in quite the same way as Allopathy, not therefore subject to the laws which govern the practice of medicine. If this view gains wide acceptance and legal sanction, Homœopathy will indeed be considered a non-medical therapy, and the United States, which once led the world in Homœopathy, might become the first country to remove it from its present status as a proper medical drug therapy."

The accessibility of homœopathy

Jerome Whitney, in explaining the rise of the lay prescriber in the UK and the move toward the "professional homœopath" offers this thought:

"What seemed to make homœopathy so accessible to the "non-medical" person began at the turn of the century. Although Kent was adamant about a homœopath receiving training in the medical sciences, the hierarchical system of ranking symptoms that he suggested was the means by which a new type of homœopath would emerge.

"Based upon the Swedenborgian system of reflexive correspondences between the planes of being, Kent had developed an effective and powerful system of truly homœopathic diagnosis. No longer did a prescriber need to rely on conventional medical training in order to treat the full spectrum of human disease. When a possible simillimum was found using mental symptoms, it could be verified by correspondence with emotional and physical level symptoms or *vice versa*.

"The Kentian tool-kit of hierarchical prescribing provided the basis for the professional homœopath that was to emerge in increasingly large numbers particularly after 1970. This allowed the cutting edge of homœopathy to shift into the sphere of the non-medically qualified practitioners who could more readily become 'homœopathic thinkers.' Because they did not have their minds cluttered with an allopathic chemical-materialistic concept of disease, they were able to utilize the reflective and associative thought processes required in homœopathic symptom synthesis."

"So the standard of Homœopathy generally practiced by laymen setting themselves up in public practice inevitably leaves much to be desired. Homœopathy is equated with every fashionable fringe therapy; healthfood stores and occult bookshops sell kits of remedies with instructions on using them; Homœopathy is misunderstood, distorted, dishonored, exploited. Self-styled teachers conduct short seminars on case-taking and prescribing for any amateurs who will present themselves, and teach them just enough to ruin their patients and Homœopathy, not nearly enough to do much good. Without proper restraint and responsibility there is much confusion…

"Then there is the movement to allow nurses and paramedics to practice Homœopathy, as they are already allowed to administer certain remedies in a role subservient and complementary to the doctor's more specifically medical one. If this movement succeeds, it will also mean that there is acceptance of the view that Homœopathy is not really medicine to quite the same degree as Allopathy; and it will tend to reserve for Homœopathy the treatment of patients who are not seriously ill, or else patients could be treated homœopathically and allopathically at the same time… Homœopathy would have rather the same status and consideration as physiotherapy, nutrition, and other adjuncts to real medicine, and a physician who treated serious illness with Homœopathy might even be liable to malpractice suits, or disciplinary measures from medical regulatory agencies.

"The legal sanction of lay homœopathic practice on the grounds that 'holistic health-care' is not medicine and Homœopathy is a part of this holistic healthcare, inevitably means that Homœopathy is no longer a proper medical drug therapy. It is important to be aware of these legal implications."

Volume 1 Number 1 of the *Homœopathic Heartbeat* in 1978 contained a note: "In view of the current activity in our homœopathic field concerning 'lay prescribing'…" and reprinted the policy that:

"Homœopathy is a postgraduate specialty of medicine practiced as a medical therapy by fully licensed physicians with the degree of MD or DO. The NCH does not advocate and has never advocated the lay practice of Homœopathy."

A memo from Kay Vargo on September 4, 1978, reiterates the point concerning lay education: "I am opposed to providing the same books on the recommended reading list for laymen and doctors." There were to be no Materia Medica or Repertory books for the lay courses. "First aid books will suffice. The layman should receive more philosophy and less materia medica."

An incident at Millersville in 1979, shows the attitude with clarity: Wendy Rue, a lay person from New Orleans, was attending the course. On the day she arrived she found the 200–book library housed at the Millersville dormitory. She was looking at the books and saw a Kent's *Repertory*. Having read about homœopathy, and about the value of the repertory, she took it from the shelf. No sooner had she opened it when Kay Vargo appeared, took it from her, and placed it back on the shelf, saying, "No, my dear, those books are for the doctors!"

In 1980, while attending the Millersville professional course, I had occasion to go to my room to get a book. I saw Kay Vargo sitting in her room and asked how come she wasn't downstairs listening to the lecture. She replied that the lectures "were for doctors" and she should not be hearing the information.

When Laren Bays, ND, taught the lay class in 1981 at Millersville, it was the first time materia medica and repertory work were openly discussed with non-medical people.

In April, 1982, *Homœopathy Today* published a long article by Richard Moskowitz, MD, discussing the dilemma of lay prescribing. He said:

"Let us not try to ostracize our lay practitioners as if we were ashamed of them. Let us rather pay them tribute, as an expression of the spirit that kept homœopathy alive all these years. And, above all, let us now try to provide effective leadership for them, in the form of educational services, professional supervision, and some realistic guidelines for their practice, before somebody gets hurt, and the FDA or the courts or some other government agency that knows nothing of homœopathy decides to do it for us."

The same issue of *Homœopathy Today* contained the statement that:

"Homœopathy is a post-graduate specialty of medicine practiced by health care professionals… The NCH has fostered lay education in Homœopathy only to the extent consistent with the concept that patients should be involved in their own health care. Education in the use of homœopathic medicines is concerned with their applicability to domestic emergencies."

But more study groups were forming, and books were becoming increasingly available. Robin Murphy began his series of seminars in 1983, and the audiences for these

But, who will listen?

With all the discussion about keeping the responsibility of practice in the hands of physicians and charging the laymen with the job of "watchdogs," how can homœopathy survive if the practitioners are dying off? Alain Naudé presented the following in his 1977 editorial.
The idea, in the most perfect of worlds, is laudable. In the world of homœopathy in the USA in 1977 (and even in 1997) it is a most unrealistic pipe-dream.

"If Homœopathy is to survive at all we must create new homœopathic medical schools in which a medical degree and the license to practice also guarantees the highest homœopathic competence. This can be brought about if enough good homœopathic physicians work together to reintroduce Homœopathy into a medical school, at first as a subject, and then as a separate department of therapy. This would eventually lead by a series of steps to the formation of a separate homœopathic medical school, and other schools would follow. But if this is to happen the dignity of Homœopathy as a proper medical drug therapy must be rigorously upheld and defended by laymen and physicians alike…

"The proper role of homœopathic lay groups is infinitely grander than anything hitherto imagined. The energy, intelligence, and dedication of laymen throughout the country has already awakened the public to the need for Homœopathy. If they unite their efforts to establish homœopathic medical schools in America nothing will be able to resist them: they will start a movement which will not only restore Homœopathy to its old glory, but give it an incomparable new brilliance and power…"

seminars were a mix of lay people and licensed medical professionals— the two sitting side by side, and learning the same material. It was the beginning of the end of the hold the National Center for Homœopathy had on general homœopathic education. It was no longer the "only game in town." Soon after, starting with Francisco Eizayaga in 1984, an influx of teachers from abroad arrived to teach all comers in the United States.

By March 1985, the National Center board of directors had a long discussion about education and lay practice and, basically, re-defined its educational position. It would not support lay practice, since the practice of medicine without license is illegal in all states. However, the distinction was made between the knowledge and the use of the knowledge. Said Richard Moskowitz, "We cannot adjudicate lay practice. Only society can do that. Persons who hang out a shingle do so at their risk— not ours [the NCH] for putting out the information." Dr. Henry Williams said it was, "possible to do good homœopathy without medical knowledge but not all the time. We must educate laymen to understand and recognize where their limits are."

The NCH stated:

> "…as a fundamental educational ethic it would freely share homœopathic knowledge, with all persons and would not deny it because of educational background… The NCH does not support the illegal practice of medicine by unlicensed persons. Those who administer homœopathic medicines should consult their state laws on the practice of medicine."

By 1990, more seminars were being held. The Pacific Academy of Homeopathic Medicine had begun a course on the west coast, the Atlantic Academy had begun teaching on the east coast. Soon students were flocking to hear teachers like André Saine, Jeremy Sherr, Vega Rozenberg, S. K. Banerjea, Roger Morrison, Ananda Zaren, Jonathan Shore, Bill Gray, Paul Herscu, and Lou Klein. Although the seminars were open to all, the majority of those attending most of the seminars (through personal observation) appeared to be "non–medically trained" prescribers.

The last of the elders

In 1983 the National Center undertook a project to collect the oral history of homœopathy from the few "elders" still alive. In many ways, *this* book is an outgrowth of that project. Adelaide Suits, an NCH director, interviewed John Renner, MD, the reclusive California homœopath who appeared at the 1984 NCH meeting in Santa Barbara. The result was a biography of Renner, *Brass Tacks: An Oral Biography of a 20th Century Physician*, published in 1985.

John H. Renner, MD
August 17, 1890 — June 27, 1989

Born of German descent in Fairfax, Minnesota, Renner became interested in medicine after two of his children were born with spastic diplegia, and conventional medicine offered no help.

He attended Hahnemann Medical College of Chicago and graduated with honors in 1920. One of his teachers was Arthur H. Grimmer.

He returned to teach at the college before setting up practice in Palentine, Illinois. He was editor of the *Midwest Homœopathic Journal* in 1928.

He moved to Santa Barbara, California in 1931 where he practiced until his retirement.

Renner was an outspoken critic of high potencies, and believed homœopathy failed in the United States because physicians were no longer being taught physical diagnosis, and they were using high potencies. Renner's ability to use information he gleaned from physical diagnosis was almost magical. Those who studied with him during his last years were amazed at the information he could extract from a physical exam of a patient— the sounds of the percussion, the feel of the skin, the color of the eye.

Renner kept a low profile for most of his life, but in his last 10 years he became more vocal about what he believed were the reasons homœopathy was dying. He pleaded with the American Institute to petition the FDA to declare illegal any homœopathic remedy above the 3X potency. He railed against those using the Kent *Repertory* and claimed no good practice could come from its use.

I have a large file of correspondence with Dr. Renner. Many of the letters from Renner express his concern that

The author with John and Marion Renner, Santa Barbara, 1984

homœopathy will not survive, and when I continually assured him it seemed to be doing OK, he was incredulous it could be working well with people who persisted in using high potencies (anything above a 3X).

A letter to me on March 7, 1989, asked if I could see the danger to homœopathy. Said Renner:

> "Actually it is almost all over. End. These enthusiastic reports, just the same words I have been reading for over 60 years, while every year they were clipped closer.
>
> "Do you at all think of our status? Won't you please tell me, how does this look to you as a lay person?"

I again assured him I saw homœopathy gaining strength, and although I understood his reservations about potencies, I did not see it as a major stumbling block.

A month later I received the letter below. Two months later he died.

John Collins, ND, while at naturopathic school, once wanted verification on a case and thought he'd phone the oldest, most experienced homœopath there was. He phoned Renner. Renner, 92 at the time, listened to the case, and asked Collins what he would give. John ventured a suggestion, and Renner agreed it was the right choice. Then Renner asked the question: "What potency will you use?" Collins, knowing Renner was adamantly opposed to higher dilutions, mentioned that he was studying with Eizayaga and was thinking of a low potency, a 6c.

"A 6c?" said Renner. "I don't mean that mystical stuff! John, I mean real medicine like a 3X. Give them something that has something in it!"

April 11- 89

Dear Winston:
A good dedicated worker, now for years! As the senior homeo Doctor I do thank you for us all.
You deserve much respect and thanks for your sincerity and your persistence for the years.
We are now such few MDs remaining. You need to depend and work for the general public.
Our lay build up is so necessary, so the reputation of homeopathic cures must not be lost.
Carry on, with the enthusiasm and with such dedicated involvement as you have demonstrated over the years.
God bless you.
for the humanitarian involvement

yours

J H Renner, MD

Great Britain: III

The Practice under common law
The rise of the colleges

Homœopathy in Great Britain: the rise of the lay movement

From the start of homœopathy in Great Britain, non-medical people were at the forefront of the movement. A rich London silk merchant, William Leaf, and the Reverend Thomas R. Everest were both early converts to homœopathy. Both were cured by Hahnemann and both spent considerable time with him in Paris. They established practices in the UK and started several free dispensaries and hospitals.

The French doctor Paul Francois Curie was brought to England by Leaf to help with the first free dispensary for poor people in the Finsbury Circus area of the City of London.

Frederick Foster Hervey Quin, a medical doctor, distanced himself from them, and concentrated on converting medically qualified people to the new system. In 1848 J. G. Rosenstein listed 73 practitioners in England, 22 of whom were lay people.

Medical homœopathy was very strong in Britain during the late 1880s, but by the early 1900s many of the important homœopaths— Burnett, Cooper, Skinner, Hughes, Dudgeon— had all died within a short time of each other, leaving a huge gap in the homœopathic ranks.

The gap was chiefly filled by John Henry Clarke, whose sympathy for the lay prescriber was heightened by his embittered feeling toward the medical profession and the "half-homœopaths" whom he regarded as traitors to the cause. He left the British Homœopathic Society and began teaching homœopathy to several lay persons. His three best-known pupils were Noel Puddephatt, J. Ellis Barker (Julius Otto Eltzbacher), and Reverend Roland Upcher.

Barker took over the editorship from Clarke of *The Homœopathic World* after Clarke's death in 1931. He restyled it, renamed it *Heal Thyself,* and began a blistering series of attacks on medical orthodoxy— all based on his view that conventional medicine had failed, yet homœopathy had not been allowed a fair trial by the medical establishment. He inspired a grassroots renaissance of lay practice during the 1930s and 1940s. He asked the lay people to take homœopathy to the masses.

Medical practice in Great Britain falls under Common Law— the term used for the laws and customs applied by the Royal Courts which emerged after the Norman

Conquest, and which slowly replaced local laws and customs. Common Law is also used, in a narrower sense, for one of a number of distinct sources of law existing within such a system— the other obvious one is statutes enacted by Parliament.

Common Law has always been particularly associated with protecting such matters as personal freedom, rights of property, rights of contract, and individual interests in reputation and bodily security. Hence: "Citizens are free to do as they like unless expressly prohibited by law." This is in contrast to Napoleonic Law, used in much of Europe, that allows one to do *only* what is allowed by statute.

Thus, under Common Law, one lay person could treat another without restriction, since neither the courts nor Parliament ever saw fit to interfere to impose restraint. Medical doctors are, of course, regulated by statute, and it is an offense to practice as such when not qualified.

Thus it is the government's right to mandate the educational qualifications of those whom it will accept to work under the guidelines of the National Health Service, but it cannot interfere with the right of one citizen to give medical help to another. Anyone can "hang out a shingle." As long as they do not misrepresent their qualifications, their ability to practice their trade freely is not impinged upon.

It is under Common Law that homœopathy, in the hands of non-medically trained practitioners, spread so readily in Great Britain and in most of the British Commonwealth countries.

After World War II, homœopathy in the UK drifted, as historian Peter Morrell says, "into a 30–year period of obscurity, becoming a quiet, quaint backwater of UK medical practice, totally marginalised by orthodox medicine, subservient to the British Homœopathic Society and the British Homœopathic Association and widely regarded (if at all) as the domain of cranks."

When the National Health Service was established, the continued existence of homœopathy was secured by the Faculty of Homœopathy Act, which established the right of patients to homœopathic care within the National Health Service (NHS), and established the Faculty of Homœopathy at the Royal London Homœopathic Hospital as the guardians of the profession and hospitals.

Yet, there were those (as in the United States) who were keeping homœopathy alive. Unlike the situation in the

Thomas Maughan

John Damonte

United States, a good many of those keeping it alive were not the dwindling number of medically trained homœopaths, but the well-trained lay prescribers. Noel Puddephatt was the teacher of Phyllis Speight whose husband, Leslie, ran the Homœopathic Publishing Company (later to become Health Science Press). Puddephatt emigrated to South Africa where he taught Sheilagh Creasy. Edwin Tomkins learned homœopathy from Dr. Percival George Quinton. Tomkins was also helped by the friendship of Dr. Otto Leeser, a German Jewish refugee whose remedies and pharmacy he later inherited.

Although the Faculty of Homœopathy remained officially aloof from the lay movement, a few members did teach homœopathy to non–medical folk. After World War II, almost anyone could listen to the Faculty's homœopathy lectures and no one batted an eye. Charles Wheeler and John Paterson, both Faculty members, had ongoing social and professional relations with many lay-practitioners.

The two major lay people to become influential in the UK were Thomas Maughan and John Damonte; well educated, and friends of both Sir John Weir and Margery Blackie. It is said that Maughan learned homœopathy from Dr. William Wilson Rorke, but there were so many people talking to each other it is hard to establish a lineage of exactly who taught what and to whom. It is known that Dr. Donald Foubister was a close friend to both men.

Both Damonte and Maughan were involved with an esoteric group, the Druids. In 1964, Maughan became the Chief Druid in the UK. Many of those trained in homœopathy were also from the Druid Order. It is hard to say just what this influence signified as there is some secrecy about their beliefs and work.

It is said that Maughan also was influential in the "hippie" or "bohemian" movements, as he attended many free festivals and similar events to freely offer his homœopathic services. Maughan was both a "classical" prescriber and a user of many three-remedy low potency combinations, some of which his old students still use. Similarly, Damonte was both a "classical" prescriber as well as a radionics practitioner who had studied under Malcolm Rae.

In 1946, a meeting of 300 people interested in homœopathy (including Maughan, Damonte, Speight, and Tomkins) met to form the Institute of Homœopathy, a non–doctor organization. Twenty–four years later on January 10, 1970,

Thomas Maughan, John Damonte, Edwin Tomkins and others met and formed a Society of Homœopaths. The group's formation was seen by some as a reaction to a perceived threat from the orthodox establishment (over a re-regulation of the Medicines Act in 1968 which sought to re-legislate the pharmaceutical industry), but the threat never materialized.

On June 18, 1972, an air crash at Staines killed a group of 15 British homœopaths and homœopathic pharmacists enroute to an international meeting in Belgium. Nelsons Pharmacy never recovered from its loss of pharmacists and the provings done at the Faculty of Homœopathy stopped with the loss of the main researchers. Despite this tragedy, the direct effect of this loss on homœopathy in the UK was negligible, although the crash did bring publicity to homœopathy. Both Maughan and Damonte, who had planned to be on the plane but cancelled at the last minute, decided to work even harder to establish a strong presence for homœopathy in the UK.

By the early 1970s, Maughan and Damonte had attracted a highly committed nucleus of students. Maughan's group later became known as the South London Group and Damonte's as the North London Group.

Secretly, some doctors enrolled in the Faculty courses began attending the lectures of Maughan as well. Between 1970 and 1975 the South London and North London Homœopathic Groups grew in size and intensity and depth of study, and a creative self-sustaining dynamic had emerged.

Damonte died in 1975 and many of his group began to attend Maughan's classes. In June 1976, Maughan died. Both the South London and North London groups continued to meet and study homœopathy.

During 1977, Robert Davidson, Martin Miles, Peter Chappell, Kaaren Whitney, Jennifer Maughan, Lynn Lovell, Mary Titchmarsh and Margaret Koolman of the South London Group began discussions to set up a homœopathic society. Later they invited Misha Norland, Kay Samuel, and Michael Haggiag of the North London Group, to share in the dialogue. The document that became the reference point for their discussions was the constitution of the earlier 1970 Society of Homœopaths of which Maughan was chairman and Damonte, secretary.

On July 26, 1978 the Constitution of The Society of Homœopaths was signed by Robert Davidson, Martin

The Druid Order

The Druid Order traces its outer modern public organization back to the 17th century and individual teacher-pupil links going back to ancient times. It is a private organization, and classes and on–going activities of the Order are open only to those who choose to formally join it. Public meetings are also held regularly and three public ceremonies are held each year at the Spring Equinox, Summer Solstice, and Autumn Equinox.

The order's fundamental philosophy is the same that has inspired the major wisdom philosophies throughout the centuries. The basic concept is that spirit works from within outward into material manifestation. That consciousness and humanity are evolving and that the way to learn to participate in that evolution is to study and learn from the cycles of nature. The philosophies and teachings of Paracelsus and Swedenborg are consistent with the Druidic teaching, just as is the philosophy of the Masonic Order, of which Samuel Hahnemann was a member.

The opening paragraphs of the Organon are Hahnemann's restatement of the ancient wisdom teaching rephrased to focus on healing; it is no accident that British students of Druidic teaching would be drawn toward homœopathy.

A major contribution Maughan and Damonte brought to homœopathy was the integration of Hahnemann, Paracelsus, Swedenborg, Rademacher, Kent, and Compton Burnett along with a study of "Subtle Anatomy," the science of the treatment of the endocrine glands and the chakras or vital energy centers associated with them. Their approach was to utilize homœopathy not merely to match the outer physical, emotional, and mental symptom picture of the patient but to match remedies to the state of the energy field surrounding the physical body and the condition of the endocrine system which is its biological counterpart.

Miles, Misha Norland, Peter Chappell, Kay Samuel, Mary Titchmarsh, Michael Haggiag, and Lynn Lovell, with Martin Miles as the first chairman.

Davidson and Miles formed the London College of Homœopathy in September 1978. The first class of students had an enrollment beyond their most optimistic expectations.

During its first years the college trained many people who are now "household names" in homœopathy, as well as college principals and lecturers at many of the 25 colleges that have since emerged. These include: Barbara Harwood, Jeremy Sherr, Ernest Roberts, Francis Treuherz, Tony Hurley, Susan Curtis, among others.

The Society of Homœopaths' Register was begun in 1978 by a group of practitioners who "grandfathered" themselves onto it and then set up the examining criteria.

The second college, the Northern College in Newcastle, was founded by Rima Handley and Dorothy Hannon-Blazier in 1981. That same year, Misha Norland established the School of Homœopathy in Devon. In 1985, Ernest Roberts started the Northwestern School of Homœopathy in Manchester. More colleges, all part-time, were founded in the next 10 years.

Perhaps another person will, someday, write a full history of all these schools. Their contributions to the spread and acceptance of homœopathy cannot be estimated.

A second society was formed in 1986— the United Kingdom Homœopathic Medical Association (UKHMA). It was founded by Pyarah Singh as an outgrowth of the Hahnemann School of Homœopathy in London, after a disagreement with The Society of Homœopaths over educational standards. The UKHMA established its own register for its graduates. In the 10 years since, the society has "evolved beyond its origins," and maintains a sizeable register of practitioners, some of whom are physicians. "On the whole, the UKHMA is less strictly classical than the Society and is more open to ways that are not accepted by more traditional homœopaths," said a summary in a "student guide."

In 1998, the professional homœopaths outnumber the medically trained homœopaths. There are 250 physicians registered with the Faculty, 548 registered with the Society of Homœopaths, 350 registered with the UKHMA, and about another 700 graduates licensed to practice by their colleges, insured through the Society of Homœopaths, and working towards full registration with the Society register.

1950s –1980s: The Diploma Peddlers

Maryland: 1950 – 1977
The questionable schools
Florida: 1979 – 1988
Arizona: 1980 – 85

"Irregulars" and the Medical Boards

While in England the practice of homeopathy would be under Common Law, the practice of homœopathy in the United States is dependent upon the laws of the individual states.

The Federal Government has no power over medical practice itself; the power is given to the states. The states, recognizing the legislature has no knowledge of things medical, generally have legislation allowing the governor to appoint a state medical board, and it is these boards which create the ground-rules for practice in the state and issue practice licenses.

In the early part of the 20th century, many states had separate boards for allopaths, homœopaths, and eclectic practitioners, but as the homœopathic and eclectic schools closed, the boards were merged. The state homœopathic societies began to lose members and cease operation.

In April 1957, the *Journal of the American Institute of Homeopathy* had an editorial titled "A Warning." It spoke of the threat to the profession posed by "irregulars," who were taking over the control of state homœopathic societies that were nearly defunct.

In November of the same year, Wyrth Post Baker wrote in the *Journal:* "Homeopathy ceased to exist as a school twenty years ago. Unless immediate action is forthcoming it will revert by default to the cultists in another decade." He expressed a concern that "cultists" have been setting up "homœopathic colleges" that will grant degrees for "homœopathic doctors," and that such schools pose a threat to legitimate homœopathic physicians. He urged cooperation with the American Medical Association to stop these "diploma mills."

In August 1958, Donald Gladish, MD, the AIH president, urged all state boards to drop homœopathic requirements because there were no longer any schools graduating homœopaths.

All this was in response to some shady happenings in the state of Maryland, soon to become endemic during the period.

Maryland: 1950 – 1977

In the mid–1950s Robert Reddick, MD, "re-claimed" the Maryland State Homœopathic Medical Society. The Society had been founded in 1875. Although it was still "on the books," it had been moribund for many years. Reddick was a 1937 graduate of Hahnemann Medical College. He worked at the Gowanda State Hospital, and eventually became chief of psychiatric services at the Eastern Shore State Hospital in Cambridge, Maryland in 1951. His reasons for reviving the group are not known, but how he used the group certainly is.

He established "The Maryland Board of Medical Examiners" as a part of the Homœopathic Society. However official the title sounds, it was not the legal body that passes on the qualifications of medical doctors to practice in the state. In the early 1950s Reddick began to issue membership to people who graduated from an "Approved School of Homœopathy teaching a Resident Course," and then offered those members licenses to practice medicine in the state of Maryland through the Homœopathic Society and the Examining Board.

As early as 1956 the Attorney General of Maryland wrote to an applicant:

"If you should attempt to practice medicine under the authority of your alleged license, you doubtless will expose yourself to criminal prosecution."

At the time there were, according to Reddick, 96 holders of "Reddick licenses."

In April 1957, Reddick was told to cease and desist his practices by a Maryland Court. Reddick was fired from his job as psychiatrist and head of the female division of the Eastern Shore State Hospital on grounds of "moral turpitude," namely, for having sold said licenses.

Reddick was tried for selling the medical licenses and was sentenced to five years in jail. He appealed to the state Supreme Court, and when his appeal was rejected in 1959, it appears he fled the state to avoid incarceration.

We next find him arrested in California, along with John F. Statham (of whom we will hear more) and, in December 1959, was again found guilty in a jury trial of trying to sell Maryland State Homœopathic Society licenses in California, with the assurance that other states would extend "reciprocity." He was sentenced to probation.

Robert Reddick, 1937

Between 1960 and 1970, the trail disappears. In 1975, Reddick was again sending out letters as the treasurer of the "Maryland State Homœopathic Medical Society" with an announcement that the Maryland Society will be meeting with the "Hahnemann Medical Society of America" in Las Vegas.

The meeting was attended by about 60 people. A summary of the meeting was sent to Dr. Henry N. Williams by Georgiana Neiswander in a letter of April 27, 1975. She mentioned Dr. John Renner "was made the patriarch of the society." Also in attendance was John Statham from Florida who was described as "a very good leader."

In discussing the meeting with Georgiana in 1997, she said her impression was that they (Reddick and Statham) were good promotional people ("they could sell anything") but their homœopathy had no depth. The recognition of the Hahnemann Medical Society by the American Institute of Homœopathy did not last long. "Allen [Dr. Allen Neiswander] didn't like them from the start," said Georgiana. "He said they were doing bad homœopathy."

In 1976, Reddick appeared as a member of the board of directors of the "American Coordinated Medical Society."

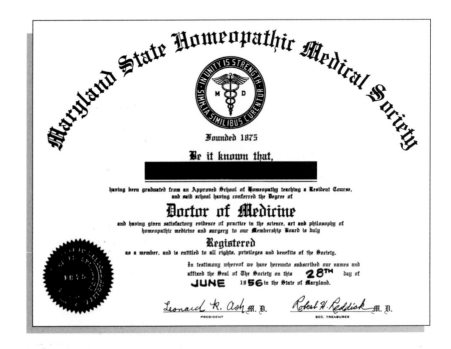

He was now signing his name as a "DO" (doctor of osteopathy) and "DC" (doctor of chiropractic) as well as "MD."

After 1976, the trail disappears again.

In the 1980 *Directory of Alumni of the Hahnemann Medical College*, Reddick is listed as "whereabouts unknown."

The questionable schools

Where were these applicants coming from? Where was the "Approved School of Homœopathy teaching a Resident Course"?

One person holding a Maryland License gained his "MD" from Fremont College School of Homœopathic Medicine which conferred a "Doctor of Medicine" in 1952. It was a branch of Sequoia University that was chartered in the State of Oklahoma. Sequoia claimed to have a School of Homœopathic Medicine and offered both a degree of Doctor of Medicine and a degree of Doctor of Osteopathy.

Fremont College
School of Homeopathic Medicine

The Trustees of Fremont College, by virtue of the authority in them vested and on the recommendation of the Faculty, have conferred upon

who has pursued the studies and passed the required examinations the Degree of

Doctor of Medicine

with all Rights, Privileges and Honors thereunto appertaining

Given at Los Angeles in the State of California on the 29th. day of May One thousand nine hundred and 5 6

The Faces of Homœopathy

In a letter of December 1, 1984, Dr. John Renner writes:

> "There were 400 or so people waiting to buy their licenses in 1957 about. I was asked to teach homœopathy at, I believe it was called Sequoia College. Chiropractors were taking the course, and given an HMD. Then they applied to the Maryland State Homœopathic Society, which did give them a regular MD license for a good substantial fee. Many got in that way. Then the Board saw what was happening. That Maryland homœopathic doctor served a jail sentence. Several hundred others did not, but kept paying lawyers fees until maybe ten years ago."

The Maryland State Homœopathic Medical Society was linked to the "American Coordinated Medical Society" of Norwalk, California through Reddick, who was on the ACMS Board of Directors. A memo from the group in 1976 lists the "International College of Homœopathic Physicians and Surgeons" and mentions the "United American Medical College" in Louisiana as one of "the schools to look forward to for professional upgrading of your degrees."

In 1983 the Federal Bureau of Investigation announced an operation called "dip-scam" which resulted in the indictments of 38 people involved in mail-order educational institutions. Among those singled out were the Homœopathic Faculty of Zurich, the Arkansas Naturopathic Homœopathic Board Inc., the Florida Homœopathic Training Center, and the Maryland State Homœopathic Medical Society.

A 1987 FBI memo listed a number of schools identified as "bogus educational institutions." Among them were: Chicago Medical College of Homœopathy, Johannes Kepler School of Homœopathic Medicine, Sequoia University, South African College of Homœopathy, and the United American Medical College.

I have seen certificates from many of these schools stating that the holder is a qualified MD in homœopathy.

Florida: 1979 – 1988

About the same time the Maryland scenario was closing, another was unfolding in Florida.

Tracy Michael Baker, Jr. (August 24, 1922 — July 3, 1988) learned of homœopathy during World War II while stationed with the United States Army Air Force in India. Homœopathy made a lasting impression upon him. A serious heart attack in 1972 forced him into partial retirement. He took full retirement from the Air Force in 1982, with the rank of Colonel. Baker was a charismatic figure. Harris Coulter described him as "a gentleman in every sense— courteous in a very Southern way, sensitive, tactful, well-meaning, kind, and generous."

From 1972 on he worked tirelessly to make the practice of homœopathy in Florida state regulated. At the time, there was no legislation recognizing the practice of homœopathy, and the state medical board in Florida as much as said that "homœopathy" was not medicine.

In 1980, Colonel Baker established the Florida State Society of Homœopathic Physicians and the Florida Board of Homœopathic Examiners, with himself as president. He

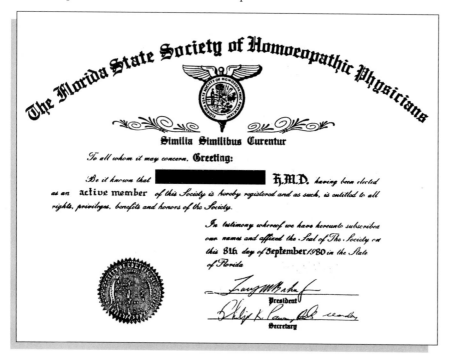

also established a corporate entity known as "The Hahnemann Medical Society of America."

Baker hired a lobbyist and convinced Representative Frank Williams to sponsor a homœopathic licensure bill. The legislative efforts in 1981 failed, although the legislature did recognize the practice of homœopathy as a profession.

During the 1981 and 1982 legislative sessions in Florida, Bill Gray testified for the need for professional regulation and the need to establish standards of practice.

A meeting with the Florida Medical Association resulted in the assurance that it would not oppose the licensing legislation. However, the Florida Medical Association did not honor its pledge and opposition to the bill was insurmountable. The legislation was withdrawn.

In 1979, Baker began a correspondence with the National Center, trying to get a "Millersville South" course begun in Florida to train the physicians who would be applying for the pending licensure. When the NCH/AFH split happened, Harris Coulter offered to arrange a summer educational program for the American Center. Through the efforts of Baker, the course was taught at the Florida Institute of

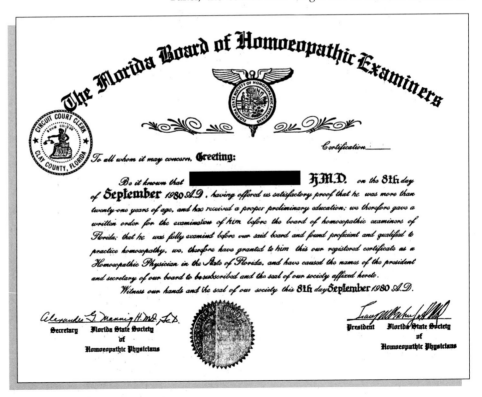

Technology in Melbourne, Florida. The director of the Medical Research Institute there, Ron Jones, PhD, was drawn into the homœopathic foray, and through Jones, the Florida Institute of Technology began to show an interest in offering a fully accredited homœopathic program. With the failure of the legislation to pass the Florida Legislature in 1982, the whole idea fell into oblivion.

But it seems Baker, in his enthusiasm, had jumped the gun. He had several people enroll in the American Center course in 1981 with the understanding it would provide them with the requirements for licensure. Afterwards he offered a course leading to certification (by the Florida Board of Homœopathic Examiners) for $650.

By 1981 the Florida State Society and the Florida Board of Homœopathic Examiners had issued more than 200 certificates granting the holders the title of "Homœopathic Physician in the State of Florida." Baker was very specific in telling all who applied that the licensure did not allow them to practice conventional medicine, which would include the diagnosing of disease and giving injections.

In 1985, 11 "self-styled homœopathic physicians" were arrested in Florida for practicing medicine without a license. The only licenses they held were those from the Florida State Society. One of those arrested was Baker, accused of doing a pelvic examination. He was convicted of practicing medicine without a license and sentenced to 18 months in jail. He died shortly after being released in 1988.

Of the incident Richard Moskowitz, MD, said in an editorial in the October 1985 issue of *Homeopathy Today*:

> "The reason I cannot support the people in Florida who do pelvic exams without licenses and proclaim themselves to be homœopaths without training is not simply or primarily because they are or are not homœopaths, but because they con their patients just as the rest of us were trained to do, with presumption and arrogance. These are qualities I find even more objectionable in homœopathy than in the prevailing system, and, I am sorry to say, no less common, whether in the physician or lay person."

As Baker was working for legislation, another person was setting up a "diploma mill" on the west coast of Florida. John Statham, ND, had been arrested with Robert Reddick in California. Statham had a naturopathic degree from Sequoia University in 1952.

By 1979 he found his way to Bradenton, Florida where

he established the "Hahnemann International Medical Association" and sold memberships for several hundred dollars. He set up the "Florida State Homœopathic Society," with himself as president. He also was selling materials under the name of "The Hahnemann Medical Society of America," which induced Tracy Baker to form a corporate entity of the same name in Washington, DC, and inform Statham to cease and desist. Needless to say there was great enmity between the two parties. Each perceived the other as a threat to "their territory."

Statham claimed to be an ND, a DC, and a DO, but was unwilling to disclose the exact place and time of his training. In a letter on the letterhead of the Inter-American Congress of Physicians and Surgeons, he signs himself as "MD." In a letter to Ralph Packman (July 16,1980) Statham says "what you do not know is that I have a legitimate MD degree in other states and countries and that I am also licensed as an ND in many states and provinces, so my ND in Florida is not my only licensure." He continues, "...the AIH membership is to all intense purposes [sic] in the deep twilight of its existence because of the age factor of its members, no one will regret more than I the passing of your members to the next world but to be realistic the preponderance of your members will have gone to their reward in short time, Mr. Packman I doubt the AIH will exist and the HMSA will become the organization of record both in the states and the National government. I do not think that you or any of your members can do anything to prevent the lawful replacement at this time of a small oligarchy by a large majority, after all the AIH members have no proprietary rights regarding homœopathic medicine in the public domain..."

The letter is signed, "John Statham, ND, MD, SCD, FIAP, FHMI, Licentiate in the Republic of India, Dominion of Canada, and numerous States in the United States."

In a reply on July 31, 1980, Packman says that he has checked the medical boards of all states, and that Statham "does not have a license in any state we can find."

At the time, Statham was running the "Hahnemann Memorial Society of America," the "Hahnemann Memorial Institute of Health Sciences," and the "Hahnemann Medical Society of America."

In mid-1980 the Hahnemann Medical Society of America published the *Organon and Rapid Repertory* which, said

Statham, "is not perfect but it will be good for the beginning student of homœopathy who has a good background in medicine."

A perusal of this book shows it to be a typewritten copy of the *Organon,* interspersed with a brief materia medica of 81 remedies (taken from "Health Through Homœopathy") and a 28-page "rapid repertory." All the parts are together— Paragraph 22 of the *Organon* is followed by the materia medica of *Opium, Petroleum, Phosphoric acid,* and *Phosphorus,* and Paragraph 36 has a repertory of symptoms from "Temper" to "Angina Pectoris." It appears to be an exercise in publishing *something* to do with homœopathy.

By 1985 Statham's Florida clinic was no longer operating and Statham had left for parts unknown.

When I visited Statham's clinic in Bradenton, Florida in 1982, I saw little evidence of any homœopathy being known or practiced. I saw no homœopathic books, save for a single Boericke's Materia Medica *upon his desk. It was basically a center for chelation therapy. Statham said he treated "snow-birds" (northerners who come south for the winter) and "they just want to have injections."*

Arizona: The Wild West

As the Florida scene was closing down, Arizona beckoned as the next calling ground.

In early 1980 several letters were received by the National Center that spoke of the effort to unify the homœopathic profession in Arizona. One of the efforts was headed (again) by John Statham of Florida. Statham had incorporated the Hahnemann Memorial Institute of Health Sciences, School of Homœopathic Medicine in Arizona on June 3, 1980. The express purpose was "to establish a college of homœopathic medicine and surgery and to grant the degree of Doctor of Homœopathic Medicine." The business was in the hands of Dr. A. E. Stewart, of Phoenix. On the same day, the same group, headed by Statham, incorporated the Arizona State Homœopathic Medical Society. In a letter dated June 23, 1980, he denounces "the diploma peddlers and medical con-men" who are involved in the "sale of phony degrees from Australia, South Africa, and Switzerland" that promise Arizona registration. In a letter to Ralph Packman on July 16, 1980, he again cites the fraudulent degrees and the "promise of an Arizona license to people totally unqualified. This of course could be the death sentence to homœopathic medicine in Arizona. We are going to try to prevent this from happening."

To do this, beginning moves were made to pass a state law legislating the practice of homœopathy.

At the same time, another organizational effort was coming from the Western Homœopathic Medical Society. The WHMS was organized in the early 1970s by a group of people who had come to homœopathy quite independently of each other. Lester Steward was trained in medicine through the US Navy and learned of homœopathy in the early 1970s while working in a drug addiction program in Perth, Australia. When he returned to the southwest, he met Dr. Harsdroff, an osteopath from Texas who was using homœopathy, and together with another osteopath, Harry Leonard, they formed the Western Homœopathic Medical Society in 1974. They tried to run a school (operating on weekends) but it failed for lack of interest. They found a bit more success when they moved the program across the border to Mexico. Then Harsdroff died (at the untimely age of 36) and the Western Homœopathic Medical Society moved into the background.

It emerges again in the late 1970s when a Phoenix businessman, David Stackhouse, joined the effort. Stackhouse was interested in alternative medicine and had received permission to sell the controversial cancer drug *Laetrile* in Arizona.

Stackhouse and Steward started the James Tyler Kent School of Homœopathy that was reported in the *Homœopathic Heartbeat* in 1980. The James Tyler Kent School was using several local homœopaths as well as having Karl Robinson and Bill Gray deliver lectures once a month. But it was 1980. The effort was premature as few were interested in learning homœopathy. The school lasted a few months and then closed.

Arizona became a seat of action partially because Phoenix was the location of the clinic for the Association of Research and Enlightenment (ARE)— the medical center that based its work on the readings of the psychic Edgar Cacye. The ARE clinic drew many conventional doctors who were interested in "alternative medicine" to the area, and several of them became interested in the pending homœopathic legislation.

In 1981 Harvey Biegelsen, MD, stepped into the fray. Biegelsen, a medical graduate of the University of Buffalo in 1965, had worked as a trauma surgeon in Vietnam. Looking for medical alternatives, he had been drawn to

Arizona by the ARE clinic. He saw the homœopathic law was close to being passed, and was aware many people pushing for the legislation were holders of dubious degrees and had a personal agenda in the process. Saying he "felt like Wyatt Earp in Dodge City," he spoke to the Governor and was able to push the legislation through with the stipulation that to be a licensed homœopathic practitioner in Arizona you must have a license to practice medicine in the United States. This effectively blocked all those trading on mail-order degrees and promised licensure in Arizona.

Shortly after the legislation was passed, an announcement for the founding of the Arizona Homœopathic Medical University, College of Medicine, appeared in the September 1983 issue of *American Homeopathy*. It was to be up and running in Arizona as a postgraduate institution. Nothing more was heard of it. The school was peripherally connected with the Arizona State Homœopathic Medical Society that now had John Statham (this time with an MD) as director.

Arizona got its Homœopathic Board in 1982. As of 1997, it is still operational, although it changed its name to the "Arizona Homeopathic and Integrative Medical Association" in May 1997. In discussing the history of homœopathy with those who were involved in setting up the board in the 1980s, all remember the involvement of David Stackhouse and recall his efforts. A few recall hearing about Statham but none remember any details about his involvement in the effort or if he actually ever made his physical presence known in Arizona. Lester Steward is still living and practicing in Phoenix. The Western Homœopathic Medical Society ceased formal operation in 1986.

And others…

During the 1980s other groups arrived and departed. A typical one, "The American Academy of Homœopathic Physicians," is described in **Appendix B**, page 533.

Despite the FBI "dip-scam," mail–order degrees were readily available. The Universal Life Church in Florida was offering an HMD degree and in 1995 The Progressive Universal Life Church in Sacramento, California was offering a "PhD in homœopathy "for $295.

1970 – 1996: The Detractors

1920 – 1982: A background
The National Council Against Health Fraud
The media
Consumer Reports
The push against homœopathy
An attack on the pharmacies
A commentary

Since its inception, homœopathy has always had its antagonists. Bradford's *Bibliography* lists 72 anti-homœopathic writings published from 1835 to 1892. The earliest work seems to be William Leo-Wolf's book, *Remarks on the Abracadabra of the Nineteenth Century*, published in 1835.

In 1842 we find Thomas Blatchford's, *The Homœopathic System; a Germanic Reverie of Transcendental Nonsense*. In the same year we find the grand author and doctor from Boston, Oliver Wendell Holmes, publishing his attack on homœopathy, *Homœopathy and Kindred Delusions*.

As Harris Coulter points out in his Volume III of *Divided Legacy*, the attack against the homœopaths stemmed from the fact that regular medicine was failing to treat many diseases, while homœopathy was enjoying successes. Furthermore the homœopath, when unsuccessful, blamed his lack on the previous allopathic treatment, thus lowering the regular doctor in the public's eyes. The homœopath was also making his appeals directly to the public— a tactic that "violated the deepest instinct of the physician and one of the most deeply rooted traditions of medicine— that the corporate body of physicians should at all costs remain united against the public."

Physicians who were becoming homœopaths were drawn from the ranks of the well-educated, and the sight of such educated people being drawn to a seemingly illogical and irrational doctrine was almost too much for the medical profession to bear. It struck out against homœopathy with anger and violence. The aim of the attacks were the same then as now— the absurdity of gaining information from "provings," the absurdity of the "law of similars," and the impossibility of the "infinitesimal dose." Accepting these basic tenets as "absurdities," the regulars of the medical profession deemed homœopathy unworthy to be given a trial "at the bedside."

Furthermore, through the 1880s, many attacks accused the homœopath of having no morals since many "half-homœopaths" were using allopathic methods as well, and therefore showed they had "no principles."

The Detractors: 1920-1982

The AMA's attack on homœopathy maintained itself during the 1920s through the work of Morris Fishbein, MD, the first AMA chairman and editor of the *Journal of the American Medical Association*.

Fishbein wrote two books discussing homœopathy and other forms of "quackery"— *The Medical Follies: An Analysis of some Healing Cults, including Osteopathy, Homeopathy, Chiropractic* (1925) and *Fads and Quackery in Healing; an Analysis of the Foibles of the Healing Cults, with essays on various and peculiar notions in the health field* (1932).

The late 1940s and early 1950s were a troubled time for any kind of non-orthodox thinking. McCarthyism was rampant in all fields of study in the United States. The National Institutes of Health was established during this time and its directions of exploration were all in the reductionist sciences. The agencies doing "medical research" were, generally, industry–funded and not interested in exploring the individual in their environment— especially when the industrial environment was criticized as contributing to ill health.

During this time the Food and Drug Administration, with the backing of the pharmaceutical and food industries, began attacking anyone who talked about "nutritional nonsense." Federal agencies intimidated anyone who openly advocated using vitamins or discussing nutrition.

The AMA set up a Committee on Quackery in 1963 and targeted, among others, the entire chiropractic profession. In 1976, a number of chiropractors sued the AMA for conspiracy and in 1987, the courts found the AMA guilty of conspiring to destroy the profession of chiropractic. A summary is found in Coulter's *Divided Legacy, Vol. IV* pages 345-349.

In 1982, Representative Claude Pepper introduced three bills in the United States Congress that would, in effect, set up a national clearing house for consumer information, increase penalties against "quacks," and create a Federal strike force to prosecute quacks. The bills all failed at the committee stage.

Four Steps

In The American Homeopath *in 1998, Harris Coulter outlines the step-wise methods that detractors follow. Step I, happens when a minority paradigm attempts to exist within the majority paradigm. The method is usually a "blacklist" with eventual expulsion from the majority.*

Step II moves to "ideological warfare." Within the history of homœopathy, we find several examples of this mode. The first move is an attempt to discredit those in the minority based on their lack of education or scientific attainments. This was difficult to do with homœopathy because most of the homœopaths were coming from the same educational background and training as those who were being critical.

The second move is an attempt to discredit the minority because they had some kind of "quirk" which prevented them from seeing the "real truth."

The third move is to discredit the minority because they turned their back on the truth for "venal" reasons— that homœopathy was more profitable— or as it was said in 1842 "they have chosen the fashionable humbug of the day." One result of this view was that homœopaths were expelled from medical societies because they were "immoral"— i.e., they were in it for the money.

Another point of ideological warfare happened in the allopaths' attempt to explain why those treated with homœopathy got better— it was either a residual result of the allopathic medication or the homœopaths were using allopathic medicines and disguising them as "sugar pills."

Step III involves Professional and Economic Coercion, which is seen as a refusal to publish articles, expulsion from professional societies, and refusal to accept ads in professional journals.

Step IV is Administrative or Judicial Coercion, of which we find an example in the 1985 North Carolina attack on homœopathic practice.

The National Council Against Health Fraud

Although the Pepper bills died, the impetus was there to protect the consumer against health fraud. A new organization was formed— the National Council Against Health Fraud. The organization had its roots in 1977 as the Southern California Council Against Health Fraud, and later merged with a similar group in Northern California to form the California Council Against Health Fraud. It became a national organization in 1984.

The NCAHF describes itself as "a private non–profit, voluntary health agency that focuses upon health mis-information, fraud and quackery as public health problems." Its funding, they say, is "derived primarily from membership dues and newsletter subscriptions."

The major figures involved in the NCAHF are John Renner, MD (not the *homœopath* John Renner) of Kansas City, Wallace Sampson, MD, a retired cancer specialist from Santa Rosa, California, William T. Jarvis, MD, a professor at Loma Linda University in California, Victor Herbert, MD, a physician from New York City, and Stephen Barrett, MD, a retired psychiatrist from Allentown, Pennsylvania. All are vociferous in their dismissal of homœopathy as a "fraud" and a "pseudoscience."

The NCAHF states, in its "position paper," that "Homeopathy's principles have been refuted by the basic sciences of chemistry, physics, pharmacology, and pathology... Homeopathy meets the dictionary definitions of a sect and a cult." It say the marketing of homœopathic products and services "fits the definition of quackery established by a United States House of Representatives committee which investigated the problem (i.e., the promotion of 'medical schemes or remedies known to be false, or which are unproven, for a profit')."

It claims the remedies often work because they have enough material in them to be effective or have been adulterated. This last claim is based on reports that some homœopathic medicines appeared to be effective in treating asthma because they contained therapeutic levels of the steroidal drugs prednisolone and betamethasone. The case cited was of a remedy made in Pakistan called "Dumcap."

The NCAHF, in its literature, asks the United States

a change...

In mid-1998, The National Council Against Health Fraud changed the name under which it issues public information to The National Council for Reliable Health Information.

Postal Service to prosecute homœopathic mail–order products that make unproven medical claims for mail fraud, and, because homœopathy is scientifically indefensible, that State Legislators should (1) enact laws requiring that medical products sold within states meet the standards of accurate labeling, truthful advertising, and pre-marketing proof of safety and effectiveness, (2) abolish state licensing boards for homœopathy, (3) do not allow homœopathy in the scope of practice of any health care provider.

They ask state food & drug regulators to take prompt regulatory action against manufacturers, wholesalers, and retailers of homœopathic products who violate the law, and they ask the state Medical Licensing Boards to discipline homœopathic practitioners for unprofessional conduct and prosecute non-physicians engaging in homœopathy for practicing medicine without a license.

Calling homœopathy a "haven for untrustworthy practitioners," the NCAHF says that "pseudosciences such as homeopathy, even if relatively benign, are magnets for cranks and charlatans... True-believing cranks may pose a more serious threat than con–men because of their devotion to homeopathy's ideology. Their sincerity may make them more socially tolerable, but it can add to their potential danger. Irrational health care is never harmless, and it is irresponsible to create patient confidence in pseudo-medicine." Pushing further on this particular edge, Victor Herbert, in an interview in the December 1993 issue of *American Health,* expounds a theory that quacks and other con–artists (and by extension, homœopaths) are born with a brain defect that short circuits their conscience, enabling them to be pathological liars.

The Media

In July 1983, Stephen Barrett wrote an article for *Nautilus* magazine titled "Homeopathy: Hokum and Bunkum," where he concludes: "There is essentially no public protection against worthless homeopathic products and those who promote them."

In January 1987, *Consumer Reports* magazine featured an article about homœopathy that was co-authored by Stephen Barrett and the editors of the magazine. The article concluded the drugs were "absurd" and the use of such

Defining "fraud"

In a 1993 letter to the New England Journal of Medicine, *Victor Herbert denies that he labels all alternatives quackery. He says he distinguishes three types: genuine, questionable, and "blatantly fraudulent." In an article in* Alternative Therapies, *David Hufford, the director of The Center for Humanistic Medicine at the Hershey Medical Center in Hershey, Pennsylvania, says of the letter:*

"Then, with neat circularity, he classifies homœopathy as fraudulent because high-dilution remedies are claimed to work but 'obviously' cannot. As in most broad attributions of quackery, claiming reasons not endorsed by officially recognized experts is treated as lying... Herbert eliminates the distinction between dissenting views and fraud. Herbert's use of 'obvious' implies that those who disagree are Brown's fools or Stalker's Yahoos.

"Alternative practitioners are often called quacks in this literature. Quackery means fraudulent treatment. But a definition of quackery is rarely given, and when it is, the importance of fraud is dismissed... Sincere alternative practitioners are grouped with quacks, and the patient stereotype follows directly from the 'quackery model.' The question becomes 'who is fooled by such patent absurdities?' Establishing this picture of quacks exploiting fools is a major goal in the cultural battle over prevalence and distribution, because it does much more than insult practitioners of alternative medicine. Its moral dimension provides the groundwork for political action. If proponents of alternatives are charlatans and their patients are incompetents who cannot protect themselves, intervention is obviously called for.

"... Herbert's attempt to establish disagreement with medical experts as fraud illustrates the struggle to capture vital language regarding authority. He is not arguing so much about alternative medicine, as he seems to be, but rather about the proper meaning of 'fraud.' If deviance from official knowledge, rather than intent to deceive, defines fraud, then all controversial discourse is quackery."

medicines whether the prescribers "are MDs, other licensed practitioners, or outright quacks" was a danger to the consumer.

As homœopathy became more visible and articles appeared about it in the national press, many articles tried to look at "both sides" and those which did often contained critical comments from one of the five "quackbusters."

In November 1992, *MD Magazine* had an editorial diatribe against homœopathy by Dr. Gerald Weissman titled, "Dancing with Fairies, Sucking with Vampires," in which he criticized the National Institutes of Health's office of Alternative Medicine as giving away money to a "murky throng from the slums and stews of the debauched brain." He ended by quoting Oliver Wendell Holmes who, he says, "took up his pen against the persistent cult of delusional fantasy that keeps banging its belief against Avogadro's number."

In early December 1992, NBC's *Dateline* had a one–hour "going undercover to investigate homœopathy." The program visited the Nevada Clinic in Las Vegas and interviewed Dr. Fuller Royal. A California food and drug inspector testified that the electrodiagnostic machines at the clinic were "illegal" and their use for diagnosis "constitute quackery." Although the program said at the outset that what was shown was not "pure homœopathy," a definition of homœopathy was never presented. Dr. John Renner was interviewed and said that "homœopathy does not work against anything" and that practitioners "border on delusional." Dr. Royal wrote a letter to NBC and to *Homeopathy Today* explaining that his quotes were taken out of context and that there was no need to use "hidden cameras," since he had opened the clinic to the press.

Two weeks later, the *Donohue Show* featured a discussion about alternative medicine. Prominent in the discussion were Drs. Stephen Barrett and George Guess— who was not identified as a physician but rather as "a believer in homœopathic medicine." Barrett claimed that homœopathy "treats people who have nothing seriously wrong with them." When an audience member mentioned that they have had success with a homœopathic remedy for jet–lag, Dr. Harvey Waxman, another panelist, said that jet–lag has "no disease process" so the ailment is a fake one and the person does not need medical help.

Consumer Reports… Again

In March 1994 *Consumer Reports* again printed an article, titled "Homeopathy: Much Ado About Nothing?" The article purported to be an honest evaluation, but again, the language used was loaded with a very deep bias against homœopathy.

The report chose to ignore significant facts and figures about homœopathy's popularity throughout the world (39% of French physicians and 20% of German physicians prescribe homœopathic medicines to their patients, 42% of British doctors refer patients to homœopathic doctors, and 45% of Dutch physicians consider homœopathic medicines to be effective).

Describing the success of homœopathy in epidemics, the article continues: "Homœopathy's fortunes began to fade a few decades later, however, as conventional medicine developed effective drugs and therapies and as training programs for physicians became standardized." The implication of this statement is that the homœopathic therapies were ineffective. So, according to the article, homœopathy had apparent successes with an ineffective therapy. And that thought is used to place homœopathy in its historical context.

The article says: "Within the past decade, products and practices have appeared that seem dubious even to some homeopaths. Practitioners may use such odd methods of choosing remedies as electrodiagnostic devices— said to measure the body's 'electromagnetic energy balance'— and iridology, a system of sizing up a person's health from the irises of their eyes." Which prompted the question posed by Dana Ullman in a reply to the article: "Does one adequately measure homeopathy and homeopathic practitioners by the small numbers of people who use unconventional methods? Does one accurately depict a subject by assessing its core or its tangents?"

The article concluded: "Consumers Union believes that these remedies deserve a closer look. Congress should remove the blanket exemption from drug laws enjoyed by homeopathic remedies. In particular, remedies being marketed as treatments for specific illnesses should be removed from drugstore shelves unless and until they are tested and shown to be safe and effective."

The Push: 1994 – 1996

During May and June, 1994, Consumers Union apparently initiated at least four newspaper articles concerning this same subject.

In July 1994, a lawyer for Consumers Union testified before a Senate subcommittee against the "Access to Medical Treatment Act." He said: "Earlier this year, Consumers Union published a three-part series on alternative medicine in *Consumer Reports*, focusing on acupuncture, homeopathy, and chiropractic. We found that studies of alternative treatments are few, and that most are poorly designed. In preparing the series, we had to sort through too little science, and too many conflicting claims, shibboleths, and hopeful hypotheses..." and again suggested withdrawing homœopathic remedies from the consumer market.

On September 1, 1994, Stephen Barrett, serving as agent for 42 others, petitioned the Food and Drug Administration to revise its regulatory policy of homœopathic remedies because they are, essentially, mislabelled. "Adequate directions for use cannot be written for products that don't work," he said.

The petition was signed by 42 people, many of whom are well–known for their opposition to homœopathy.

"Exhibit B" in the petition consisted of the chapter on homœopathy (called "The Ultimate Fake") from the book *The Vitamin Pushers: How the Health Food Industry is Selling America a Bill of Goods* by Drs. Barrett and Herbert. The chapter begins: "Homeopathic 'remedies' enjoy a unique status in the health marketplace: they are the only quack products legally marketable as drugs."

The section describing homœopathic theory is titled "Basic Misbeliefs," while the second section is titled: "The 'Remedies' are placebos." This chapter contains two statements by Varro E. Tyler, PhD (another signer of the petition) in which Tyler speculates about the popularity of homœopathy here and abroad. Says Tyler:

"Homeopathy retains its popularity in Germany because it was devised there. The Germans, like many other peoples of the world, are not about to give up a medical system that was devised by one of their own, even though most medical and pharmacy professionals in that country recognize that it simply doesn't work."

"Homeopathy has enjoyed a resurgence in the United

States because practically no one here understands it. It is no longer taught in medical or pharmacy schools, so most professionals know little or nothing about it. Not understanding it themselves, they cannot explain it to patients and consumers; and since the FDA permits homeopathic remedies to be sold, people think they must be good."

The report shows an ad for OTC homœopathic remedies that proclaim their safety and criticize conventional medications for having "side-effects," to which Drs. Barrett and Herbert comment: "…it falsely suggests that standard OTC drugs are inferior to homeopathic products. Products that never produce side effects are too weak to exert therapeutic effects."

Shortly after the petition was filed, *The Bulletin*, a current affairs program on KYW–TV in Philadelphia, had a segment on alternative medicine. When the reporter asked Dr. Barrett what a person, who finds that conventional medicine is not helping them, should do, Barrett replied: "They should learn to live with it rather than go on a wild goose chase."

An Attack on the Pharmacies

In January 1995, Donald Driscoll, a California attorney, filed six lawsuits in California against several drug chains including Payless, Long's, and Walgreens, charging that package inserts indicating specific uses for homœopathic remedies constitute false advertising.

The law under which these were filed, was passed by California legislators in 1977. The Unfair Competition Act bans "unlawful, unfair or fraudulent business practice and unfair, deceptive, untrue or misleading advertising."

In September 1996, just before the cases were to go to trial, Long's Drug Stores and Payless Drug Stores agreed to a settlement with the stipulation that all terms of the agreement will remain confidential. Wallace Sampson, chair of the board of directors for the National Council Against Health Fraud, filed similar suits against other manufacturers and retailers. The suits are still in litigation.

"It is the most ingenious approach to consumer protection I've ever seen," said Dr. Barrett. He expressed hope that this is the first of many waves of lawsuits in California challenging unconventional medical products that claim to work.

And, in summary…

When an article titled "Homeopathy: Real Medicine or Empty Promises?" appeared in the December 1996 *FDA Consumer*, William Jarvis was quick to reply. Saying that "Homeopathy is a fraud perpetrated on the public with the government's blessing," he cited six reasons why users of homœopathy may say homœopathic remedies work:

1. The placebo effect. (Which he extends to animals because "animals also respond well to attention by humans" and because "whether the animal is better or not is determined by humans observing the creature, not objective reporting by the animals.")
2. Natural ups and downs of symptoms or natural remission.
3. The remedy contains an effective dose of real medicine. (Most products are not 24X dilutions).
4. Adulteration. (Remedies may be spiked with real medicines).
5. Denial of discomfort. ("believers are delusional and see only what they want to see").
6. Liars ("with a financial interest in selling the products or with a self-interest in selling a good story").

A commentary about language

The book *Other Healers,* published by Johns Hopkins Press in 1988, was a summary of various "alternative" medical practices. The editor, Norman Gevitz, describes his work as providing "a scholarly perspective" of unorthodox health movements, saying previous books have been "pro-alternative" or "anti–cult," whose "primary motive has not been to advance knowledge, but to convince the public of the successes or failures, the rightness or wrongness, of such phenomena."

Most literature against homœopathy has been couched in language with a heavy emotional content. The language is not that of discourse, but rather antagonism. Many who call themselves defenders of "science" and accuse others of being non-scientific, often use judgmental words rather than objective ones— referring to homœopathy as "nostrums," "silly," "inane," "absurd"— to name a few.

When Stephen Barrett wrote the first article for *Consumer*

Reports, he sent it to several people within the homœopathic community for comment— Jay Borneman, Harris Coulter, Richard Moskowitz, Dana Ullman, Jacquelyn Wilson, David Wember, and me.

Many corrections I suggested had to do with the language usage and not necessarily with the facts presented. Although several changes were incorporated, those dealing with the language were not. In a letter of November 25, 1986, Barrett says he left the articles with the editors of Consumers Union who made more changes and the "article became more negative."

What were these suggested changes in language?

• "Homeopathy is based on 19th century theories that the scientific community considers absurd…"

Suggested change: "…that the scientific community considers as unfounded…"

• "Hahnemann proposed his law of similars…"

Suggested change: "After much experimentation and observation, Hahnemann developed the law of similars…"

• "[when pharmacists were asked]… the law of similars did not find a single supporter, and all but one said the law of infinitesimals was wrong also."

Suggested change: "the law of similars was found difficult to comprehend" or "the law of similars does not fit into the scientific paradigm being used…"

• "We advise our readers who have been considering homeopathic treatment or the use of homeopathic remedies to forget them."

Suggested change: "…who have been considering… to approach it with caution and open skepticism."

Another subtle use of language can be seen in the 1994 *Consumer Reports* article which describes homœopathy as an "attractive alternative to the torturous and ineffective medical treatments of the time." If the medical treatments were "ineffective" is homœopathy, by default, "effective"? Yet in the next sentence the author talks about homœopathy's "apparent successes during cholera epidemics." The word "apparent" is a loaded one. Should we talk about the "apparent" failure of conventional medicine in similar epidemics? The historical records show that those who used homœopathy fared much better than those who didn't. It is only "apparent" if you are doubting it in the first place.

"Scientific"

A good exercise: When you see the word "scientific" in any article or story, see how the paragraph reads without the word. If the meaning remains the same, the word is describing nothing.

A commentary about science

Another word that is over used to the point of becoming a buzzword is "science" or "scientific." Charles Singer, in the *Encyclopedia Britannica*, suggests that "science may perhaps be regarded as the mood in which the world is considered." As such, there is no scientific absolute— just a constant exploration, and even that is dependent upon the paradigm which is accepted within the culture, a concept that was clearly elucidated by Thomas Kuhn in his 1962 classic *The Structure of Scientific Revolutions*.

The argument is always put forth that homœopathy is not scientific. David Hufford has suggested that what passes for "scientific" is often "scientistic"— that which looks like science.

The *Scientific Method* can be described as the following procedures:

1. Recognition of a problem (observing a phenomena)
2. Collation of data through experimentation and observation
3. Development of a hypothesis
4. Testing the hypothesis

The development of homœopathy fulfills these basic criteria, yet does not fit into the mechanistic paradigm under which western medicine operates.

Hahnemann observed the phenomena (the relationship of *Cinchona* to intermittent fever); collected data (other cases cured by similars); developed a hypothesis (the law of similars); and tested the hypothesis (prescribed for disease based on proving similarity).

When Hahnemann first published his "Essay On A New Principle" in 1796, he suggested the principle be tried. Those who did became homœopaths. Those who didn't had their objections on purely theoretical grounds.

If a physician *today* would observe the same, test it as Hahnemann did, and propose it as a therapeutic modality, would they be listened to?

1985 – 1996: The Legal Battles

North Carolina
George Guess
Florida
Other places, other cases

North Carolina

As homœopathy was slowly gaining acceptance, the opposition (which has always been present) became visible. This took the form of state boards of medicine bringing charges against practitioners, scientific research being questioned, and the rise of formal "quackbusting" organizations which counted homœopathy among its targets.

The most prominent homœopathic legal case was that of George Guess in North Carolina.

In 1985, George Guess, a medical doctor practicing in Asheville, North Carolina, was called before the North Carolina Board of Medical Examiners. He was charged with unprofessional conduct, and told if he persisted in practicing homœopathy, his license to practice medicine in North Carolina would be revoked.

According to the North Carolina Medical Statutes, unprofessional conduct includes "any departure from or failure to conform to the standards of accepted and prevailing medical practice, or the ethics of the medical profession, irrespective of whether or not a patient is included…"

It seemed to be the intent of the medical board to "cleanse" North Carolina of anything outside the board's view of conventional therapy. It was the beginning of a seven–year legal battle that would see its way to the State Supreme Court.

In January 1986, the medical board ruled that Guess should desist from practicing homœopathy or have his license revoked. He was given a two–year probation, however he obtained an injunction that let him continue practicing as further legal appeals were made.

In May 1987, Judge Robert Farmer of the North Carolina Superior Court found the medical board had been "arbitrary and capricious" in attempting to revoke Guess' license. The medical board appealed to the State Supreme Court.

In 1988 the North Carolina Court of Appeals upheld the ruling, saying the medical board's purpose was to protect the public from harm, and as the board failed to demonstrate the practice of homœopathy was a risk to the public, it could not censure it. The appeal continued.

On July 28, 1990, the North Carolina Supreme Court reversed the two earlier appellate decisions and said it is within the power of the medical board to determine what are "acceptable and prevailing standards" and it is not necessary to say specifically how a deviation from the standards might harm the public. That homœopathy was accepted elsewhere was held to be of no consequence.

Justice Frye, of the State Supreme Court, dissented, recognizing the statute's intent was to protect the public from harm, not from unorthodoxy. "This is not the case of a quack beguiling the public with snake oil and drums, but a dedicated physician seeking to find new ways to relieve human suffering," he said.

Exhausting his appeals, Guess re-located to Virginia.

In the summer of 1993, a grass-roots group, the Carolinians for Health Care Access, was successful in having the state's Medical Practice Act amended by a legislative vote of 104-1. The Medical Board now can not revoke or deny licensure solely on the basis that the practice of a therapy is "experimental, non-traditional, or departs from acceptable and prevailing medical practices unless, by competent evidence, the board can establish that the treatment is generally not effective."

George Guess, MD, DHt
November 1, 1947 —

Guess did his undergraduate work at Old Dominion University, in Virginia and his medical degree at the Medical College of Virginia in 1973.

Says Guess: "I had suffered during my brief medical career a nagging dissatisfaction with medicine in general and came to recognize all too well the shortcomings of the allopathic system of medicine. During a six-month stay in Alaska, where I worked on a *locum tenems* in family practice in Anchorage, I met a naturopath practicing there. During our few meetings she would regale me with stories of the efficacy of naturopathy and gently chastise me for knowing so little of natural medicine. Periodically I would read of astounding cures effected by natural health care means. I became curious and resolved to make of study of them. At the naturopath's suggestion, I wrote several alternative practitioners asking if I could observe their practices over a two month period. They were of many varying disciplines.

George Guess

441

Of all the inquiries, only a homœopath wrote back—Dr. Clyde Reynolds of Beaverton, Oregon. He very graciously permitted me to live and practice with him. While my own preferred method of practicing homœopathy now differs greatly from the way Dr. Reynolds introduced me to, I observed several interesting positive clinical outcomes in Dr. Reynold's practice, enough to intrigue me. I also read all the books he suggested and, I guess, became enamored with the aesthetics of homœopathic practice— you know, the hands on, non-technological style of bedside practice described in the many books of yore. I became intrigued by the profound cures I read of which were effected by so unlikely a method of medicinal application.

"Subsequently, I happened upon the tapes of George Vithoulkas's first US conference at Stanford. I can only say that there was an immediate resonance in my heart and head with his message. I resolved then and there, like an aspiring acolyte, to study with Vithoulkas and to see if I might become a decent homœopath. In 1978 I went to the NCH course at Millersville at David Wember's suggestion. While there I heard Bill Gray lecture and was so taken with the clarity of his lessons that I subsequently signed on for the first IFH Professional Course, a direct route to more exposure to Vithoulkas.

"Every year for several years after finishing Bill Gray's course I attended seminars in Greece and the US given by Vithoulkas. In 1984 I went to Greece to work and study for a year with Vithoulkas. I was there at the same time as Roger Morrison. We enjoyed ourselves and learned a lot.

"After my year in Greece I returned to North Carolina resolved to begin a full-time practice in homœopathy. Previously I had been very quietly practicing homœopathy while also working part-time as a conventional physician in a hospital emergency room. It was very soon after I put up my shingle announcing my homœopathic practice that the North Carolina Board of Medical Examiners initiated their campaign against me."

Guess is currently practicing in Charlottesville, Virginia. He is the editor of the *Journal of the American Institute of Homeopathy* and the president of the American Board of Homeotherapeutics.

Florida

In late 1989, Philip Parsons, a dentist from Keystone Heights, Florida, was charged by the Florida Department of Professional Regulation with using homœopathy.

The DPR said that "prescribing homeopathic preparations and remedies is not within the scope of dental practice" and the practice would be considered "experimental" and therefore must have full informed consent of the subjects. Parsons was also charged with removing amalgam fillings and replacing them with non-amalgams which "fails to meet minimum adequate standards of performance."

Parsons had studied homœopathy with the National Center at Millersville and with Vithoulkas. He was a faculty member at the NCH Summer School.

In 1991 he was found guilty of using homœopathy in his dental practice, but his lawyer pointed out that homœopathic remedies are legal drugs recognized in Florida statutes, and Parsons, as a licensed dentist, is allowed to prescribe drugs.

A second trial found the practice of homœopathy "cult–like and experimental" and fined Parsons $1,000, asked him to take 18 hours of continuing education in pharmacology, and required him to have a signed consent form before he could use homœopathy with a patient.

In June 1995, Elizabeth Brinkley, an MD homœopath in Tallahassee, Florida, ran afoul of the "powers that be." She was working as a pediatrician in a Health Maintenance Organization (HMO) and during a routine chart review the HMO found she was using homœopathy with her patients. She was dropped as an HMO provider for "giving sub-standard care." She filed a lawsuit against the HMO in October 1997. At the time of this publication, there has been no resolve.

Brinkley also ran afoul of a local hospital when (with consultation) she gave *Arnica* to a hospitalized patient. The nursing staff complained the patient was given remedies while in hospital, and Brinkley received a threat of "serious consequences" were she ever to use homœopathy in the hospital again. After Brinkley informed the hospital that the homœopathic remedies are covered under the 1938 Federal Food, Drug, and Cosmetic Act (a requirement for any medication given in the hospital) she did not hear from the hospital again.

Other places, other cases...

By 1997, nine states (Alaska, Colorado, Georgia, Massachusetts, New York, North Carolina, Oklahoma, Oregon, Washington) had freedom of practice legislation. Of them, Massachusetts had legislation in place for the longest time.

Massachusetts General Law Annotated, Chapter 112, Section 7, says "Section two to six, inclusive, and section eight shall not be held to discriminate against any particular school or system of medicine." The law has been on the books since 1901.

In the other states, the legislation has been similar to that passed in Alaska in 1990, which says a State Medical Board "may not base a finding of professional incompetence solely on the basis that a licensee's practice is unconventional or experimental in the absence of demonstrable physical harm to a patient."

An interesting situation can be seen in Texas. Since 1846, Texas has been the only state with a constitutional provision for medical freedom: "The Legislature may pass laws prescribing the qualifications of practitioners of medicine in this state, and to punish persons for malpractice, but no preference shall ever be given by law to any schools of medicine" [Art.16, Sect.31].

An additional statute since 1907 mandates that "Nothing in this act shall be construed so as to discriminate against a school or system of medical practice. . ." [Sect. 3.06 (a)]. However, both provisions are currently dysfunctional. In addition, Texas adopted a mini–FDA act in 1985, but in one glaring omission dropped the *Homeopathic Pharmacopoeia* from both the definition of Drugs, [Sect. 431.002 (14)] and definition of the Official Compendium. [Sect. 431.002 (26)].

It is important to recognize these freedom of practice laws are for protection of state licensed physicians. All other health care practitioners who do not fall under the aegis of the State Medical Board are not protected by these acts.

In late 1997, two professional homœopaths, certified by the Council for Homeopathic Certification and registered with the North American Society of Homeopaths, were brought before Medical Boards in their respective states (Connecticut and Georgia) on charges of practicing without a license. The cases are still pending.

1980 – 1996: Research

Research and homœopathy
Clinical research
The work of David Taylor Reilly
Jennifer Jacobs
The Nicaragua study
Non-clinical research
The "Benveniste affair"

Research and homœopathy

Although homœopathy has been used, successfully, since the early 1800s, documenting its success was all done within the homœopathic community.

The conventional medical community, by shutting out the homœopaths and dismissing them as "quacks," left no openings for the homœopaths to prove the efficacy of their treatments within the conventional model.

The attitude of the American Medical Association (well expressed by George H. Simmons who said, "Of all the medical systems of present or past times, there is none which in my opinion has a scantier basis of fact or reason, a poorer excuse for existence, or a more fantastic set of principles and methods, than homœopathy.") was hardly likely to draw the communities together.

An attempt was made in 1913 when a group of homœopaths convinced the AMA president, Abraham Jacobi, to conduct a test of homœopathy. The testing was to be done under the auspices of the Rockefeller Institute in New York and the McCormack Institute in Chicago. However, the two institutes refused to participate. The AMA asked the AIH to suggest other acceptable laboratories, and the AIH, sensing (rightly or wrongly) little enthusiasm for the project on the part of the AMA, dropped the matter.

Until recently, the efficacy of *any* treatment was determined by clinical application. While the homœopaths were using the methodology outlined in the *Organon*, and finding the "appropriate remedy" through the knowledge of drug provings, the allopaths, increasingly, were getting their information from the drug manufacturers and from testimonials offered by physicians who had used a specific product.

As the numbers of conventional drugs began to climb, a technique was needed to separate the less effective drugs from the more effective ones. In the 1930s, British statistician Austin Bradford Hill suggested models for controlled clinical trials and randomized clinical trials. The first major controlled clinical trial was the 1946-1948 study of *streptomycin* in tuberculosis.

The use of the controlled trial grew in the 1950s and received its major impetus as a result of the 1962 Kefauver-Harris amendments to the Food, Drug, and Cosmetic Act. For a drug to be introduced to the market, "substantial

The perils of clinical trials I

Can a clinical trial meet the stringent requirements for the use of human subjects? When Dr. Michael Carlston did a survey about alternative medicine at the University of San Francisco, the Committee on Human Research at the University would allow him to send only ONE follow-up letter, saying any more letters would be too emotionally stressful to the recipients.

The perils of clinical trials II

Where is the money going to come from? Dr. Carlston mentioned a research project that was a "survey of attitudes" where the postage for the project cost $11,000.

evidence" of efficacy became a legal requirement. Although the term "substantial evidence" was not defined, it was eventually interpreted to mean "randomized" and "controlled" clinical trials *à la* Hill's suggested models.

But within the medical community, questions arose. During such trials, how can one take into account the unique nature of the person being tested? The "idiosyncratic" nature of people will prevent everyone from reacting in the same way to everything. Coulter says, "…the opinion of the FDA reflects that of the majority of physicians— who are convinced that, for purposes of medical and pharmacologic research, the individuals 'idiosyncrasy' or 'abnormality' is less important than the features he possesses in common with others, i.e., his 'normalities'… If this heterogeneity is ignored or assumed out of existence, the 'controlled clinical trial' must be judged a failure."

With the "double blind, randomized, clinical trial" accepted as the "gold standard" of research, how can homœopathy— which relies so much on the very "idiosyncratic" nature of the patient— be tested?

Even before we ask *that* question, there are others that must be asked. The old adage says, "If you don't know where you are going, you won't know when you get there." What exactly do we want to test? What should we look for in our research? Do we want to look for the effectiveness of remedies in clinical use? Do we want to test the efficacy of high dilutions? Do we want to be able to measure the high dilutions? Do we want to investigate the bio-magnetic field? Do we want to investigate the relationship of the healer to the patient? Do we want to be able to define the "placebo response" so we can discard it from our trials?

Wayne Jonas and Jennifer Jacobs say that, "With homœopathy, we have hardly a clue as to how it *could* work or what the rules it follows might be. It is unlikely that any fundamental advances in our understanding of homœopathy can be made without this knowledge." Does this mean investigating the "mechanism of action" of the similar? How does one begin to do that?

Much of this comes down to a question of finance. A well controlled double-blind study can be very expensive. A single trial can cost upwards of $60,000 to produce. Research has to be supported, and the lack of potential profit from homœopathic research is always a problem.

The perils of clinical trials III

Under FDA rules, there must be an "Investigational New Drug" application (IND) for every drug used in research on a serious (i.e., prescription) diagnosis even if the drug is already available over the counter for other uses (e.g., aspirin had to have an IND number when it was used in trials about heart disease). For a homœopathic trial every drug in every potency will have to have an IND number, unless an exemption is granted.

The perils of clinical trials IV

Dr. Edward Chapman, in conjunction with the University of Pennsylvania, conducted a study of the usefulness of homœopathy with Premenstrual Syndrome (PMS). It seemed to be a good subject, since most homœopaths in practice have great success treating cases of PMS. 105 volunteers applied for the study. Questionnaires were sent to all to determine the baseline of symptoms. Only 87 questionnaires were returned. Of those, only 31 had PMS based on the prior set definitions. After personal interviews, 10 were dropped leaving only 21 in the study. All were given placebo. Eleven improved and were dropped from the study. Of the remaining ten, half received a remedy, half received placebo. Five improved. Of the five who improved, three had been given placebo. Of the five remaining, all were re-interviewed and given the indicated remedy. Three improved, two did not. None of the data was statistically significant. The placebo response was 57% versus a usual placebo response of about 35%. Does that say something unique about the classification of PMS? Did the interview have anything to do with it? Starting with 105 subjects, the trial concluded with only ten. The results were inconclusive and it cost over $10,000 to do.

While a new drug makes profits for its manufacturer because it is patented and widely distributed, homœopathic medicines, derived from common plants and elements, are generic and cannot be patented. The manufacturing procedures are simple, and the final product is inexpensive. With little money to made from the final product, who would be interested in financing the research?

An overview

The scientific approach we are so accustomed to using has evolved from Greek tradition through the Renaissance. One premise of the science which evolved from this tradition is that phenomena become understandable and amenable to mathematical modelling if one divides the whole into small enough parts. But by doing so one often loses whatever it is that one was looking for in the beginning. The "method of science" may not always be suitable for investigating living bodies and their interaction with the environment. The sum of the parts do not equal the whole, any more than looking at individual bees would tell anything of the complexity of the hive.

The interaction between homœopathy as a holistic discipline and science as a reductionist methodology can be mutually beneficial. Science can benefit from acknowledging the shortcomings of its philosophy and use it only in areas where it is applicable. Hopefully, some will find a way of enlarging the tool box of scientists so the class of phenomena on which science can shed light becomes larger in the future.

As we read about the research done in homœopathy in this chapter, we should keep in mind the current status of all research: nobody has the foggiest idea of how and why homœopathic remedies work. There exists, to date, no machine capable of distinguishing between placebo and homœopathic remedy, although some have made claims. The only such device known to us to be able to measure remedies is a living entity (vide Endler's work on tadpoles, provings, etc.). If and when advances will be made in the above areas is currently unclear. While all the research is pointing toward a deeper understanding of the mechanism of homœopathy, there exists no firm indication that a significant advance is imminent.

Clinical Research

Dr. David Taylor Reilly of Glasgow commented, upon seeing all the books in the Glasgow Homœopathic Library, "that if five-percent of this is true the implications of this is absolutely stunning for the population and medicine itself."

Yet although homœopathy has 200–years of clinical use, the case reports in the literature are considered "anecdotal" in the contemporary world of the double-blind clinical trial.

On February 9, 1991 *The British Medical Journal* published an overview of homœopathic trials (Kleijnen, J. et. al., "Clinical Trials of Homeopathy", 302, pages 216-23). 107 controlled trials were found in the literature. Of them, 105 had interpretable results and of the results, 81 were positive. Pointing out that the trials generally were of low methodological quality and complicated by publication bias (i.e., they had appeared in homœopathic journals), the authors said, "The amount of positive evidence came as a surprise to us. The evidence presented in this review would probably be sufficient for establishing homœopathy as a regular treatment for certain indications."

They suggested, although evidence of the clinical trials is positive, it is not enough to draw definitive conclusions. "This indicates that there is a legitimate case for future evaluations of homeopathy," was the conclusion.

Among the trial looked at in the overview were:

• The 1980 trial of the use of homœopathy in rheumatoid arthritis by R. G. Gibson and published in *The British Journal of Clinical Pharmacology*, 9, pages 453-459. 23 patients receiving the active medicine and 23 receiving placebo. There was a significant improvement in the first group and none in the second.

• The 1986 trial of the use of homœopathic mixed pollens in hay fever by David Taylor Reilly, MD, published in *The Lancet* October 15, pages 881-886. Testing the hypothesis that homœopathic remedies are placebos, a double–blind trial was held. No evidence emerged to support the idea that placebo action fully explains the clinical response to the homœopathic drug.

• The 1986 trial of stillbirths in pigs by Christopher Day, published in the October issue of the *International Journal for Veterinary Homeopathy*, pages 26-28. *Caulophyllum* 30C was given to 10 sows, and 10 sows received no treatment.

"…it can't work…"

In March, 1994, Consumer Reports *contained a report about homœopathy. In the course of the article* Consumer Reports *showed the 1991 overview of homœopathic trials published in the* The British Medical Journal *to two people well versed in clinical trial analysis. One found some methodological problems with the studies and said that "until homœopathic research is evaluated by such standards, it's hard to say whether additional studies are worthwhile." (And between the lines, the assumption is that further studies are NOT worthwhile.) The other found one study "flawed" but two others were "impressive." Yet, would he prescribe these remedies for patients with the conditions that were tested? Without hesitation, the reviewer answered "no." "Ultimately, it gets to the issue of plausibility and how well it fits into your scientific view of the world," he said. "This doesn't fit."*

And there it is. Homœopathy doesn't fit into their conceptual model, so they don't want to study it. It suggests that unless research fits into their theories, they will not accept the research. It appears they want science to fit facts around theories rather than make theories around facts. It all comes down to the same thing: "We can't believe it works, so we don't think you should use it."

Stillbirths were 8% in the control and 3% in the treated group— a statistically significant difference.

• The 1989 trial with fibrositis by Peter Fisher, published in *The British Medical Journal*, 229, pages 365-6. "The improvement experienced by our patients while receiving active treatment was at least as great as that reported for any other treatment that has been assessed double-blind."

• The 1989 study of treatment of influenza-like syndromes by J. P. Ferley, et. al., published in *The British Journal of Clinical Pharmacology*, 27, pages 329-335. This was a "triple-blind" study— neither the patients nor the physicians administering the drug knew it was *homœopathic*. 237 cases received the active drug and 241 received placebo. The authors say, "The effect was modest… but nevertheless is of interest. A 7% difference in efficacy as defined would be a respectable proportion in most drug trials," said an article in *The Lancet*. The remedy being tested was a proprietary remedy used for the early stages of colds and flu called*Oscillococcinum*, made by Boiron.

On December 10, 1994, *The Lancet* published a double-blind study using homœopathic medicines. Authored by Dr. David Taylor Reilly, of Glasgow, Scotland, the article was titled "Is Evidence for Homœopathy Reproducible?"

After his previous study (*The British Homœopathic Journal* titled, "Is Homœopathy a Placebo Response?"), Reilly approached independent (non-homœopath) colleagues at the University of Glasgow to find out if the results of the two previous trials could be reproduced in a third trial. The studies used "homœopathic immunotherapy" (i.e., the use of remedies made from the allergens) in inhalant allergies. The first two trials had used hay fever as a model, while the third trial used asthma produced by house dust mite as a model. The report in *The Lancet* was the review of the last study and a meta-analysis of all three trials together.

The overall results showed homœopathically–treated patients had a 33% reduction in symptoms and physical signs of breathing distress. Placebo patients had a 10% reduction in signs and symptoms. There was only a 4-in-10,000 chance that the results were a fluke (P=0.0004).

Editors of *The Lancet* certified Reilly's studies as "done with exceptional rigour." Nevertheless, the journal repeated

the orthodox medical view, "…What could be more absurd then the notion that a substance is therapeutically active in dilutions so great that a patient is unlikely to receive a single molecule of it?" the journal said. The editors then carefully accepted the trial had validity, but suggested the reason for its success *must* lie elsewhere.

Said Reilly, "They invite us to choose between two interpretations of this activity: either there is something amiss with the clinical trial as conventionally conducted… or the effects of homœopathic immunotherapy differ from those of placebo. Yes, the dilution principle of homœopathy is absurd; so the reason for any therapeutic effect presumably lies elsewhere."

Another factor which is often used as a "negative pivot" of such tests is the preparation of the remedies themselves and the nature of the placebo. In this case, the batch of alcohol used to prepare the remedies to a 30th potency, was also used to make an identical preparation of serially diluted and succussed alcohol with no antigen added. Both these preparations were placed onto granules. The "live" medicine was a 30th potency of the antigen, and the "dummy" was a 30th potency of nothing but the alcohol.

"inexplicable— but reproducible"
Comments by David Reilly, MD

"Could the explanation be three false–positive results? The patients were carefully selected, had clearly defined diagnoses, and the results are not due to any change in conventional treatments. Double–blinding and randomisation rule out observer or patient bias. The patterns appear orderly, and are similar in the three studies. Analysis shows the absence of random or chance factors, and the results have proved reproducible under independent conditions. The positive results from the meta-analysis of the 202 patients in this series of three trials do not stand in isolation.

"But homœopathy is not an orthodox treatment; it has long been regarded as having 'inherent implausibility.' So can positive trial results validate claims of biological efficacy for solutions thought to be lacking any trace of their original solute? Where should this debate now proceed? When

The criticism

After publication, The Lancet published several letters trying to discredit the research. The following were among the criticisms (and the replies to them):
- *The subjects and practitioners correctly guessed who was on homœopathic medications more often than chance would predict, suggesting the trial may not have been adequately blinded. (The study could not be considered inadequately blinded simply because the subjects noticed obvious differences pre-and post-medication.)*
- *Past financial support of the primary author has been given by homœopathic foundations, therefore the author was biased. (No homœopathic company or foundation funds were accepted for this study, and all grants went directly to the university.)*
- *Patients were allowed to continue on conventional drugs during the study. (Yes. The study showed that there was no difference in drug intake between the groups.)*
- *The study has a large drop-out rate. (Initially, 28 subjects were enrolled in the study, 4 of whom dropped out (14%). This is not considered a large drop-out rate for a study of this size.)*
- *There is a chance the homœopathic medicine was contaminated with some of the original allergenic material. (Each medicine was diluted 30 times, in a different and fresh vial. Checks for traces of the allergen were performed and found to be negative.)*
- *The subjects given the homœopathic medicine did not experience the aggravation of symptoms soon after medication which is a hypothesis of homœopaths. (An aggravation of symptoms after taking a homœopathic medicine is sometimes but not always observed. The fact that it was not observed in the asthma study is not significant.)*
- *Because the homœopathic medicines are so dilute, they are simply water. Comparing this water with placebo is simply comparing one placebo with another. (This criticism is steeped in serious denial of the scientific method. It represents a cynical view of science because it suggests that double-blind, randomized studies are inadequate for measuring outcomes.)*

The Faces of Homœopathy

Bias— again

Although the editors of The Lancet *described this study in their editorial as carefully done, the press release sent to the media upon the publication of the article noted the results obtained from homœopathic treatment were "nowhere near that obtainable with conventional medicines." Because the trials reported in* The Lancet *did not compare homœopathic medicines with conventional medicines, this statement had no basis in fact or experimentation.*

The subtle anti-homœopathy bias expressed by The Lancet *is typical and represents an anti-scientific attitude which has no place in high calibre scientific or medical journals.*

does one 'believe the unbelievable' as an editorial in *Nature* asked?

"Over a century ago the UK General Board of Health omitted the success of homœopathic treatments in the London cholera epidemic in their statistical return to Parliament as they would 'give an unjustifiable sanction to an empirical practice alike opposed to the maintenance of truth and to the progress of science.'

"Does this still hold true today and must we likewise reject the contemporary trial results as spurious? If so, we must ask if the technique of randomised controlled clinical trials is fundamentally flawed, and capable of producing evidence for effects that do not exist, by, for example, the clinicians' expectation of outcome transmitted by subtle effects which circumvent even double–blinding?

"To question the tool which has built most of today's pharmacological practice is no less perplexing than asking whether homœopathic treatments are active. Either answer suggested by the evidence to date— homœopathy works, or, the clinical trial does not— is equally challenging to the current medical evidence.

"The usual response to the possibility that homœopathic treatments are effective is to call for a mechanism of action — asking 'how?' before asking 'if?'— is a bad basis for good science when dealing empirically with things which may as yet evade explanation. The speculation which follows should be considered in that light.

"For today's science, however, the main barrier to acceptance of homœopathy is the issue of these serially vibrated dilutions which lack any molecules at all of the original substance. Can water or alcohol of fixed biological composition encode differing biological information? Using current metaphors, does the chaos-inducing vibration, central to the production of a homœopathic dilution, encourage biophysically different new fractal-like patterns in the diluent, critically dependent upon the starting conditions? Theoretical physicists seem more at ease with such ideas than pharmacologists, considering the possibilities of isotopic stereo diversity, elathrates, or resonance and coherence within water as possible modes of transmission, while other workers are exploring the idea of electromagnetic changes. Nuclear magnetic resonance changes in homœopathic dilutions have been reported, and if reproducible, may be offering us a glimpse of a future territory.

"For now the critical tests remain clinical. Our results lead us to conclude that homœopathy differs from placebo in an inexplicable but reproducible way."

The Lancet... again

On September 20, 1997, *The Lancet* published the most significant and comprehensive review of homœopathic research. The article, by Klaus Linde and Wayne Jonas, was a meta-analysis of 89 blinded, randomized, placebo-controlled clinical trials. The authors conclude the clinical effects of homœopathic medicines are not simply the results of placebo and that homœopathic medicines seem to have clinical effects.

The researchers uncovered 186 studies, 119 of which were double-blind and/or randomized placebo-control trials, and 89 of which met pre-defined criteria for inclusion into a pooled meta-analysis. The researchers found by pooling the 89 trials together, homœopathic medicines had a 2.45 times greater effect than placebo.

Jennifer Jacobs, MD, MPH
November 10, 1950 —

Born in Huntington, West Virginia, Jacobs graduated in 1976 from Wayne State University School of Medicine in Detroit. Entering into a family practice residency in Florida, she soon became disillusioned with conventional medicine.

Says Jacobs, "I realized that most drugs did not cure patients, and often created side effects that required more medicines. I began to feel like a glorified pill pusher. Without knowing anything about homœopathy I started thinking that symptoms were the body's way of trying to heal and that it didn't make sense to suppress them. I began doing home births for friends on the side as midwifery was the only positive side to medicine I could see."

The local doctors, upset at her working with birthing, asked her to choose between birthing and her residency. She quit the residency and moved to California to pursue home births in a less hostile climate. Attending a midwife conference in San Diego, she heard Robert Schore speak on homœopathy.

"No effects"

The Lancet *concurrently published two critiques of the homœopathic research. Jan Vandenbroucke, MD, acknowledged, "The meta-analysis is completely state of the art." And yet, despite its results, he asserts homœopathic medicines "cannot possibly produce any effect," and British professor M. Langman questioned whether it was appropriate to analyze a group of experiments which used disparate remedies for different conditions.*

"It was the proverbial light bulb going on in my head as I realized there was a whole system of medicine that saw health and disease as I did and that I had at last found my calling."

Jacobs attended NCH Summer School in 1978, then moved to San Francisco and joined the Hering Clinic.

To supplement her income she got a part-time job doing histories and physicals at the Marshall Hale (formerly Hahnemann) Hospital, which had a full library of homœopathic books and the late Frederic Schmid on the staff.

"Fred took me under his wing. I subbed in his practice when he had a heart attack. I continued in a preceptorship at Hering under Corey Weinstein, Randy Neustaedter, etc."

She took the IFH course, taught by Dean Crothers and Bill Gray in 1981. "I knew Dean for over a year before Cupid struck," said Jacobs. "We eventually wound up in Seattle."

Frustrated by the lack of research in homœopathy, Jacobs decided to get a Masters of Public Health as a way of learning how to do research.

"I laid low as a homœopath until my fellow students and professors accepted me. The 1990 diarrhea pilot study was my Masters thesis. I am now on the faculty at the University of Washington as Clinical Assistant Professor in Epidemiology. The department first voted to refuse my appointment, because they didn't want to be seen as supporting homœopathy. Once the *Pediatrics* paper was published, they had no choice but to accept me."

Jacobs lives in Edmonds, Washington and is in practice with Dean Crothers.

The Nicaragua Study

On May 9, 1994, *Pediatrics* magazine published a clinical trial of homœopathy. Authored by Jennifer Jacobs, it was titled "Treatment of Acute Childhood Diarrhea with Homeopathic Medicine: A Randomized Clinical Trial in Nicaragua." It was the first time a trial of homœopathy had been published in a conventional medical journal in the United States.

The clinical trial was a randomized double-blind test comparing homœopathic medicine with placebo in the treatment of acute childhood diarrhea. The clinical diagnosis of "childhood diarrhea" was chosen because it would be amenable to treatment with homœopathy while the conventional therapy, oral rehydration, could be used at the same time. In effect, all the children in the trial were getting the standard therapy, but some would also be getting homœopathic remedies. The trial was carried out in Nicaragua with eighty-one children aged six months to five years. An individualized homœopathic medicine was prescribed for each child and daily follow-up was done for five days.

The treatment group had a statistically significant (p<.05) decrease in duration of diarrhea, defined by the number of days until there were less than three unformed stools daily for two consecutive days. There was also a significant difference (p<.05) in the number of stools per day between the two groups after 72 hours of treatment. The study concluded that "Further study of this treatment deserves consideration."

Eighteen different homœopathic remedies were prescribed, but nearly sixty percent of the cases required *Podophyllum, Chamomilla,* or *Arsenicum.* Other remedies prescribed were *Calcarea carbonica, Sulphur, Mercurius, Pulsatilla, Phosphorus, China, Gambogia, Aethusa, Aloe, Belladonna, Bryonia, Colchicum, Croton tiglium, Dulcamara,* and *Nux vomica.*

All the statistical analysis of the results was done before the randomization code was broken.

Says Jacobs, "Initially *Pediatrics* refused the manuscript. They sent comments from three reviewers, two of which were very positive. The third reviewer launched into an impassioned diatribe against homœopathy, saying nothing about the merits of the actual study. The tone of this review was very condescending; full of such phrases as 'all children presumably received' and 'the claim is made' and other not so subtle suggestions that the authors were lacking in integrity. The reviewer said, 'I will only accept that homœopathic medicine works if the practitioners of this art can tell me in plausible ways, why they think it works.'

"I was advised by a colleague to point out that one of the reviewers was 'hostile to the manuscript' and to ask for new, impartial reviewers. I figured I had nothing to lose by asking, and was surprised when the editor wrote back, agreeing to another review and asking me to recommend 'experts in this subject' who would be qualified to review the manuscript."

The perils of clinical trials V

"The Human Subjects Committee at the University of Washington initially turned down my application, stating that a substance had to be proven effective in adults, before studies could take place in children. They also expressed concern about using 'unproven' substances in the developing world, with the fear that the University would be accused of using third–world children as 'Guinea pigs.'

"I arranged for a meeting with the committee, who knew very little about homœopathy. They remained skeptical, but what really turned the tide was when I passed around a bottle of "Hyland's Teething Tablets" I had purchased at a local drug store. Once they realized homœopathic medicines were already being sold over-the-counter for children in the United States, they became much more cooperative and the study was approved."

There were, of course, letters to the editor pointing out every possible flaw in the research design, methodology, analysis, and conclusion that can be used to cast doubt on the findings. The rigorous methodology of the study helped to call for further research in this area.

How many studies are needed to convince someone that homœopathy works? This particular study shows only that homœopathy might work for diarrhea.

Hopefully, as we continue to do research in other areas, we will reach a critical mass where someone might conclude that since homœopathy has been shown to be effective for hay fever, influenza, diarrhea, fibrositis, asthma, head trauma, etc., that it must be effective in general.

Says Jacobs, "I am working hard to convince myself that homœopathy is more than the placebo response. It appears to work, from my clinical experience, but maybe I am living in a delusional world (along with a lot of other people). If homœopathy is legitimate, then we should be able to document this in a scientific way. As a physician practicing homœopathy for more than fifteen years, I am tired of being considered a quack by my colleagues. I believe that we need to be able to show that homœopathy is effective by the rules of modern science, in order for our healing art to take its rightful place as a respected modality in the health care system."

A second trial has since been conducted in Nepal with positive results. At the time of this writing, the study has not yet been published.

Non-clinical research

Although the real test of homœopathy is to be found at the bedside, the exploration of the remedies themselves and possible explanations of the sub-molecular dose have occupied another, but smaller, part of homœopathic research.

In 1963, Garth Boericke and Rudolph Smith, began experiments to explore the remedies themselves. A series of remedies, both simple dilutions and succussed dilutions, were looked at with the help of Nuclear Magnetic Resonance Spectroscopy. The work continued for a few years, with a second report appearing in the 1968 October-December issue of the *Journal of the American Institute of Homeopathy*.

An editorial by Allen Neiswander, in the same issue, spoke of the increasing use of NMR and "worthwhile results" in looking at homœopathic potencies. But as the article was being prepared for publication, Garth Boericke died, and the interest in the work was lost.

In 1983, Adam Sacks, a student at the John Bastyr College of Naturopathic Medicine, duplicated some of the Boericke/Smith experiments and published the results in 1983 Fall-Winter *Journal of Holistic Medicine*.

His experiment measured nuclear magnetic resonance spectra on 23 homœopathic remedies prepared in a solution of 87 percent ethanol and 13 percent water. NMR curves were compared with a control ethanol-water solution. The experiment found distinct differences between controls and homœopathic remedies in the hydroxy regions of the NMR spectra. He postulated that the process of dilution and succussion of homœopathic remedies produces a change in configuration of water and/or hydroxy groups, or a change in the interactions between them, which is detected by NMR.

Some of this work is continuing through the efforts of Rolland R. Conté, Henri Berliocchi, Yves Lasne, and Gabriel Vernot, who co–authored a book, *Theory of High Dilutions and Experimental Aspects*, in 1996. They explore the differences between succussed and non–succussed solutions, how these differences are seen through NMR spectroscopy, and what the meaning of these differences are.

Conté says "Hahnemann's 'dynamic principle hidden in high dilutions' can be entirely validated using physical measurements (NMR, Beta radiation emission) and be mathematically interpreted" by a variety of methods and suggests the potentizing process (i.e, dilution and succussion) creates "white holes" in solutions and the emission of a Beta particle (an electron).

Conté has found that saliva and urine also emit these Beta particles which can be "mapped" to obtain a spectrum indicating a person's state of health.

Homœopathic dilutions can be measured in the same way and a remedy can be chosen based on a comparison of the "map" of the person to the "map" of the medicine. At the time of this writing, the work is on-going.

Another piece of research that emerged in 1996 was authored by Shui-Yin Lo, an associate researcher at Stamford.

Lo investigated differences between ordinary water and samples, which were prepared in a way very similar to homœopathic remedies. Lo speculated that in a homœopathic dilution, the ions of the solute function as crystallization centers for the water molecules, which are attracted to them and form something akin to an ice crystal around them. Lo calls these formations "Ie–crystals," but others say he is describing "hydration shells," a concept that has been known for a while. Unfortunately, however, contrary to common practice in the scientific community, Lo did not disclose full details to allow independent repetition of his experiments. In the paper Lo forwards a theory which, upon closer examination, does not seem to add significantly to common knowledge of physical chemistry. Also, the experimental evidence which he reports has been considered as highly questionable in several key points. Independent reproduction of measurements by one other laboratory on samples supplied by Lo have failed to show any evidence of "Ie crystals." The dilutions examined by Lo correspond, on a homœopathic scale, to a maximal potency of 13X, which is still well below the Avogadro limit. Therefore, the critical question of the non-material action of homœopathic remedies is not addressed in this paper at all.

It is important to note that research concerning the mechanism of homœopathic action can be divided generally into two groups: those papers which have been published in non–scientific journals, with the publication geared toward the scientific lay audience, and work which has passed the scientific peer–review process and thus appeared in indexed and referenced scientific journals. The work above falls into the first category. Conté's work was published in his book and has not appeared in any peer–review journals, and as such, has been seriously questioned by a number of people. The work described below all falls into the second category of research.

The first work to appear that discussed research into homœopathy was *The Scientific Foundations of Homeopathy*, by Resch and Gutmann. Published in 1987, it contained a number of essays summarizing homœopathic research.

In 1995 Paolo Bellavite, MD, a hematologist and professor of general pathology at the Verona School of Medicine in Italy, and Andrea Signorini, MD a practicing homœopath, wrote *Homeopathy: A Frontier in Medical Science*.

In the book the authors construct a model, based on conventional paradigms, to explain the action of homœopathic remedies. They discuss a number of complex subjects, including molecular biology, immunology, neoplastic proliferation and receptor theories. By applying the theories of fractal geometry, chaos and complexity, quantum physics, coherence, electromagnetic phenomena, and Boolean networks, the authors attempt to construct a hypothesis that explains the law of similars and the principle of dilution.

The authors argue there are some physical theories making it plausible that homœopathic remedies contain specific information, comparable to the specific molecule necessary to activate a certain type of receptor, which is read by the organism in a very specific sense, and propose that homœopathy fits well into the emerging picture of complex systems. They carefully show homœopathy and the current theory in biomedicine do not contradict each other.

Of the work, Harald Walach, a homœopathic researcher from Germany says:

"But still there are many missing links in the chain. There is no single basic research paradigm yet which has consistently been able to show that homœopathic potencies act in a simple system. There is no clinical paradigm which has repeatedly been able to show the effects of high potencies, except the models of David Reilly. None of the research has stood the final test of scientific fact: reproducibility in the hand of other researchers. I read the database of homœopathy in a different way: I see promising beginnings which never hold up to the end. I see exceptional data, which cannot be replicated. I see a host of anomalies but no clear pattern emerging. In the light of that type of data, I myself would be very hesitant to promise that a biophysical view will vindicate homœopathy. I disagree with the authors of this book in the interpretation of this database, and I disagree with them in the view that a biophysical outlook will change the picture and that can be integrated into modern biology and that will be part of normal science in the not too distant future."

Two other books appearing in 1996 were *Signals and*

Images by Madeleine Bastide— a collection of 23 full scientific papers from more than 50 contributors to the last two meetings of the International Research Group on Very Low Dose and High Dilution Effects, and *Ultra–High Dilution Physiology and Physics*, a series of essays edited by P. C. Endler and J. Schulte.

Claiming to be the first serious multi-disciplinary work to investigate scientifically the actions of ultra high dilutions (those dilutions above the Avogadro number), the book is a compilation of papers and reviews from leading physiologists, physicists and biophysicists.

One paper re-investigates Kolisko's well-known model of the effects of homœopathically–prepared silver nitrate on the development of wheat seedlings in the late 1930s. A zoological study by Endler et al., examining the effect of *Thyroxine* 30X on amphibian development, has a very detailed protocol, positive results, and uses an evaluation technique with potential for the investigation of other biophysical phenomena. Several contributions find homœopathic dilutions can affect living systems even when sealed in glass vials, and this represents a crucial discovery found in physiological studies using ultra-high dilutions.

Endler and Schulte's book contains papers postulating many theories, such as a coherent interaction between the electromagnetic fields of the molecules of the mother tincture and the dipoles of the solvent water molecules resulting in the permanent polarization of water or the isotopic diversity inherent in many types of atoms which in turn confers two more properties of atoms in molecules— the diversity in mass and abundance. This isotopic diversity of the solvent may be influenced by the preparation process of the ultra-high dilutions and can perhaps affect living biosystems.

Most interesting is the paper which suggests the electro-magnetic nature of the molecular signal. Citro et al. attempted to transfer the speculated molecular information contained in the polarized coherent water dipoles of ultra-high dilutions to pure water using a special electronic device. It was discovered the water that had received the 'information' from a sample of *Thyroxine* affected a particular stage of the amphibian development more significantly than the control.

In a review of the work in *The British Homœopathic Journal* by Aaron K. Vallance and Kim A. Jobst, the reviewers point out that although the book "promotes the need for high methodological standards in research by presenting research done exactly in this manner, as well as encouraging a more interdisciplinary approach… It is a great pity that some of its contents have not been addressed by non-homœopathic publications, a step which has all too often eluded homœopathic research and yet is vital if is to have any future impact in orthodox science."

Those investigating the mechanism of action are, in effect, admitting there *is* a mechanism and that homœopathy actually does work within living systems. At the same time others are trying to develop trials showing homœopathy *is* capable of treating diseases states. And *that* will be the task of the research in the next century.

The "Benveniste affair"

Jacques Benveniste, MD, is a specialist in immunology who worked for INSERM, the French Biomedical Research Institute. In 1982 he was a Nobel Prize finalist. According to the *Scientific Citation Index*, 13 of his articles have been cited more than 100 times, making them "classics" in the field, and one article in the *Journal of Experimental Medicine* has been cited more than 640 times. He was awarded the silver medal from the French National Research Council for his allergy and asthma work.

In 1987, while searching for a new blood test to identify allergies, he found antibodies that react with certain blood cells continued to react when they were diluted beyond a point where there were, theoretically, no antibodies left in the solution.

Benveniste approached the reputable journal *Nature*, with his work, and it suggested the work might be a fluke and needed verification before submitting it for publication. Benveniste was certainly known to *Nature* as it had already published four of his articles.

In response to the suggestion, Benveniste had similar work conducted at five laboratories— two in Israel, one in Canada, one in Italy, and one in France.

The article appeared in the June 30, 1988 issue of *Nature* magazine under the title "Human basophil degranulation triggered by very dilute antiserum against IgE."

Jacques Benveniste, MD, 1989

461

An editorial, in the same issue, was titled "When to believe the unbelievable," and while suggesting the work might give "aid and comfort" to homœopathy (because of the dilute nature of the substances used), it spoke of the threat to conventional science: "Where, for example, would elementary principles such as Law of Mass Action be if Benveniste is proved correct?" and it suggested the Benveniste's observations "strike at the root of two centuries of observation and rationalization of physical phenomena."

Within a month, *Nature* had sent an investigating team to the Benveniste labs, and printed a follow-up declaring the original experiments to be "a delusion."

The team investigating the work was comprised of John Maddox, the editor of *Nature;* James Randi, a sleight-of-hand artist and professional "magician" known as "the Amazing Randi," who is a debunker of paranormal phenomena; and Walter Stewart, a self-appointed investigator of science fraud from the National Institutes of Health. None of the investigators were schooled in any specialized areas of biology. The investigating team did not have an immunologist in the group. Furthermore, the team only looked at Benveniste's lab; the other four labs were never questioned.

The group's composition pointed to the pre-conceived idea that Benveniste had committed fraud, and that was what they were looking to prove. Either Benveniste made up the data, or he had committed serious errors in the interpretation of the data. Benveniste, in reply, likened the inquiry to a "Salem witch hunt," and warned his laboratory colleagues elsewhere to "never let these people get into your lab."

"The only way to confirm science is to have the experiments performed again in other laboratories," said Benveniste. "There are only two possibilities. Either all of us are wrong, but in good faith, or these results are true."

The sub-text of the episode was to avoid giving support, in any way, to homœopathy. Stewart told Harris Coulter, in a private conversation, that the group had performed a "crucial experiment" which "disproved the whole of homœopathy."

On September 3, 1988, shortly after the *Nature* article appeared, there was a debate about the article on British television. Present were Stewart, Randi, Benveniste, and

David Taylor Reilly. Also present was Dr. Jonathan Miller, the presenter of the TV series *The Body in Question*. Of all the statements made during the program, the most telling was by Miller. He described homœopathy as "blasphemy" and said he had no interest in any experiments since, if they were shown to be repeatable, "they would bring into question the entire nature of the physical universe as we now know it."

And *that* is the entire reason to consider homœopathy as dangerous. Because if it does work, then the model of the universe many people have had all these years might have to be re-built.

The treatment of Benveniste by the medical establishment followed the "four-steps" described by Harris Coulter and outlined on page 429. He was shunned by his colleagues and subjected to a conspiracy of silence. He was blacklisted within the community. When he repeated his experiments and refined the procedures, both *Nature* and *Science* refused to publish the results.

Since the science community decided to shun Benveniste, he took his case to the press. He was ordered by his superiors, in 1989, to cease publishing articles in the popular press. *Le Monde*— where many of his articles appeared— received letters from scientists complaining it should not make space available to a person who had been excluded from the scientific community.

In 1994 his laboratory was closed by INSERM. He continued to work at the privately–funded Digital Biology Laboratory in Paris.

In late 1997, Benveniste sued three scientists who had said in *Le Monde* that Benveniste's work may have been fraudulent. One colleague said Benveniste suffered from "psychotic delusion" leading to "distortion in his perception of reality" and, ultimately, to "unintentional fraud." 1985 Nobel Prize recipient Francois Jacob, one of those sued, said "It is impossible to have a scientific discussion with Jacques Benveniste."

In the 10 years since the publication of the *Nature* article, Benveniste has continued to do his work, and refine his experiments. He is still finding substances that, when diluted to the 60X potency, continue to have activity on the cellular level. He has postulated that the water being used as the diluent, has a "memory" which can retain the "energetic information" placed upon it through the original dilution and succussion.

An article in *Nature* magazine, reporting on the law suit said of Benveniste, "He claims to be able to routinely transmit biological activity to water and cultured cells electronically and to store such signals on computer disks." This is referring to the work reported in Endler and Schulte's *Ultra-High Dilution Physiology and Physics* by Citro et al. describing the attempts to transfer the speculated molecular information contained in the polarized coherent water dipoles of ultra-high dilutions to pure water using a special electronic device.

When questioned about the connection with homœopathy, Benveniste shrugs. "I am an immunologist, not a homœopath," he told a group at Temple University in 1993. "I have found a phenomenon that I can not explain. I am looking for explanations. Closing your eyes to it will not make it go away."

1980 – 1996: Homœopathic Pharmacy

The new legislation
Questionable pharmacy and slick marketing

The 1938 FD&C Act

*Although those interested in homœopathy are aware Royal Copeland made sure the Homœopathic Pharmacopoeia was written into the 1938 legislation, it is important to understand the legislation of Copeland's **created** the Food and Drug Administration. Copeland presented the suggested legislation to the Senate on June 12, 1933. It was finally passed on June 25, 1938, a few days after Copeland died. All along the way he actively defended the legislation and pushed it through several failures to get a Senate vote.*

The fact homœopathic medicines were made legal by the legislation is a very minor part of the whole. The legislation provided for the regulation within interstate commerce of any food, drug, device, or cosmetic that has been adulterated or mis-branded. It established definitions and standards for foods that have been mis-branded or adulterated. It established new drug application procedures. It established regulation and standards defining the adulteration of cosmetics, and it established factory inspections to assure the standards are upheld. Those in the United States are so used to living under these regulations that it is hard to imagine the lack of regulatory environment prior to Copland's legislative bill.

Although the "quackbusters" speak in derogatory terms of Senator Copeland and how he "snuck" the Homœopathic Pharmacopoeia into the legislation, they should remember that without his efforts the entire edifice of the FDA and the regulations it enforces might not even exist.

In June 1938, the Pure Food, Drug, and Cosmetic Act was passed into law. Enacted as a response to an increasing number of severe poisonings with adulterated or untested products, the Act was introduced by Senator Royal Copeland, MD. The Act recognized the *USP (United States Pharmacopoeia)* and the *HPUS (Homœopathic Pharmacopoeia of the United States)* as the two "official" compendiums. Because of this recognition, homœopathic remedies are considered legal drug products in the United States.

From the 1940s to the 1960s, homœopathy in the United States (at least in the eyes of the FDA) was almost non-existent. The market share homœopathy represented within the total pharmaceutical market was negligible— probably a true "homœopathic dilution"— a 12X of the market (1/1,000,000,000,000 of a part!).

In 1962, the FDA ruled all homœopathic drugs were "prescription only" items, but the ruling was never enforced. There was little effort made by the FDA to take any interest in the industry, especially since the agency was very busy with approving many new drugs, vaccines, and busy with the "side effects" of drugs like Thalidomide.

From the mid–1960s to the 1980s, the FDA regulated homœopathy by a series of "institutional understandings," i.e., agreements reached between the homœopathic pharmaceutical industry and whoever the senior FDA official was at the time. As FDA officials came and went, these "understandings" had to be re-negotiated with each administration.

But even with these "understandings," there were a number of small incursions in enforcement by the state agencies. *Gelsemium* 6X was once taken off the shelf in Pennsylvania because it was deemed "poisonous"; *Apis* was seized in another state because it had "no indications for use" on the label; Arkansas decided that all homœopathic remedies must be prescription only; and several remedies were seized in Louisiana because they were labeled in Latin rather than English.

Furthermore, the morass of bureaucracy was evident everywhere. At one point, a phone call was made by an FDA employee to a teacher of pharmacy at Hahnemann University in Philadelphia. The questions he asked were referred to the Hahnemann Archivist, who referred it to me. I referred it to Jack Borneman who informed the person who asked the questions in the first place that the answer could have come from the FDA Division of Compliance which was three doors away in the same building. One arm did not know what the other was doing.

The reaction to this inconsistent enforcement at the state level culminated in a series of meetings between the FDA and the homœopathic pharmaceutical industry to discuss the problems of regulation.

In the early 1980s homœopathy was beginning its resurgence. New interest was fueled by the advent of the use of homœopathic remedies prescribed via "Electrical Acupuncture Voll" — a technique which used machines measuring "energy flow through the meridians" as a method of determining a suitable remedy. Most of these remedies were being imported from Germany as injectables. When these remedies came through customs they drew the attention of the FDA, because they were injectable products more than because they were "homœopathic." The FDA started to renew its interest in regulating homœopathic remedies.

Another related point was the opening of the United States market to foreign pharmacies. As long as the manufacturing pharmacies were the long-standing native "small" businesses (Boericke and Tafel, Borneman, Ehrhart and Karl, Luyties, Standard, Washington) the FDA seemed happy, but when foreign pharmacies began importing remedies for use by EAV practitioners, United States Customs Service, followed by the FDA, took notice.

A series of meetings, held between 1982 and 1988, with the FDA and an ad hoc committee of the HPCUS (The Homœopathic Pharmacopoeia Convention of the United States) resulted in an agreement with the FDA to establish a new regulatory environment.

The FDA, in effect, recognized the homœopathic pharmaceutical industry's efforts to regulate itself. The industry welcomed the FDA's actions against individuals and companies that falsely applied the label "homœopathic" to their products.

At this time, homœopathic remedies were available without prescription as long as they were at dilutions that were not toxic.

Some remedies— mostly combinations— had prescribing indications on the label (i.e., number 346, "bronchitis,"

The HPCUS

Although Charles Hempel suggested, in 1868, that a committee be formed by the AIH to establish a "Dispensatory," it was not until 1886 that the AIH formed a committee to study the possibility of working with other countries to create a uniform pharmacopoeia.

Boericke and Tafel published a homœopathic pharmacopoeia in 1882, and this book formed the basis for the first official Pharmacopoeia that was published in 1897. Subsequent editions were published in 1901, 1914, 1936, 1938, 1941, 1964, and 1981.

Realizing the importance of producing a homœopathic pharmacopoeia, a committee of the AIH was formed with Wyrth Post Baker as head. Shortly after, Baker formed a group of industry representatives, physicians, and lay persons and incorporated the Homœopathic Pharmacopoeia Convention of the United States in 1980. The purpose of the group was to publish and sell the Pharmacopoeia, and undertake all that was necessary to do so. The original board of directors of the HPCUS was Wyrth Post Baker, MD, Willard Eldredge (from Humphreys Pharmacal), John A. Borneman III, Harris L. Coulter, and Allen Neiswander.

The HPCUS has since evolved into the organization representing homœopathy to the Food and Drug Administration and acts as the intermediary between the industry and the government.

"indications"

In most other countries, legislation governing manufacture and sale of homœopathic remedies specifically prohibits them from being labeled in a manner which indicates they are "for a condition." Generally, the labeling of any product with a "proscribed claim" will require the product being subject to more specific controls.

The EC Directive requires homœopathic medicines be labelled as "homœopathic medicinal product without approved therapeutic indications." If indications are listed it may only be after clinical trials.

If we must use indications, which ones should be used? Obviously, the indication must be for a self-limiting condition. In the case of a remedy like Lachesis, *the description of the symptoms takes up 90 pages in Hering's* Guiding Symptoms. *Do you use the indication "hot flashes in menopause"? Or do you use "sore throat, left side, worse from swallowing liquids"? Or the symptom "Headache from occiput to eyes"?*

What happens when a woman with hot flushes is prescribed Lachesis *and she sees on the label that it is for "sore throats"?*

The homœopathic industry in the United States has recognized this problem. It suggested to the FDA there be three classes of homœopathic products: those needing prescriptions (non-official products and those unsafe at the dilution i.e., Aconite *tincture); those with indications on the labels i.e., combinations for specific symptom complexes— are available on the shelf; and single remedies— to be stored behind the counter and available for the asking (With the legend, "to be used according to standard homœopathic indications"). This last option puts the burden of responsibility on the consumer— if they ask for it, they should know about it.*

The FDA refused to entertain this option since it would create a third class of substances, and faced with the prospect of the absurdity of having to put indications on single remedies or accepting all homœopathic products as prescription only, the industry, in the USA, chose the former option.

etc.). All the others, generally, were simply labeled "To be used according to standard homœopathic indications."

The FDA wanted the remedies to fall into two categories— as do all other drug products: over the counter products (OTC) and prescription only products. To be classified as OTC, the remedy *must* be labeled with an indication that is for a "self-limiting condition." The FDA has a list of 45 self–limiting disease categories. Urinary complaints may be "self–limiting" while bladder or kidney problems are not self–limiting and need a physician's attention.

The final guidelines were read into the *Congressional Record* on May 31, 1988, reaching the final "phase-in" on June 1, 1990.

According to the new *Compliance Guidelines*, a drug may be sold OTC if it is:

- claimed for a condition which is self-limiting
- claimed for a condition which does not require medical diagnosis or monitoring
- non-toxic in the dosage form and package delivered.

A homœopathic drug product not meeting these criteria may be sold only by prescription. For a product to become "official" (i.e., listed in the *HomœopathicPharmacopoeia*) it must have sufficient clinical data or provings to show its homœopathic use.

By 1988 several manufacturing facilities, owned by overseas companies, were operating in the United States. Dolisos (France) had begun its operation in Las Vegas in 1981, Boiron (France) had purchased a substantial share of Borneman in 1982 (absorbing the company in July 1986), VSM (Netherlands— part of the Schwabe Group from Germany) purchased Boericke and Tafel in 1988, and BHI-Heel (Germany) opened a facility in Arizona.

The homœopathic market in the United States is growing. The American Homeopathic Pharmaceutical Association's (AHPhA) estimate of sales for 1997 was $230,000,000 with a growth rate of 12%.

A chart of the relationship between the historic pharmacies in the United States can be found in **Appendix A**, on page 520.

Questionable pharmacy and slick marketing

When Frederick Humphreys sold his first "specific" in 1855 he paved the way for the "allopathsizing" of homœopathy. People wanted the "pill" that would cure their ills.

Since 1855 there have always been homœopathic specifics on the market, but with the public's beginning to accept homœopathy in the 1980s, there came marketing schemes to cash in on the new safe and natural craze.

Several companies promoted "male-enhancers" designed to improve sexual performance. The main ingredient was a potency of *Yohimbinum*. In material doses, this South American plant produces a lasting erection. In theory, a homœopathic dose should be good for taking a persistent erection away (what it can cause it can cure). Even so the products were marketed, generally one step ahead of the FDA enforcement officers.

"Natural Sex" was marketed with the claim that it contained a "sexual enhancer" called *Avena sativa* that has been "known to homœopaths for almost 200 years." According to homœopathic literature, *Avena sativa*, the common oat, is indicated for "functional irregularities" in the male sexual sphere, mostly where there is "general debility, insomnia, inability to keep the mind fixed upon any one subject, etc., more especially when apparently due

An ad for remedies for male sexual disturbances by the Irving Homœopathic Institute in New York City. From the 1892 catalogue.

to nocturnal emissions, masturbation or sexual intercourse."

1985 saw the rise and demise of a multi-level marketing scheme from "HOMERICA… a new business opportunity that is filled with adventure, excitement, and fabulous earning potential…" The marketing plan was simple. You buy remedies that are not succussed. You then succuss them yourself, and sell them back to "Energy Enhancement Centers" who will use the products. "For a few shakes and a small investment, you can be knee deep in dough!" Since this is un–regulated manufacturing of drug products for sale, it was quickly moved upon by the FDA.

There were a number of homœopathic "weight loss" formulas. 1987 saw "Slimco" labeled as "Homeopathic Medicine for weight loss." It contained 15C *Hypothalamus*, *4C Thyroid, 4C Nephrine, 6C Ferrum metallicum* ("a great source of iron to keep you feeling great!") and 6C of *Graphites* ("for the tendency toward obesity"). Advertised as, "Completely safe with no harmful side effects and may be taken for years without interruption," the statement is in bold disregard of homœopathic principles.

Then there was "Slenderage homeopathic weight loss tablets," which contained several ingredients including *Phytolacca* 6C. It had been reported in the old homœopathic literature that the juice of the *Phytolacca* berries was useful for shedding fat, and several older pharmacies (including Washington Homeopathic and Boericke and Tafel) offered *Phytolacca* Berry tablets. But the *Phytolacca* used in the weight loss formula was the homœopathic remedy which is derived from the root of the plant. It shows no symptoms of weight loss in any of the provings.

This advertisement (circa 1925) is but one of many that presage the glut of "quick-fix homœopathic" products that began to come to market in the 1980s.

There was the "Sore throat formula" from an Oregon marketer which was so typical of the quick-fix products being offered to an unsuspecting public under the banner of homœopathy. It contained: *Echinacea* 1X, *Baptisia* 3X, *Belladonna* 3X, *Merc sol* 3X, *Phytolacca* 3X and *Pyrogenium* 30X. All in a "homœopathic fluid."

Anybody who has ever played with mercury knows it will not dissolve in water. According to the *Homœopathic Pharmacopoeia*, mercury must be triturated until the 6X (one part in 10, serially for six times— resulting in a dilution of 1 part in 1,000,000) before it can be dissolved in water or alcohol. How could the product have 3X *Mercury* in a 20% alcohol base? The lowest liquid potency for a product that must be triturated (*Mercurius, Ferrum phos, Silica, Phosphorus*) would be either a 4c or an 8X— the step after converting a trituration to a liquid potency.

1988 saw the first of the homœopathic "diet patches." Advertised as "Appetite Control Patches" they were touted to be "FDA–approved safe method." The reality was that they violated FDA regulations, since trans-dermal application is not an accepted homœopathic delivery method.

One of the diet-patches contained potencies of: *Calcarea, Graphites, Anacardium, Antimonium crudum, Ignatia, Natrum sulphuricum*, plus a grouping of amino acids in potency. The amino acids are not recognized as "official" drug products in the *Homœopathic Pharmacopoeia* and, therefore, not legal for non-prescription sale in homœopathic potencies.

In late 1996 I was shown a "homœopathic medicine" containing 24 different remedies in 69 potencies. I was told the remedy has "great success by lots of people" and it was the "new way" to use homœopathy. It was sold for "deep level 'toxin-specific' homœopathic treatment." The dosage suggested was 10 drops three times a day. It contained:

Cuprum (5 potencies; 12X, 15X, 20X, 30X, 60X), *Formilinum* (3 potencies), *Plumbum* (5 potencies), *Aluminum* (4 potencies), *Amalgam* (4 potencies), *Stannum* (4 potencies), *Aurum* (3 potencies), *Mercurius* (4 potencies), *Cadmium* (4 potencies), *Allium sativa* 1X, *Allium cepa* 1X, *Thiosinaminum* (4 potencies), *Silica* (4 potencies), *Solidago* 1X, *Formic acid* (3 potencies), *Selenium* (3 potencies), *Fagus sylvatica* 2X, *Niccolum* (3 potencies), *Merc corr.* (4 potencies), *Hypericum* 3X, *Apis* 4X, *Belladonna* 4X, *Chelidonium* 1X, and

Berberis vulgaris 1X. It should be noted that of this list, *Amalgam* is not an "official" drug product and, therefore, illegal to sell without a prescription.

The "symptom profile" was: spasms, scar tissue, fatigue, kidney discomfort, headaches, chronic nose obstruction, colds, cramps, convulsions, dry skin, nervous symptoms, insomnia, stress.

What kind of proving symptoms could be elicited from the daily taking of *Aurum* and *Silica?* A cold, fearful person who wants to jump from a window? This is the application of allopathy to homœopathy at its best. There was no attempt at individualization. All the symptoms were general ones, those considered useless in homœopathic prescribing.

If these marketing schemes were not enough to get Hahnemann rolling in his grave, the following was received in a mailing in August 1992:

"Publish your own book in a field where you are the expert. Imagine 'Homeopathic Remedies' by Dr. John or Jane Doe. Your own book, name as author, title, knowledge, expertise, and PROFITS, PROFITS, PROFITS!" A retired doctor would be contracted to write the book for you— for a payment of $7,500. The book was to be written in "easy to understand layman's terms… You can sell the book to other professionals as a reference, at seminars you participate in, through direct mail, as correspondence course materials, or to college instructors teaching homeopathy."

1980 – 1996: The Literature

The rise of new literature
The treasures that were lost

The "five foot shelf"

H. C. Allen's *Keynotes*
T. F. Allen's *Hand Book*
Arndt's *System of Medicine*
Baehr's *Science of Therapeutics*
Bell's *Repertory of Diarrhoea*
Boenninghausen's *Lesser Writings*
Boenninghausen's *Pocket Book*
Boericke's *Materia Medica*
Boger's *Boenninghausen's*
Boger's *Synoptic Key*
Burnett's *New Cure for Consumption*
Carleton's *Medicine and Surgery*
Choudhuri's *Materia Medica*
Clarke's *Dictionary*
Clarke's *Homœopathy Explained*
Close's *Genius of Homœopathy*
Cowperthwaite's *Text-Book*
Dewey's *Therapeutics*
Dudgeon's *Lectures on the Theory*
Dunham's *Science of Therapeutics*
Farrington's *Clinical Materia Medica*
Gentry's *Concordance Repertory*
R. Gibson Miller's *Outlines*
Gross' *Comparative Materia Medica*
Guernsey's *Keynotes to Materia Medica*
Guernsey's *Obstetrics*
Hahnemann's *Chronic Diseases*
Hahnemann's *Lesser Writings*
Hahnemann's *Materia Medica*
Hahnemann's *Organon*
Hering's *Analytical Therapeutics*
Hering's *Condensed Materia Medica*
Hughes' *Manual of Pharmacodynamics*
Jahr's *Forty years' Practice*
Jahr's *Repertory*
Joslin's *Principles*
Kent's *Lectures on Materia Medica*
Kent's *Lesser Writings*
Kent's *Philosophy*
Kent's *Repertory*
Knerr's *Repertory*
Lee and Clark's *Cough and Expectoration*
Lilienthal's *Homoeopathic Therapeutics*
Nash's *Leaders*
Pulford's *Pneumonia*
Raue's *Special Pathology*
Royal's *Textbook*
Schuessler' *Tissue remedies*
Wheeler's *Principles and Practice*
Wheeler's *The Case for Homoeopathy*

Homœopathy exists through its literature. It would be a difficult science if one had to transmit the knowledge only through the spoken word. The books are its life–blood.

In 1931, Dr. Benjamin Woodbury presented a paper to the Connecticut Homœopathic Medical Society titled "The Literary Armamentarium: The books we cannot do without." In the paper he wondered aloud which books one would need to have the "five-foot shelf of classics." Beginning with a listing of over 300 books he narrowed the selection to 55 books— 14 materia medica, 15 books of homœopathic philosophy, 14 repertories, and 12 books about therapeutics. This did not include the ten volumes of Hering's *Guiding Symptoms* nor the 10 volumes of Allen's *Encyclopedia*— of which he said, "no library could be complete without them." The list appears on the left, minus a few books which are no longer in print.

Often, however, the literature was difficult to obtain. We read of Dr. Erastus Case hand-copying Boenninghausen's *Repertory* because he could not locate a copy to purchase. Several books, among them Von Grauvogl's *Textbook of Homœopathy*, were mentioned by Bradford in his *Bibliography* as being rare or in short supply. And as the schools closed and the physicians died, the libraries were often sold as scrap or assigned to the trash.

As the practice of homœopathy dwindled, the availability of its literature also faded. During the 1930s Boericke and Tafel, long a supplier of homœopathic books, began reducing its stock. It was a standard practice for the company to print books but to leave them wrapped, unbound, uncut, and to have 10 or so bound at a time, as needed. When the pharmacy moved from Philadelphia in 1992, the attic was full of unbound books. None of them were real "classics."

Most pharmacies continued to sell small pamphlets about homœopathy and very abridged domestic manuals. Boericke and Tafel continued to sell its "bible," the black–bound *Materia Medica* of William Boericke. Ehrhart and Karl continued to print Kent's *Repertory* into the 1950s.

But few new books were being written, and the old books were difficult to procure. One of those written during this time was the *Home Prescriber* by A. Dwight Smith— a 42-page domestic manual published by Ehrhart and Karl in 1960.

Homœopathic books continued to be written and printed in India by a number of publishers, and Health Science Press in England was still printing the works like Clarke's

Prescriber and Tyler's *Drug Pictures*. Several pamphlets of materia medica by D. M. Gibson were published in England during the 1960s, but little of this material found its way to the United States.

With the reviving interest in homœopathy in the early 1970s several new books became available. Vithoulkas' *Homeopathy: Medicine of the New Man* was published in 1971; *Homeopathic Medicine*, a small book on philosophy by Harris Coulter, was published in 1972; Coulter's *Divided Legacy Volume III* was published in 1973; and Stephenson's *A Doctor's Guide to Helping Yourself with Homeopathic Remedies* was published in 1976.

In 1986, Catherine Coulter wrote *Portraits of Homœopathic Medicines*. This was the first original materia medica material published in the United States since Alfred and Dayton Pulford authored *Graphic Drug Pictures* in 1944.

Within ten years, the market in homœopathic literature bloomed. New repertories were developed (*The Complete, The Synthesis, The Homeopathic Medical Repertory*) and quickly became the standards; Frans Vermeulen (Holland) re-combined several old materia medica standards and gave us several grand reference books; Roger Morrison authored the *Desktop Guide*; Ananda Zaren and George Vithoulkas both authored materia medicas; Paul Herscu gave us invaluable information about children from his clinical practice; Jeremy Sherr (Great Britain) gave the community several provings of remedies that are showing their worth (*Chocolate, Hydrogen, Scorpion, Diamond, Neon, Germanium*); Rajan Sankaran (India) gave us new ways of approaching cases; Jan Scholten (Holland) wrote two materia medica exploring ways of looking at mineral remedies and the periodic table of elements; and Wenda Brewster O'Reilly and Stephen Decker celebrated the 200th anniversary of homœopathy by producing a new and complete English translation of Hahnemann's *Organon*.

A look through catalogs from homœopathic booksellers will show many more volumes— transcriptions of seminars, re-prints of older books, and any number of basic books explaining homœopathy.

One bookseller who began his business in 1988 with 75 titles, has, in 1997, more than 800 titles on homœopathy in his catalog.

Homœopathy is back in print!

Frans Vermeulen

Jan Scholten

Catherine R. Coulter
January 21, 1934 —

A graduate of Columbia University, Coulter first became interested in homœopathy in 1960 while she and her husband were vacationing in France. On a recommendation, she sought out a homœopath for relief from her allergies. The homœopath told her to return the next day after he studied the case. When she returned, he gave her a number of remedies to take (he was obviously not a unicist prescriber!) and told her he had consulted with a great homœopath, Dr. Kent, in the United States about her case. She was impressed with his diligence.

When it came time for her to return to the United States, she asked about finding Dr. Kent. "Oh no," said the doctor, "Dr. Kent's been dead since 1916!"

Upon her return, she found Elizabeth Wright Hubbard lived just around the corner from her home. However, Dr. Hubbard was not about to speak to a lay–person about homœopathy. In the early 1960s there were few books available on the subject, but Hubbard's secretary told Coulter about the Boericke *Materia Medica*. She obtained a copy. "I read it at night, in bed, and at any other spare moment I had," she said.

She began to treat her immediate family with homœopathy, and then began helping friends.

About six years later, she was able to obtain a used copy of the 10 volumes of Hering's *Guiding Symptoms*, and began to study it in the same depth she had done with Boericke's book. "I still had never heard of Kent's *Repertory*, or even seen one." she commented. "I finally got a copy of it about three years after I got the Hering set."

In the early 1970s she met David Wember and several other young medical doctors who were learning homœopathy. Recognizing her mastery of materia medica, they asked her to guide them in their studies.

In 1977 Coulter was invited to spend two months at the Hering Clinic in Berkeley, California, where she delivered a series of lectures on materia medica. In 1978, a sudden vacancy in the staff at the NCH course at Millersville found her teaching materia medica in the professional course. During the next 11 years she honed her lectures and finally formalized them in her first volume of *Portraits of Homœopathic Medicines*.

Catherine Coulter with Hering's Lachesis

She has served as a preceptor for an endless stream of physicians, under whose aegis she can practice.

"You learn everything from patients," she said. "I find I have a difficult time learning anything from reading cases in the old journals. They are interesting, but they aren't *my* cases. Homœopathy is a very simple idea. The difficulty is in its implementation. You can't learn it unless you practice it and see the remedy pictures in the patients. That is what my books are about."

Catherine Coulter lives in Arlington, Massachusetts and continues to preceptor physicians.

Some personal notes...

I first met Catherine Coulter when I took the National Center's course at Millersville in 1980. Every morning, for two weeks, we were treated to an amazing lecture about a single remedy (*Natrum muriaticum* took two mornings...). Her rapid fire delivery had those present begging her to slow down. She didn't. When her first book came out, I was thrilled to know that I had heard it in person.

Catherine came from the "era between." On one side were the old-guard— Elizabeth Wright Hubbard, Julia M. Green, Arthur Grimmer— all dying in the 1960s. They were followed by those who are now the elders— Maisie Panos, Henry Williams, Allen Neiswander— who had learned homœopathy in the late 1940s and early 1950s.

Then there was a gap before the new generation— Gray, Wember, Moskowitz, Chase, etc. began practicing in the mid-1970s. Catherine Coulter and James Stephenson are among the few who discovered homœopathy in the 1960s. And Coulter is the one who taught the next generation.

Coulter is truly amazing because she is completely self-taught. "One can teach oneself anything by reading," she told me, "and only a very few books are needed." That's how she taught herself homœopathy at a time when the doctors wouldn't talk to lay people, and no new doctors were coming on the scene.

She learned her homœopathy from Boericke's *Materia Medica* ("a work of genius"), Hering's *Guiding Symptoms*, Boger's *Synoptic Key*, and from seeing people in practice and figuring out the remedies needed.

A visit to Lachesis

In 1989, Catherine Coulter, David Wember, and I went to pay homage to Hering's original Lachesis snake at the Museum of Natural Sciences in Philadelphia. The snake, along with a large collection of insects and plants from South America, was donated to the Museum by Dr. Hering. The herpetologist at the museum knew nothing of Hering's connection to Hahnemann Hospital— only that there are many items in the South American collection which bear Hering's name.

The snake was taken from the bottle of alcohol in which it is stored, and stretched out upon the table. It was a bit over six feet long. The bullet hole in its head was clearly visible ("After I milked the venom I dispatched it," wrote Hering).

The three of us were like kids in a candy store. In the same room as the original Lachesis!

"forbidden desire"

Catherine was flying somewhere at the time her second volume of Portraits *was about to be released. The woman at the airline ticket counter looked at her ticket and asked if she was a writer. Catherine said she was. "Oh!," said the woman, "I just read your new book and I loved it!" Catherine was baffled, as her book was not yet released, and the ticket agent did not seem to be a type deeply into homœopathy. Further discussion revealed that the ticket agent thought she was "Catherine Coulter"— the author of such great romance novels as* Calypso Magic *("in the heat of the tropics, she surrendered to forbidden desire..."). As Catherine says, "That is why I am Catherine <u>R.</u> Coulter!"*

Her understanding of materia medica developed through her practice, which gave her the insights she shares in her books.

"I began to see patterns," she said. "You must see enough cases to notice how the *Natrum muriaticum* patients have that quality— where their whole face changes when they smile. Then when you see that in a case, you start to think about *Nat mur.*"

Her role as a preceptor is simply to empower and build confidence.

"I've seen so many people who learn a bit and then think they must know more to practice. So they go to seminar after seminar trying to get that 'knowledge' that will help them practice. The only way to learn homœopathy is to sit down and practice it— not in theory. You learn from the patients, not from lectures. 98% of the cases you will see can be understood with just the three books: Boericke, Kent's *Repertory,* and Boger."

The treasures that were lost

A while ago, someone asked me for some figures about the homœopathic success with the flu epidemic of 1918. I gave them the information quoted earlier in this book. They asked if any of the original data, from which these figures were derived, still existed. Unfortunately it does not.

Much of the information Kent used in his *Repertory* was derived from the work of E. J. Lee, who in turn received clinical verifications from several people including Edward Rushmore, MD (who supplied more than 300 pages of information), S. A. Kimball, MD (who transcribed additions from Wesselhoeft's personal repertory), and Edward W. Berridge, MD (from the UK).

Where is the information now? We can see the result in the *Repertory,* but that is one step removed from the source. What happened to Kent's papers? What happened to Kent's library?

The fate of some old journals is related by Allen C. Cowperthwaite, MD, in a letter to James William Ward dated March 26, 1918. Ward had asked Cowperthwaite about some bound *Transactions,* to which Cowperthwaite replied:

> I have had a somewhat unfavorable experience in regard to medical journals. For over forty years I carefully filed and had bound all my journals. I must have had nearly a thousand volumes including many like the old "Medical Investigator" that have long since been out of existence. I had an Index Rerum made at great expense, of all the articles on Materia Medica that appeared in these volumes. Sometime before leaving Chicago, I presented these books and about 100 volumes of other medical books to the library of Hahnemann Medical College of Chicago. I considered them a very valuable acquisition. Since coming to the Coast, I have learned from reliable authority that the whole lot of books were sold to a Junk Dealer. You can imagine how I felt to have these accumulations of a life-time sold for waste paper.

While sorting through NCH files, I came upon a folder labeled "library bequests." The contents reveal another piece of the history that was a casualty of "the unpleasantness."

On October 28, 1947, Grace Stevens, MD, in Northampton, Massachusetts, wrote to the American Foundation for Homœopathy: "Plumb Brown [a homœopath in Springfield, Massachusetts] left his books to the Wesson Memorial Hospital in Springfield, MA— where they are not wanted. I am afraid they will be thrown away."

The Wesson Hospital was founded by Daniel Wesson, an ardent homœopathic supporter and founder of the arms company, Smith & Wesson. The reply from Robert Ferry Hovey, MD, was shocking:

"I went to the hospital and found the books have been disposed of already. Dr. Stevens placed great value on these books and told me they should all be saved… Our hospital has had several sets of books left. The library space is limited and they wish to keep up with modern literature— so all the old books are destroyed. I am sorry I failed to send all these books to you." This was a typical story of the times.

As the older physicians began to die, Dr. Julia M. Green's house in Washington, DC, became a repository for the libraries of many of these great practitioners. By 1954, Dr. Green wrote that her "basement was crammed full," and when she died in 1963, her basement was still full of books.

At this point the history becomes a bit fuzzy. Julia Green kept meticulous records of her correspondence.

arms and homœopathy

Daniel Wesson was not the only arms-maker who supported homœopathy. Samuel Colt (1814-1862), the inventor of the Colt Revolver, and a prominent citizen of Hartford, Connecticut, used a homœopathic physician. In Colt's "final illness" his wife writes, "… his friend and physician, Dr. John F. Gray, of New York, was telegraphed to come at once."

John F. Gray was, as we know, the second homœopath in New York after Gram.

The Indians

Homœopathy was planted in India in the mid-1830s by John Martin Honigberger, and it took off like a duck takes to water. There could be many theories as to why this happened, but the fact remains that during the later part of the 19th century and the early part of the 20th century, a fair number of Indians came to the United States to learn homœopathy from Allen and Kent.

While homœopathy declined in the United States, it remained vibrant and alive in India, breeding practitioners who authored many books— Phatak, Sankaran, Dhawle, Banerjee, Chatterjee, Chitkara, Choudhuri, Farokh Master, Kamthan, Bose, Mathur, Shinghal, Patel, Fayazuddin, to name a few. A number of printing houses came into existence to publish these works— Roy and Co. in Bombay, Jain and Aggarwal in New Delhi, and Sett Dey in Calcutta— and have been publishing homœopathic books since the 1930s.

Most of the classic homœopathic literature is available only from the Indian publishers. Although the quality of the binding and paper is often poor, the prices can't be beaten. While original copies of Hahnemann's Lesser Writings *are rarely found and will fetch over $300 when available, the Indian edition is available for just $12.00.*

Aside from the printing of the old literature, the clinical experiences imparted by the Indian authors in their works are a mine of treasures.

After her death the paperwork gets a bit thin, so my information comes from people who were there at the time. Some time later, probably in about 1964 or 1965, Harris Coulter spent about two months sorting the books in Dr. Green's basement. When finished, he kept two of each edition for the American Foundation library, and packed the rest of the books for sale. He delivered them to a bookstore in New York City, but, as he told me, it was the late 1960s and no one was interested in homœopathy. He eventually retrieved them from New York, and stored them in the basement of Ralph Packman's house in Philadelphia. Some were bought by the new National Library of Medicine in Bethesda, Maryland.

In 1974 or so, Coulter contacted a few people he knew interested in purchasing homœopathic books. They came to Philadelphia and bought the books for a dollar a copy.

When I visited the American Foundation library in Falls Church, Virginia in 1980, I saw shelves filled with books and journals. They still had many duplicates, and I was told if they had three of an identical volume they would sell the one in the poorest condition. I was able to buy a number of these books at that time. I was not familiar with the homœopathic journals, but Richard Moskowitz recalls "eyeballing several shelves" of homœopathic journals on a visit to the office during that time.

After the American Foundation and the National Center split, the library remained at the offices of The Homeopathic Headquarters of America in Falls Church. By the spring of 1982, Harris Coulter had left the organization, and with him went his watchful eye on the library. In May of 1982, *American Homeopathy* reported that Dr. Keller, from Germany, found (and used for research) a complete set of *International Hahnemannian Association Transactions* at the headquarters.

By March 1983, the American Foundation moved to California, the library was packed, the building sold, and the United States Homeopathic Association took over the existing membership organization.

In April 1983, the National Center and the American Foundation reached an agreement under which the AFH library would be given in trust to the NCH.

These books are now housed in the Maesimund Banning Panos Library in the NCH offices in Alexandria, Virginia.

In looking through the AFH records in 1992, I found that a large number of books donated to the AFH are no longer in the NCH library. Some were, undoubtedly, sold in the early 1970s. Others (among them all of the homœopathic journals) disappeared between January 1981 and the time the library was received by the NCH in 1983.

To give some idea of the quantities we are talking about:
• Grace Stevens, MD, bequeathed all her books— 152 volumes. Only four remain in the NCH Library.
• Hahnemann Medical College in Philadelphia sent a new set of Hering's *Guiding Symptoms* and all its homœopathic journals: *Homœopathic Observer, North American Journal of Homœopathy, Medical Advance, Medical Investigator.* None remain.
• Benjamin Woodbury's library— eight large boxes were received. Only 30 books of Woodbury's are in the Library.
• The Grosvenor Library in Buffalo was discarding its homœopathic books. The AFH received 100 books. Only six books are in the library.
• Margaret Burgess Webster, MD, sent her complete library— three cartons. Only one of her books is in the Library.
• Dr. Griggs sent all of his *Homœopathic Recorders.* The NCH has none of his books in the Library.
• Garth Boericke, MD, had all of Dr. Rudolph Rabe's library in his basement— 16 cartons. He donated them to the AFH. The NCH has no books belonging to Rudolph Rabe.
• H. Leslie Fry, MD, sent 118 books. The NCH has 25 books belonging to Dr. Fry.
• Warren Bradbury of Randolph Center, Vermont, sent the following to Julia M. Green: *Medical Advance* 04-09; *American Homœopathist* 97-01; *Clinique* 02-06; *American Journal of Surgery* 07-10; *Medical Century* 1900. The NCH has none of these journals.
• R. S. Faris, MD, Richmond, Virginia, sent bound *IHA Transactions* 40-46; bound *Journal of Homœopathics* 1-4; *Critique* 05-07; *Medical Advance* 06-11. The NCH has none of these journals.

Between the spring of 1982 and the spring of 1983 almost all the old journals held at the library in Falls Church disappeared. I know of one occasion where several boxes of *AIH Transactions* were found on the sidewalk outside the offices. When the person who found them inquired about them, he was told they were old journals and had all been microfilmed. He took them home. They eventually found their way to me, and then back to the National Center. No one I have spoken to (Packman, Coulter, Zack) recalled ever having any journals microfilmed except *The Layman Speaks*.

In the one year between 1982 and 1983, a large portion of our homœopathic history went missing.

If anyone reading this book has ANY volumes belonging to any of the people listed, PLEASE let me know. Several people and I are working on developing a database of all known books that had belonged to the older homœopaths. It would be good to know that these books have found their way into good hands and are still extant.

1980 – 1996: The Electronic Age

The personal computer
Information exchange

The personal computer and data sorting

With the amount of information to be sorted and related in a well-taken homœopathic case, it is only logical that a systematic way of searching through the mass of information contained in the materia medica be developed.

The first step was an "index" to the symptoms in the materia medica. Although Hahnemann had several ideas for such an index, it was Boenninghausen who developed the first index, or repertory.

After 1900, several ideas were implemented to bring the information in the repertory into a form that could be manipulated— where the information in the rubrics could be extracted and synthesized. Most of the ideas were in the form of punch card repertories. Tyler developed a set of cards in 1912. Dr. Richard Field developed a huge (6,460 cards in a four-drawer cabinet) card repertory in 1922. Dr. Marcos Jimenez (Mexico) developed a card repertory in 1925. Boger developed his punch cards in 1931. Robert Farley, MD, developed a card repertory in 1950, P. Sankaran (India) did a 389–card repertory in the mid-1960s, about the same time Dr. Flury (Switzerland) did a card repertory.

A card from the Farley
Card Repertory

180   G   URINE SUPPRESSED

PUNCH CARD SPINDLE REPERTORY OF THE HOMEOPATHIC MATERIA MEDICA.
COMPILED BY ROBERT H FARLEY, M. D.
SPINDLE IDEA CONTRIBUTED BY JOSEPH G WEISS, M. D.

ABBREVIATIONS ARE LIMITED TO FOUR LETTERS. COMPOUND WORDS AS AMMONIUM MURIATICUM WILL SHOW A CAPITAL LETTER FOR EACH PORTION OF WORD - AM-M.
MERC AS USUAL FOR MERCURIUS: MERC FOR MERC. CORROSIVUS:
MRIF FOR MERC. IOD. FL., ETC.
ACID IS ABBREVIATED WITH A CAPITAL X, AS MURX FOR MURIATIC ACID: MURX FOR MUREX
SOME WELL KNOWN ABBREVIATIONS WILL SEEM DISTORTED, I. E

STRM - STRAMONIUM
STRN - STRONTIUM
SLPH - SULPHUR
TRAX - TARAXACUM
TRNT - TRANTULA
ANRX - ANTHRACINUM
COLC - COLOCYNTHIS
CRBA - CARBO-ANIMALIS
CRTC - CROTALUS CASCAVELLA
LYCV - LYCOPUS VIRG.
CLCA - CALCAREA ARS.

PACK   SYMPTOM

Printed in U.S.A.   REMINGTON RAND   P-17556

Jugal Kishore (India) did a large set of cards in 1959 (3497 cards, 8869 for the second edition in 1967); Dr. George Broussalian translated Kent's *Repertory* to 1861 cards in 1969 (France); and Hans Leer (Germany) did a 3,000–card repertory in about 1975.

Anyone who has ever looked at a repertory (which is simply, as Hahnemann conceived, an index to the materia medica) can understand it is a prime candidate for being accessed through a computer program. It was not until the mid–1980s and the development of personal computers, that several people, almost simultaneously, began developing computer repertories. The first program was a very simple one called *Lamnia* developed in Australia. It used a very abbreviated repertory based on Kent's work.

As the conception of the computer-assisted repertory developed, three main programs gained prominence: *MacRepertory, RADAR,* and *CARA.* There are others which, though not as "full-featured," are used by many. Among them are *Homeopathy@Work, Homeopathic Assistant, PC Kent* (an outgrowth of the Broussalian card repertory), *Polycrest,* and *Hompath.*

An obvious outgrowth of entering all the information from a known repertory (such as Kent's) into a computer data base, is that additions can be made to the data base which can *then* serve as a source for a new printed repertory.

In the 1990s two new repertories were produced and have become the standard of the profession. *The Synthesis Repertory,* edited by Frederick Schroyens of Belgium, grew from additions made to the *RADAR Computer Repertory* program.

The Complete Repertory, edited by Roger van Zandvoort of the Netherlands, grew from additions that were made to *MacRepertory—* a Macintosh–based computer repertory.

MacRepertory and ReferenceWorks

David Warkentin, PA
August 20, 1951 —

David Kent Warkentin

Warkentin was introduced to homœopathy through the California group, having attended the Esalen seminar in 1980. He received his Physician Assistant degree in 1985 and studied homœopathy with Bill Gray.

Warkentin was working at the Hahnemann Clinic when he bought his first Macintosh computer.

Says Warkentin: "My major in college was Computer Science which left me with a deep dislike for computers and the way that they depersonalize everything they touch. I had never intended to touch a computer again. Then while I was teaching at the Hahnemann Clinic I had to type up my notes. My manual, non-correcting typewriter wasn't making it and a friend lent me his brand new Macintosh 128. I was blown away with how easy and fun it was. It was obvious to everyone that repertorizing was begging to become faster and it was perfectly suited to the computer. There were a few homœopathic programs already in the world but they were very unfriendly and ugly, so I started playing, imagining how one could model the therapy in the computer so that it felt familiar and enjoyable; so that the computer became more human/real-world instead of people having to become computerized. The response to my simple designs was *very* enthusiastic and the next thing I knew I hired a programmer to realize them."

Warkentin's "test team" were his colleagues at the Hahnemann Clinic. He never intended the effort to turn into a business. He figured when he sold 50 programs (and got back his development outlay) he'd call it quits.

"I had no idea of how to find a programmer, but one day I was borrowing a kayak from a friend of a friend. He mentioned he was a programmer; I mentioned that I was looking for a Macintosh programmer (very unusual at that time) who could write a database/outlining program like *ThinkTank*. The friend replied he was indeed a Macintosh programmer and had just finished a version of *ThinkTank* for the Atari!" And so David met Mike Hourigan.

Mike originally scanned everything in ("A big mistake," says Warkentin) but found so many errors that the data had to be re-entered by hand. The program's "look" was all David's conception. The beta test version was released in early 1986, and the program started selling, officially, in the fall of 1986.

"Those days were a wonderful time for me. There was so much enthusiasm for what we'd made. I remember going to Holland and showing the program to 21 doctors. It was a rather stern quiet group and I wasn't sure if they were excited by what they were seeing— they didn't smile, didn't move, it was very quiet. When I finished there was tremendous clapping and in the end 18 of the 21 bought the program and went out and bought computers. When I go to seminars now, it is gratifying to see so many Macintoshes. I know that homœopathy is now about 90% Macintosh because of our program. "

In 1990, Warkentin released *ReferenceWorks*— a searchable database of materia medica. Again, all the information was entered by hand. The programmer, again, was Mike Hourigan. Says Warkentin: "I think a lot about what is the appropriate use of the computer; why is it here now in homœopathy. It has a danger built in that it will make prescribing more mechanical and heartless; that the mystery will be stripped out. Yet I can feel that it also has the potential to move the therapy to a new level.

"So, why do we even have a repertory? Because the

The MacRepertory selection screen. Each icon represents a chapter in the repertory. The icons on the left select the different "clipboards" in which the rubrics can be placed, different analysis strategies, and a "key" for selecting "Keynote files."

materia medica and provings are just too difficult to remember. Is it a perfect tool? Not at all. The grades are inconsistent and mostly work only for polychrests, it is terribly incomplete and the symptoms have been robbed of their picture. But things are different now. We have a tool that can remember all of the materia medica and use it directly to analyze cases. We can really match an individual patient to an individual prover or cured case. Thus we created *Reference Works*.

"Actually my dream is that we will no longer use a repertory in a few years— I think that the repertory has done a lot of harm to homœopathy and is best left in the past…"

MacRepertory "Analysis" window. The rubrics are at the left, the remedies are graphed to the right.

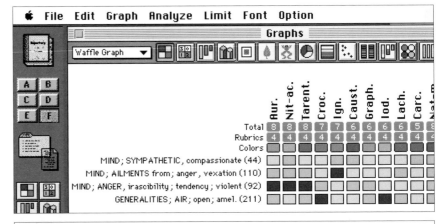

The *Reference Works* window. In this example, the search was for the word "dreams" in the same sentence as "dogs."

The search yielded 141 references (in the 190 books), and 41 different remedies.

The first reference is found in Hughes' *Pathogenesy* under *Abrotanum*. The entire reference is readable in the bottom window.

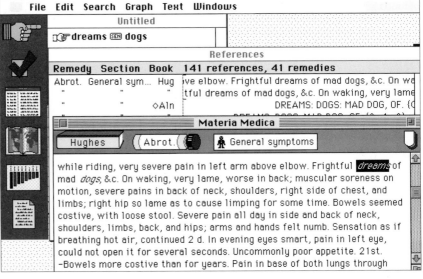

Roger van Zandvoort
November 30, 1958 —

Van Zandvoort was born in Heerlen, Netherlands. After a stint in the army, he went to naturopathic school and became interested in herbalism and later homœopathy. He bought the *MacRepertory* program in 1987 to help in his practice. He began adding remedies and rubrics to *MacRepertory* from the common sources— Kent's *Materia Medica*, Hahnemann's *Materia Medica Pura*, *The Synthetic Repertory* of Barthels and Klunker.

David Warkentin saw the work, liked it, and van Zandvoort agreed to publish it. Van Zandvoort now has worked with a team of about 50 people to cull the information needed to produce the *Complete Repertory*. It was released in print in 1996— a massive book of 2800 pages. The computer version is *Complete* 4.5 and is available on both *MacRepertory* and CARA.

CARA (Computer Assisted Repertorial Analysis)

David Witko
August 10, 1953 —

In 1982, Witko was working in London as a computer software designer for a major retail bank. He developed a personal interest in homœopathy and started attending public lectures and seminars to gain more knowledge.

At a meeting of the Hahnemann Society, Witko heard Michael Jenkins, from the Royal London Homœopathic Hospital, lecture about new developments in homœopathy. One of these new developments was the imminent availability of low cost personal computers. Witko's interest was immediately fired and he discussed this matter with Jenkins. Shortly thereafter Jenkins and Witko started a project at the Royal London Homœopathic Hospital to design and build a computer software program to allow homœopaths easier access to the repertory.

The program, running on MS-DOS, was given the name CARA, an acronym for "Computer Assisted Repertory Analysis." Considerable effort was spent adding repertory data from Kent's *Repertory* into the system and hospital

volunteers spent long hours keying in data.

In 1986, Witko moved away from London and the project effectively stopped. At the time only a small portion of the Kent *Repertory* was actually input. The Royal London Homœopathic Hospital became discouraged with the amount of time and effort required to complete the program, and ceased its involvement. Witko kept working on CARA and it was first released as a product in 1988.

In 1991 Witko decided to create a software program to run under the *Windows* platform. He approached John Stevenson, an experienced software engineer, to jointly develop the program. The program was released in 1992, with version 2 released in 1995, including the *Complete Repertory* and Murphy's *Homeopathic Medical Repertory*.

The CARA selection screen. Each icon represents a chapter in the repertory.

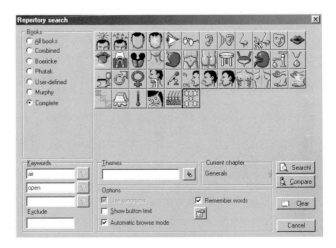

CARA "Analysis" window. The rubrics are at the left, the remedies are graphed to the right.

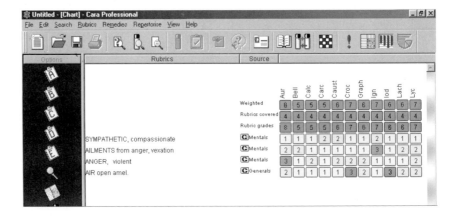

RADAR (Rapid Aid in Direct Access to Repertorization)

The RADAR program began with assistance from the Department of Computer Information at the University of Namur in Belgium. A mathematics professor, Jean Fichefet, whose son was cured by homœopathy, became intrigued with the amount of information a working homœopath needed to access in all the books.

He took on the project as an exercise in data retrieval. When first introduced in the United States in 1987 it was sold for $12,000— included the hardware (an IBM platform). It originally included a choice of Kent's *Repertory* or the *Synthetic Repertory* of Barthels and Klunker, as well as the text of Hahnemann's, Allen's, Hering's, and Clarke's *Materia Medicas*.

It is (in 1997) available for both IBM and Macintosh platforms. The resident repertory is the *Synthesis*. The *Materia Medicas* are available as a separate program called "ExLibris."

Frederik Schroyens, MD
January 12, 1953 —

Schroyens is a 1977 medical graduate of the State University of Ghent (Belgium) and a 1978 graduate of the one-year Homœopathic Training Course at the Faculty for Homœopathy in London (MFHom). In 1981 Schroyens became the president of VSU, the largest homœopathic school in Belgium.

One of the earliest RADAR users in 1986, Schroyens became the homœopathic coordinator of the RADAR project soon afterwards. In 1987 Schroyens was the main link between Vithoulkas and the programming team at the University of Namur during the development of the Vithoulkas Expert System— an algorithm duplicating Vithoulkas' "thought process" which suggests possible remedies for the case at hand.

Culling the homœopathic literature for repertory additions, Schroyens and a team of homœopaths corrected the Kent *Repertory,* incorporating a number of additions in the RADAR program.

491

In 1993 Schroyens edited a printed version of *Synthesis,* the expanded *Repertory* linked to the RADAR project. A computer version of *Synthesis* exists in seven languages. Translations into various other languages are ongoing. Since 1995, several books based on *Synthesis* have been published in several languages, such as *1001 Small Remedies* and *Arzneimittelbilder von Gemüt und Traume.*

The RADAR selection screen. Each icon represents a chapter in the repertory. The icons on the left select the different "clipboards" in which the rubrics can be placed. A "key" is for selecting "Keynote files."

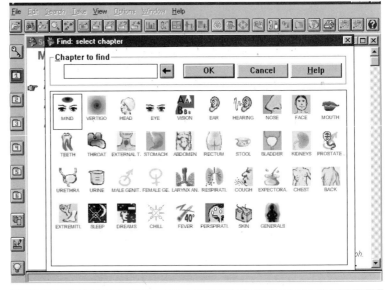

RADAR "Analysis" window. The rubrics are listed in the top window, the remedies for the rubrics, are displayed in the bottom window.

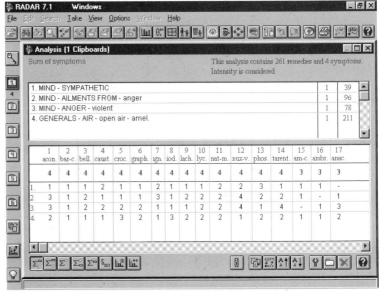

The personal computer and information exchange

In 1986, David Warkentin, working with the Tides Foundation and the Association for Progressive Computing (APC), established a "homœopathic network" called *HomeoNet*. Using the developing technology of e-mail and the expanding global Internet, *HomeoNet* was intended to link the homœopathic community throughout the world. Shortly after *HomeoNet* was formed several people created the first HANP exam. With questions being mailed back and forth between the writers, a project that would have taken several months using regular mail, took just a few weeks. It was a great beginning.

But not many people understood the advantages of such communication, and still more were computer phobic. Although more than 200 people had signed up with *HomeoNet,* only about 20 became regular users.

In 1987 I received a postal letter from someone who I knew was also on the net. I sent an e-mail reply that day. Two weeks later, I received a phone call asking me if I received the letter and why had I not replied. I said I had sent an e-mail reply. "Oh," said the caller, "I never check that."

By the early 1990s the personal computer was becoming commonplace. As more people became acquainted with the personal computer, access to the "world wide web" became less threatening. The computer interfaces changed drastically with the advent of the Macintosh computer and then with the introduction of a similar interface, *Windows,* for IBM–based computers.

With increasing access, Internet providers flourished.

Access to *HomeoNet,* meanwhile, was still limited to those who could access the APC network. The combination of access limitations plus the burgeoning supply of Internet providers and users, reached a "turning point" in the homeopathic community.

The next move came from the UK. In December 1994, Jon Haworth, a barrister in England with an interest in homœopathy (his wife was attending a homœopathic college), set up an unmoderated mail–list for people interested in homœopathy.

Originally serviced by the provider "dungeon.com," the "dungeon" mail–list slowly became larger. In April 1996

Just a few years ago…

In 1939, my father visited his cousin who was working at MIT. His cousin took him to a room that was filled with wires, vacuum tubes, motors, and fans. At one end was a typewriter. It was a very early computer that could do simple math. My father asked if it could ever get smaller and was told it MIGHT get to be "desk size" eventually.

In 1982, I bought my first PC. It was an Osborne. It was portable. It was the size of a small suitcase. I showed it to a friend. She told me that when she was working at IBM in the early 1970s, they were struggling to get 9K of memory in something the size of a desk. Now I was carrying something with 64K of memory. It needed floppy disks to operate. Each disk held 180K.

In 1986 I bought my first Macintosh. It had 1000K (1MB) of memory. It had a 20MB disk drive. I was thrilled.

As I write this I am working on a machine no larger than a thick pad of paper. It has 24MB of memory. It has an internal hard drive with 1.4GB of space. It has ReferenceWorks installed— the text of 190 books.

Life is grand!

the provider changed to "lyghtforce.com." With the growth of electronic communications, the "lyghtforce" computer is in Texas, the mailing list is managed by Jon (now a judge), in the UK, and the messages are received by people in 41 countries— from Canada to South Africa, from Pakistan to the Netherlands, from the USA to New Zealand.

As of December 1998, the lyghtforce mailing list had more than 1400 subscribers.

April 1996 also saw the introduction of *Homeopathy Online*, the first electronic media magazine about homeopathy. It was edited by Dr. Christian Kurz, PhD.

A search (in December 1998) of the "world wide web" for the word "homeopathy" (using <www.yahoo.com> uncovered 97 web–pages now devoted to the subject.

The first page of the first issue of *Homeopathy Online*.

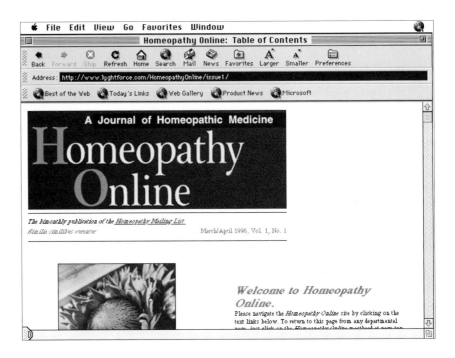

Epilogue

The move for certification
Issues for the future

The move for certification

The 1992 July/August issue of *Homeopathy Today* contained a lengthy article about the need to establish standards of practice.

In a long letter, Edward Chapman, MD, discussed the effort of the newly–formed Council for Homeopathic Certification to establish a "certification of competency in homeopathy" for *all* health care providers. Chapman urged the community to understand the differences between a "certification" (which establishes qualification in a skill) and "licensure" (which is controlled by the state).

The Council for Homeopathic Certification (CHC) grew out of the desire to establish an across-the-board certification to set a standard of competency in homœopathy, regardless of licensure. The certification is available to both medically trained and non-medically trained practitioners. The certification does not hold any legal weight regarding practice— it simply certifies the person has passed an exam and has met a standard in homœopathic knowledge, skill, and competence.

The CHC had its first formal meeting in September 1991 in San Francisco. Present at the meeting were Harry Swope, ND, DHANP; Durr Elmore, ND, DHANP, DC; Richard Pitt, RSHom; Peggy Chipkin, RN, FNP; Stephen Messer, ND, DHANP; Joanna Daly, RSHom; Peter Borregard, DC; Randall Neustaedter, LAc OMD; and David Warkentin, PA.

From that meeting a board was formed, with Harry Swope as president. In 1998 there are 175 people holding the "CCH" (Certified Classical Homeopath) designation. Of the group, 33 were naturopaths and 12 were MDs.

The North American Society of Homeopaths (NASH) was founded in 1990 by Lou Klein, Eric Sommeman, and Valerie Ohanian. They saw the need for an organization to help unify and support non–licensed professional homœopaths. The organization was modeled after the Society of Homœopaths in the UK. NASH maintains informal ties with the SOH and offers an exam leading to registration, the "Registered with the Society of Homeopaths" [RSHom(NA)]. In December 1998, NASH has 60 registered members.

The Smithsonian Exhibit

When the Smithsonian Institution was assembling material for its "Centennial" Building in 1975, it looked through the catalog of the 1876 Centennial Exposition in Philadelphia to see who had exhibited and if, by chance, any of the businesses still survived.

Boericke and Tafel had exhibited at the 1876 Exposition, after which the company moved the large exhibit to its store at 1011 Arch Street in Philadelphia. There it sat until the Smithsonian asked if it could have it.

The large carved mahogany display cabinet was dis-assembled, moved to Washington DC, and lovingly restored to its original condition. It is now housed in the Centennial Hall.

It contains a number of books that B&T printed, cardboard cylinders (black with gold labels) that held tincture bottles, a selection of bottles, corks, mortars and pestles, and other paraphernalia of the homœopathic trade. It is topped by a bronze bust of Samuel Hahnemann. The two white "columns" on either side of the display are made of glass tubes— each filled with a different size of homœopathic sucrose granules.

The author at the Smithsonian Exhibit

Issues for the Future

In 1963, the historian Lewis Mumford was asked if he would like to revise the text of his book, *Technics and Civilization*, first printed in 1934. In the book, Mumford traced the history of technology and its influence to the present day.

Mumford, in reply said, in a new introduction, that he would rather leave the book as it was— 1963 was too close to 1934 to really understand the meaning of what was happening at the present time. He said, "So, though the technical history of the last thirty years is lacking in this survey, the basic insights necessary for interpreting these events and their consequences actually pervades the whole book. Hence my readiness to sanction this unrevised text."

Can I do less? I have often been asked, "Where do you see homœopathy going?" and I really can't answer that. In the context of the United States, could we, in 1992, think that within a year of George Guess being forced to move from North Carolina to maintain his homœopathic practice, that a Freedom of Medical Practice Act would be passed in that very state?

In 1995 George Vithoulkas produced a journal— *The European Journal of Classical Homeopathy*. In the first issue he offered an editorial attacking the work of Rajan Sankaran and suggesting the downfall of homœopathy will be due to a "number of 'artistic distortions' that are injected into the main body of knowledge by the 'imaginations' and 'projections' of some 'teachers' of Homœopathy," and that the teaching of Sankaran falls in this category.

When a reply to the article suggested that Vithoulkas himself might do with "a bit more modesty," Vithoulkas replied that "people who state with presence what they think is right, usually are not liked and frequently hated by others." The criticism devolved, as one writer said, into "pure condescension and vitriol."

I found myself looking back at the debate when the second issue of the same journal contained an article about the "paranoid side of *Veratrum album*."

Should I comment further on this? I think not. As with Mumford, we are too close to see the ultimate resolution. I can visualize ways in which the "imaginative" works of Sankaran and Scholten— the stuff "pushing the envelope" in homœopathic thinking— can become integrated within conventional homœopathic practice, just as Vithoulkas' "essences" which pushed the envelope just 20 years ago have been modified and integrated into general thinking.

But we are too close to it. The eventual resolve will not come from the personalities, but from people who integrate the information and practice it.

The correctness or falsity of the doctrine (and of any other "edge") will be shown in the successes or failures in practice. That which works will remain. And it is for someone else— in 40 years— to write about it.

In 1981–1982 I took a year–long sabbatical from teaching at the University of the Arts in Philadelphia.

I was wanting to take time off and explore the idea of pursuing homœopathy and medicine as a career. I obtained the mailing list of the National Center and called on people in every place I was going to be. There were pockets of study groups over the whole country, and they all felt as if the National Center had forgotten them. I visited them all. I talked with them about what the NCH was doing, and gave them an overview of homœopathy in the USA as I was finding it. I met with people who were on both sides of the "great unpleasantness." I had come to the NCH in the aftermath and knew none of the personalities. It was an eye–opening six months. When I returned, I summarized my findings to the NCH Board of Directors in a 45–page document. At the end of the report I posed a series of questions.

The issues that homœopathy was facing in 1982 are the same as they are now, 17 years later. We can look around us and find that although some of the details are gaining clarity, the essential issues remain:

- What is homœopathy? Is there more than one way? Are there limits? Where do we draw them?
- Who will do the research that is needed?
- Should the role of the players be defined?
- What is the exact nature of the interaction between the medical professional, the pharmacist, and the lay person?
- How do we recruit new practitioners?
- How do we convince the "rational" school of the efficacy of homœopathy?
- Who will set the standards for homœopathic education?
- How do we set up teaching organizations?
- How do we train our teachers? From where do we draw them?
- How is competence determined?
- What is the role of the lay prescriber?
- How do we support the pharmacies?
- How do we educate those that sell OTC products in stores?
- How do we get the public to support homœopathy?

Three ways

Those who practice homœopathy generally adhere to one of three "schools" of prescribing:
Unicist: *often called "classical," it is giving a single remedy at a time, as outlined in Hahnemann's* Organon. *Often the remedy is given as a single dose.*
Pluralist: *Often referred to as the "French School," this approach often gives more than one remedy at a time with the idea that there is more than a single disease to treat. Often a medium potency (12c-15c) remedy is given daily, with a lower potency (6X) of an "organ specific" remedy given in the morning for "drainage," and then a high potency (30c) nosode given on the weekend.*
Complexist: *several remedies are combined into a single dose and given, often daily.*

- What publications are needed? How are they supported?
- What is the value of machines like the EAV Dermatron, the Vega Test, and the like?

In 1833 when Quin came before the Royal College of Physicians, one of the censors advised to "Let Quin alone, as homœopathy cannot last more than two years."

Two years later when Hahnemann arrived in Paris, he applied for permission to practice. Several members of the Academy wrote to the Minister of Education and Public Health, protesting Hahnemann's practice and method. Guizot, the Minister, replied, "Hahnemann is a scholar of considerable merit. Science must be free for all. If homœopathy is a chimera or a system without inward application, it will fall of itself."

In 1989 when Martin Kaufman, the author of *Homeopathy: The Rise and Fall of a Medical Heresy*, was asked to write a chapter on homœopathy for the book *Other Healers*, he titled it "The Rise and Fall and Persistence of a Medical Heresy."

At the end of the last decade of the 20th century, homœopathy has shown itself not to be a chimera and has certainly persisted. As we pass the 200th anniversary of Hahnemann's first paper on homœopathy, we should be proud to say that, in the USA and world-wide, homœopathy is alive and well.

Appendix A

The book magnet
Ugly Sam
For the good times…
The succussion myth
The conversion experience
Divine healing
Homœopathic kits
Humphreys' Home Council
The Gavel Book
Middletown cases
Powder papers
The "AIH Two-Step"
American pharmacies

Christopher Ellithorp in his library

The book magnet

Christopher Ellithorp is a book magnet. Homœopathic volumes somehow find their way to him. There are 14 entries for "Kent, J. T." in Bradford's *Bibliography*. Most are for pamphlets containing lectures he gave (this was in 1892— before his major books were printed). There is but one book: *Sexual Neuroses*, published in St. Louis in 1879, just as Kent was becoming a homœopath. Most booksellers have never seen the volume. It is a rare one. Yet, Chris has a copy of this little red book. He found it at a flea market *in* Johnstown, New York (where he lives). It found its way to him. As did a five foot long photograph of the AIH meeting on the White House lawn in 1922. As did Volume 1 and Volume 2 of Dunham's *Lectures*— both having belonged to Ellis Santee. Both volumes were signed by Santee, and were found two years and 400 miles apart. Chris supplied me with a signature from Margaret Tyler— the book found its way to him from England, and he had the signature of Federal Vanderburgh in another book.

Sitting in his library, with the green-shaded library light on the desk, Chris absorbs the literature. Having Edward Bayard's spirit hovering over is probably of help. Bayard is buried in a cemetery in Johnstown— just around the corner from Chris's house.

When I wanted someone to proof-read this manuscript for historical accuracy, Chris did the job.

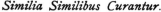

Similia Similibus Curantur.

HAHNEMANN.

Ugly Sam

Of all of the likenesses of Hahnemann in existence, this sneering countenance is certainly the strangest. It is found on many title pages of several homœopathic theses written for the Hahnemann Medical College, and now in the Hahnemann Collection at the Allegheny University of Health Sciences, in Philadelphia. It is also found in a small booklet published in 1888 by the Irving Homœopathic Institute in New York.

For the good times…

The good old days

The following describes the "riot" that took place at the Cleveland Homœopathic College in 1852 just three years after its founding. It was part of a larger article that appeared in the Hahnemann Annual *in 1899. Do we long for the "old days" when things were quieter? Thanks to Chris Ellithorp for finding this bizarre piece of homœopathic history.*

The second course of lectures opened with an enthusiastic class. The faculty had been strengthened by the addition of Professors B. L. Hill and H. P. Gatchell, from the Eclectic College of Cincinnati. Everything glided along smoothly until February 22, near the end of the session, when the college was attacked by a mob. A man named Johnson, who lived on the West Side (then known as Ohio City), found upon examination of the grave of his daughter, that the body had been removed. The story of the robbery was immediately published in the newspapers, and created great excitement, the two medical colleges being at once suspected. Search was made, and a body hacked and cut was found in an out-closet of the Homœopathic College. It appears that Dr. George Turrill (father of the present Prof. Geo. E. Turrill) was in the habit of dissecting in summer or winter, whenever he could find a body. In September he found a "floater" on the beach near Gordon Park, which, with the assistance of another student named Gilson, he removed and placed in pickle. The Demonstrator of Anatomy was Dr. Owens, of Cincinnati, and after he returned home, early in February, Turrill and Gilson took this pickled body (a man) into the college, but its odor was so strong that they were obliged to remove it to prevent detection by the Faculty. It was, therefore, cut into pieces and placed in the out-closet of the college. It was this body that Johnson and his party found. They took it in secret to the coroner, summoned Johnson's family physician Dr. Ackley, who examined it and swore it was the body of a woman, and, that he knew it was Johnson's daughter because it showed an amputated ring finger on the left hand, which he had amputated after death to remove a ring. Upon publication of this story the people became wrought up to such a pitch of excitement that a mob, composed of all the toughs in the city, was formed the next day, and about 10 a.m., with Johnson at their head, they started for the college.

Prof. Witherell was delivering a lecture upon anatomy at the time, and the first intimation he received of the appearance of the mob was given by the janitor, McCabe, who rushed into the room crying out: "The are a lot of devils coming to kill the students and destroy the college." Dr. D. M. Dake, a bold and fearless man, was

Of all those connected with the 1852 riot, the only likeness I could find was that of Dr. Seth Beckwith.

503

in the room at the time, and told Prof. Witherell to go on with his lecture. But this was impossible. Doors and windows were hastily barricaded, and Bitely, of Paupau, Mich., and S. R. Beckwith went into the hall with Dr. Dake and the janitor, armed with a good supply of heavy clubs, furnished by the latter. The front stairway was very wide. Dr. Dake stood on one side, Beckwith on the other, the janitor in the center, while Bitely, a very powerful fellow six feet two inches in height, guarded the back stairs. The mob soon made a charge up the stairs, but the first man to reach the top was knocked backward against his comrades by a terrible blow from the janitor, who swung his club with both hands, forcing the crowd down several steps. At every blow the janitor would yell: "Take that, ye divils. I've got more for yez of the same sort." Many were soon bleeding freely from severe wounds on the head, and the crowd becoming pretty well covered with blood, became discouraged, and went to the rear. The janitor then ran to help Bitely. The fighting continued for about two hours, when the crowd dispersed. In the afternoon the Faculty came in. The Mayor, Wm. Case, was seen and he promised protection on the following morning. The students remained in the building all night. Professors Williams and Brainard obtaining food for them from the Prospect House, on the opposite side of the street.

About nine o'clock the next morning the mob reappeared. The fire department was ordered out and the engines surrounded the building. Mayor Case soon appeared on the scene with two policemen. He mounted a flour barrel, read his proclamation, and tried to induce the leaders of the mob to permit students and professors to leave the building but they refused. He then placed the building in charge of the two policemen and told the students and professors to leave, that the city would be responsible for the safety of the college property. But as soon as he left the mob rushed into the building, the students trying to escape. Some of the boys armed with thigh bones and whatever weapons they could find managed to fight their way out singly; others, headed by Dr. Dake, S. R. Beckwith, and the janitor, armed with their clubs, charged down the front stairway and escaped. The fight was a terrible one and many of the students were severely bruised. Dr. Dake and Professor Gatchell mingled fearlessly with the crowd. Professor Gatchell saw student Greenleaf run into a butcher shop pursued by a crowd of

rioters. Rushing into the shop he grabbed a knife and cleaver, and, swinging these weapons savagely he succeeded in getting the student across the Square to safety. The college property was wrecked. The building was twice set on fire but was saved by the fire department which also tried to disperse the rioters by throwing streams of water upon them but without avail. Wildly excited, the mob placed portions of dissected bodies on poles and paraded the streets, while barber poles, like the gate posts of cities in ancient times, were decorated with human heads and other anatomical structures.

The Cleveland Grays were ordered out and led by General Sanford attacked the mob. A volley was fired with blank cartridges but this failing to intimidate them a bayonet charge was made which cleared the field. A number were wounded and numerous arrests were made, but the trial which followed proved to be a farce, the prisoners being discharged. During the riot nearly every article in the college was destroyed. John T. Otis, a very tall man, now a judge in Chicago, placed a skeleton on his shoulder and ran up Prospect street closely pursued by the mob. One fellow managed to get near enough to grasp a dangling foot and wrenched off the femur at the hip joint but the rest was saved. The heroine of the second day's fight was the wife of a physician from near Warren, O. She had a room in the building and in it kept the mannequin and fœtal head belonging to the college. She fearlessly stood in the doorway armed with a pistol and dagger and threatened to kill the first man who attempted to enter the room. No one entered.

The lectures were necessarily discontinued for the remainder of the term; but, the second annual commencement exercises were held in the Baptist Church on the corner of Champlain and Seneca streets before an interested and appreciative audience.

At a banquet ten years after this, a physician who had been a student in the Eric Street College at the time of the riot and had a personal knowledge of the theft of the body of Miss Johnson, stated that the body was concealed in his college and was shipped out of the city during the riot. One of the students who assisted in the removal of the body from the cemetery was in the front ranks of the mob with Johnson until the attack was made on the college when he retired.

Fun and games at Ann Arbor (or "boys will be boys")

Dr. James C. Wood tells of a Halloween prank the students pulled at the University of Michigan in 1887.

"A yearling heifer had been heroically medicated with *Croton Oil*, a most drastic purgative, and carried bodily up the outside stairway to the upper lecture room of the Homœopathic Department. The results were devastating and no lectures were possible on the following morning in that particular room."

Dr. Wood, in his autobiography, recalls that, as a student at Ann Arbor, the homœopathic students took the general medical lectures with the regular medical students. Dr.

Palmer, a regular lecturer, was of the opinion that the "sugar pills" were perfectly innocuous.

On one occasion, the homœopathic students armed themselves with two vials— one containing blank granules, the other containing *Glonoine* 2X. The homœopathic students all were seen to be taking their "sugar pills" and the allopathic students said, "pass the sugar"— at which point they were passed the bottle of *Glonoine*. Within five minutes all the allopathic students were doing a short but effective proving of *Glonoine*— holding their throbbing heads and paying little attention to the lecture.

The succussion myth

A story is told by way of explaining how Hahnemann "discovered" the idea of shaking the remedies to increase their effectiveness.

The story has been that Hahnemann discovered potency because in those days people didn't have automobiles so they used horses and wagons to get around. The roads were very rough. As Hahnemann made his rounds to his patients, he noticed that the people in the country were getting well faster than those in the city. This made him think that the shaking of the remedies as they traveled in the back of the wagon or in the saddlebags might be the reason, so he decided to shake up all the remedies and potentization was discovered.

It is very difficult to ascertain the truth of this story.

The likely source of the myth of Hahnemann's discovery of potentization can be found in a footnote by Hahnemann in the *Organon*, and an article in Stapf's *Archives*.

In the first edition of the *Organon* Hahnemann talks of "eight drop doses of tincture" but in Par. 250, he says: "If dilution is also employed (whereby the dose gains a greater power of expansion), an excessive effect is easily produced. But there is no small difference in the effects of a dilution which is, as it were, only superficial, and a dilution which is so intimate and uniform that every smallest part of the fluid medium contains a due proportion of the dissolved medicine; the former is much less powerful than the latter."

In the following paragraph he speaks of putting a single drop of tincture in a pound of water and shaking it vigorously.

It appears that it was his effort to have the dilution become "intimate and uniform" that led to the development of succussion.

In the *Organon* 4th edition (1829), he says (Par. 269): "The homœopathic healing art develops for its purposes the immaterial (dynamic) virtues of medicinal substances, and

to a degree previously unheard of, by means of a peculiar and hitherto untried process..."

In Par. 270, he speaks of using one drop of alcohol and one drop of plant juice mixed, and then mixing those two drops with 98 drops of alcohol, "...and the whole twice shaken together, the medicine becomes exalted in energy (potenzirt) to the first development of power..." He then recommends making similar preparations to the 30th potency.

In a footnote, he says he prefers two shakes to every vial. He had used more previously, but it developed the energy to too great a degree.

"On the contrary, there are homœopathists who, in their visits to the sick, carry about their persons the medicines in a fluid state, which, they nevertheless affirm, do not in time become increased in energy by the frequent agitation to which they are thus subjected."

Hahnemann goes on to say that, in his experience, such agitation does, indeed, raise the energy of the medicine.

This statement, and the footnote, is repeated again in the *Organon* 5th edition.

Francis E. Boericke, in *Three Lectures on Homœopathic Pharmaceutics*, published by F. E. Boericke in 1878, says the following: "One of the early homœopaths, in a dissertation on potencies published in the *Archives*, cautions his fellow practitioners, especially the country physician as they had frequently to go on horseback, against carrying in their pocket cases liquid potencies. The trotting of the horse, he thought, would be potent enough to potentize every medicine they carried higher up."

So although the idea of the remedies getting potentized when carried as liquid on horseback existed, it seems that Hahnemann's original intent was simply a thorough mixture.

The Conversion Experience

The "conversion" experiences of the old homœopaths could (and have) filled books. Of all the experiences I have read, the one of Dr. Felix R. McManus (in 1837), the first homœopath in Maryland struck a particular chord. Here it is in his words:

I saw an announcement in a paper of a homœopathic physician by the name of Radcliff, and at that time I had a very singular case, and I did not know what to do with it. It was a case that I defined to be neuralgia, rheumatic pain, or rheumatism. The neuralgia was intermittent neuralgia. The lady was 19 years of age, very sensitive in her organization and nervous system. Every day at two o'clock after an intermission of six weeks, she was taken with what she called a needle pain. She felt as if a needle were stuck into her heart, and that was immediately followed by a convulsion which lasted from 30 minutes to two or three hours. I commenced the treatment with the tonic plan: I commenced with sulphate of quinine. Still the pain came at two o'clock. Then I resorted to a preparation of arnica flowers and a solution. Finally I anticipated the paroxysms by sinapism [mustard plasters —JW] anteriorly and posteriorly. These were applied to the heart. I thought by the time we began to irritate it would produce some effect. I thought by this plan we might break up the paroxysms. I did not know what to do.

I saw this advertisement and said, "I do not know Dr. Radcliff; nobody can tell me who he is, I will go see him." I went and told him the object of my visit. I asked if he had ever treated such a case. He said, "No." He was a very intelligent man and very agreeable in his presence, bearing, and conversation. He listened to my story patiently, and after hearing my case said, "Doctor, I think a dose of *Spigelia* in the thirtieth will cure that case."

"One dose of *Spigelia*," said I. "You do not mean the Maryland pink root?"

"Yes," he replied, "I will give you a dose."

It was then 10 o'clock in the morning. "What will I do with it," said I.

His reply was: "You put this powder on the tongue of the patient."

I saw him pour out the pellets in a little sugar of milk. I had the curiosity to take up the bottle; It bore the mark:

"*Spigelia*, 30." I left the house and thought to myself, "This man must be a fool, and yet he told me with assurance that would baffle suspicion." I thought, "If this dose of *Spigelia* will cure her, I will try it."

I went to see the young lady and put the powder on the end of her tongue. I thought to myself it was a real piece of folly, but I told her I would come again in the afternoon. I was very busy, but told her I would go to the house at about 5 o'clock. Now, you must recollect that this patient had not missed a spasm in six weeks. Her mother met me at the door. She was standing on the portico and she raised her hand and said: "Mary missed her pain today."

"Missed her pain. Had she any spasm?"

"Not at all. Come in."

I went in. The girl was sitting up. The first thing I did was feel her pulse.

"Well, Mary, how do you feel?"

She answered, "I feel better than I have in a long time. I think it is because I missed the pain."

"Had you no symptom of it?"

"No," she said. "I never had any premonition at all until it came like a needle sticking in my heart. But today I had nothing of it."

I looked at the girl and I looked at myself. What conclusion could I come to? It must be the effect of the *Spigelia*. I waited till the morrow, and at 5 o'clock went to see the girl, who felt remarkably well. That night I went to see the doctor. "Well," he said, "Did that powder have any effect upon that young woman?"

I said, "Really I do not know how to answer that question. I called at four or five in the afternoon and the girl had neither pain, spasm, nor convulsion, and I called this afternoon and she had neither the one nor the other."

"Well sir, you told me that if I would cure the case—and I have cured it with one dose of medicine— that you would believe in homœopathy"

"Well doctor, if I tell you that I believe, you will say that I am a very visionary man. How could one dose cure that girl after I had done so much? How could one dose do it?"

He replied, "The dose of *Spigelia* that I gave was what the girl's case required, and what you did amounted to nothing."

Divine Healing

William Gentry

While digging through Bradford's *Scrapbooks* at the Hahnemann Archives, I came across an interesting set of clippings about Dr. William Gentry.

Gentry, an 1880 graduate of the Missouri College of Homœopathy in St. Louis, wrote *Gentry's Concordance Repertory*— a six-volume set published by Chatterton in 1890. Gentry had written several articles (found in the *Scrapbooks*) about homœopathy, including a lengthy letter in which he points out that Dr. Swan was using *Tuberculinum* almost 20 years before Koch came out with the tuberculin vaccine.

A few years later, Gentry turned away from homœopathy. In Gentry's words, "My mind, in 1892, was directed to the subject of divine healing."

By 1900 he was traveling around the country preaching the gospel: "That the Lord Jesus Christ is the great physician that never lost a case."

A large, front page article, announced Gentry was being sued by a woman in New York who claimed she never had headaches before he "healed" her. In the article he is compared with practitioners of Christian Science. In his rebuttal, he calls all the others, including the Christian Scientists, charlatans and quacks, and says, "I alone can speak to you in the name of Jesus Christ."

James Bell

On a similar subject, James Bell, MD, who wrote the well-known treatise on *Diarrhœa*, was nearly expelled from the Homœopathic Medical Society in Massachusetts in 1892, because he said religious faith can be as curative as homœopathy in some cases, and that he acknowledges the power of God in the healing process.

Mary Baker Eddy and Christian Science

There is also a connection between Mary Baker Eddy, the founder of Christian Science, and homœopathy. On page 137 of the book *Mary Baker Eddy— The Years of Discovery* by Robert Peel, there are a few paragraphs which give an interesting insight into the person of Mary Baker Eddy:

"This system of medicine [homœopathy] had been growing tremendously in favor during the past decade or two, and her own favorable results with it in 1853 had started her off on a long series of experiments, and had also led Daniel Patterson [Mrs. Baker's second husband] to practice homœopathy as a sideline to his dentistry.

"In her possession was a copy of Jahr's *New Manual of Homœopathic Practice* edited by A. Gerald Hull, and popularly known as "Hull's Jahr." Myra Smith told of Mrs. Patterson's devotion to this huge volume which, next to the Bible, probably constituted her chief reading matter at the time. The blind girl also told how some of the neighbors would come to Mrs. Patterson for medicine; and her own later accounts of her experiences with these rustic patients shows the immense importance homeopathy had in the development of her thought."

Mr. Peel describes homœopathy and Hahnemann's concept of the "vital principle." He tells of a case of a woman with dropsy who came to Mrs. Patterson. She was given a 4C of *Argentum nitricum* and later a higher potency of *Sulphur.* Mrs. Patterson then gave her some unmedicated pellets and found that while the woman was taking the placebo she improved, but when she ceased taking the placebo, the improvement stopped. Later, Mrs. Eddy wrote that the episode was "a falling apple to me— it made plain to me that the mind governed the whole question of recovery."

In her autobiography, she made the statement, "One drop of *Natrum muriaticum* in a tumbler full of water mixed with the faith of the ages, would cure patients not affected by a larger dose."

The kits

Many of the older doctors assembled kits for their patients. These were often labeled only by number. When a patient called with a problem the doctor could listen and say, "Take one of number 30 and call me in the morning."

Many of these kits are still around, but after the doctors died, the codes were lost.

While cleaning up Boericke and Tafel's Philadelphia premises in 1991, I came across an envelope of index cards listing many of the kit's ingredients. It appears most of the kits were made up by B&T.

In the hope that this list will help someone out there, I offer the codes below. It is also instructive to see, given a finite number of bottles, which remedies each doctor chose to include.

Dr. Wright Hubbard's large kit

Dr. Wright Hubbard's small kit was discussed within the main text on page 294. Her large kit (all 200th except as noted) contained the remedies listed below. The card had a note: "Drs. Stephenson, Gutman, Whitmont, Eisfelder, Hubbard, have key to kit."

1. Acon	21. Con	41. Mag p
2. All c	22. Crot tig	42. Merc c
3. Aloe	23. Cubana	43. Merc v
4. Anac	24. Cup	44. Nat m
5. Ant t	25. Dros	45. Nux v
6. Apis	26. Ferr.	46. Phos (30th)
7. Arn	27. Ferr p	47. Phyt
8. Ars (30th)	28. Gels	48. Podo
9. Ars i	29. Glon	49. Psor
10. Bell	30. Graph	50. Ran b
11. Bry	31. Hepar	51. Rhus t
12. Calc c	32. Hyos	52. Rumex
13. Calc p	33. Hypericum	53. Sep
14. Canth	34. Ign	54. Sil
15. Carbo v	35. Ipecac	55. Spig
16. Caust	36. Kali bi	56. Spong
17. Cham	37. Kali c (30th)	57. Sulph
18. Chel	38. Lach (30th)	58. Thuj
19. Chin	39. Led	59. Tub b
20. Coloc	40. Lyc	60. Verat a

Dr. Whitmont's kit (all 200th with three exceptions)

1. Acon	19. Ferr p	37. Podo
2. Anac	20. Gels.	38. Puls
3. Apis	21. Hepar	39. Ran b
4. Ars. (30th)	22. Hyper.	40. Sep.
5. Arum t	23. Ipecac	41. Sil
6. Baptisia	24. Kali bi	42. Spong
7. Bell.	25. Lachesis	43. Sulph
8. Bryonia	26. Ledum	44. Verat a
9. Calc	27. Lyc	45. All c
10. Canth	28. Mag p.	46. Rhus t
11. Capsicum	29. Merc v	47. Ferr m
12. Carbo v	30. Merc sol	48. Placebo
13. Cham	31. Merc i f	49. Arnica
14. Cina	32. Merc i r	50. Eup per
15. Coloc	33. Nat m	51. Bacill (30th)
16. Crot t	34. Nux v	52. Placebo
17. Dios	35. Phos (30th)	53. Influenz
18. Euphrasia	36. Phyto	

Dr. James Stephenson's emergency kit (all 12X)

1. Aconite	10. Euphrasia	19. Lyss.(30th)
2. Apis	11. Ferr p	20. Mag p
3. Arnica	12. Glonoin	21. Nux v.
4. Bell.	13. Hepar	22. Rhus t
5. Cactus grand	14. Hyper.	23. Ruta
6. Canth.	15. Ign.	24. Stram
7. Carbo v	16. Lachesis	25. Urtica
8. Coloc.	17. Laurocer.	26. Verat. alb
9. Crot horr	18. Ledum	

American Foundation kit (all 30X)

1. Aconite	8. Cantharis	15. Lachesis
2. Apis	9. Carbo veg	16. Ledum
3. Arnica	10. China	17. Phos
4. Arsenicum	11. Crot horr	18. Rhus tox
5. Cactus	12. Ferrum p	19. Ruta
6. Calendula	13. Hypericum	20. Symph
7. Camphora	14. Ipecac	21. Urtica

Humphreys' Home Council

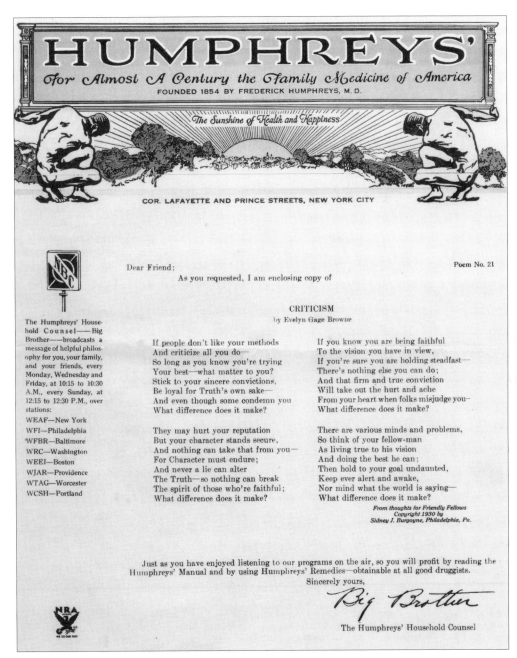

The weekly mailing from "Humphreys' Home Council" radio show, 1930.

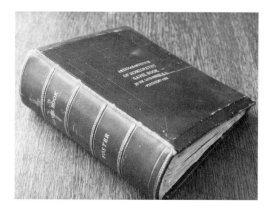

The "Gavel Book"

Aside from the possessions of Hahnemann's housed at the Robert Bosch Institute in Stuttgart, Germany, those at The Faculty of Homœopathy in London, and those in the Hahnemann Collection at the Allegheny University of Health Sciences in Philadelphia, homœopathy has few "relics."

The American Institute of Homeopathy gavel (and the "Gavel Book" that describes it) might be one of the genuine relics of homœopathy in the United States.

It was the idea of William Davis Foster, MD, the AIH president in 1909.

Dr. Foster wrote to relatives of all the grand old homœopaths and asked for a small piece of wood from something that had belonged to their ancestor— a chair, table, settee, etc. These pieces were assembled into the gavel, with each piece numbered so the genealogy of the piece may be traced in the book.

As an example, piece number nine was donated by Calvin Knerr and came from a piece of wood from the Allentown Academy. Piece number 10 was from a church in which the first lectures on homœopathy were delivered in Cleveland by Dr. Beckwith in 1850. Piece number 59 was from an old mahogany chair used in the office of Dr. Gosewisch in Wilmington, Delaware in 1839.

The handle of the gavel was made from a piece of an ebony walking cane that belonged to David Glass, MD of Hopkinsville, Kentucky. There is an ivory piece inlaid in the gavel's handle from a scalpel handle used by Dr. Foster in field operations during the Civil War. The end of the gavel handle contained a pebble from Hahnemann's grave in Paris. The end surfaces of the gavel itself were made from gold sheet.

The "Gavel Book" contains a listing of all the parts plus letters of reply. Letter number 59 is duplicated on the following page.

The *Journal of the American Institute of Homeopathy* in January 1935, contained a letter discussing the gavel and the book, and commenting that its whereabouts were unknown. All who were asked knew nothing about it. Somehow, from somewhere, it reappeared. The gavel is in possession of the American Institute of Homeopathy. The *Gavel Book* is at the National Center for Homeopathy in Alexandria, Virginia.

U. S. DEPARTMENT OF AGRICULTURE

WEATHER BUREAU

Keokuk,Iowa March 1,1909

Dr William Davis Foster

Kansas City,Mo

Dear Sir

In response to your kindletter of 8th inst requesting
some memento of my Father,Dr J.C.Gosewisch of Wilmington,Del,to be
incorporated in a gavel,I take pleasure in mailing to you this date,
under a separate cover,a piece of an old mahogany chair,which he used
in his office,as the most suitable article I can recall for the purpose desired.

Herring,Wesselhoeft,Rauh,and Lippe were intimate friends and co-
workers of my Fathers,in my boyhood days,at the beginning of the battle
with the pracitioners of the"Sangrado""school,who deemed bleeding and
calomel the sovereign remedies for all the ills the flesh was heir to,
and I believe there are now some seventeen physicians enjoying a good
practice in Wilmington,the field my Father opened.

Yours sincerely

Fred. J. Gosewisch.

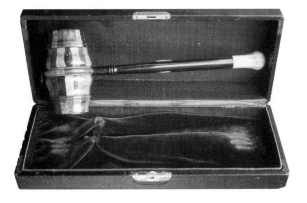

The American Institute of Homeopathy Gavel in its felt-lined box. The various sections of the head are clearly visible. Each bears a stamped number indexed back to the letters in the *Gavel Book*.

Middletown cases

In 1997, Janet Madow accessed some files of the Middletown State Hospital in Middletown, New York. She came away with several cases transcribed from the longhand notes. It is an interesting look into the "homœopathic" therapeutics practiced at the hospital.

CASE 1:

Name has been blackened out.
Admitted: June 28, 1894 at 7:15 a.m.
by Dr. G. S. Kinney, accompanied by Dr. Franklin Neal
approved by Judge A. T. ?

Age: 33
Civil condition: Single. No children.
Nativity: U.S.
Father: Germany
Mother: Germany
Occupation: Laborer
Religion: Protestant
Education: Reads only common school.
Tendencies: Temperate. Insane
Relations: No.

Present physical condition: Pulse: 76 Tongue: Clean Temp. 98 1/2. Eyes: Light Pupils: Normal. Bowels: Normal. Appetite: Good. Speech: Asks questions, coherent. Gait: Normal. Weight: (blank). Heart: Weak. Lungs: Normal. Skin: Moist. No. of admissions: 1. Other hospitals. 0. No. of attacks: 1. Age at first attack: 33 years. Duration of present attack: 2 months. Alleged causes: Predisposition, Ex: Masturbation. Diagnosis: Mania. Stage: (acute is crossed out and underneath reads Dementia term c.).

Continued History: Partial sun stroke two years ago. Uses Tobacco and Liquor moderately. That he was in fear of arrest. Also that he was afraid of his life. That he wished they had put him in lock up so that he might be protected from his pursuers. Said he had pain in his head and could not sleep nights also that he was in the habit of masturbating. He seemed quite willing to answer all questions. Drowsy and depressed. Making proposals of marriage to the young ladies of the town, visiting their houses and insisting on marriage. His friends say he does not sleep nor eat and wanders off thinking someone is pursuing him. Also that he is unsafe to be about.

On admission, patient states that he had a slight sun stroke about two years ago and ever since while in the sun his head hurts. Head throbs and pains him. Says the girls in Ellenville have been very fond of him and waited to marry him. Feels depressed a good deal. Acknowledges that he has masturbated. Says everyone was teasing him and making fun of him about his girls and he got to worrying and could not rest. Feels depressed and heavy all the time.

RX: *Glonoine* (3/3 hrs)
July 3rd: Masturbates daily. Eating and sleeping well. Plays checkers.
July 5th: Has hallucinations of sight and hearing. He hears women talking to him and sees women.
July 7th: Was restless and excited last night and removed from 2 Hall to 2 floor.
RX: *Belladonna* 3/2 hrs.
July 23rd: Thinks his mother and sister are in the house. Physically he is looking better.
August 1: So slowly gaining, physically and mentally is unstable and is easily excited. Does a little work at the hospital.
September: Same.
October: Physically stronger, but he does not improve. He is acting with little self control.
January 1, 1895: Sleeps five to eight hours. Mind dull. Is not acting as bright as he was three months ago.
April: Sleeps from five to eight hours. Does not talk much. Very careless of his person. Seems to have no ambition.
July: Sleeps from five to seven hours. Mind dull. Careless of his clothing. Does not talk much.
October: Eats and sleeps well, but is demented. No ambition.
January 1896: At present is doing very well. Is exhibiting good self control.
April: Does not improve. Careless of his person. Not inclined to talk.
May: Was sick at his stomach and vomited last night.
RX: *Nux vomica* (1/hrly?) Better this morning.
June: Stomach aches at the present.
June: Vomited this afternoon. **RX:** *Agnus castus* (3 hrly?)
July 8: Vomited in the night, very jaundiced in color. Hot water enemas. **RX:** *Merc* (Prs 1/3hrs.)
July 9th: Slept 7 hours. Is today looking better. Skin more clear. Free from pain.
October: Quiet. No ambition. Will not go out walking. Seldom talks much. Demented.

March 1897: No change. Walks the grounds.

July 1898: Does not change. Still works on his law suit against the builder of the Napinoch Reformatory.

October: Does not change. Good physical health.

January 1899: No change since last (?)

April: Expects to go out every day and look up his enemies in the Napinoch Reformatory.

July: No change.

October: Eats and sleeps well.

January 1890: Goes out walking and is in good bodily condition. Will do no work. Pleasant. Has an air of importance. Will not work.

July: No change in delusions. Condition stationary.

December: 148 lbs.

January 1901: Unchanged.

CASE 2:

January 11, 1895 by Dr. D.H. Arthur at 3. p.m. accompanied by hospital attendant Winfield and Dr. ?.

Order: Public.

Medical certificate by A.P. Francis of Florida (NY) and Dr. H.H. Robinson of Goshen, approved by Judge R.C. Coleman of Surrogate.

Age: 83.

Civil condition: widower, three children.

Nativity: England.

Father: English.

Mother: English.

Occupation: House carpenter.

Religion: Protestant.

Education: Reads only common school.

Tendencies: Homicidal and criminal insane

Present Physical condition: Pulse: feeble. Tongue: (blank). Temp: 101 1/2 . Eyes, pupils, Bowels, appetite and speech are blank. Weight: 123. Gait, heart, lungs, skin: blank. No. of admissions here. 1. Other Hospitals: 0. No. of attacks: 1. Age at first attack: ? Duration of present attack: ? Accompanying diseases: blank. Alleged causes: (something) senility. Ex: (too light to read). Diagnosis: (too light to read).

Continued History: Has served a sentence of ten years in state prison Pennsylvania for aiding in causing the Car Rock Railroad disaster 1868. Filthy. Is excitable and destructive, not homicidal nor suicidal. When asked his age, he replied that he was a small boy in the time of protection of Oliver Cromwell. He also said, displaying his fingers that they were of equal length, contrary to fact, continuing incoherently, he said that the Americans could easily whip the English. The patient was sleeping in bed, was aroused by an attendant and assisted to a sitting posture. Without any leading questions, he extended both hands and stated that his fingers were all of equal length. He pulled the stockings from his feet and said that his feet were sore and frozen. Inspection revealed no lesions about the feet. Such as indicate partial Senile Dementia. His manner seems such as to indicated that he had no realizing sense of his situation. He took no intelligent (something) in the examination and asked no questions. He was apathetic, which condition was attributed to an opiate administered to restrain violence. His attendant says that he wanders about his room the entire night, attempts to leave his room in a nude condition and would not be controlled without opiates or mechanical restraints.

On admission was brought from Orange Farm, Goshen, NY. Patient's lower limbs are paralyzed. Is 83 years old and can give no account of himself. Brought to the County house one week ago, clothing new. Put to bed. Temp 101 1/5, Pulse 90, Resp 22. Noisy and restless. Resistive and profane.

RX: *Acon.* 1/hrly.

January 12th: Patient states to Dr. H. that he lead a very good and Christian life, never did any harm to anyone. He is deceitful and malicious. (Dr. H.). Temp last night: 101 1/5. Pulse: 90, Resp 22. PM: temp: 100 1/5. Pulse: 74. Resp: 23.

January 13th: Temp: 100 Pulse: 8o. Resp: 22. . PM: Temp 99 3/5 Pulse: 80, Resp: 24.

January 14th: temp 98 4/5. pulse: 68. resp: 22. Does not say anything that is at all coherent. Denies anything wrong in his past and says he has "been one of the best of ?" Eats well. Sleeps poorly and is noisy at times during the night. Does not appear to suffer any pain. **RX:** *Nux vomica* 1/2 hrs.

January 28th: Cough towards night.

RX: *Belladonna* 2/hrly. *Ant. Tart.* 3/3 hrs.

March 19th: Noisy and restless.

April: Restless sometimes noisy. Demented. Filthy. Eats well. Sleeps poorly. Unsteady on his feet. Almost helpless.

About 3:40 p.m. patient soiled his bed, after changing clothing he sat up in bed for a minute and talked to attendants. Suddenly fell back in bed, became blue in face and gave three gasps for breath and then expired. Post mortem revealed a rupture of his left ventricle of heart.

April 24 1895: Discharged dead.

How To Fold Powder Papers

We often read of remedies being prepared in "powders," but the practice is not so common today.

The remedy was often given as a single granule— usually smaller than a number 10— that was placed in a small quantity of milk-sugar, and then folded into a small paper package.

When local homœopathic pharmacies were still operational, a doctor's prescription was often written for a month's worth of powder papers, numbered from 1 to 30, with the active dose in number one, and all the rest blank powders. The patient was to take them sequentially.

Most homœopathic pharmacies sold boxes of "powder papers." The paper was very thin (.0015 inch— regular writing paper is about .004), and was generally 3"x 4" in size.

Bernard Haviland recalled several jars of folded powder papers of varying colors in the office of Dr. Eugene Underhill in Philadelphia. Haviland said Underhill would give a dose on the tongue in his office, and then write a prescription which was given to the secretary. She would go to the jars and take out the folded papers. The prescriptions were on the order of: "Take one blue packet every day, and take a pink one on Sunday." In discussing this with the secretary several years after Dr. Underhill's death, she admitted that they were all the same— all plain milk sugar— and she would spend hours preparing them.

Here are instructions for folding powder papers as I learned it from Henry N. Williams, MD.

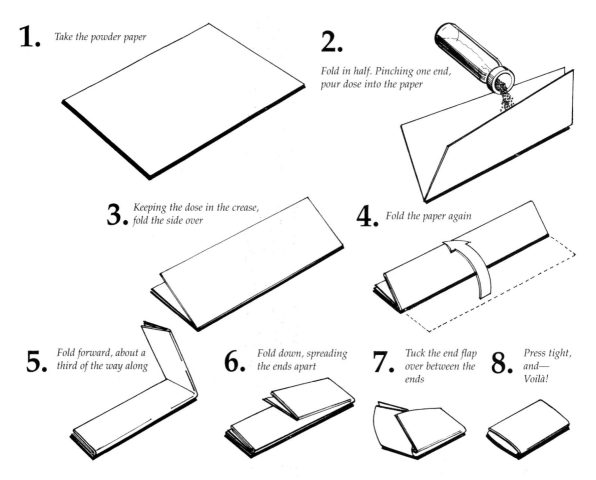

1. *Take the powder paper*

2. *Fold in half. Pinching one end, pour dose into the paper*

3. *Keeping the dose in the crease, fold the side over*

4. *Fold the paper again*

5. *Fold forward, about a third of the way along*

6. *Fold down, spreading the ends apart*

7. *Tuck the end flap over between the ends*

8. *Press tight, and— Voilà!*

The AIH Two – Step

This sheet music is in the collection William Kirtsos in Old Chatham, NY. The tune was written for the AIH Convention that was held in Richland Springs, New York during June, 1901. The composer was Frank Thompson.

The video, *The Faces of Homeopathy*, uses it as the music track for parts of the story that take place at the turn of the century.

It is a wonderful piece of homœopathic ephemera.

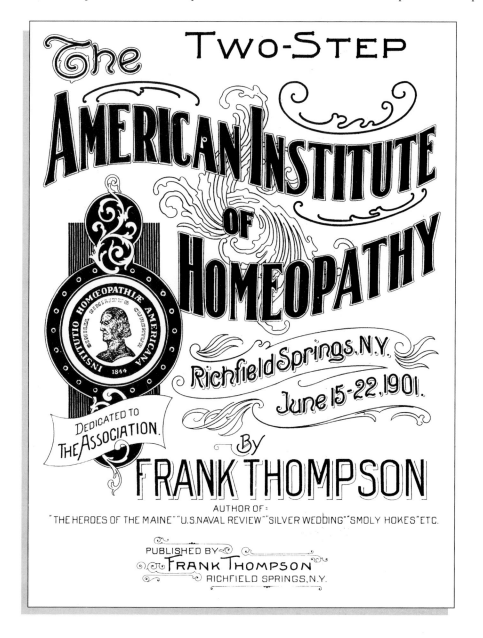

THE AMERICAN INSTITUTE OF HOMEOPATHY.
TWO STEP.

FRANK THOMPSON.

The American Pharmacies

A brief historical overview. The founding dates are in parentheses. The pharmacies listed were operating in 1892, and were listed in Bradford. Most closed during the 1920s. Some remained in operation through the 1950s. There were many other, smaller, pharmacies operating through the first half of the century. Those pharmacies still operational under the name listed are indicated by a star (★).

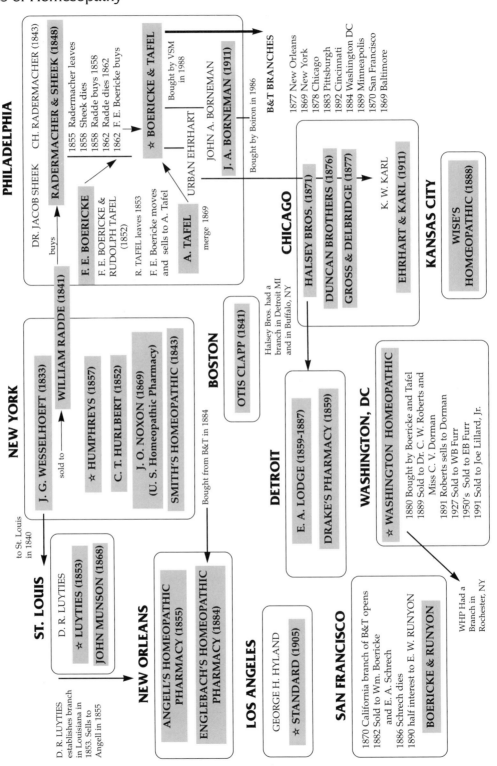

PHILADELPHIA

DR. JACOB SHEEK   CH. RADERMACHER (1843)

RADERMACHER & SHEEK (1848)

1855 Radermacher leaves
1858 Sheek dies
1858 Radde buys 1858
1862 Radde dies 1862
1862 F. E. Boericke buys

★ BOERICKE & TAFEL

Bought by VSM in 1988

F. E. BOERICKE

F. E. Boericke & RUDOLPH TAFEL (1852)

R. TAFEL leaves 1853
F. E. Boericke moves and sells to A. Tafel

A. TAFEL

merge 1869

URBAN EHRHART

JOHN A. BORNEMAN

J. A. BORNEMAN (1911)

Bought by Boiron in 1986

B&T BRANCHES

1877 New Orleans
1869 New York
1878 Chicago
1883 Pittsburgh
1892 Cincinnati
1884 Washington DC
1889 Minneapolis
1870 San Francisco
1869 Baltimore

CHICAGO

HALSEY BROS. (1871)

DUNCAN BROTHERS (1876)

GROSS & DELBRIDGE (1877)

K. W. KARL

EHRHART & KARL (1911)

Halsey Bros. had a branch in Detroit MI and in Buffalo, NY

KANSAS CITY

WISE'S HOMŒOPATHIC (1888)

NEW YORK

J. G. WESSELHOEFT (1833)

sold to →

WILLIAM RADDE (1841)

★ HUMPHREYS (1857)

C. T. HURLBERT (1852)

J. O. NOXON (1869)
(U. S. Homeopathic Pharmacy)

SMITH'S HOMŒOPATHIC (1843)

Bought from B&T in 1884

to St. Louis in 1840

BOSTON

OTIS CLAPP (1841)

DETROIT

E. A. LODGE (1859-1887)

DRAKE'S PHARMACY (1859)

WASHINGTON, DC

★ WASHINGTON HOMŒOPATHIC

1880 Bought by Boericke and Tafel
1889 Sold to Dr. C. W. Roberts and Miss C. V. Dorman
1891 Roberts sells to Dorman
1927 Sold to WB Furr
1950's Sold to EB Furr
1991 Sold to Joe Lillard, Jr.

WHP Had a Branch in Rochester, NY

ST. LOUIS

D. R. LUYTIES

★ LUYTIES (1853)

JOHN MUNSON (1868)

D. R. LUYTIES establishes branch in Louisiana in 1853. Sells to Angell in 1855

NEW ORLEANS

ANGELL'S HOMŒOPATHIC PHARMACY (1855)

ENGLEBACH'S HOMŒOPATHIC PHARMACY (1884)

LOS ANGELES

GEORGE H. HYLAND

★ STANDARD (1905)

SAN FRANCISCO

1870 California branch of B&T opens
1882 Sold to Wm. Boericke and E. A. Schrech
1886 Schrech dies
1890 half interest to E. W. RUNYON

BOERICKE & RUNYON

Appendix B

"The great unpleasantness"
Kent's school
New York: 1984

"The Great Unpleasantness"

In the last 20 years the business of American homœopathy between 1978 and 1981 has been referred to as "the great unpleasantness."

But that title conveys nothing of what really happened, any more than it would if we referred to the Vietnam War by the same name.

In looking through the minutes of Kent's Post-Graduate school, we find Dr. Baldwin was removed as a teacher for "deviating from the *Organon.*" His exact infractions were never mentioned, and we are left to speculate exactly what he did that was deemed so wrong.

In writing this record of the history of homœopathy, I do not want people guessing about what might have happened. I believe I owe it to future generations to describe what did happen at that time.

And, in 1997, it is certainly possible to do so. The general outline is in the main text. These are the details. I apologize for any duplication.

The background

In the mid to late 1970s, a group within the NCH Board became very interested in obtaining funding to educate young physicians. The "elder" most supportive of this effort was Dr. Maesimund B. Panos. Believing a good part of the NCH's mission was education, Panos sought funding to send several doctors to Greece to study with George Vithoulkas.

But the NCH relied on funding from the American Foundation and was not permitted to raise its own funds. The American Foundation was obligated to fund the National Center because its tax-exempt status depended upon it. The AFH gave the NCH about $100,000 annually. Were the NCH to raise, let's say, $20,000, the AFH would then fund the NCH with only $80,000. So the NCH was held at a specific spending level.

Most players in the drama had strong personalities, and interpersonal frictions were increasing. In looking through correspondence from the time, it becomes obvious some of the people were "big-picture" (global) folk and some were "detail" (linear) folk. These types talk very different languages and often appear (to each other) to have very different priorities. As the correspondence shows, one person is debating if the word "and" or the word "or" should be used in the latest press release, and another person is saying, "let's just get it out!" It was a pressure cooker with no safety valve.

In July 1978, the AFH decided the magazine, *The Layman Speaks* was running at a loss for too long, and ceased its publication. In August 1978 it was replaced with a four-page newsletter, *The Homœopathic Heartbeat.* It had, according to the legal statement, a paid circulation of about 1,800. The masthead featured the name superimposed on a ECG reading. It was pointed out by Sandra M. Chase, that the reading was of a patient in cardiac arrest. It was not a good omen! The masthead was changed.

In 1977 Christine Zack DeZutel, from Chicago, Illinois, was elected to the National Center board of directors and, in 1978, she was elected by the board as vice-president. DeZutel had taken the lay course at Millersville in 1973 and the professional course in 1976. Her father was in the heating and air conditioning business and she inherited the business from him. The company specialized in engineering cooling apparatus for electrical generating plants and other large installations.

DeZutel was the chief officer of the Zack Foundation— a philanthropic organization whose primary purpose was to pay annual stipends to college students who were children of employees of the Zack Company, and whose second purpose (at the time) was to contribute to other 501(c3) [i.e., not for profit] charities.

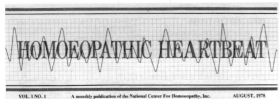

VOL. 1 NO. 1   A monthly publication of the National Center For Homoeopathy, Inc.   AUGUST, 1978

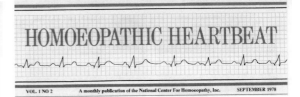

VOL. 1 NO 2   A monthly publication of the National Center For Homoeopathy, Inc.   SEPTEMBER 1978

The 1979 elections

For the NCH board of directors elections in 1979, there were six nominations:

Steffe G. Witney, RN (Pittsburgh, PA), Nick Nossaman, MD, (Denver, CO), Sandra M. Chase, MD, (Fairfax, VA), Willard Eldredge, (NJ— Humphreys Pharmacy), J. Laurence McCarty, (Mc Lean, VA— a lawyer), and Sheldon Clark, (Sandy Spring, MD— a lawyer).

According to Christine Zack (in 1997), the NCH board was operating with a large division. Panos, president of the NCH board of directors, was on one side—supporting classical homœopathy— and Packman, the executive director, was on the other— a businessman who "saw the economic potential of this modality if it could be unhinged from its cultish facade."

Says Zack, "At its barest roots it was a power conflict between two groups. It was WAR, plain and simple. Without any doubts, a line was drawn in the sand, all the players lined up on one side or the other, and the battle commenced. Then the tactics got dirty."

When the election for the NCH board was held at the 1979 membership meeting, proxy votes were used for the first time. 100 proxies were submitted. Richard Monet, who had counted the votes for the board, brought it to the board's attention that of the 100 proxy votes, 64 were brought by a single member— Forrest Murphy, one of the AFH trustees. It was also pointed out that the 64 people who submitted proxies had become members of the NCH to vote— none had been members prior to the election. The result of these 64 proxy votes on the final tally was that Dr. Chase (who was supportive of Dr. Panos' position) lost the election, and Mr. McCarty won.

Of the incident, Dr. Richard Moskowitz later said, "The use of proxy votes was unprecedented… and reflected the growing split between the broad-based membership of the National Center and the overriding financial interests of the Foundation, which sought to control the Center 'from above.'"

Chase recalled she had become increasingly vocal about the amount of control the executive director was wielding, and noted that Harris Coulter, who was *not* on the board of directors was often at meetings and was allowed to vote. She had raised this as an issue, and was removed from the board by the proxy votes.

That year, the American Foundation moved to Lee Highway in Falls Church, Virginia. It had bought a building for about $120,000 as the headquarters for the American Institute

of Homeopathy, the National Center, the American Association of Homeopathic Pharmacists, and the American Board of Homeotherapeutics. All American homœopathy was now under a single roof.

Over the next year, the friction between the board of directors continued. Packman appeared to be asserting control in the direction of the organization, and Panos, the elected president, expressed the sentiment that in a membership organization, the chain of command comes from the members, through the president, and *then* to the executive director who implements the ideas.

Added to this were issues few wish to discuss— even now, 20 years later. Most of the underlying discontent had to do with the organization's financial control and the increasing sense that Packman was working to keep the status-quo and was involved in "shady" financial dealings with NCH funds.

As one older homœopath said, "There is a sense of honor about those times, and people still don't want to talk about it."

Such dealings have been alluded to but never spoken of directly in any of the conversations I have had with those involved in the organization at the time. It was, certainly, a time of increasing stress.

It was under these circumstances the stage was set for the membership meeting in Chicago in 1980.

The 1980 elections

At that meeting, the following were nominated for the board:

John A Borneman, III (Borneman Pharmacy in Norwood, PA), Sheldon Clark, Christine (Zack) DeZutel, George Guess, MD, Richard Moskowitz, MD, Elaine Ryan, (the President of the Washington DC Layman's League), Frank Vargo, and Jacquelyn Wilson, MD.

One hundred members attended the meeting, and 277 proxy votes were cast. The proxy votes were in the hands of four people— Drs. Henry Williams, Maesimund Panos, David Wember, and Ann Panos Jones. The result was the election of Guess, Moskowitz, Wilson, and Ryan— and the removal of DeZutel and Clark.

Said Moskowitz (in 1997), "It was a defensive move. Like FDR stacking the Supreme Court. It was the way we could survive."

Says Ms. Zack, "As for me, the exit was clearly marked. Time bears out that the actions in Chicago followed by the new board's directives, brought the whole house of cards tumbling down. Their fondest wish was to be financially and directionally independent from the AFH. Their wish came to fruition."

Harris Coulter, in the *Homoeopathic Heartbeat*, wrote of the results: "The block vote was employed to deny re-election to two board members, Christine DeZutel and Sheldon Clark, whom the majority had counted on to serve for several more years and one of whom had made a considerable financial contribution to the National Center… The board was counting on DeZutel to assume presidency… When a board member has been trained for two years to take the highest office, and is prepared to do so, it is politically frivolous to vote that person off the board."

The person who "made a considerable contribution" was DeZutel who, Packman told me, had given the NCH about $30,000 and "had promised more."

The *Homoeopathic Heartbeat* reported that the first move of the new board was a certified audit to be carried out through the executive committee and a request by the executive committee to have the executive director "exercise expenditure control." Harris Coulter (at the time), viewed the meeting as an inquisition into Packman's management of the NCH.

The board, according to Moskowitz, was interested in looking at "the top–heavy administrative staff" which accounted for two-thirds of the annual budget. According to Moskowitz's recollection, the new group had many questions about the past policies of the AFH— going back as far as the splitting of the NCH into a separate entity. Had the split been necessary? Were there *real* legal reasons for doing so? Or were there other motives?

As the group began to ask these questions, they were cautioned by the AFH trustees to cease the inquiry— which, said Moskowitz, "Made us even more suspicious that there was dirty-pool going on."

The new group of six began to see the financial ties to the AFH as a liability to the NCH rather than an asset. It began to investigate the organization's finances.

There were other issues as well. The NCH summer school the previous year had attracted only four medical doctors, and the six-page *Homoeopathic Heartbeat* had little to offer the membership. When the NCH requested funds for scholarships to Athens, or clinical preceptorships, they were turned down. And with Packman working for both the NCH and the AFH, was there a conflict of interest?

"After the election," said Moskowitz, "we had a clear majority on the board favoring decisive action to end our financial dependence on the Foundation and to get homœopathy back into the mainstream of the burgeoning holistic health movement."

The ultimatum

At a meeting of the NCH board of directors on January 21, 1981, Directors Eldredge, McCarty, Witney, and Weaver requested "the dissident majority" to resign.

On January 23, Dr. Nossaman, the NCH board president, received notice to vacate the premises.

On January 25, Panos told McCarty the six new members would not step down.

On February 3, 1981, a compromise was offered, which included the following:

- The NCH board would be reduced from 11 members to 9 members.
- Four of the members would be: Eldredge, McCarty, Witney, and DeZutel (Mrs. Weaver would step down and DeZutel would step in).
- Nossaman would remain as president of the board.
- Four of the six (Guess, Moskowitz, Ryan, Wilson, Panos, Wember) would remain on the board of directors.
- The election of the board by the membership would be suspended (i.e., the board would become self-perpetuating).

The rejection

All six "dissidents" rejected the proposal. Nossaman resigned the presidency. Of the times, Nossaman writes (1997):

"From the very beginning of my time on the board, there was a very strong 'us vs. them' theme everywhere I went, and everyone was aligned with one side or another. The tremendous polarity was something I hadn't experienced before on anything near that scale, and I— by my personality, as a natural life-long peacemaker— had the naive belief that I could help heal the rifts, and bring the community together.

"The rifts, however were deep and incurable, and I gave up on that idea finally. In retrospect, the outcome was as it should have been for the best of the organization, although the new administration was like jumping from the frying-pan into another frying-pan. I was really glad I left when I did, though I felt like a failure at the time."

On February 18, 1981, Dr. Wyrth Post Baker, the chairman of the AFH board of trustees, wrote the following letter to the homœopathic community:

"The Trustees of the Foundation have been disturbed for the past two years by evidence of dissent between members of the governing boards of the National Center for Homopathy. We have further been disturbed by its failure to use funds for maximum effectiveness and economy, and apparent neglect of certain responsibilities… The Trustees of the Foundation have become so disturbed and disappointed by the events of the past year that they have reluctantly and with profound regret withheld all funds from the National Center as of December 31, 1980, and requested the officers to vacate the premises owned by the Foundation as of February 12, 1981."

An injunction was obtained to prevent any of the new NCH board members from entering the premises.

Packman had signed a contract with the NCH before the election and was, officially, still its executive director. He was asked by the remaining NCH board to assist them in finding alternate funding. A week after vacating the premises in Falls Church, Packman had made no attempt to assist in fund-raising and his contract was cancelled by the new NCH board.

The aftermath

A committee called "The Ad Hoc Committee for the Preservation of Homœopathy in the United States" was formed by Harris Coulter, Christine DeZutel, Willard Eldredge, Steffe Witney, and J. Laurence McCarty.

They produced a seven-page letter to the homœopathic community that said, in part:

"The board acquired a majority of six physicians (of whom five were inexperienced in the conduct of homœopathic affairs on the national scene)… furthermore the loss of a lawyer (Sheldon Clark) and a businesswoman (Mrs. Christine DeZutel) meant, in our view, a definite impairment of the Board's capacity to deal with the many important issues confronting homœopathy today."

They said that, "The six directors have taken possession of the NCH files and records."

The rancor was thick enough to be cut with a knife.

What few files the NCH were able to rescue from the Lee Highway offices were removed to Dr. David Wember's office in Falls Church, Virginia. Space was made for a temporary office, and two volunteers, Millie Donaldson and Grace King, sorted through all the paperwork in an attempt to re-establish contact with the NCH membership. In the transition the entire membership listing of the north-east United States was lost.

In discussing the times with Harris Coulter in 1997, he admitted that, in retrospect, he picked the wrong side to come down on. He said, at the time, he was afraid if the NCH lost its funding, it would cease operating. "What I did

not consider was that Maisie would step in and finance it herself." [The NCH gained financial independence through the generosity of several private contributors, among them Maisie's husband John Holtvoight — JW]

"My loyalties were divided between Packman and Maisie. Packman had obtained a $15,000 grant from the Foundation in the early 1970s for me to write *Homeopathic Science and Modern Medicine*. It was the only grant I ever got. It was hard for me to go against Ralph. And Maisie was working with the younger docs and I felt out of the loop. I decided to go with the money.

"Here I made another mistake by trusting Ralph's political judgment more than Maisie's. She obviously knew the homœopathic world better than he did. But I thought his guidance, together with the DeZutel millions would keep the Center alive."

In March of 1981 a mailing was sent to all known NCH members, and in April 1981 the first four-page issue of *Homœopathy Today* was mailed out.

The aftermath: The unwinding

In early 1981, Dr. Wyrth Post Baker and Ralph Packman approached Christine Zack DeZutel with an idea to form a new organization. Within a month, "The Ad Hoc Committee for the Preservation of Homeopathy in the United States" formed the new organization: The American Center for Homeopathy. It was funded primarily by the AFH although, according to Zack (in 1997), "In time we were able to support ourselves from our own activities and contributions." DeZutel became president of the new organization. The other members of the Board were Willard Eldredge, Harris Coulter, Steffe Witney, and J. Laurence McCarty.

The ACH remained in the Lee Highway offices in Falls Church and shared the space with the AFH, AIH, and the AAHP. Its goals were similar to those of the National Center for Homeopathy:

- Training physicians
- Training laymen in domestic situations
- Formation of an Advisory Council
- Fiscal and fiduciary responsibility

It offered a free subscription to the new four-page magazine, *American Homoeopath*, until end of 1981. It was edited by Harris Coulter.

Coulter was also busy organizing an educational program for the ACH. Held in Melbourne, Florida, it was timed to run concurrently with the NCH course at Millersville— an undisguised effort to undermine the NCH program. Among the teachers were Drs. Ahmed Currim and Karl Robinson.

While Coulter admitted of the split that, "the sad facts were these disputes were all over personalities," it did not stop the flow of barbed rhetoric with the pen of Moskowitz writing for the NCH and Coulter writing for the ACH.

By August 1981, sensing the name was too close to that of the National Center, the name of the organization was changed to "The Homeopathic Headquarters of America," and the magazine was renamed *American Homeopathy.* Robert Williams was hired as "manager" and later served as executive director until July 1982.

In March 1982, representatives from 21 homœopathic organizations met in Washington, DC. Arranged by the Homeopathic Headquarters and called "The Joint Conference for the Preservation of Homeopathy," it was attended by representatives of all the homœopathic pharmacies and of the newly formed International Foundation for Homeopathy, as well as representatives from the AIH and the AFH. The National Center was prominently absent from the meeting, never having been invited.

By April 1982, Coulter was no longer part of the organization. Coulter said (in 1997) he had the feeling that Williams had been hired just to keep an eye on him. He subsequently found, upon returning from a successful educational program in Florida, that one of the AFH trustees reported to the Foundation that Harris had embezzled school money. Coulter found out about this allegation from another AFH trustee much later. He was never confronted directly about it.

"It became clear that my own board was turning against me," he said.

Coulter began to question the organization's finances and discovered the ACH had paid Packman about $6000 for "unspecified services." Coulter asked about the accounting.

"This caused considerable commotion, and I understand they spent a whole weekend on conference calls." Coulter was voted off the board, and the next day all the office locks were changed.

Within a short time of the organization's founding the ties with Packman were severed because, as Zack suggested in 1997, "of unethical side activities."

Williams became editor of the newsletter. John A. Borneman III replaced McCarty as treasurer.

When I asked Jack Borneman (in 1997) about his involvement in the organization, he gave me a very candid answer:

"I didn't know any of the people. I was busy running the family pharmacy in Norwood. I was not involved in any of the organizations and I guess I was politically naive. They asked me if I'd be treasurer, and I said 'OK.' There really wasn't much to do. There was very little discussion. Chris made all the decisions. I'd go down for a meeting, listen to it all, and then sign the checks."

In April 1982, the AIH voted to leave the "umbrella" and locate itself with the NCH in Washington, DC. In September the same year the American Board of Homeotherapeutics also moved to the National Center.

In July, 1982, executive director Williams was replaced by Arden Hyde, and Jonathan Harger became editor of *American Homeopathy.*

In the masthead in August 1982 we find Joe DeZutel (Chris' husband) listed as a vice president along with Eldredge.

In 1982, the Homeopathic Headquarters of America sponsored a seminar in Melbourne, Florida, in conjunction with the IFH. It was a one day introduction to homœopathy taught by George Vithoulkas.

By January 1983 the magazine was accepting advertising. There were large ads from the two new French pharmacies in the USA— Boiron and Dolisos. At that time, Dolisos was working closely with a group, including Floyd Weston and F. Fuller Royal, MD, at a clinic in Las Vegas— all of whom were using EAV machines and a new machine called the Accupath— and "machine homœopathy" became a prominent feature of the writing in the magazine.

In April 1983 the Homeopathic Headquarters of America changed its name to the United States Homeopathic Association (an easy acronym: USHA) and moved from Lee Highway in Falls Church, Virginia, to Lee Highway in Arlington, Virginia. At this time, the AFH left the premises and took possession of the library.

The new board was Chris DeZutel as President, Joe DeZutel as vice president, and Marion Power and Rolf Mayer— who

Volume 1 No. 1   *A monthly publication of the American Center for Homeopathy*   April, 1981

Vol. 2, No. 11   November, 1982

swapped secretary/treasurer positions.

The magazine's content drifted toward more general "health" issues, and less homœopathy. The October 1983 edition had a large article on chelation therapy. The same issue also announced the formation of "the advisory council"— a group of prominent physicians and pharmacists consisting of Wyrth Post Baker, MD, Tariq Kuraishy from Dolisos, Robert Mendelsohn, MD, Richard Pitcairn, DVM, John Renner, MD, and F. Fuller Royal, MD.

The council's role was obviously limited, since when I asked Pitcairn (in 1997) about his responsibilities, he said he remembered nothing about it at all and was surprised to find he was listed!

At this time several different magazines, all with basically the same content, were produced— an affiliate edition (for health food stores and marketing— in green), a professional edition (for practitioners— in red), and a consumer edition (in blue). It appeared the organization was trying to find its niche and was casting out several nets. Says Zack, "Our publication grew in scope, size, and quality. Our paying membership grew exponentially. The wonder of it was we reached a lot of people brand new to homœopathy with no philosophical prejudices. We developed thousands of new members."

In May 1984 Joe DeZutel died unexpectedly of an aneurysm. The organization seemed to "stumble" and then right itself with just Chris DeZutel, Power, and Mayer at the helm. In August 1984 *American Homeopathy* became a glossy covered publication that supported "all approaches to homœopathy."

In 1984, the USHA successfully marketed the *Homœopathic Pharmacopoeia of the United States*. Shortly after it funded an animal experiment at the University of Georgia. According to Zack:

"A PhD there had developed a protocol a few years before wherein chickens could receive identical blows from a machine to their breast tissue. The initial experimentation had been developed at the request of the Georgia Poultry Growers' Association. Their members were suffering financial losses because the chickens developed serious bruising in transport and were down-graded in quality after slaughter. It turned out to be a perfect protocol to test homœopathic dilutions of *Arnica* on animal subjects, not influenced by the placebo effect. The rapidity of healing in the treated groups was astounding as compared to the control and un-medicated group. The 6X, 30X, and 200c potencies were utilized. A quite unexpected correlation became apparent when the data was tallied. The youngest of the chickens were most

benefited by the 6X potency whereas the older chickens benefited from the 200th potency. We were promised that the data would be published in a national veterinary magazine, but it never happened."

In late 1985, the United States Homeopathic Association ceased as an entity.

Says Zack, "although the USHA experienced some remarkable successes, it was never able to generate the level of funding necessary to experience great growth. Perhaps, in a real sense, I had seen too much, been lied to way too frequently, and completely lost the desire to play Don Quixote. The Board unanimously voted to cease operations."

The rights to the magazine, *American Homeopathy*, were bought by the Society for Ultra Molecular Medicine in Las Vegas, Nevada. It was under the editorship of Trevor Cook. The magazine was published for a brief time, and then ceased.

The name "United States Homeopathic Association" was purchased by a multi-level marketing company, headed by Floyd Weston, who tried to market a series of combination remedies using the pyramid marketing approach. The remedies were all "Approved by the United States Homeopathic Association." The group faded as fast as it came.

The aftermath: The rise

In the aftermath of the split from the AFH, the NCH board decided that they *must* continue three things: the annual meeting, the newsletter, and the summer school.

The annual meeting was set for May 1981 in Washington DC. One incident alone would describe the level of rancor: the hotel at which the meeting was to be held received an anonymous phone call telling them that the "NCH did not have the funds to run the meeting" and they should "get all the money in front."

But the meeting went on, and a new board was elected.

The summer school fell into place with Dr. Henry N. Williams serving as dean.

The NCH had several executive directors before the board decided that they— the directors— were doing pretty well developing the NCH policy and what was really needed was an efficient office staff. An office manager was hired in 1989 when the current executive director left for another position. Sharon Stevenson, who first attended the summer school in 1985, had been working in the office since 1988. She became the office manager in 1990 and was appointed executive director in 1994.

The rest of the story is in the main text.

Kent's Post–Graduate School in Philadelphia, PA

The following is a summary of the Post–Graduate School of Homœopathics' board meeting minutes, referred to on page 163. This document provides many insights into the school's workings. Since the "office of the corporation" was Kent's residence, the document provides us with an accurate accounting of when Kent moved to various locations within the city.

1890

"A meeting of persons interested in promoting the formation of an association to support an educational institution for the higher education of physicians in the philosophy and methods of homeopathy was held on Tuesday evening, October 28th, 1890 at 1419 Walnut Str., Philadelphia."

The first meeting of the Post Graduate School of Homœopathics was convened at the office of Dr. Kent, 1419 Walnut Street, Philadelphia.

Present were: John Pitcairn, Theo. P. Matthews, W. A. D. Pierce, R. B. Johnstone, William F. Kaercher, Robert Farley, Milton Powel, Franklin Powel, W. H. A. Fitz, John Massey, and William Baldwin.

John Pitcairn was elected president of the association. T. P. Matthews, solicitor, explained the steps necessary for incorporation.

December 11: A Bond of $5,000 was obtained by the board. Milton Powel resigned from the board, on advice of lawyers, to assume the treasurer position.

December 16: Discussion centered around the topic of a space for the school. They wanted a building in which they could operate a clinic, and the clinic would pay for the space above it. Faculty were suggested: Kent: materia medica and philosophy; Pierce: clinical medicine; A. G. Allen: eye and ear; F. Powel: Surgery; Fitz: obstetrics; Jennie Medley: diseases of women; Jean J. McKay: diseases of children. Kent was elected school dean, and Milton Powel registrar.

1891

January 15: To facilitate smooth transitions, the terms of the directors were staggered. The charter was approved. A suitable building was found at 1317 Ridge Ave. The rent was $45 a month. The fee for the spring semester was to be $50. Clinic hours were discussed. There would be two courses of lectures each year. The general clinic will be open between 12 p.m.

and 1 p.m. daily, except Sunday. Eye, ear and obstetrics were open Monday and Thursday; children's clinic and the Tocology clinic was opened Wednesday and Saturday; the surgical clinic was opened Tuesday and Friday.

Feb. 14: The charter was incorporated on Jan 21, 1891. The beginning income consisted of donations in the amount of $580. Each board member contributed $10. Pitcairn gave $500. They had $248 in expenses. 500 copies of the charter were to be printed. Permission was granted for the dean to advertise the school.

March 19: No meeting, since Kent was moving his office.

April 16: Office was moved to 1605 Walnut Street. No quorum.

May 21: First statement of income and expenses. Balance in hand was $216.64. Some expenses included: fixing clinic door, $1; 20 pounds of pellets, $3.60. Kent nominated as clinical assistants: W. R. Powel, Milton Powel, J. A. Tomhagen, W. W. Baldwin, C. A. Reger, Frederica Gladwin, and William Kaercher.

June 2: Kent nominated a group of people as honorary members of the Post Graduate School of Homœopathics. The list was voted and approved.

July 16, August 20, September 17, October 15: No quorum present, meetings adjourned.

November 19: Each member had to sign the following statement identified only as Article II:

"Section 1: The *Organon* of Samuel Hahnemann, edition of 1833, shall furnish the sole groundwork of principles to be taught in this school, and no principles at variance with the said work shall be taught at any time or under any circumstances, and any professor, tutor, or assistant found guilty of violating this principle must be removed from office.

Section 2: The said *Organon* must be accepted as teaching the only homœopathy recognized by this association, vis: the employment of the single remedy, dynamized medicines, and the minimum dose, not singly but collectively.

Section 3: Potentized medicines shall be used in the clinics of the school or schools maintained by this association under all circumstances, and under no circumstances shall crude drugs be made use of, either internally or externally for dynamic diseases (non-surgical) in the teaching or the clinics.

Section 4: It shall not be the object of the institution to teach the mechanical branches of the healing arts, such as belong to surgery, yet it shall not be considered opposed to the interests of the school to attend to any surgical case that may come under the care of the clinicians."

Kent and Matthews were to devise a seal for the institution. Kent presented the wording of the diploma that will be given. The diploma was approved to be printed.

December 17: Meeting cancelled— all the directors ill.

1892

January 4: No quorum present, meeting adjourned.

January 6: Letters of resignation were read from W. W. Baldwin, Milton Powel, Franklin Powel, and William R. Powel. Letter from W. W. Baldwin was to be returned to Dr. Baldwin with the statement : "This Board declines to consider any communications not from a member of the association assuming to criticize the board, and the writer will refrain from further impertinence of this character, and any further communication will remain unanswered."

A resolution was made by T. P. Matthews, concerning Dr. Baldwin's resignation of his lectureship.

"Dr. Baldwin began his course of lectures in accordance with the announcement on page 15 under the head of philosophy and undertook to teach the truths in the *Organon* of Hahnemann fearlessly in truth and verity and not abridged and distorted to suit the prevailing theories of the day, but that almost immediately he departed from this course and began teaching doctrine so opposed to those of the *Organon* that the members of the class and instructors protested to the Dean against being obliged to listen to such heretical teaching, and thereupon, the Dean having examined into the matter and found that W. W. Baldwin, MD, was teaching principles at variance with the said *Organon* and, therefore, in pursuance of his duty as set forth in section 1 article II of the constitution, immediately removed the said W, W. Baldwin, MD from his office as assistant lecturer."

January 21: Report on prescriptions filled in the clinic (2355 to Jan 15th). There are seven matriculates in the spring course, and eight in the winter course. New officers were elected.

February 18: Financial report: $66. 43 on hand, $47.86 spent. Kent says that coming year will have about $745 in expenses. Kent moved that Dr. W. Johnson become head of clinical medicine and the registrar of faculty. Kent said that he was advertising the school in several journals at his own expense. A contract for ads in *The Medical Advance* was presented at $30. He was given the OK to sign the contract.

March 17: 537 prescriptions were filled in February. A price of $75 for copper plate or $85 for steel plate of the diploma was presented. A. G. Allen resigns.

April 21, May 19, June 16, July 21, Sept 15, Oct 20: no quorum present, meetings adjourned.

November 17: Number of prescriptions filled: July, 561; Aug, 613; Sept , 566; Oct , 597.

Drs. Keith, Mary H. Johnson and Rosalie Stankowitch get $300 scholarships. NY Central Homeopathic Union donates $100 for scholarships. Kent nominates Allan S. Ironside for membership.

November 21: Minutes from year approved.

December 20: Balance of $27.21. 100 new patients and 513 old patients at dispensary. Allan S. Ironside was approved for membership after he signed Section II as above.

1893

January 19, February 16: No quorum present, meetings adjourned.

February 23: Balance $75.45 "The free dispensary attached to the Post Graduate School of Homœopathics was opened on Jan 24, 1891. The need for it and the measure of its usefulness are shown in the following significant figures taken from its official reports: During its second year, 7,234 prescriptions were made to 1026 patients in the clinics and 878 outside visits." A leaflet to be printed, annual subscriptions are invited. The free dispensary is described as having visits gratis "… the patients are very poor have received treatment from skilled physicians, and have benefitted thereby. Otherwise they would have languished in suffering and misery."

"Should you know of any persons (irregardless of age, sex, race, creed, or color) suffering from disease, who are too poor to employ the services of a skilled physician, it will be a charitable act to inform them that they can receive at this dispensary skilled medical treatment, free of charge without attendant expenses"

March 16, April 20: No quorum present, meetings adjourned.

May 18: There were 73 new cases and 487 old cases seen in April. Gladwin moved up to clinical instructor.

September 21: Fix gas fixtures.

October 19, October 31, November 16: No quorum present, meetings adjourned.

December 21: $88.38 on hand. F. A. Davis Co. donates a set of Hering's *Guiding Symptoms* to the school.

1894

January 18: Annual report: 13 have matriculated, 3 degrees granted, 7,181 prescriptions have been written, 663 out patients visited, 1,335 prescriptions were written for 940 new patients. $75.05 balance.

January 30: No quorum present, meetings adjourned.

February 1: Dr. Keith read a letter from T. M. Dillingham in NY saying the Philadelphia Post-Graduate school will soon be dead. A letter will be written asking Dr. Dillingham if that is true before any action is taken.

February 15: No quorum present, meeting adjourned.

March 15: 758 old cases, and 117 new cases were seen in February. $107.14 balance.

April 19: No quorum present, meeting adjourned.

April 26: $11.64 balance. 759 old cases and 166 new cases were seen in March. C. Louis Olds is added as a clinical instructor.

May 17: 635 old cases and 103 new cases were seen during April.

June 21: No quorum present, meeting adjourned.

August 16: During June-August there were 271 new cases seen and 1706 old cases seen. The classes are growing and there is a need to find a new building before the beginning of the fall term.

August 21 A discussion of moving to 1223-1225 Ridge Ave. for $75.00 a month. No action taken.

September 20: 628 old cases seen and 11 new cases. $71.76 balance.

October 5: 587 old cases seen and 69 new cases. Mr. Massey, a real estate agent, has offered two properties. He outlines the terms upon which 613 and 615 Spring Garden Street could be purchased for $7,500.

October 18: Balance on hand $239.43. 529 old cases seen and 67 new cases, 2 new home visits, 58 old home visits. Authorization to buy the Spring Garden Street properties.

November 15: 638 old cases seen, 91 new cases, and one obstetrics case.

November 23: The Board moved to accept a $7,000 debt. The building was purchased from Charles E. Trommer.

1895

January 17: During 1894, 961 outside visits were made and a total of 8997 prescriptions were filled.

January 24: Minutes read and approved. New board elected.

March 28: No quorum present, meeting adjourned.

June 17: Draft of an appeal to the public to help with the dispensary. To be worked on.

July 18, August 15, September 19, October 17: No quorum present, meetings adjourned.

November 21: text of draft circular:

"Were you ever critically ill? If so, you remember the relief and comfort you experienced when you were visited by your own physician. You can imagine how distressing it would be if you were very sick and were unable to procure the services of any physician to treat you according to your preference. There are thousands of poor people in this city in that very predicament. Look at the figures which prove it.

"The free dispensary attached to the Philadelphia Post Graduate School of Homœopathics was first opened January 24, 1891 at 1317 Ridge Ave. By the close of the year it had made 2,806 prescriptions at the dispensary and made 100 visits to patients at their homes. The numbers have steadily increased until, in the close of 1894 the dispensary was driven to seek more commodious quarters at its present location 613-15 Spring Garden Street. Last month it treated 1,047 patients. Its total record to July 1, 1895 shows 32,375 patients prescribed for at the dispensary, and 4,245 patients at their own homes. This grand total is being added to month by month in an increasing ratio.

"In all those thousands of cases those treated have been at no expense whatever. They have not been called to pay for the services of the physician. They have not spent a single penny for drugs or medicines. The services have been to them as free as air. Of course it cannot be carried on without expense. The pecuniary burden this far has been borne by the few earnest workers who inaugurated and have carried on the work; but it has grown too great for them and is still growing. Without the aid of the charitable public they will break down under its weight and this great charity will be destroyed. Won't you lend us a helping hand? We will be glad to have you as an annual contributor in a sum that you feel justified in giving. Failing in that, will you not give us a some contribution for our present needs, no matter how small? A dime or a quarter which you will not miss from your superfluity will enable some sick and suffering brother to receive the care and attention that he craves and so greatly needs."

Year	prescriptions	out patient
1891	2,806	400
1892	7,234	878
1893	7,181	663
1894	8,997	961
1895(7/1)	6,157	1,343

grand total 36,620

November 30, December 6, December 19: No quorum present, meetings adjourned.

1896

January 16: A verbal report by Kent about the school year in 1895.

February 27: A. S. Ironside read a letter from T. P. Matthews dated Feb 21, 1896.

"Dear Doctor:

When you were last at my office you made a confidential communication to me to the effect that Dr. Kent, in delivering his lectures at the Post Graduate School of Homœopathics took the occasion to infuse his homœopathic teaching with the "New Church" doctrine to an extent that was giving the school a reputation as a Swedenborgian institution, and that to such an extent that two directors, Hopkins and Pierce were withholding their pecuniary support upon the declared ground that it had become sectarian in character; to use your own words, "it is common talk with Dr. Hopkins and Dr. Pierce that they are not going to give anything to support a Swedenborgian School."

These charges, were they true, would show that a course of action was being pursued such as would seriously impair the usefulness of the school and I have felt it my duty to investigate the matter with the result that I find these charges wholly unfounded. I am satisfied that Dr. Kent does *not* couple Swedenborgian teachings with his homœopathic doctrines, and both Dr. Hopkins and Dr. Pierce, in reply to a direct question, unequivocally and with emphasis deny that they have ever said or thought the institution was a sectarian one or that any theology is or has ever been taught within.

I have, of course, preserved your confidence hitherto, and have not revealed the identity of my informant. If these communications had been made to me alone, the matter might drop here, but in the course of my inquiry it has become evident to me that you have conveyed to others the same charges and thus occasioned the spread of an opinion— as I believe without warrant of fact to support it— which is hurtful to the school as well as to Dr. Kent. I therefore request you to make these statements openly to the board of directors, which, under the circumstances is your plain duty to do, and permit them to be properly investigated by a duly appointed committee."

A discussion followed. Dr. Pierce was not able to recollect ever having made such statements to Dr. Ironside. Ironside withdrew his comments but then said it was his belief that Kent had introduced Swedenborgian doctrine to the injury of the school, and such a grievance should be presented to the board. If founded in fact, the practice should be stopped. Kent asked a committee to investigate.

March 19: No quorum present, meeting adjourned.

April 16: Meeting at 2009 Walnut St (Kent moved again).

May 21: No quorum present, meeting adjourned.

July 1: 2,000 announcements were distributed. Report of the committee on the "Ironside affair" through the President, John Pitcairn. The charge and specification take up about eight pages in the ledger book (from page 240). A summary is offered here:

"The accusation should take such a form as will enable all the parties interested, both the accuser, the accused, and the judges, to know with certainty and definitiveness, exactly what disputed points are being tried in this case.

1.The doctrines which are distinctively those of Emanuel Swedenborg are numerous and range over wide fields in science, philosophy, theology, and religion. The accusation is merely that Swedenborgian doctrine had been introduced into teaching at the school, without defining or specifying which doctrine is alluded to.

2. "…a doctrine might be introduced casually by way of an illustration of the subject matter, without injury but with positive benefit."

3. "Injury might result if the Swedenborgian doctrine so introduced was at variance with the the system of homœopathy as taught in the *Organon* of Samuel Hahnemann, Edition 1833. Injury could also occur from the teaching of theology of any character which would be at variance with homeopathy if the class instructed was thereby made to consider that restraint or coercion was being exercised upon their individual freedom of choice as to religious beliefs…"

The committee decided that the accusations were "…vague, general, and indefinite…" and they did not contain any specifications.The board asked Dr. Ironside to offer specific charges. They asked for it in writing. Two letters were sent to him, copies of which are in the minutes. He did not comply with either request. On May 2nd he replied that he had nothing to say on the matter.

The committee finds that without specific charges, and since Ironside did not say that Kent was *not* teaching the *Organon* (as stated in the by-laws), he was not at variance with the principles to those which were to be taught. Since there are no specific charges, it has no way to take any action and Dr. Ironside's complaint is only an opinion.

The committee consisted of Pitcairn, Glenn, and Kaercher.

Exhibits were attached, and the board asked for Ironside's resignation. It also wanted his diploma back. ("requested to return to the board for cancellation the diploma evidencing the Degree of Master of Homœopathics").

November 19, November 23: No quorum present, meetings adjourned.

December 17: General business and reading of minutes.

1897

January 4, February 18: General business and reading of minutes.

March 18: A report on clinic visits in March. 137 new patients, 798 old patients. 168 new home visits, 429 old home visits.

May 20: No meetings were to be held during the summer.

October 21: General business and reading of minutes.

November 18, December 20: No quorum present, meetings adjourned.

1898

January 20: No quorum present, meeting adjourned.

February 17: A report that the north wall of building in poor condition and should be repaired.

March 17: A report that the building is in need of considerable repair.

April 21: The wall has been re-pointed and other repairs made.

May 18: Harvey Farrington is listed as a lecturer for the first time.

June 16, July 21, Aug 18, September 15, October 20: No quorum present, meeting adjourned.

November 17: Verbal report on school and dispensary.

December 15: List of active members read.

1899

January 19: Minutes read.

February 16, March 16: No quorum present, meetings adjourned.

May 18: Julia Loos resigns because she is moving to Harrisburg.

June 15, July 20, Aug 17: No quorum present, meetings adjourned.

Sept. 21: The place of meeting was moved to 2133 Walnut Street.

1900

January 18: The 10th annual meeting.

Kent read aloud two communications: one from the faculty

of Dunham College, in Chicago, and one from the board of directors of Dunham College. A proposition was made to affiliate the Post Graduate School with the Dunham College. A request was made by the faculty and the Board of Directors to have the dean and the faculty move to Chicago. E. D. Seaton, manager of the Dunham College in Chicago, was empowered to agree on the terms of affiliation.

It was decided that the affiliation should be accepted, and the details were to be worked out at the next meeting.

February 24: A special meeting was held to discuss the proposal from Dunham College. The following points were made:

1. The usual course of instruction in medicine in the US had been three years.

2. Now, the colleges are all becoming four–year institutions. Taking the Post–Graduate course makes the medical education five years.

3. Many students could not bear the expense of "taking instruction in an institution located at a distance from the college at which they receive their degree, in consequence the Post–Graduate School is deprived of many students who would otherwise attend classes."

4. There is restrictive legislation in the Commonwealth of Pennsylvania, making it difficult to form a full school. "…and there is other restrictive legislation of this commonwealth which tends to hinder and embarrass this school in the discharge of the duties which it was incorporated to perform."

5. Dunham College is duly incorporated, has a four-year course, and teaches pure homœopathy.

5. Dunham asked that the Post–Graduate School move to Chicago as an extension of the Dunham College.

6. That the Board of Directors of the Post–Graduate School of Homœopathics accepts the invitation with the following conditions:

Condition 1: The Post–Graduate School of Homœopathics be allowed to operate under its constitution and its own name.

Condition 2: that the Post–Graduate School be allowed to operate under its own by-laws.

Condition 3: That the Dean of the Post–Graduate School be James Tyler Kent.

Condition 4: That the curriculum remain the same.

These conditions were accepted by E. D. Seaton, director of Dunham College.

March 15: Kent verbally resigns from the organization. The dispensary will close on April 1.

April 5: The building would be taken back by Charles Trommer, the mortgage holder.

It was reported that Drs. Gladwin and Ives took records from the record cases without permission.

Farrington reported that the Lippe *Repertory* was missing.

It was reported that Dr. Farrington was in possession of the Kent *Repertory* used at the clinic.

It was requested by several doctors (Hess, Stokes, Lewis, Phelps, Burgess, Baer, and Boggess) that they wish to continue the clinic as a charity to the poor. They plan to rent a room opposite the present clinic. It will be, they hope, self supporting. They wish to buy some of the furnishings.

Mary Ives wrote on March 20, asking the janitoress be allowed to stay in the building because she has no other housing at the present time. She also asks if she can take the medicine case that was in use.

F. E. Gladwin wrote on March 22, and asks if she could obtain one of the record cases for her use. Also, if she could buy some of the supplies at cost.

It was reported that before Dr. Kent left for Chicago, he expressed his disapproval of the use of the clinic, "expressing his fear that Dr. Cooper did not know these persons as well as he— Dr. Kent— did, and the opinion that we ought not permit them to continue any work in our name, or so as to assume any recommendation on our part. The doctor had, on the other hand, expressed great confidence in Dr. Ives, saying that whatever she should undertake to do we could depend upon as being right."

It was said that some of the patients were so poor that the 10 cents usually expected could not be counted upon. T. P. Matthews suggested turning the whole operation over to Dr. Cooper, but to disallow the use of the Post–Graduate School name. The persons who took the records should be asked to return them.

April 17, April 20: No quorum present, meetings adjourned.

April 25: Meeting was held in room 1304 of the Land Title building in Philadelphia.

The property at 613-15 Spring Garden St. was sold to Charles Trommer.

New York: 1984 Different people, same story

The American Academy of Homeopathic Physicians, from page 425

In 1984, a letter from the American Academy of Homeopathic Physicians from Old Westbury, New York, was received by a number of homœopaths in the USA. Until then, no one had heard of this organization. The letter read:

Dear Doctor:

The nomination committee of the American Academy of Homeopathic Medicine has the honor to inform you that you have been selected for Fellowship in the 1984 Register of the Academy.

To activate your Fellowship, kindly complete the enclosed form and return it with your check or money order for $150.

You will be proud to display the beautiful Fellowship Diploma in your home or office and you will be one of those privileged to use the designation FAAHM (Fellow of the American Academy of Homeopathic Medicine).

It was signed by Gregory Miller, MD, FAAHM.

When the letter was brought to my attention I phoned Dr. Miller to find out more. Miller claimed to be the "leading homœopath in the country" and had been a member of the AIH for "some time." He said he was "in public health" but wouldn't give a name of the hospital he was working at. When the National Center was mentioned he said, "I'll give you a run for the money…"

Within two weeks, another piece of mail arrived from the same address:

The newly formed Board of Homeopathic Medicine is the first organ to offer BOARD CERTIFICATION that will be recognized nationally and internationally. Check one:

❏ I have been in the active practice of homeopathic medicine for more than five years. I request a certificate based on the Grandfather Provision and Rules of the American Board of Homeopathic Medicine. I have enclosed copies of my credentials and a certified check for $500.

❏ I would like to sit for the specialty exam to be given in July 1985. Enclosed is a check for $300. I understand that upon passing the board examination I will be required to remit $200 for the certification fee.

Gregory Miller, it seems, had gone to medical school in Mexico, and was trained there in homœopathy. According to a letter from Dr. James Stephenson, he was not registered as a physician in New York. Miller had never been a member of the AIH, although he had subscribed to the *Journal*.

The AAHM published one magazine (with several articles taken from other journals, and a logo copied from the AIH's mark) and advertised a "national conference" with a list of prominent speakers. Two of the speakers told me they had never been contacted by the organization and knew nothing of it.

The journal listed 45 names as "Charter Fellows and Editorial Advisory Board." I knew 11 of those names. All, when asked, knew nothing of the organization or why their names had appeared.

Within six months, the AAHM was no longer visible. The phone had been disconnected. An informed source said, about a year later, that Gregory Miller had died.

Appendix C

The graduates
The practitioners

The graduates

King's four–volume *History of Homœopathy in America* gives a history of each of the homœopathic schools at the time (1905) and includes a list of all the school's graduates.

Some schools listed the graduate's name, graduation year, and where they were from; some schools listed the graduates by last name with first initials only; and one school (Hering in Chicago) listed the graduates but without the graduation year.

In 1993 I databased King's listing of 15,003 names. With this information I could easily plot the rise and the beginning of the fall of homœopathic movement.

But what happened after 1905?

Many schools closed within 10 years, and the records of graduates disappeared into the ether. Few papers were kept.

I have a *1941 AIH Directory of Homeopathic Practitioners* in my library and it lists the practitioners along with the schools they attended and their graduation dates. I entered *that* data into my pre-existing database. Of the 6,698 entries, 112 were listed as "not in practice" and 166 were listed as "retired," bringing the number of those claiming to be homœopaths in the USA in 1941 to 6,420.

There were many physicians trained before 1905 who were still in practice 40 years later. 2,205 of those listed in 1941 were found in King's work. The oldest, Thomas Steven Dunning, graduated from Hahnemann Philadelphia in 1870 and was still practicing in Philadelphia 71 years later!

There were 68 people in the 1941 listing who graduated before 1905 but were, somehow, missing from King's work.

I am doubly fortunate because my 1941 book had been the personal copy of S. Alexander Klein, MD, who was on the AIH Membership Committee, and it was carefully annotated— listing new practitioners in the margins, and crossing out those who had died. The work was obviously done late in 1942 because there are entries that are marked "died 11/20/42."

Through this listing I can now document those who had graduated from homœopathic schools between 1905 and 1940. It is, of course, a general figure— I do not know how many of the graduates had died earlier than 1940, or how many of them were not in practice and chose not to be listed. Of the 21 graduates of Cleveland in 1904, 11 were still in practice in 1940, and of the 66 graduates of Hahnemann Philadelphia in the same year, 28 were still listed as homœopaths 36 years later.

When I compared the number of graduates in the Hahnemann *Yearbook* for 1933 against the number of 1933 graduates listed in the *Directory* I found that of the 114 graduates, 97 were listed— roughly 85%. And of the 120 who graduated Hahnemann in 1937, 119 were listed!

Of the 6,698 people in the 1941 directory, 317 (a bit over 4%) had not graduated from "homœopathic schools," i.e., they learned homœopathy after graduating from a conventional medical school.

The database was brought up to a more recent level by including the graduates listed in the *Homeopathic Directory of 1963*. Included were those who had "received undergraduate training in homœopathy in the course of obtaining their MD degree." What this means is that all graduates of Hahnemann Medical College were asked if they wished to be included in the directory, and those who returned the request were listed. Not many were practicing homœopaths, but there is no way to determine the exact figure. I once looked at the Pennsylvania listings with Jack Borneman. His commentary was like this: "Hmm… oh! He's a heart specialist… he does mostly surgery… hmmm… this one is a urologist… this one… my dad helped him through school and now he won't look at homœopathy… hmm… oh! him… he orders only *Gelsemium* and *Nux*…"

The information extracted from the expanded database can be graphed and the rise and decline of homœopathy can be seen at a glance.

The decline in numbers after 1941 was rapid. It might be accounted for by the fact that homœopathy was de–emphasized at Hahnemann after 1935. In 1941 the Hahnemann Medical College had a graduating class of 128. By 1963 only 34 of the class of about 90 are listing themselves in the homœopathic directory. The graduating class of 1945 had 121 people. 18 years later only 17 of the class claim to be homœopaths. From a 1952 graduating class of 77, only 5 were listed in the *Directory* of 1963.

But even with the influx of new "homœopaths," practitioner numbers dropped precipitously in the 22 years between 1941 and 1963. California, which boasted 389 practitioners in the *1941 Directory*, had only 49 listed in 1963; Illinois which had 395 practitioners in 1941 had but 19 in 1963; New York went from 1,685 to 123; Tennessee went from 12 to none. The drop can also be clearly seen in the cities: Brooklyn, New York, boasted 383 homœopaths in 1941; there were but 30 listed 22 years later.

Across the river, New York City had 686 homœopaths

listed in the 1941 directory. By 1963 there were only 51.

And of the 1,477 practitioners listed in the *1963 Directory*, only 217 were AIH members.

A measure of the "true homœopath" might be to count those attaining the DHt. Of those in the 1963 listing, there were only 81 DHts listed— a bit over 5%.

It may be noted that there are 191 practitioners listed in the 1963 Directory who graduated prior to 1940 but were not found in the *1941 Directory.*

The figures graphed here are approximate, at best. I have yet to correlate all the obituaries found in the *Journal of the American Institute of Homeopathy* with the graduation lists found in King's work and with the practitioner lists found in the various directories. Such a cross reference might yield a few more details and a more accurate figure for the period between 1905 and 1960.

Yet the graph presents a clear picture. The first peak was in 1881 with 442 graduates. There was a slight drop, with the number rising to the high of 490 graduates in 1897.

The last accurate figure is from King in 1905 where he lists 198 graduates. I have databased 149 graduates from 1906, although the figure is probably between 10% and 15% higher through the years from 1906 to, perhaps, 1930.

It is clear by the time the Flexner report was published in 1910 that the schools were already in a sharp decline. The rise from 1925 to 1940 was composed, in the large part, of graduates of New York Homœopathic and Hahnemann Medical College in Philadelphia.

The women graduates were, on average, about 12% of the graduate population— 11.21% to be exact. The largest percentage of women graduates was in 1859— with 11 women from 54 graduates.

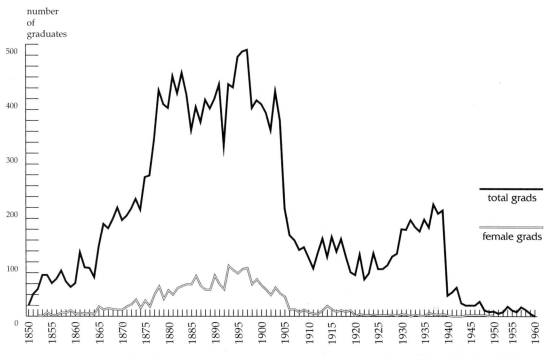

graduates of homœopathic medical colleges in the USA 1850–1960

The practitioners

Determining the number of homœopathic practitioners is a difficult task. The questions arise: Who is counted? Is the physician who uses only a handful of remedies with a smattering of knowledge a "homœopath"?

The figures presented here are gleaned, primarily, from the *Directories* that were published by the American Institute of Homeopathy. They do not list *only* AIH members, but they *do* list only licensed physicians. While there were not many people other than "physicians" who were practicing homeopathy between 1900 and 1930, many other health professionals, mainly chiropractors and naturopaths, used homœopathic medicines from 1930 on. These people do not begin to appear in any *Directories* until the 1990s.

The "professional homœopaths" who arose during the late 1980s were not listed in the *National Center Directory*, which was limited to only those with a license to practice a health-care profession in one state.

Yet, while the chart may not be completely accurate, it is instructive. We can see the AIH membership was always lower than those practicing, and of those members, the numbers who were also members of the IHA or held DHts were smaller still.

year	number of practitioners	AIH members	IHA members
1902	15,000	1,896	93 +38 associate
1911	n.a.	2,442	131+ 47 associate
1925	8,720	2,855	186
1931	7,676	2,596	207
1941	6,698	1,957	142
			DHt holders
1963	1,477	217	81
1980	128	n.a.	n.a.
1988	n.a.	88	16
1996	410	n.a.	52

The 1902 figure was quoted by James C. Wood, MD, to the AIH Meeting in 1902.
In 1998 there were 1150 members of the HANP, 57 of whom held the HANP diplomate. There were 175 practitioners recognized by the Council for Homeopathic Certification, and there were 60 registered members of NASH.

Appendix D

The states

Homœopathy in the United States

In assembling the following brief history of homœopathy in each state I relied on the work of T. L. Bradford who wrote brief accounts in Volume I of William Harvey King's *History of Homœopathy in America*. I also included information found in part II of Bradford's *Homœopathic Bibliography* where State societies, hospitals, and schools are discussed.

Because I have a separate Appendix on *Homœopathic Hospitals*, I did not dwell on those institutions within the state information.

Since Bradford's book was published in 1892 and King's work in 1905, the period from then until now has been unrecorded. I have used the *AIH Directory of Physicians* from 1941 and from 1963 to bring some of the figures a bit closer to our time.

Some states (e.g., New Mexico) have a very brief history while others (e.g., New York or Pennsylvania) have such full histories that it was impossible to condense the amount of information (New York has 67 pages in King's) to a paragraph. Much has been left out. If anyone who is reading this desires more specific information about a particular town or area, I'd suggest finding a copy of King's work (large libraries might have it, the library at the NCH in Alexandria, Virginia has two copies) or formulate the question and send it to the NCH. If they cannot supply the answer, they will probably send it on to me.

Having assembled the information from Bradford's work, I made no effort to convert his writing into contemporary usage. I trust you will enjoy the flavor!

I hope that the tid-bits I have given here will encourage others to delve into the histories in their own states and to be able to "flesh out" the picture. I would certainly appreciate copies and/or notes of all research done.

Alabama

The first homœopath in Alabama was a layman who dispensed remedies in Montgomery as early as 1843. In 1845, Drs. Ulrich and Schafer established themselves in the city and treated the epidemic of fevers raging on the nearby plantations.

There was never a large following in this state, with only eight homœopaths in 1857 and 12 by 1904.

Dr. A. L. Monroe relates that when he moved to Birmingham in 1883 he found homœopaths had to pass an examination before the allopathic board of examiners. "It is really a delightful experience to pass this examination and turning this allopathic weapon back upon themselves enter practice with their forced endorsement."

The Homœopathic Medical Association of Alabama was formed in 1889, "although on account of its limited membership meetings are occasionally held in conjunction with the Tennessee Homœopathic Medical Society."

There were six practitioners listed in Alabama in 1941 and 3 in 1963. The 1996 *NCH Directory* lists one practitioner and one study group.

Alaska

Little is known other than Dr. James Johnson was practicing in Sitka in 1877. In 1896 William Egbert, a graduate of Cleveland in 1875, began practice in Juneau. In 1899, Dr. Edwin Rollin Gregg and Dr. James K. Perrine were in practice in Dawson City. In 1898, Dr. Harrison Pelton, a graduate of San Francisco in 1888, sailed as the ship's surgeon, bound for Kotebue Sound. The boat went up the Kowark river and wintered. Dr. Pelton cared for all the people on the boat and at a community several miles away. He was frozen to death in a blizzard. Dr. Horatio Marsh, was practicing homœopathy in Barrow in 1904.

There were two practitioners listed in 1941. The 1996 *NCH Directory* has no listing for the state, but nine study groups were listed in the *1995 Directory*.

Arizona

Dr. H. J. Morrison was recorded as being in Sacaton in 1876. In 1886, John Miller, a graduate of Ann Arbor, located in Clifton. In 1890, Dr. Fetterman, a graduate of Hahnemann in Philadelphia, was reported in Tombstone. By 1896 there were practitioners in Phoenix and Tucson. In 1904 there were 12 homœopaths in the territory— three in Phoenix, three in Prescott, one in Chloride, one in Mesa, one in Troy, one in Tombstone, and two in Tucson.

The Arizona Homœopathic Medical Association was formed in 1900, "but no meets have been held since 1902, it being difficult for the members to assemble."

A Homœopathic Medical Board was established in Arizona in 1982.

There were nine practitioners listed in 1941, and four in 1963. The 1996 *NCH Directory* lists 12 practitioners and three study groups.

Arkansas

The first homœopath was Dr. E. D. Ayers who came to Little Rock in 1859. He practiced till his death in 1903. Dr. Pierce was in Fort Smith about 1869, Dr. John Brooks and L. S. Ordway introduced homœopathy to Hot Springs about 1874, and Dr. E. W. Chambers was in Bentonville in 1874.

The Arkansas State Homœopathic Medical Association

was founded in Little Rock in 1903.

In 1876 there were nine homœopaths in the state, and by 1904 there were 36. In 1941 there were nine practitioners. The 1996 *NCH Directory* lists two practitioners (both veterinarians).

California

Homœopathy entered California with the migration of people during the 1849 "gold rush." The first homœopath was Dr. Benjamin Ober, who settled in San Francisco in 1849. He was followed in 1850 by Dr. Moritz Richter.

Dr. William Robert Reud introduced homœopathy to Sacramento in 1870; Dr. George Barnes was the first homœopath in San Diego in 1869; and Dr. Weisecker was the first in Los Angeles sometime before 1871.

The Hahnemann Medical College of San Francisco was begun in 1883 by Drs. C. B. Currier, E. J. Canney, J. N. Eckels, and William Boericke.

The first attempts to start a homœopathic hospital foundered in 1888 when the hospital head, Dr. James W. Ward, was arrested for violating a city ordinance that prevented a hospital from being set up within a certain distance of City Hall. Ward took the suit to the Supreme Court and won the case.

In 1899 there were 88 homœopaths in San Francisco and 57 in Los Angeles.

With the 1901 election of E. E. Schmitz as Mayor of San Francisco, the city gained an ardent supporter of homœopathy. James W. Ward was appointed its Health Commissioner, and served in that capacity through the 1906 earthquake.

The name of the Homœopathic Medical College was changed to the Hahnemann Medical College of the Pacific, and it remained in existence through the 1930s. The homœopathic libraries donated by Drs. Lilienthal and Cowperthwaite moved to the University of San Francisco, along with the only existing copy of the 6th edition of Hahnemann's *Organon*, purchased by Boericke and Ward in 1921. The hospital changed its name to the Marshall Hale Hospital shortly after Ward's death in 1939.

The California State Medical Society of Homœopathic Practitioners was formed in 1871. Other societies were formed and by 1877 they all merged into the California State Homœopathic Medical Society— a group still operating today.

The Southern California State Asylum for the Insane and Inebriates which was opened in Patton, in 1893 ran under homœopathic supervision.

There were 389 practitioners listed in 1941, and 49 in 1963. The 1996 *NCH Directory* listed 76 practitioners and eight study groups.

Colorado

Denver was the only town in the territory in which there

was a homœopathic physician before 1871. In 1863 Dr. Ingersol located in Denver, practiced there a short time, then left. In 1866 Dr. M. L. Scott, a Vermonter, came to Denver, practiced two years, then returned east. In 1869, Dr. Squires came and practiced a few months and then yielded to Dr. A. O. Blair, formerly of Cleveland, who visited Denver in search of relief of chronic asthma. His stay, too, was short, and he was followed in the spring of 1870 by Dr. Martin Marix, a German, who had practiced homœopathy in Leipzig in 1852. Like others he came to Denver for the good of his health and remained there until his death in 1877.

Dr. George Pyburn, an Englishman, practiced in Canada, and graduated in 1859 from the Western College of Homœopathic Medicine in Cleveland. After practicing in several locations in the United States he became interested in the Union Colony and in 1870 went to Colorado as one of the settlers of the town of Greeley.

Homœopathic treatment was introduced in the Arapahoe county jail and poorhouse hospital in 1881. It became allopathic after 1884.

There were several state societies: Colorado State Homœopathic Medical Society (Denver, June 1881); Homœopathic Medical Society of the County of Arapahoe (Denver, 1888); Denver Academy of Homœopathic Medicine (Denver, 1879. Merged with Arapahoe); Homœopathic Club of Denver (December 1890).

The Denver Homœopathic College and Hospital was founded in 1894. By 1905 it had graduated 75 students. There is no mention of it in the Flexner report. It had closed by 1909.

According to Bradford (1892) The State Board of Medical Examiners was appointed by the Governor and had nine physicians: six allopaths, two homœopaths, and one eclectic.

In 1869 there was only one homœopathic practitioner in the state, while in 1900 the number was more than 120.

In the *1925 AIH Directory*, there are 119 homœopathic physicians listed. By 1941 there are 70, and in the 1963 AIH listing, there are only six. The 1996 *NCH Directory* lists seven practitioners and two study groups.

Connecticut

King's *History* devotes 10 pages to Connecticut, with a full listing of the earliest practitioners in almost each county. Bradford says (in 1904), "there is no county and hardly a single town that has not at least one homœopathic physician."

In 1837 Dr. Federal Vanderburgh, visiting an old doctor friend in New Milford, prescribed for the friend's wife. The doctor, George Taylor, was so impressed with the cure he studied homœopathy and began practice in about 1840. When it was found out he was using homœopathy, he was dismissed from the State Medical Society. Taylor's son, Charles Taylor, took over his father's practice and worked in New Milford till his death in 1890.

Grace Homœopathic Hospital in Hartford was opened in 1892. It was the state's first homœopathic hospital. It became allopathic sometime after 1911. The Norwich State Hospital for the Insane was still functioning as a homœopathic institution in 1941.

The Connecticut Homœopathic Medical Society was founded in 1851. In 1904 the membership was 105. The society still operates today.

In 1857 there were 42 homœopaths in the state. By 1904 the number had risen to 153. The high point was in 1925, with 163 practitioners. The number dropped to 122 by 1941, and to 32 by 1963. The 1996 NCH Directory lists 14 practitioners and two study groups.

Delaware

Delaware's first practitioner was J. C. Gosewisch, a pupil of Wesselhoeft and a graduate of the Allentown Academy. He settled in Wilmington in 1839. Gosewisch passed his examination with the Delaware medical board but was prevented from practicing based upon an 1835 law that excluded homœopathic practice in Delaware. Gosewisch petitioned the legislature and the law was reversed in 1843.

The second practitioner was Dr. Caleb Harlan who settled in Wilmington in 1847.

The Delaware State Homœopathic Medical Society was formed in 1874 and incorporated in 1889. It had 30 members in 1903.

The Homœopathic Hospital in Wilmington (Memorial Hospital) opened in 1888 and was still using homœopathy in 1941.

In 1904 there were 30 practitioners in the state, 21 being in Wilmington. There were 38 practitioners in 1941 and 15 in 1963. The 1996 NCH Directory lists three practitioners and two study groups.

District of Columbia

Dr. John Piper, a regular graduate from University of Maryland, learned homœopathy from Felix McManus in Maryland, and settled in DC in 1841. By 1857 there were five homœopaths, by 1870 there were 17.

The Washington Homœopathic Medical Society was formed in 1870, with Tullio Verdi as the first president.

Dr. Susan Edson came to DC in 1861 and worked as a nurse during the civil war, after which she established a medical practice in the city.

The National Homœopathic Hospital was founded in 1881. It was open to allopaths in 1928. It was still operating in 1941.

There were 63 practitioners in 1925, 35 in 1941, and 11 in 1963. The 1996 NCH Directory lists six practitioners and one study group.

Florida

The first homœopaths seem to be Dr. A. C. McCantz and Dr. J. A. Mitchell, who were practicing in Jacksonville in 1857. Little is known about their background. Dr. Charles R. Doran, a graduate of the Homœopathic Medical College of Pennsylvania, located in Jacksonville about 1869. At the same time, Sarah M. Ellis, a graduate of Cleveland, began a practice in Jacksonville. Dr. Samuel Fowler practiced in Gainesville from 1883 until 1888.

The State Homœopathic Medical Society of Florida was organized in Jacksonville in 1889.

In 1857 there were three practitioners of homœopathy in Florida, and 30 by 1904. There was a high of 81 in 1925. It dropped to 68 in 1941 and 27 in 1963. The 1996 NCH Directory listed 29 practitioners and 13 study groups.

Georgia

Georgia's first homœopath was Dr. James Banks Gilbert, who settled in Savannah in 1842. He was a former student of Dr. John F. Gray. He became a member of the Georgia Medical Society, and his success attracted the attention of a fellow member, Dr. James M. Schley, who soon went to study with Dr. Gray, and on his return began practicing homœopathy. Before long both men were arraigned for trial before the medical society for practicing homœopathy and they were expelled, but their practices continued to expand. Dr. Gilbert died in 1853, and Dr. Schley in 1874.

Dr. W. H. Banks settled at an early date in Savannah, becoming a partner with Dr. Gilbert. In 1850 Dr. Francis Hodgson Orme studied with Dr. Gilbert and completed his studies in the medical department of the University of New York. He graduated in 1854, returned to Savannah and entered into partnership with Dr. Banks. During the yellow fever epidemic of 1855, of five homœopathic physicians then resident in Savannah, Dr. Orme alone was able to practice, the others having sickened and left the city. His great success with homœopathic remedies caused the system to become very popular. Dr. Orme eventually moved to Atlanta. In 1878 he was a member of the Homœopathic Yellow Fever Commission.

Dr. Louis Knorr also was an early practitioner of homœopathy in Savannah. He was a graduate of the University of Munich in 1848, and became a convert to homœopathy in 1850.

Dr. Louis Alexander Falligant located in Savannah in 1858, associating himself with Dr. Schley. At the commencement of the Civil War he entered the Confederate Army, serving from 1862 to 1864 as health officer at Savannah.

Dr. Edward Worthington Starr settled as an allopathic physician in Columbus in 1836, but soon adopted homœopathy in his practice.

Dr. William Elliott Dunwody practiced allopathy in

Marietta from 1845 to 1856, when he adopted homœopathy.

Bradford, in 1892, notes the existence of the Atlanta Medical Club— a homœopathic group. It was "extant" but no other information was given.

There were no hospitals, dispensaries, or "homes and asylums" listed in Georgia.

There were 19 homœopaths in the state in 1925, 10 in 1941, and one in 1963. The 1996 *NCH Directory* lists seven practitioners and one study group.

Hawaii

There are no entries or information about Hawaii in the 1911 or 1931 *International Directory*. The 1941 *Directory* lists 20 practitioners. Of interest is 12 of them graduated from Jefferson Medical College, a conventional medical school in Philadelphia, Pennsylvania. A number of those listed were with the US Army at Schofield Barracks or in Honolulu.

In 1963 the *Directory* lists 3 practitioners. In 1996 the *NCH Directory* lists two practitioners.

Idaho

There has never been much homœopathy in Idaho. In 1877, Dr. D. G. Strong was practicing in Idaho City. In 1886 there were five homœopaths in the territory, and there were 12 in 1904. The number increased to 20 in 1925, and then dropped to five in 1941. By 1963 there were no homœopaths listed in the state. In 1996 there was one study group in Sandpoint.

Illinois

Dr. David S. Smith, an allopathic convert, brought homœopathy to Chicago (a small town of 20,000) in 1843. Dr. George Shipman, a student of Federal Vanderburgh, introduced homœopathy to Peoria in 1844 and then moved to Chicago in 1846. In 1848 he started the *Northwestern Journal of Homœopathia.*

Shipman also opened a small homœopathic hospital in 1854. Although it existed for only three years, it was the precursor to the larger institutions that followed.

Dr. Reuben Ludlam came to Chicago in 1852 and Alvan E. Small arrived in 1857. Both became influential in establishing the state's educational institutions.

The Chicago fire in 1871 served to unite the homœopaths and the allopaths, as they both worked to help those suffering from the devastation. The fire destroyed the printing house of Gross and Delbridge who had printed much of the homœopathic literature. It also destroyed the printing plates and remaining stock of *A Textbook on Homœopathy* by Von Grauvogl— translated and printed by Dr. Shipman. The book was never re-printed and remains one of the more rare homœopathic editions.

The Illinois State Homœopathic Medical Association was formed in 1855 and incorporated in 1881. With a good number of homœopaths in the state there were a number of smaller local societies: The Northern Illinois Homœopathic Association, The Chicago Homœopathic Medical Society, The Illinois Valley Homœopathic Medical Society, etc.

The Hahnemann Medical College of Chicago was organized in 1855 and graduated its first class in 1861. The Chicago Homœopathic Medical College was opened in 1876 in a building at the corner of Michigan Avenue and Van Buren. Both Colleges opened associated hospitals in 1894. In 1901 Allan C. Cowperthwaite became president of Chicago Homœopathic. In 1905, Chicago Homœopathic merged with the Hahnemann Medical College of Chicago. The school closed in 1922.

Hering College was founded in 1892 by H. C. Allen and J. B. S. King, as an institution to teach pure homœopathy. Dunham College, espousing similar principles, opened in 1895. In 1900 Dunham College hired Dr. J. T. Kent, and absorbed his Post–Graduate School of Homœopathics. In 1903, Dunham College merged with the Hering College. The Hering College continued until 1914-1915.

The Cook County hospital had both allopathic and homœopathic wards.

In 1870 there were 40 homœopaths in the state, and by 1904 there were 532. In 1941 there were 395 homœopaths in the state; by 1963, only 19. The 1996 *NCH Directory* lists 12 practitioners and three study groups.

Indiana

Isaac Coe, an allopathic physician, was treated by Dr. A. G. Hull in New York. The homœopathic cure so impressed him that he studied homœopathy with Hull. In 1840 he settled in Indianapolis where he formed a partnership with Dr. L. H. Van Buren. They eventually moved to Kentucky.

The next homœopath was Dr. Shard, who settled in Indianapolis in 1855. He was followed by Dr. Augustus Wright, who stayed for a few years and then moved to Nebraska in 1862.

The "father" of homœopathy in Indiana was Dr. Oliver Perry Baer, who settled in Richmond in 1849. He found two other physicians "trying to do something with the Hahnemannian system, but not at all to their satisfaction." He was advised not to stay, as homœopathy "would not pay five dollars per annum." He found a property, set up an office, and made more than $1000 in his first year of practice. "I used thirtieth dilution entirely and succeeded far beyond my most sanguine expectations." He practiced in Richmond until his death in 1888.

The Indiana Homœopathic Institute was organized in 1867 and was reorganized as the Indiana Institute of Homœopathy in 1882. In 1903 it had 150 members.

There were 21 homœopaths in the state in 1857, 308 in

1904, 162 practitioners listed in 1941, and 21 listed in 1963. The 1996 *NCH Directory* lists four practitioners and two study groups.

Iowa

Bradford comments that "while there is no lack of homœopathic history in Iowa, the profession has recorded so little of its interesting annals..."

The pioneer was Dr. Beck who settled in Dubuque in about 1852. "He stayed for about a year and then... yielded to the pressure of adversity and betake himself to a more congenial neighborhood..."

He was followed in Dubuque by Dr. Nathan Dodge who stayed only two years. Dr. Wilmot Horton Dickinson was in Des Moines in 1858. Dr. Maria W. Porter located in Davenport in about 1860. She was the first female physician to settle between the Mississippi River and the Rocky Mountains.

Despite the adversity, the number of homœopaths grew from 19 in 1857 to 370 in 1904. This large increase was due, in part, to the formation of a homœopathic department at the State University. In 1877 the state legislature passed a bill to create a department of homœopathy at the Iowa State University. The first degree was conferred in 1878. Dr. Alan Cowperthwaite was the first professor of materia medica. In 1892 he was succeeded by Dr. George Royal. The department of homœopathy ceased in the early 1920s.

The Iowa Homœopathic Medical Association was founded in 1862 and collapsed due to the Civil War. The Society of Homœopathic Physicians of Iowa was organized in 1870 and changed its name to the Hahnemann Medical Association of Iowa in 1879. There were local societies in Hardin County, Linn County, Polk County, Scott County, Woodbury County, as well as several others.

In 1941 there were 154 practitioners listed. By 1963 the number had dwindled to six. In the 1996 *NCH Directory* there was only one homœopath listed in the state.

Kansas

Dr. John Doy was educated in England and came to the United States in 1846. At that time he was practicing homœopathy. He was in the first group of 29 who settled in what is now Lawrence, in 1854.

Homœopathy grew in Kansas so that by 1870 there were 17 homœopaths in the state. In 1904 there were 188.

The Homœopathic Medical Society of Kansas was organized in Levenworth in 1869. The Topeka Homœopathic Medical Society was formed in 1881; the Southern Kansas Homœopathic Medical Association was formed in 1886; and the Shawnee County Homœopathic Medical Society was formed in 1890.

The Kansas Surgical Hospital of Topeka (1882) was homœopathic, as was the Wichita Homœopathic Hospital (1888).

There were 76 practitioners in 1941, and one in 1963. In 1996 there was just a single study group in Manhattan.

Kentucky

The first practitioner was Dr. I. G. Rosenstein, who settled in Louisville in 1839. He was using homœopathy as early as 1836, when he published a book in Albany, New York, in which he discussed his training with Dr. Biegler. In 1840, while in Louisville, he wrote a book *Theory and Practice of Homœopathy*. He left for Canada in 1842. A third book was published in Montreal in 1846.

Dr. Rosenstein was, from all accounts, welcomed into the medical community by the allopaths, and remained on good terms with them throughout his stay in Louisville— one of the few instances where the allopathic physicians in the town gave homœopathy a fair hearing.

Rosenstein was soon followed by Dr. Logue who joined with Dr. Richard Angell in 1844 when Angell moved from Mississippi. Angell stayed in Louisville until 1847, when he returned to the south.

Dr. Edward Caspari, a graduate of the Allentown Academy, began his practice in Louisville in 1846 and remained there until his death in 1870. His practice was assumed by Dr. William Breyfogle.

The Kentucky State Homœopathic Medical Society was informally organized in 1849, and formally organized in 1873. It had 75 members in 1904. The Western Kentucky Homœopathic Medical Society was formed in 1892. In 1903 it had 35 members.

The Southwestern Homœopathic Medical College was opened in Louisville in 1893. It continued through the early 1920s. In 1895 it reached an agreement with Louisville Hospital to allow entrance to its students, effectively making Louisville Hospital quasi-homœopathic.

In 1857 there were 13 homœopaths in the state. By 1904 there were 117. The *1941 Directory* listed 46 practitioners, and only two were listed in 1963. In 1996 there was one practitioner and one study group.

Louisiana

Homœopathy was brought to Louisiana by Dr. Joseph Martin, a physician in the French navy who learned homœopathy in France in 1834. Martin settled in New Orleans in 1836 and practiced there until his death in 1861. Shortly after Martin settled in New Orleans, a layman named Formel established a practice there as well.

The French and American sectors of New Orleans were quite separate. The first homœopath to bring the system to the Americans in the city was Dr. Robert Glass of Hopkinsville, Kentucky who, from 1840 until 1844, spent his winters in New Orleans.

The name most connected with homœopathy in Louisiana is that of William H. Holcombe— often spoken of as "the Hering of the South." A graduate of University of Pennsylvania, he settled for a time in Cincinnati, Ohio where he became acquainted with the work of Hahnemann and Swedenborg. He practiced in Natchez, Mississippi from 1852 until 1855, at which time he moved to Waterproof, Louisiana. In 1864 he settled in New Orleans, and remained there until his death in 1893. During the yellow fever epidemic of 1853, Dr. Holcombe was appointed to the Mississippi State Hospital, an appointment not received with favor by the conventional medical community. He was a prolific author on both medical and non-medical subjects.

In 1880, the few homœopathic physicians in the state formed the Hahnemann Medical Association of Louisiana. It was succeeded by the Southern Homœopathic Medical Association in 1885. In 1903 there were 22 physician members. The Association continues to this day, meets annually, and has 16 members.

In 1904 there were 26 homœopathic physicians in the state. By 1941 there were 22 practitioners listed, and by 1963 there was but one. In 1996 there is one homœopath (a veterinarian) listed in the *NCH Directory.*

Maine

Homœopathy came to Maine in 1840. Dr. D. F. Sandicky, a Polish itinerant doctor was the first to practice in the state. Dr. William F. Payne, came to Bath in 1840, and was converted to homœopathy by Sandicky.

From 1840-1850, homœopathy spread from Bath to Bangor, Portland, and Kennebunkport. The first meeting of the AIH in 1844 had delegates from Maine— Albus Rea, Eliphalet Clark, and John Merrill— all of Portland. Homœopathy made great inroads while treating the cholera epidemic of 1849 and the diphtheria epidemic of 1860.

The Maine Homœopathic Medical Society was formed in 1867 in Augusta. In 1903 it was still meeting and had 66 members.

By 1890 there were 100 practitioners in the state. There were 38 in 1941, and five in 1963. In 1996, the *NCH Directory* listed seven practitioners and eight study groups.

Maryland

Dr. Felix R. McManus is often credited with being the state's first homœopath. He took his degree in medicine at the University of Maryland in 1829, and began an allopathic practice in Baltimore. In 1837 the loss of a patient so disturbed him that he turned in another direction in the hope of arriving at "some satisfactory conclusion respecting the evident mistakes of that school's methods, and at the same time to provide himself with more rational and sane means of cure."

It was then that his attention was called to homœopathy by one of the Catholic clergy. He was led to investigate, and began practice.

A Dr. Schwartz, is mentioned as being the first homœopathic physician in Baltimore, in 1837. However, he stayed in the city only one year.

In 1836, contemporary with Dr. McManus, Reverend Jacob Geiger took up the practice of medicine in connection with his pastoral duties, and continued both until his death in 1848. Nine of his children were graduates of homœopathic colleges and medical practitioners.

Another of the Baltimore pioneers was Dr. Adolph Ferdinand Haynel. He had been a personal student of Hahnemann's and had accompanied Hahnemann from Leipzig to Köethen. He came to America in about 1835, and resided in Pennsylvania. Dr. John Gray says Haynel established himself in Baltimore as early as 1838, returning to Germany in about 1870.

In 1875 there were 57 homœopathic practitioners in Maryland, 35 of whom were in Baltimore.

The Maryland State Homœopathic Medical Society was formed in 1887. In 1904 it had about 75 members.

The Southern Homœopathic Medical College and Hospital was chartered in 1890. It was located at 323 N. Paca Street in Baltimore. The college opened in 1891. Some time between 1905 and 1909 it changed its name to the Atlantic Medical College and ceased its homœopathic affiliation. It closed shortly after the Flexner report.

There were 119 homœopaths listed in Maryland in 1925, 71 of them in Baltimore. By 1941 the number was reduced to 75. By 1963 there were 11— two in Baltimore. The 1996 *NCH Directory* lists 11 practitioners with seven study groups.

Massachusetts

King's *History* devotes 30 pages to Massachusetts, with the state's first homœopath being Samuel Gregg. A graduate of Dartmouth in 1825, Gregg learned of homœopathy through two patients who had been cured by Vanderburgh in New York. He consulted Vanderburgh, bought some books, and studied the "new system." Gregg started homœopathic practice in Medford in 1838. In 1839 he was joined by Josiah Flagg, an 1815 graduate from Harvard, who had become interested in homœopathy through his own cure.

The Homœopathic Fraternity of Massachusetts was formed in 1841 by the state's six homœopaths. In 1851 it became the Massachusetts Homœopathic Medical Society. The membership was 375 in 1903. King says there were 645 homœopathic physicians in Boston alone in 1904.

The Massachusetts Homœopathic Hospital opened in 1855 and was said to be, in 1904, the largest hospital in the States under homœopathic management. The Hampden Homœopathic Hospital was founded in Springfield in 1900, largely through the benevolence of Daniel Wesson, the co-founder of the Smith and Wesson Arms Company. Other hospitals in the state are mentioned in the "Hospital" **Appendix**.

The New England Female Medical College was absorbed by Boston University in 1873. Boston University taught homœopathy until about 1920.

There were 85 homœopaths in Massachusetts in 1941, and 47 in 1963. The 1996 *NCH Directory* lists 35 practitioners and three study groups.

Michigan

The beginnings of homœopathy in Michigan are uncertain. Some say Dr. S. S. Hall, an allopath, took up homœopathy in Detroit, sometime between 1841 and 1843. Others credit Dr. John Mosher, of Somerset, as the first practitioner in 1843.

King has 12 pages of biographies of the early homœopaths, and lists 80 homœopaths practicing in Michigan before 1860.

Dr. S. B. Thayer, who began homœopathic practice in Detroit in 1847, was influential in securing a department of homœopathy at the University of Michigan. As early as 1855 the state legislature passed an act authorizing at least one professorship of homœopathy in the State University.

In 1847, eight practitioners formed the Michigan Institute of Homœopathy. It merged into the Homœopathic Medical Society of the State of Michigan in 1871. By 1904 there were 501 homœopaths working in Michigan. The state supported more than 20 other homœopathic medical societies.

John Ellis opened a homœopathic pharmacy in Detroit in 1850, and in 1859 it was taken over by Edwin Lodge and in 1875 by his son, Albert Lodge.

Grace Hospital, founded in 1888, was homœopathic and allied with the Detroit Homœopathic College which was founded in 1872. The Detroit college closed sometime before 1920 and its library went to Ohio State University in Columbus.

The Medical School at Ann Arbor maintained a homœopathic department until the mid 1920s. The Library at Ann Arbor is one of the few that did not destroy their homœopathic books, and the full collection is available, from the stacks, by appointment.

There were 189 practitioners listed in 1941, and 38 in 1963. The 1996 *Directory* listed 11 practitioners and eight study groups.

Minnesota

Dr. Sperry began practicing homœopathy in St. Paul in 1852— six years before Minnesota gained statehood.

Dr. George Hatfield came to St. Paul in 1854 and left in 1859 but, while there, published a bi-monthly journal— *The Minnesota Homœopath*. An early practitioner in St. Paul was Reverend Father Clemens Staub, a priest at the German

Catholic Church of Assumption. He practiced homœopathy without fees. He died in 1886.

The first homœopath in Minneapolis was Dr. Philo T. Hatch in 1858. He later taught at the University of Minnesota and was the state's ornithologist.

King list 57 homœopaths practicing in Minnesota before 1870. The State Homœopathic Medical Society was formed in 1867.

The Homœopathic Hospital of Minneapolis was founded with a $30,000 bequest from Dr. William A. Penniman. It opened in 1883 and closed in 1896. The Maternity Hospital in Minneapolis was incorporated in 1887 and was still operating under homœopathic management in 1904. The St. Paul homœopathic hospital was opened in 1887 and was still going in 1904. The State Hospital for the Insane at Fergus Falls was opened in 1890 and was under homœopathic management through the 1930s.

The Minnesota Homœopathic College was incorporated in 1886. In 1888 it closed and the faculty moved the whole school to the University of Minnesota. In 1909 the University closed the homœopathic department.

The *1941 Directory* lists 71 practitioners. In 1963 there were only five— the same number as in the *1996 Directory*.

Missouri

Homœopathy was brought to Missouri by Dr. John Temple who settled in St. Louis in 1844. In 1845 a professor at St. Louis Medical College denounced homœopathy. Dr. Temple wrote a reply, but neither the medical journals nor any of the city newspapers would allow him space. He published his answer in a pamphlet and distributed it throughout the city. It resulted, said Dr. Temple, "in all classes trying it."

In 1848, Temple established the *Southwestern Homœopathic Journal and Review*. It lasted for three years and did much to spread homœopathy in the state.

The Missouri Homœopathic Institute was an outgrowth of several state societies— the earliest formed in 1853. The Institute had about 250 members in 1904.

St. Louis boasted a number of homœopathic hospitals, as well as serving as the home for several homœopathic pharmacies including Luyties Pharmacal.

Dr. William Curran brought homœopathy to Hannibal in 1856, and in 1859, Dr. Joshua Thorne introduced it to Kansas City. King lists 41 homœopaths in Missouri prior to 1860.

The Homœopathic Medical College of Missouri was incorporated in 1857 but did not begin in full until after the Civil War. Several other homœopathic colleges came and went, but the Homœopathic Medical College of Missouri weathered the minor storms. It ceased operation by 1910.

The Kansas City Homœopathic Medical College was organized in 1882. In 1896 the College of Homœopathic

Medicine and Surgery of Kansas City University opened. In 1902, Kansas City Homœopathic merged with the latter institution, and the name was changed to Kansas City Hahnemann Medical College. The school ceased operations in 1923.

There were 104 practitioners in Missouri in 1941, and four in 1963. The 1996 *Directory* lists four practitioners and two study groups.

Mississippi

The first homœopath was Dr. Augustus Frederick Davis who, looking for alternatives to conventional practices, studied with Dr. Pulte in Cincinnati in 1846 and returned to Natchez to practice in 1847.

The second practitioner in the state was William H. Holcombe who became a partner of Dr. Davis.

Both doctors were appointed to staff the Mississippi State Hospital at Natchez— the first time a state hospital passed to homœopathic control.

Notwithstanding the small numbers, a state homœopathic medical society was founded in 1889. King list 15 practitioners in the state before 1870. There were four practitioners in the state in 1904, five listed in the state in 1925, two listed in 1941 and currently none in the state since before 1960.

Montana

Montana's first practitioner was Dr. Stephen Roby Mason who, in 1864-65, journeyed through the gold regions of Montana, Idaho and British Columbia. He opened an office in Virginia City, and introduced homœopathy.

In 1876, Drs. A. E. Ingersol and C. S. Ingersol were practicing at Helena. In 1886 Dr. Robert M. Whitefoot was located in Bozeman; Drs. Charles W. Clark, Frederick Hiller, J. W. January, Adolph Mamor, Winfield S. Norcross and George B. Sarchet were in Butte City; Drs. Maria M. Dean, Thomas Eccles and Charles S. Thompson were in Helena; Dr. Fox E. H. Canny was in Waterville.

In 1886 there were 10 homœopathic practitioners in the territory; in 1896, 15; in 1904, 19, of whom six were located in Butte.

There were 31 homœopaths listed in the 1925 AIH *Index*, and 19 in 1941. Only one homœopath was listed in the 1963 AIH *Index*. The 1996 *Directory* lists five practitioners and one study group.

Nebraska

Dr. Augustus Wright was the first to practice homœopathy in the Nebraska territory. He settled in Omaha in 1862, and remained until 1874 when he moved to California because of failing health.

Dr. Jacob H. Way, a graduate of Jefferson Medical College in Philadelphia, practiced homœopathy for a few years in Nebraska City.

Dr. William Sisson began homœopathic practice in Omaha in 1868 and continued till his death in 1873. His practice was taken over by Dr. F. Saxenburger, who stayed but a year. In 1868 Dr. Orlando Wood established a homœopathic practice in Omaha.

Dr. W. A. Burr located in Lincoln in 1869, to be followed by Dr. L. J. Bumstead and Dr.. Edwin Taft Hurlburt in 1873.

Although homœopathy was fully accepted, most homœopaths who came to Nebraska seemed to move on within a few years. King lists 42 practitioners in the state before 1880, but many of them stayed for only a short time.

The Nebraska State Homœopathic Medical Society was organized in Lincoln in 1873, and the Omaha Homœopathic Medical Society (Douglas County Homœopathic Society) was formed in 1889.

The 1925 *Directory* listed 81 homœopaths in Nebraska. The number fell to 43 in 1941 and one in 1963. The NCH lists one practitioner in 1996.

Nevada

Nevada's first homœopath when it was a territory, was Dr. Frederick Hiller in Virginia City in 1862 . He remained there until 1870 when he moved to San Francisco. He is said to have travelled, at times, more than 300 miles to see his patients.

In 1904 there were but two homœopaths in the state, Dr. Philipina Wagner in Carson City, and Floyd Nutting in Searchlight. The number increased to six in 1925, then dropped to four in 1941, and two in 1963. The 1996 *NCH Directory* lists six practitioners and one study group.

New Hampshire

Homœopathy was introduced to New Hampshire by Dr. Moses Atwood, who had studied with Gregg in Boston. Atwood lived in Francestown for a short time before moving to Nashua, then to Concord, and Manchester, before settling in New Boston.

Dr. James Peterson, of Weare, learned homœopathy from Atwood. "I prescribed my first globule in 1843," he said.

The state's third practitioner was Dr. Joshua F. Whittle, a nephew of Dr. Peterson, who settled in Nashua in 1843.

King lists 47 practitioners in the state before 1860.

The New Hampshire Homœopathic Medical Society was formed in 1851 and incorporated in 1853. In 1904 it had 75 members.

In 1941 there were 26 practitioners in the state. In 1963 there were seven. In 1996 there were three practitioners and three study groups.

New Jersey

King devotes 18 pages to New Jersey. Although Constantine Hering published *The Family Advisor* in

Camden in 1838, the state's first practitioner was Isaac Moreau Ward. A graduate of Rutgers College in 1829, he saw the comparative results of allopathic and homœopathic treatment in the cholera epidemic of 1832. He studied homœopathy with Dr. Alonzo Ball of New York. In about 1839 he began practicing homœopathy in Newark.

By 1846 there were enough homœopaths in the state to start a branch of the AIH, and by 1854 the New Jersey Homœopathic Medical Society was organized. Bradford lists 16 societies within the state.

By 1857 there were 46 homœopaths in the state; by 1904 there were 333.

There were several hospitals in the state in homœopathic hands until the 1920s.

The 1941 *Directory* lists 528 practitioners in the state. By 1963 there were 123. The 1996 *Directory* lists 14 practitioners and four study groups.

New Mexico

There is little in the way of history in this state. In 1893 there were eight physicians in the territory, and by 1904 the number had reached 12.

The early practitioners were Drs. M. D. Allen, J. M. Cunningham, and J. H. Sutphin in Las Vegas; Dr. C. L. Kendall in Lordsburgh, and Dr. William Eggert in Santa Fe.

There were 11 practitioners listed in 1941, and six in 1963. In 1996 there were 12 practitioners in New Mexico.

New York

While it is impossible to condense King's 67 pages to a paragraph or two, mention should be made of the following milestones in New York's homœopathic history.

It arrived, of course, in 1825 with Gram and was spread across the state by his pupils.

The New York Homœopathic Society was formed in 1835, and by 1850, became the Homœopathic Medical Society of the State of New York. By 1852 there were 301 practitioners in the state, and by 1904 there were 1,206 practitioners. The Homœopathic Medical Society is still operating.

With such a large base of practitioners there were 91 other societies formed in various parts of the state.

The state supported many homœopathic hospitals and educational institutions, the largest being The Homœopathic Medical College of the State of New York that began its first session in 1860. The name was changed to the New York Homœopathic Medical College in 1869. It was joined with the New York Ophthalmic Hospital in 1872 in a building at the corner of Third Avenue and 23rd street. In 1887 the name was again changed to The New York Homœopathic Medical College and Hospital, and new quarters were found on Eastern Boulevard (now York Ave.) between 63rd and 64th Streets. This eventually became the site for the New York Medical Center. In 1890 a new building was constructed on the site through a grant from Roswell B. Flower and was called the Flower Hospital. It was later moved to a site at 5th Ave and 105th street where it remains as the Flower-Fifth Avenue Hospital.

The College absorbed the New York Medical College for Women in 1918. The school changed its name to the New York Medical College, and ceased teaching homœopathy in the early 1930s, although a portrait of Hahnemann was still seen on the school seal through the 1970s. The College still exists, with operations in Valhalla, New York.

In 1941 there were 1,685 practitioners listed in New York. There were 626 in 1963. The 1996 *Directory* lists 31 practitioners and nine study groups.

North Carolina

The first homœopath was Dr. William K. Freeman, who graduated from the Charleston Medical School in 1847. In 1848 he moved to Wilmington, where he practiced allopathy two years and then publicly announced his belief in homœopathy. His action at that particular time required great moral courage; there was no homœopathic practitioner south of Virginia, and for 20 years he was the only one in the whole state of North Carolina. He died in Wilmington in February, 1879.

Dr. Barton Munsey was another of Wilmington's early practitioners. A native of New Hampshire, he learned homœopathy from Dr. Atwood in Manchester. In 1846 he went to Harvard University, and the next year applied to the New York Medical School for a course, but Dr. Mott informed him that "he would not be allowed to graduate with homœopathic notions." He went to South America, introducing homœopathy in Curacoa, then returned to the United States and located in Wilmington, where he practiced dentistry and homœopathy. He attended the first course of lectures at the Homœopathic Medical College of Pennsylvania and graduated in 1850. He then returned to Wilmington. He worked as a surgeon in the Union Army.

Dr. W. Storm graduated in 1877 from the New York Homœopathic Medical College, and soon after settled in Wilmington. Dr. Storm was still practicing in 1941.

The health–giving properties of Asheville attracted Dr. Horatio P. Gatchell, from Kenosha, Wisconsin. He spent the rest of his life in Asheville, and died in 1885.

In 1857 there were but two homœopathic practitioners in the state, and in 1870 Dr. Freeman was the only homœopath there; in 1886 there were five; 1896, three; in 1899, six; and in 1904, eight. The 1941 *Directory* lists nine practitioners. There were two in 1963. The 1996 *Directory* lists six practitioners and six study groups.

North/South Dakota

As early as 1877 Dr. E. O. Plumbe was located in Canton, F. L. Richter was in Fargo, Dr. N. C. Whitfield in Rapid City, and Dr. Charles Evans in Vermillion. Who was the first in the territory is not recorded.

The Dakota Homœopathic Medical Association was organized in 1884. The organization was dissolved when the Dakota Territory gained statehood, and in 1893 the South Dakota State Homœopathic Medical Society was formed. It was still operational in 1905 and had about 50 members.

In 1941 there were there were seven practitioners in North Dakota, and eight in South Dakota. There were none in 1963, and one study group in North Dakota in 1996.

Ohio

King devotes 23 pages to the state of Ohio. The early history of homœopathy in Ohio is clouded in vagaries. It is generally accepted that Dr. Cope was the state's first in 1836, practicing near Plymouth, Richland County. He was a high-potency prescriber, "giving a single pellet and repeating the dose at the end of fourteen days, if the case required such 'radical' treatment." There is mention of an unknown German doctor in Delaware County who treated his patients with "very little pills, and whose habit was in typhoid cases to give the patient one dose and then return at the end of the week to see how it was working."

Dr. Wilhelm Sturm was the next practitioner, settling in Cincinnati in about 1839, followed by Dr. Pulte in 1840.

The Western College of Homœopathic Medicine was started in Cleveland in 1850. It eventually became the Cleveland College of Homœopathic Medicine. The Pulte College was begun in 1872 in Cincinnati, with the major amount of funding being granted by Dr. Pulte.

The Pulte College was absorbed by Cleveland in 1909, and in 1914, both were absorbed by the medical school of Ohio State University in Columbus. OSU continued teaching homœopathy until 1922.

The Homœopathic Medical Society of Ohio was formed in 1846, and is still operating. In 1892, Bradford reported 40 different homœopathic societies in the state.

By 1857 there were 120 practitioners in the state, by 1904 there were about 1,000. There were 458 practitioners in 1941, and 110 in 1963. The 1996 *Directory* shows 10 practitioners and 10 study groups.

Oklahoma

Oklahoma received statehood in 1907. When Bradford wrote the history of the region in King's work in 1904, little information was available. Nathan Van Wert, a graduate of St. Louis Homœopathic, settled in Okmulgee, Indian Territory in 1881, where he practiced for 12 years. There were 41 homœopaths in the Indian Territory and Oklahoma in 1904. There were 26 practitioners in 1941, and three in 1963. There were none listed in the 1996 *Directory*. There was

never a state homœopathic society.

In a biography of the children's author Laura Ingalls Wilder, mention is made of the Ingalls family being cured of malaria by a black doctor who was a homœopath in the Indian Territory.

Oregon

Dr. Leslie Jacob Coombs settled in Oregon in 1853. He was a graduate of Washington University in Baltimore, and learned homœopathy from Dr. Charles Geiger of Manchester, Maryland. It was reported he had an extensive practice and treated both homœopathically and allopathically. By 1876 there were only 11 homœopaths in the state— the number swelling to 60 in 1899 and dropping to 40 in 1904.

The Oregon State Homœopathic Medical Society was founded in 1876 and was still extant in 1904.

The Portland Methodist Hospital opened as an allopathic hospital in 1886 and became homœopathic in 1895.

In 1941 there were 33 practitioners in the state, there were three in 1963. The 1996 *Directory* has 13 practitioners and two study groups.

Pennsylvania

King devotes 52 pages to Pennsylvania's history as the state was a veritable center for homœopathy. It has supported Hering, the first homœopathic school, the first homœopathic college, several pharmacies, and a large number of hospitals and societies.

Homœopathy in Pennsylvania began, of course, when Detwiller gave the first dose of *Pulsatilla* on July 23, 1828. The rest of the history can be read elsewhere in this book— the history of homœopathy *in* Pennsylvania is often *the* history of homœopathy.

The first homœopath west of the Allegheny Mountains was Reverend Father Byer, a Catholic priest stationed in Pittsburgh. Byer wrote to Hering and asked for a physician to settle in Pittsburgh. Hering presented the request to the class at Allentown, and the offer was taken up by Gustavus Reichhelm, who had trained in medicine in Berlin before immigrating to the USA.

Reichhelm began work in Pittsburgh in 1837. He developed a large following, despite being denounced by the medical community and boycotted by druggists. He was the physician in charge at the Catholic Orphan Asylum. It is reported that "more children died within one year after Reichhelm was superseded by an allopathic physician than during his whole term of service."

Before 1860 there were 117 homœopaths in the city of Philadelphia and 208 practitioners elsewhere in the state. It was estimated that by 1903 numbers had grown to more than 700. Bradford reports that there were 60 homœopathic societies in the state.

The Homœopathic Medical Society of Pennsylvania was formed in 1866, and in 1903 had 358 members. It is still in operation today.

In 1941 there were 1443 practitioners in the state, and in 1963 there were 626. The 1996 *Directory* lists 23 practitioners and 14 study groups.

Rhode Island

The first practitioner was Dr. Louis Parlin, who settled in Providence in 1839. Parlin became involved with "the Dorr Movement" which sought to overthrow the established system of government. Parlin was forced to leave the state when the leaders of the movement were dispersed. It is reported that the allopaths greeted his departure with approval. It is also reported that he spent the rest of his life "in foreign parts."

Most of the homœopathy came from outside the state. Wells visited from Brooklyn, Channing visited from New York, Flagg visited from Boston. Dr. Abraham Howard Okie, a graduate of the Allentown Academy, settled in Providence in 1842. Okie was one of the first translators of *Boenninghausen's Therapeutic Pocketbook* to English. In his later years he left homœopathy. Says Bradford: "It is a great pity that a man of such talents, and even genius, is as good as lost to the profession, having taken for the last decade, no interest whatever either in society meetings or in other enterprises concerning homœopathy."

In 1844 Dr. Peleg Clark came to East Providence from Coventry. He practiced there till his death at the age of 91 in 1875.

The Rhode Island Homœopathic Society was organized in 1847. It had 47 members in 1903.

The Rhode Island Homœopathic Hospital was opened in 1886. In 1891 it was sold under mortgage foreclosure proceedings.

There were 38 homœopaths in the state in 1941, and 12 in 1963. The 1996 *Directory* lists three practitioners in the state.

South Carolina

"The story of homœopathy in South Carolina is but a meager one," says Bradford. In 1853 Dr. John Henry Hazzard, a homœopathic graduate from Pennsylvania in 1851, came to Charleston from Alabama. He worked arduously during the yellow fever epidemic of 1854, and returned to Alabama in 1856.

Dr. John Pfonts settled in Columbia in 1854, but moved to Pennsylvania at the start of the Civil War.

Joshua Adams Whitman came to Beaufort in 1874. He brought a case of homœopathic medicines and a book of practice. He cured many cases considered hopeless by the allopaths. His friends persuaded him to get a diploma, and he attended a course at the Chicago Homœopathic Medical

College in 1886, after which he returned to Beaufort.

In 1904, there were four homœopaths in the state: Whitman in Beaufort, Nichols in Greenville, Hood in Greenwood, and Cleckley in Charleston. In 1941 there were but three; in 1963, only one. The 1996 *Directory* lists four practitioners in the state, two of them veterinarians.

Tennessee

"The doctrines of Hahnemann have never gained a strong foothold in this state," says Bradford. The first homœopath was Dr. Philip Harsh who moved to Nashville in 1844. He was joined by Dr. P. M. Wheaton in 1847. Dr. Sheffield settled in Nashville in 1855, the same year Dr. John A. Williams introduced homœopathy to Memphis. In 1869, Dr. J. H. Morgan settled in Knoxville and Dr. E. H. Price located in Chattanooga.

In 1869, Dr. Jabez Dake, who authored the *Cyclopedia of Drug Pathogenesy* with Dr. Richard Hughes in England, settled in Nashville. He was instrumental in forming the Homœopathic Medical Society of Tennessee in 1875, but "the society has never been numerically strong." The Chattanooga Homœopathic Medical Society was organized in 1888.

In 1874 a bill was introduced to the legislature— "An Act to protect the citizens from quackery"— which provided the regulation of medicine in the state be placed in the hands of the State Medical Association of Tennessee. Articles appeared in the newspapers assailing the idea, and when it came up for a vote, it received only three votes— all from allopathic physicians.

In 1941 there were 12 homœopaths practicing in the state. In 1963 there were none. The 1996 *Directory* lists three practitioners and one study group.

Texas

The first homœopath in Texas was Dr. Henry C. Parker who, discouraged with conventional medicine, learned homœopathy from Dr. Logue in Meridian, Mississippi. He settled in Houston in 1848. There were 16 allopaths in Houston at the time, but Dr. Parker opened his library to them and was soon consulting with them on difficult cases. Worn down by treating the yellow-fever epidemic in 1853 he soon retired, beginning practice again in 1867.

Dr. Edmund Blake, who learned homœopathy from Parker took over his practice. In 1899 there were seven homœopaths in Houston.

Dr. James Angell began practicing homœopathy in Galveston in 1854, and homœopathy was introduced to both Austin and Dallas before 1870. In 1904 there were 74 homœopaths in Texas.

The Texas Homœopathic Medical Association was formed in 1874 and had a membership of 45 in 1903.

There were 38 homœopaths listed in the state in the 1941 *Directory*, and only four listed in 1963. The 1996 *Directory* lists six practitioners and 14 study groups.

Utah

Dr. Isaiah White settled in Salt Lake City in 1875. He had graduated from the City University of New York and was a homœopathic convert. By 1904 the state had 16 homœopaths.

The Utah Homœopathic Medical Association was formed in 1892, and "maintained a healthful existence but since 1895 it has become decadent." There were nine homœopaths in Utah in 1941 and none in 1963. The 1996 *Directory* lists one practitioner and one study group.

Vermont

Homœopathy was introduced in Vermont by David H. Baird, who was not a graduate of any school of medicine. He administered the little homœopathic doses in Coventry and Troy in Orleans county as early as about the year 1840, and thus became the pioneer in the Green Mountain state.

The second practitioner was Dr. T. C. Taplin, who met Mr. Baird, took up studying homœopathy and settled in Montpelier, where he died in 1864.

The next homœopath in Orleans county was Dr. Gershom Nelson Brigham, who began practice in Waitsfield in 1850.

In Bennington county Dr. H. Smith was in practice at Bennington in 1857, and in the same year Dr. R. B. Bruce was at North Bennington.

In Windsor County homœopathy was introduced in 1844 by Dr. A. T Pike and Dr. Amos Dean, who came from Lowell, Massachusetts and located at Woodstock. Woodstock was the seat of the Vermont Medical College and more than half the population was related to allopathic physicians by marriage or otherwise. One who was then a student there wrote: "In 1852 a clinical case of indolent ulcer came before the class. The professor pronounced it incurable and so dismissed it.

"A dentist, then a resident of the town, and attending lectures at the time, invited the patient into his office, and proposed to cure the case if he would take homœopathic pellets. He prescribed for him and in a few weeks the ulcer was healed. At that time one-fifth of the class were homœopaths, but such was the abuse of the system, and ridicule of those who believed in it, that every one kept his own counsel, and it was not until after years that they knew each other as homœopaths at the Vermont Medical College."

Within 20 years there were about 35 practitioners in Vermont. As early as 1854, the Green Mountain Homœopathic Medical Association was organized and in 1858, it became the Vermont State Homœopathic Medical Society. It was operating in 1904.

Several smaller groups were established— the Caledonia County Homœopathic Medical Society, the Connecticut and Passumpsic Valley Homœopathic Medical Society, and the Champlain Valley Homœopathic Medical Society— to name a few.

The number of homœopathic physicians in 1904 was 54. In 1941 there were 14, in 1963 there was one. The 1996 *Directory* lists six practitioners and one study group.

Virginia

Virginia was the third state to be introduced to homœopathy. About 1830 a lay practitioner named Kuper was working in Norfolk. He remained for a year or two. Two brothers, Adolph and Edward Caspari, students at the Allentown Academy, resided at Norfolk between 1832 and 1838.

In 1838 Dr. F. T. Campos went to Norfolk and in 1839 commenced practice. He is said to have graduated in medicine in Lisbon, Portugal, and to have practiced several years in Brazil. He was active in the epidemic of yellow fever during the summer and winter of 1855.

The Hahnemann Medical Society of the Old Dominion was organized at Richmond in 1880, and reorganized in 1893. It was operating in 1904.

In 1899 there were 31 homœopaths in Virginia, of whom eight were located in Richmond. In 1904 there were 30 homœopathic physicians in the state.

In the 1925 AIH listing there are 30 practitioners. There were only five in 1963. The 1996 *Directory* lists 10 practitioners and ten study groups.

Washington

Washington's first practitioner was Dr. Alvan Bagley, an 1855 graduate of Cleveland, who settled in Seattle, some time before 1875. Dr. Charles Grove settled in Spokane in 1889, and Dr. Ferdinand Southworth began practice in Tacoma in 1888. By 1876 there were four homœopaths in the state, in 1904 there were 58.

The Washington State Homœopathic Medical Society was organized in 1889. The Tacoma Academy of Homœopathic Medicine was organized in 1890. The Homœopathic Society of King County was organized in 1889.

In 1941 there were 56 practitioners listed. In 1963 there were but three. The 1996 *Directory* lists 13 practitioners and two study groups.

West Virginia

The history of homœopathy in West Virginia pre-dates the separation of the state from Virginia in 1863. Reverend William Hunter was the first to use homœopathy in the area in 1848. He trained several homœopaths who went on to earn medical degrees.

Dr. Alfred Hughes and his sister Eliza began practicing homœopathy in Wheeling in about 1849. He subsequently gained his degree from the Homœopathic Medical College of Pennsylvania in 1853. Espousing the Confederate cause, he was arrested in 1861 and eventually moved to Richmond

The Faces of Homœopathy

and then to Baltimore. Eliza C. Hughes eventually earned her degree from the Pennsylvania Medical College in 1860. She was the first woman practitioner in the Virginias.

The West Virginia Homœopathic Medical Society was organized in 1898, at Wheeling, by Drs. M. L. Casselbury and C. M. Boger among others. This society was still active in 1904.

There were 30 homœopaths in the state in 1904. In 1941 there were 15 homœopaths in the state. By 1963 there were but two. The 1996 *Directory* lists two study groups in the state.

Wisconsin

Although Dr. Henry Hull Cator practiced homœopathy when he settled in Milwaukee in 1846, tradition says homœopathy was first used by the wife of an Episcopalian clergyman in Green Bay. Homœopathy spread rapidly in the state, with 32 practitioners in 1857 and 234 in 1904.

The animosity between the regular practitioners and the homœopaths was rampant. One doctor received a severe reprimand by the medical board for even saying hello to a homœopath on the street. The Homœopathic Medical Association of the State of Wisconsin was formed in 1858—an outgrowth of the Wisconsin Institute of Homœopathy which had been formed in 1848. The association had 115 members in 1904.

Dr. Tracy, a partner of Cator, published a small journal, *The Milwaukee Homœopathic Medical Reporter*, in about 1848.

We find several people practicing with no medical degree. W. P. Butler and his family located in Woods County in 1855, and Mrs. Woods became the only homœopathic practitioner in the county, while David Graham was practicing in Door County in 1852, saying, "I began to prescribe for my neighbors and was soon given the title of Dr. Graham."

Dr. Giles and Dr. Bowen were the first practitioners in Madison in about 1850.

The 1941 AIH *Directory* had 83 practitioners in Wisconsin. By 1963 the number had dwindled to three. The 1996 *Directory* lists 11 practitioners and four study groups.

Wyoming

Dr. John Bowman, an 1874 graduate of NY Homœopathic settled in Cheyenne in 1875— the first homœopath in Wyoming. He left a year later and was succeeded by Dr. G. E. Gorham. In 1904 there were seven homœopaths in the state, although 22 homœopaths had come and gone by that time. In 1941 there were six practitioners. By 1963 there was one. The 1996 *Directory* has no listing for the state.

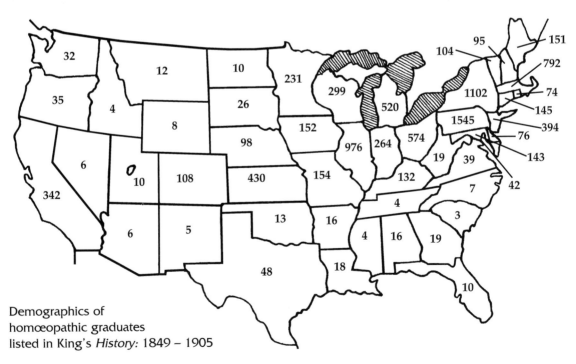

Demographics of
homœopathic graduates
listed in King's *History:* 1849 – 1905

Appendix E

The Hospitals

The Homœopathic Hospitals

The following is a list by state of most of the hospitals listed in several sources: Bradford's *Bibliography*, published in 1892, *The International Homœopathic Directory of 1911*, *The International Homœopathic Directory of 1931*, and *The AIH Directory of 1941*.

I have not listed the small hospitals that Bradford includes which existed for only a few months in the 1850s-1880s. There were undoubtedly other, smaller hospitals. In the 1911 listing, 175 hospitals responded to the questionnaire. 94 others did not respond *or* were smaller than 30 beds.

The larger hospitals were, generally, state–supported. The smaller ones were supported by patient fees and donations. A "hospital" at the turn of the century was a far cry from the technological behemoths we know today or see on the popular TV shows like "Chicago Hope"or "ER." Many of these private hospitals were operated by a single doctor and a staff of nurses. The patient population was often less than 20.

Many of the larger hospitals begun as homœopathic institutions slowly allowed non-homœopathic physicians entrance— often only to keep the fees coming in. Many were taken over by allopaths and remain today, with only a change of name. Many hospitals reverted to allopathic management during the 1930s. For example, The Yonkers Homœopathic Hospital in Yonkers, New York became Yonkers General Hospital, and the J. Lewis Crozer Home and Hospital for Incurables in Chester, Pennsylvania is today the Crozer Medical Center.

Those hospitals listed with *italic* headings were listed in Bradford or the 1911 listing, but did not appear in the 1931 listing. Either they closed or became allopathic. No further information was available.

Those listed with **bold** heading were listed in the 1931 *Directory*. This *Directory* had separate listings, which here appear with the following codes: (H) a full homœopathic staff; (M) a mixed staff of allopaths and homœopaths, with the latter in the majority; (G) a general hospital with the homœopaths in the minority.

Those that were funded in whole or in part by state or local funding are marked with an (F). All others were supported by patient fees, endowments, or donations.

Those marked with an asterisk (*) were listed in the 1941 *Directory*. Some of these were not in the 1931 *Directory*.

Wesson Memorial Hospital
Springfield, Massachusetts

National Homœopathic Hospital
Washington, DC

CALIFORNIA

Los Angeles:
*Allan Cowperthwaite Endowed Clinic and Homeopathic Hospital. 1510 N. Main St. (H)
State Reform School Hospital. opened 1891. (F)
Oakland:
Oakland Homeopathic Hospital opened 1876. Moved to 1057 Alice St. in 1883. Name changed to Fabiola Hospital in 1886. Moved to Moss Avenue and New Broadway, 1888.
Patton:
*Southern California State Hospital, Patton, California. Opened 1896. For the Insane only. (H) (F)
San Diego:
Hospital of the Good Samaritan. opened 1889.
San Francisco:
*Hahnemann Hospital of San Francisco. 1887. 312 Page Street. 100 beds. Became the Marshall Hale Hospital in the early 1940s. (H)
Maria Kip Orphanage, San Francisco, Calif. 1870. 120 beds. (F)
*San Francisco Homeopathic Polyclinic. Opened 1881, ceased 1885. Opened again. Mills Building corner of Valencia and 27th St.
San Francisco Nursery for Homeless Children. Opened 1878. 80 beds.
Santa Barbara Cottage Hospital. Opened 1891.

COLORADO

Golden:
Colorado Industrial School for Boys. Opened 1881. 372 beds (F)
Denver:
Denver City and County Hospital, Homœopathic Department, Sixth Ave. and Cherokee Street. Opened 1876. 300 beds. (F)
Belle Lenox Nursery. 1897. 79 beds.
Colorado Springs:
Nordrach Ranche Sanitarium. 1901. 155 beds. Tubercular paying patients only.

CONNECTICUT

Greenwich:
Crest View Sanitarium. Opened 1894. 35 beds. For treatment of nervous, alcoholic and insane cases only.
New Haven:
Grace Homeopathic Hospital. Founded 1892. West Chapel Street. 100 beds. (F)
*The Evans Private Hospital. 1488 Chapel Street.
Norwalk:
*The Elmfield Health Resort and Health School.

Norwich:
*Norwich State Hospital for the Insane. Incorporated 1904. 2,652 beds. (H) (F)
South Norwalk:
*Dr. Wadsworth's Sanitarium. 35 beds. Mental and nervous diseases only. (H)
Stamford:
Barnes' Sanitarium, Stamford, Conn. 1894. 160 beds. For alcoholic, nervous and insane patients.
Given's Sanitarium. Opened 1891. 250 beds. For alcoholic, nervous and mildly insane cases.

DELAWARE

Wilmington:
*Homeopathic Hospital of Delaware. (The Memorial Hospital) 1888. 1501 Van Buren. 110 beds. (M)

DISTRICT OF COLUMBIA

*National Homeopathic Hospital. 1881. In 1886 moved to N and 2nd street. 85 beds. Opened to allopaths in 1928. (G) (F)

FLORIDA

Jacksonville:
Homeopathic Department, St. Luke's Hospital. The homœopathic ward was opened in 1878. It was closed between May 1888-May 1889, after which it re-opened.

ILLINOIS

Bloomington:
The Kelso Sanitarium and Hospital. 1920. 30 beds. (H)
Chicago:
Baptist Hospital of Chicago. 541 North Halstead.
Chicago and Cook Country General Hospital. Homeopathic wards established in 1882. (F)
Chicago Foundlings Home for Mothers and Infants. 15 Southwood St. 1871. 40 beds for mothers, and 60 for babies.
Chicago Homœopathic Hospital. 354 Southwood St. 1903. All cases but alcoholics and insane. 40 beds.
Chicago Nursery and Half Orphan Asylum. 175 Burlington Street. Opened 1850. 200 beds.
Garfield Park Sanitarium, 3813 Washington Boulevard. Opened 1893. 50 beds.
Hahnemann Hospital of the City of Chicago. 1855. 170 beds.
Illinois Masonic Home. 1884. Supported by the Grand Lodge of the State of Illinois. 80 beds.
*Streeter's Private Hospital. 1890. 2646 Calumet Ave. 35 beds.
Women's Model House. 3040 Calumet Ave. Opened 1893. Supported by Women's Clubs of Cook County. 35 beds.

Elgin:
Illinois Central Hospital for the Insane. Incorporated 1869. For the insane only. 1280 beds. (F)

Moline:
Moline Public Hospital. 1894. 42 beds. (F)

Rockford:
Rockford Hospital, Homœopathic Department. Opened 1883. 35 beds.

INDIANA

Kramer:
Mudlavia Sanitarium. 1890. All cases except maternity and insane. 200 beds.

South Bend:
Epworth Hospital. Opened 1894. 50 beds.

IOWA

Cedar Rapids:
Home for the Friendless. 1884. "This Institution has been receiving all the cases from the Juvenile Courts. Doing splendid work." 70 beds. (F)

Council Bluffs:
The Jennie Edmundson Memorial Hospital, Homœopathic Department. 1884. 60 beds.

Des Moines:
The Home for the Aged in the State of Iowa. 1896. 80 beds.
Des Moines Home for Friendless Orphans. 1882. 50 beds.
Benedict Home. 1882. 43 beds. (F)

Iowa City:
Hahnemann Hospital of Iowa City. 1886.
Homœopathic Hospital of the State of Iowa. 1876. 8 North Clinton Street. (F)

Sioux City:
Samaritan Hospital and Training School for Nurses. 1882. Corner of 17th and Pierce Street. 65 Beds.

KANSAS

Atchison:
The Soldiers' Orphan Home. 1887. 200 beds. (F)

Topeka:
Kansas Surgical Hospital of Topeka. 1882

Wichita:
Wichita Homœopathic Hospital. 1889. 2nd and Riverview.

KENTUCKY

Hopkinsville:
Western Kentucky Insane Asylum. 1859. 1,100 beds. (F)

Lexington:
Eastern Kentucky Insane Asylum. 1867. 1,045 Beds. (F)

Louisville:
City Hospital, Homœopathic Department. 1882 250 beds.
Deaconess Home and Hospital. 1896. 35 beds.

LOUISIANA

New Orleans Homœopathic Hospital. Ground dug in 1892 on State Street. No record of it ever opening.

MAINE

Biddeford:
Trull Hospital. 1901. 40 beds.

Portland:
Maine Homœopathic Hospital, Portland. 1891.

MARYLAND

Baltimore:
Maryland Homeopathic Hospital. 1890. 323 N. Pace St. 58 beds. (F)

Forest Glen:
Carroll Springs Sanitarium. 1886. General, nervous, and maternity cases only. 40 beds. (H)

Laurel:
Brewster Park Hotel-Sanitarium. 1893. 30 Beds.

MASSACHUSETTS

Brighton:
*Hahnemann Hospital. 1892. (Listed only in the 1941 Directory, the corporation was established in 1892, and by 1939 had enough money to construct the hospital. Located at 1515 Commonwealth Ave., it opened in March, 1941. It had room for 15 patients. The medical and surgical staff were all Hahnemannian homœopaths, several being direct pupils of Kent. Although it maintained its homœopathic library and stocked remedies in the pharmacy into the early 1980s, it ceased providing homœopathic care when Ray Spalding, the last homœopath on its staff, died in the late 1960s.)

Boston:
Boothby's Hospital. 1-5 Worcester Square, Boston. Opened 1891.
Emerson Hospital, Forest Hills. 1904. 50 beds.
Massachusetts Homœopathic Hospital. 1855. Moved1876 to E. Concord St. between Harrison and Albany. 375 beds.
Talitha Cumi Maternity Home of the New England Reform Society. 1836. 204-206 West Brookline St. This home is for the care of maternity cases only. 30 beds.

Brockton:
Brockton Hospital. 1890. 45 Beds. (F)

Chelsea:
  Rufus S. Frost's General Hospital. 1894. 50 beds.
Dorchester Center:
  Cullis' Consumptive's Home. 1864. 40 beds.
Gloucester:
  Addison Gilbert Hospital. 1897. 30 beds.
Haverhill:
  Haverhill Hospital. 1904. 45 beds.
Lowell:
  Lowell General Hospital. 1893. 70 beds.
Malden:
  Malden Hospital. 1890. Three allopaths and three homœopaths on staff. 75 beds.
Newton:
  Newton Cottage Hospital, Washington Street. 1886. Four allopaths, four homœopaths. 150 beds.
Quincy:
  Quincy Hospital, Quincy. 1890.
Roxbury:
  New England Baptist Hospital. 1893. 53 beds.
Rutland:
  Massachusetts State Sanatorium. 1895. For incipient consumptives. 350 beds. (F)
Sandwich:
  White's Private Asylum for the Insane. 1891.
Somerville:
  Somerville Hospital. 1891. 45 beds.
South Framingham:
  Framingham Hospital. 1890. Open to both schools of medicine on equal terms. 60 beds.
Springfield:
  Wesson Maternity Hospital. The staff has six physicians, three of whom must be homœopaths. 72 beds.
  *Wesson Memorial Hospital. 1900. 140 High Street. 70 beds. (M)
Taunton:
  Morton Hospital. 1889.
Waltham:
  Waltham Hospital. 1885. 111 beds.
Westboro:
  *Westboro Insane Hospital. 1884. 1,000 beds. (F)
Worcester:
  *Worcester Hahnemann Hospital. 1896. 281 Lincoln St. 100 beds. (G)

MICHIGAN

Ann Arbor:
  Homœopathic Hospital of the University of Michigan. 1880. 125 beds. (F)

Detroit:
  Detroit Free Hospital (Grace Hospital). 1888 150 beds. 2,700 in-patients in 1910.
Grand Rapids:
  Union Benevolent Association Hospital. 1873. In 1891 the trustees voted to allow homœopaths access and the entire allopathic staff resigned. 70 beds.
Highland Park:
  *Jordan Hospital. 30 Beds. 14131 Woodward Ave.
Ionia:
  Michigan Asylum for Insane Criminals. 1883. 425 beds. (F)
Kalamazoo:
  Borgess Hospital. 1889. 125 beds.
Muskegon:
  Mercy Hospital of Muskegon. 1903. 40 beds.
Smyrna:
  Andrew B. Spinney Sanitarium. 35 beds.

MINNESOTA

Fergus Falls:
  Fergus Falls State Hospital. 1897. Hospital for the insane only. 1,650 beds. (F)
Minneapolis:
  City Hospital. 1890. 175 Beds.
  Homœopathic Hospital of Minneapolis. 1884. 25th Street and 4th Ave. S.
  Lawrence Sanitarium. 1890. 60 beds.
  Maternity Hospital. 1886. 2529 4th Ave. S. 30 beds.
  Minneapolis Medical and Surgical Institute. 1890. 1st Ave. S. and 9th St.
  Washbourne Memorial Asylum. 1883. 117 beds.
St. Paul:
  City and County Hospital. 1871. Jefferson Ave. and Colburn St. Seven homœopathic physicians on staff. 350 beds. (F)
  St. Joseph's Hospital. 1854. 130 beds.
  St. Luke's Hospital. 1873. Supported by endowments, providing for seven homœopathic physicians on the staff. 100 beds.
  St. Paul Homeopathic Hospital. 1887. 800 Agate Street.

MISSOURI

Kansas City:
  Elliott Sanitarium. 1909. 35 beds.
  Kansas City Homœopathic Hospital. 1889. 817 E. 8th Street
St. Louis:
  Girls' Industrial Home. 1854. 5501 Von Versen Ave. 90 beds.
  Good Samaritan Hospital of St. Louis. 1861. Pratt St. and O'Fallon.
  St. Louis Children's Hospital. 1880. 100 beds.
  Women's Homœopathic Hospital of Missouri. 1891.

NEBRASKA

Lincoln:
"Green Gables" Sanitarium. 1901. 75 beds.

NEW JERSEY

Atlantic City:
Galen Hall. 1894. 200 beds.
Camden:
Camden Homeopathic Hospital. 1885. Moved to West and Stevens in 1888.
West Jersey Homeopathic Hospital. 1887. Mt. Ephraim and Atlantic Avenues. 40 beds. (H)
East Orange:
Homeopathic Hospital of Essex County. 1903. 120 beds.
Hackensack:
Hackensack Hospital. The hospital has a homœopathic ward.
Irvington:
Bethany Home. 1900. 86 Beds.
Montclair:
Montclair Community Hospital. 1923. 120 Harrison Street. 61 beds. (M)
Neptune:
Fitkin Memorial Hospital. 1905. 100 beds. Had been the Ann May Memorial Homeopathic Hospital in Spring Lake, New Jersey before a change of location and name. Corlies Ave. (M)
Newark:
Baptist Home for the Aged. 285 Roseville Ave. 1891. 33 beds.
Passaic:
St. Mary's Hospital. 1895. 50 beds.
Plainfield:
Children's Home. 1877. 40 beds.
Plainfield Sanitarium. 1889. 60 beds.
Trenton:
Trenton City Hospital. 1889. Brunswick Ave.
William McKinley Memorial Hospital. 1889. Brunswick and Ferrier Ave. 75 beds. (H) (F)

NEW YORK

Albany:
Albany House of Shelter. 1868. 35 beds.
Albany City Homeopathic Hospital. 1872. 75 Division Street. 35 beds.
Babylon:
Muncie Seaside Sanitarium. 1895. 100 beds.
Binghamton:
New York State Asylum for the Chronic Insane. 1881. 1,325 beds.
Brooklyn:
Brooklyn Homœopathic Hospital. 1852. From 1890 it was at Cumberland St. and Myrtle Ave.

Brooklyn Homeopathic Maternity Hospital. 1870. 48 Concord St.
Brooklyn Nursery and Infants' Hospital. 1871. 399 Herkimer St. 195 beds.
Brooklyn Women's Homœopathic Hospital (The Memorial Hospital). 1883. 200 South Oxford St.
Carson Peck Memorial Hospital. Albany Ave. and Crown. (G)
Cumberland Street Hospital. 1902. 312 beds. 39 Auburn Place. Became Cumberland Hospital in 1918. (G) (F)
Muncie Sanitarium. 1895. 119 Macon Street. 30 beds.
Prospect Heights Hospital and Brooklyn Maternity and New York State School for Training Nurses, Washington Ave. and St. John's Place. 190 beds. (H)
The Bethesda Sanitarium. 1884. 952-954, St. Mark's Ave. 40 beds.
Buffalo:
Buffalo Homeopathic Hospital. 1872. In 1885 moved to 74 Cottage Street. 65 beds.
Buffalo Ingleside Home and Hospital. 1870. 13th and Vermont. 70 beds.
Erie County Hospital. 1894. 500 beds. (F)
Geneva:
Geneva Institute. 1854. 80 beds.
Geneva City Hospital. 1892. 35 beds.
Goshen:
Interpines Sanitarium. 1890. For alcoholic, drug, insane and nervous cases. 68 beds. (M)
Helmuth:
Gowanda State Hospital. 1894. For the insane only. 1,288 beds. (F)
Jamestown:
Women's Christian Association Hospital. 1887. 55 beds.
New York City:
Baptist Home for the Aged. 1869. 68th Street. 100 beds.
Chapin Home. 151 East 66th Street. 1869. Has two attending homœopathic physicians. 68 beds.
Children's Hospital of the Five Points House of Industry. 155 Worth Street. 77 beds. (F)
Florence Hospital of New York City. 1890.
*Governor Flower Hospital 450 East 64th St.
Hahnemann Hospital of New York. 1870. Park Ave. and 68th Street. 90 beds.
Helmuth House. 1886. 41 East 12th St.
Hospital of the New York Medical College for Women. 1863. 213 West 54th St. then 19 West 101st St. 50 beds.
Hospital of the Protestant Half-Orphan Asylum. 1835. 67 West 10th St. 210 beds.
Laura Franklin Free Hospital. 1886. 17-19 111th St. Under charge of the Episcopal Sisterhood of St. Mary. 50 beds.

*Metropolitan Hospital. Welfare Island, New York City. 1875. Previously the New York Homœopathic Charity Hospital of Ward's Island. 8,915 patients treated in 1910. 1,500 beds. Supported by the City of New York. (M) (F)

*New York Homeopathic College and Flower Hospital. 1890. Originally at East 63rd Street. 60 beds. (H) (F) Continued today as the Flower-Fifth Avenue Hospital, at 5th Avenue and 105th St., it maintained hospital privileges for a few remaining homœopaths through the 1940s.

New York Ophthalmic Hospital. 1852. 201 East 23rd St. 57 beds. (M)

Middletown:

*Middletown State Homœopathic Hospital for the Insane. 1870. Ten homœopathic physicians on staff. 3,092 beds.

Owego:

"Glenmary." 1889. For alcoholic and insane cases only. 35 beds.

Rochester:

Hahnemann Hospital. 1889. 9 Oakland Street. 75 beds.

Rochester Homœopathic Hospital. 1889. 233 Monroe Street. 140 beds. Re-located in 1893 to Alexander Street, the name was changed to Genesee Hospital in 1926.

The Lee Private Hospital. 1898. 179 Lake Ave. 51 beds.

Syracuse:

Syracuse Homœopathic Hospital. 1895. 116 East Castle St. 38 beds.

Utica:

St. Luke's Home and Hospital. 1872. 29 Hamilton Street.

Faxton Hospital. 1875.

Yonkers:

*Yonkers Homeopathic Hospital of Maternity. 1896. 127 Ashburton Ave. Staff consists of eight homœopathic physicians. 30 beds. (F)

OHIO

Renia:

Ohio Soldiers' and Sailors' Orphans' Home. 1870. 835 beds.

Chillicothe:

Chillicothe Emergency Hospital. 1893. 38 beds.

Cincinnati:

Cincinnati Orphan Asylum. 1833. 75 beds.

Home for the Friendless and Foundlings. 1855. 50 beds.

Ohio Hospital for Women and Children. 1881. 325 West 7th Street.

Cleveland:

City Hospital. 1889. 375 beds. (F)

*Cleveland Homœopathic Hospital. 1864. (Huron Road Hospital) 8811 Euclid Ave. 120 beds.

Cleveland Protestant Homœopathic Hospital. 1868. 66 Huron St.

Dorcas Invalids' Home for Incurables. 1862. 50 beds.

Glenville Hospital. 1907. 701 Parkwood Ave. Seven homeopathic physicians. 30 beds.

*Grace Hospital. 1910. 2307 West 14th. (G)

Home for Aged Women. 2206 East 46th Street. 60 beds.

Maternity Hospital 1892. 2364 East Seth St. 30 beds.

McGregor Home. 1929. 50 beds.

The University Sanitarium. 1903. 1948 101 St., N.E. 50 beds.

Columbus:

Parkview Sanitarium. 1895. 50 beds.

Dayton:

Miami Valley Hospital. 1890. 160 beds.

Elyria:

Elyria Memorial Hospital. 1907. 35 beds. (F)

Marion:

Sawyer Sanitarium. 100 beds.

Toledo:

Toledo Protestant Hospital. 1877. 171 Union Street.

Toledo Hospital. 1876. 125 beds.

Zanesville:

Bethesda Hospital. 1888. 50 beds.

OKLAHOMA

Oklahoma City:

*Hubbard Hospital, 1501 North East 11th St.

OREGON

Portland:

Children's Home. 100 beds.

*Hahnemann Homeopathic Hospital. 1935. 1132 East Second Ave. 75 beds. Name changed to Holladay Park Hospital in 1947. Closed June 1994.

PENNSYLVANIA

Allegheny:

Western Home for Women. 1868. 423 Locust St. 30 beds. (F)

Allentown:

*Homœopathic State Hospital for Insane. 1901. 1,429 beds.

Chester:

*J. Lewis Crozer Homœopathic Hospital. 1897. 85 beds. (H)

Easton:

Easton Sanitarium. 1894. 36 beds.

Eire:

Hamst Hospital. 1881.

St. Vincent's Hospital. 1875.

Johnstown:
*Lee Homeopathic Hospital. 1897. 65 beds. (M)
McKeesport:
St. Barnabas Free Home. 1900. 100 beds.
New Brighton:
Beaver Valley General Hospital. 1894. 55 beds. (F)
Philadelphia:
*Children's Homœopathic Hospital of Philadelphia. 1877. Moved to 914 N. Broad Street in 1883. 55 beds. Absorbed by:
St. Luke's Homœopathic Hospital. 1896. Thompson & 8th. 300 beds (H) (F)
Eye and Surgical Institute of Philadelphia. 1886. 18th and Mt. Vernon.
*Homeopathic Hospital of the Hahnemann Medical College Philadelphia. Incorporating the older Homeopathic Hospital of Philadelphia. 1850. Race and Broad St. 592 beds. (H) (F). When Hahnemann Medical College ceased teaching homœopathy in 1959, the hospital itself ceased homœopathic involvement, although some of the older homœopaths still had hospital privileges. It was absorbed by the Allegheny Health Consortium in the early 1990s.
Philadelphia Home for Infants. 1873. 4618 Westminster Ave. 52 beds. (F)
West Philadelphia General Homœopathic Hospital and Dispensary. 1905. 1234 North 54th St. 32 beds. (F)
*Woman's Southern Homeopathic Hospital. 1896. 744 Spruce St., Philadelphia, Pa. Opened 1896. In 1930, re-named **Broad Street Hospital** and re-located to 739 South Broad St. 110 beds. (H) (F)
*Women's Homeopathic Hospital. (Medical, Surgical, and Maternity Hospitals of the Women's Homœopathic Association of Pennsylvania). 1882. Moved to 20th and Susquehana in 1887. 200 beds.(H) (F)
Pittsburgh:
*Christian Home for Women. 1868. 1423 Liverpool St.
*Homeopathic Medical and Surgical Hospital of Pittsburgh. 1866. Second Avenue and Smithfield Streets. 220 beds. (F)
Pittsburgh Sunshine Children's Home. 1906. 31 beds.
* Shadyside Hospital, 5230 Center Ave.
Pottstown:
*Homeopathic Hospital. 1914. 1212 High St. 62 beds.
Reading:
*Reading Homeopathic Hospital. 1891. 135 North 6th Street. 75 beds. (H) (F)

Scranton:
Florence Crittenden Home. 1894. 40 beds. (F)
*Hahnemann Hospital and Training School for Nurses. 1897. 316 Colfax Ave. 125 beds. (M) (F)
Walters Park:
The Walter Sanitarium. 1876. 140 beds.
West Chester:
*Homeopathic Hospital of Chester County. 76 beds.
Wilkes-Barre:
*Wyoming Valley Homeopathic Hospital. 1912. 149 Dana Street. 80 beds. (H)

RHODE ISLAND

Providence:
Children's Friend Society. 1835. 70 beds.
*Rhode Island Homeopathic Hospital. 1878. 825 Chalkstone St. 200 beds. (M)
St. Elizabeth Home. 1882. 183 Atlantic Ave. 37 beds.

TENNESSEE

Knoxville:
Knoxville General Hospital. 1899. 125 beds. (F)
Pleasant Hill:
*Uplands Sanitarium. 1922. 16 beds.

VERMONT

St. Johnsbury:
The Sparhawk Sanitarium. 1887. 30 beds.

WASHINGTON

Seattle:
Northwestern Hospital. 100 beds. (M)

WISCONSIN

Kenosha:
Pennoyer Sanitarium. 1857. 100 beds.
Milwaukee:
Milwaukee Orphan Asylum. 1850. 2,125 beds.
Knowlton Hospital. 1900. 40 beds.
Oconomowoc:
*The Summit Hospital.

Appendix F

The world

A brief synopsis of homœopathy— worldwide

The task of finding out who brought homœopathy to where and by when is not an easy one. There are few sources to go to, and little of it is in one place.

I began with Volume II of the 1876 *Transactions of the American Institute for Homœopathy*. The Philadelphia meeting was the first international gathering with reports from around the globe.

I then moved to the 20th century with Volume I of the *International Homœopathic Congress* in Atlantic City, New Jersey in 1906— which contains summaries of homœopathy in many countries.

I then consulted the *International Homœopathic Directory*— 1912 and 1931; both edited by E. Petrie Hoyle, MD. Some information was found in Richard Haehl's two volumes (*Samuel Hahnemann: His Life and Works*), and still more was culled from Bradford's *Pioneers of Homœopathy*.

I also used the database I developed of 15,000 graduates of homœopathic colleges in the USA listed in William Harvey King's *History of Homœopathy in America*, and I traced journals through *Bibliotheca Homœopathica* by Baur, Gypser, von Keller, and Thomas. The final source came from correspondents on the Internet homœopathy list.

In all the written works, information came from local informants. In some cases, very few historical details were printed. In others, only a list of practitioners appeared.

It was difficult to find the exact trail. A name was often given as the first person to bring in homœopathy, but where did THAT person get it? We can only assume they read the work of Hahnemann. We must remember in the medical world of the time, Hahnemann's theories were "all the talk."

Dates often conflicted with sources— was it 1850 or 1852? And while three sources mentioned Dr. Martins from Lisboa, one source spoke of Dr. Martins and Dr. Lisboa. Is this a translation error, or a missing piece of information?

And, of course, the world was a different place. In 1876, some countries did not exist, and some which did are now long gone. I've tried to report using the geographical units as we now know.

A fuller history of each country lies beyond this book. I hope this information becomes a starting point for expanding individual histories. Much of this information began as a short history compiled for the European and International Councils of Classical Homœopathy (ECCH/ICCH).

A common thread through all of the history is the way the laity carried the homœopathic torch. In many countries it thrived despite the lack of trained professionals. Dr. Hoyle urged the laity to form homœopathic organisations to insure the survival of the art and science. I wonder what he would have thought of the professional homœopath.

Another factor in the spread of homœopathy during the early part of the 1900s was the Missionary School of Medicine, founded in England in 1903. It was connected with the Faculty of Homœopathy in London. The Missionary School's goal was to teach missionaries enough about medicine and homœopathy to serve as health care providers. In 1934 when Dr. Neatby's obituary was printed in the *British Homœopathic Journal*, there were more than 700 graduates of the Missionary School. The missionaries were, undoubtedly, an important diaspora for homœopathy.

In 1880, Joseph C. Guernsey, MD, wrote in the *AIH Transactions*, "Letters had to be written to all parts of the country for essential information, many of which are yet un-noticed."

Fifty years later E. Petrie Hoyle, MD, wrote in the *International Homœopathic Directory*, "We expect there are many others, but we have not been able to obtain any direct reply to our letters."

Now, 67 years later, amid the advent of overnight mail services, faxes, and the Internet, communication has not much improved. Human nature still has people not replying to letters. The brief histories here have been gleaned from that with which I have been furnished. Many requests for information have gone unanswered, and I did not hold off publishing until replies came in.

Africa:

Dr Benoit Mure was the first homœopath in Egypt and Sudan in 1851. There were also probably French homœopaths in the Mahgreb regions.

The 1931 Directory lists practitioners in Rhodesia (1), Natal (1), the Congo (2), Kenya (1), Liberia (1), and Egypt (2).

Antarctica:

Fosteri Aptenodytes introduced homœopathy to the Emperor in 1900.

Argentina:

The "liberator of Argentina," General San Martin, arrived from Spain in 1812. He carried a homœopathic medicine chest, now in the Museo Sanmartiniano de Mendoza. The first Argentine physician homœopath was Dr Guillermo Darrouzsin, in the mid 1880s. The *Boletín Homeopático* was the Argentine Hahnemannian Society magazine, from 1865 to 1875.

During the 1870 yellow fever epidemic, Dr Pierre Petit de Murat treated hundreds of people with homœopathy. Dr. Murat formed the Argentine Homœopathic Society in 1877, but homœopathy foundered and by 1931 there were only seven doctors and seven chemists.

In 1933 the Argentine Homœopathic Medical Association was formed with Dr Tomas Paschero as a leading member. The first *Organon* was printed in Argentina in 1967 using the 1927 Mexican translation of Romero.

During 1964 the first course of homœopathic medicine was taught at a university, but the continuous attacks lead to its demise. In 1972 Dr Paschero founded the "Escuela Médica Homeopatica Argentina Tomas Paschero," and in 1975 Dr F. X. Eizayaga founded the "Fundacion Homeos." Both institutions are still operating.

The estimate of numbers of practitioners in the country ranges from a low of about 700 to a high of about 2,000. It is not known how many are unicist or complexist, or how many alternate allopathic and homœopathic methods.

The national organization is Federation of Argentine Homeopathic Medical Associations (FAMHA). You must be an MD to practice.

The country is represented in the LMHI.

Australia:

Mr. Thienette De Bergny, a layman (he was referred to as Dr. Bergny in NZ in 1855), is credited as the first to introduce homœopathy in Victoria in about 1850, although some say it was Dr. John Hickson in Melbourne. Some homœopathy was introduced with the English settlers. There were several medical doctors. Stephen Simpson, the author of *The Practical Advantages of Homœopathy* (1836) "was discouraged [in the UK] and took to a sheep run in Australia." He practiced homœopathy in Queensland, and eventually returned to England.

In 1858, Benjamin Wilson, a Baptist clergyman, settled in Brisbane and practiced homœopathy. In 1857 a Benedictine monk, Rosendo Salvado, was using homœopathy among the Aborigines near Perth.

The first homœopathic pharmacy was established by E. G. Gould in Melbourne in 1864.

The Melbourne Homœopathic Hospital was founded in 1869 and survived until 1936 when it became allopathic and re-named Prince Henry Hospital. There were two homœopathic hospitals in Tasmania at the turn of the century.

King lists 17 graduates from Australia who studied at US schools between 1850 and 1905.

William Moore, a retired homœopath, left money to establish the Sydney Homœopathic Hospital in Glebe in 1902. The last homœopath, Leigh Deck, resigned in 1945. However, the terms of Moore's will allowed the hospital to continue operating under the public hospital system provided a bed was always available for homœopathic treatment. The hospital continued receiving the bequest against the time when interest in homœopathy might revive.

In 1985 the Australian Medical Homœopathic Society for Research and Education (AMHSRE) approached the Sydney Homœopathic Hospital to use the accumulated funds in Moore's bequest to have the hospital extended and modernised to include a homœopathic clinic and dispensary. The Central Sydney Area Health Services vetoed the proposal, and closed the hospital in 1989. At that time the AMHSRE was replaced by the Australian Medical Faculty of Homœopathy (AMFoH) which lobbied the health department to provide hospital facilities to satisfy the growing demand for homœopathic treatment. Eighteen months later, on August 1, 1990, a homœopathic outpatients clinic was opened at the nearby Balmain Hospital, which still operates today.

A journal, *Australian Homœopathic Progress*, was published in Melbourne in 1870.

Dr. Hoyle mentioned homœopathy was declining— there were 27 doctors in 1911 and 19 in 1931. The was one homœopath in Western Australia and "the laity prescribe for themselves to the limits of their courage."

The Australian Institute of Homœopathy was formed in 1946. Membership was open to qualified homœopaths, but students were allowed to attend meetings. Although the numbers of qualified members dropped severely it was carried on by Mrs. Gwen Reynolds who held regular weekly meetings at her home. She practiced part-time with Dr Buiys, a Dutchman. The Institute was mainly responsible for promoting and advertising homœopathy, by giving regular talks to Lions Clubs, Rotary, etc. The Institute established the first course in Homœopathy when the Nature Care College in Sydney was formed. This attracted 20-25 students every year and the course ran for 4 years.

Over the years several homœopathic societies were founded in the different states. The Australian Federation of Homœopaths became a national organization of affiliated state branches by the late 1980s. By mid 1990 the AFH changed its name to the Australian Homœopathic Association, and became a truly national organization; 80% of homœopathic practitioners are members.

By early 1998, nine homœopathic associations had amalgamated to become five. A National Competency Standard was established and awaits government endorsement at the time of writing.

As in the UK, under Common Law, the professional homœopath is allowed to practice. Medical doctors may practice homœopathy, and there is a homœopathic society for MDs, The Australia Medical Faculty of Homœopathy. It will not amalgamate with the non-medical association but has been instrumental in helping endorse the competencies.

There are about 450-500 professional homœopaths (not all association members) and perhaps 20 serious medical homœopaths with another 130 MDs who use some homœopathic remedies. There are about 10 recognized specialist schools and several naturopathic colleges teaching homœopathy to a professional standard, and there are three manufacturing pharmacies.

The country is represented in the LMHI.

The Faces of Homœopathy

Austria:

Although Hahnemann studied in Vienna in 1777, homœopathy came to Austria in 1818 with Prof. S. Veith, a veterinarian, in Bohemia. In 1819 we find Dr. Fleischmann in Vienna and Dr. Marenzeller (who first learned homœopathy in 1815) in Prague. After successes with the 1831 cholera epidemic, practice was legalized in 1837. The first journal was published in Wien in 1844. In 1842, a group of homœopaths, oriented toward "specifics," formed the Verein homœopatischer Aerzte Oesterreichs fuer physiologische Arzneipruefung (association of homœopathic doctors for physiological drug testing). In 1843, there were 17 members. In 1873, the association was renamed to Verein homœopatischer Aerzte Oesterreichs (association of homœopathic doctors in Austria). It then had a membership of 43, which dwindled as the years passed.

At the turn of the century, there were only a handful of known homœopaths, but the body of knowledge was being passed on to and adopted by priests, pastor's wives and lay people.

By 1931 Dr. Hoyle notes a "marked decease" in practitioners with "no young men" filling the ranks. "25% of the letters sent came back marked 'deceased'."

Between the two World Wars, several doctors (Schreiber, Rosendorf, Wancura and Gutman) tried to revive homœopathy in vain. Gutman immigrated to the United States in 1938.

After World War II, Robert Seitscheck and a pharmacist couple (Erich and Maria Peithner) established contact with homœopathic doctors.

In 1953, Seitschek and Mathias Dorcsi founded the Vereinigung Homœopatisch interessierter Aerzte (association of homœopathy-interested doctors). Seitschek built linkages abroad and in 1958 an international homœopathic league congress was held in Salzburg. In 1969, the association was renamed the Oesterreichische Gesselschaftt fuer Homœopathische Medizin (OGHM). The membership in 1995 had about 1000 doctors.

In 1973, the association was officially recognized in the form of a research contract with the ministry of science. A journal, *Homœopathie in Oesterreich*, was launched in 1989.

In 1985, Dorcsi obtained a teaching contract in the Institute for Pharmacognosy, and regular year-long homœopathy lectures are now held in the Vienna Faculty of Medicine. The campuses in Graz and Innsbruck soon followed.

In 1991, a second homœopathy society was founded, the Ärzte der Klassischen Homöopathie/ physicians of classical homœopathy (ÄKH). They have a separate curriculum and maintain a separate roster but the quality of education is comparable between them.

As of 1997, the OGHM has 310 recommended homœopaths on its roster, and the ÄKH had 100.

Only medical doctors are allowed to practice in Austria.

The country is represented in the LMHI.

Barbados:

In 1931 there was one doctor and one chemist. King lists 11 graduates from the "West Indies" who studied at US schools between 1850 and 1905.

Belgium:

The first homœopath was Dr. Pierre Joseph deMoor who began practice at Alost in 1829. In 1832, Dr. Varlez and Carlier brought homœopathy to Brussels. The earliest journal was published in Brussels in 1856.

Dr. Jahr, fleeing Paris in 1870 during the Franco-German war, settled in Brussels. More than 50 Belgian doctors were educated in homœopathy by Jahr himself. In 1894, 70 doctors officially used homœopathy for their patients and 50 pharmacists were delivering medications to patients.

In 1871, a society of homœopathic physicians was established. The "Society Royale Belge d'Homoopathie" (SRBH) is still active today.

In 1926 the "Association Homoopathique Belge" (AHB) was created for legal purposes (the SRBH was created for scientific matters). The AHB published the *Belgian Homoeopathic Journal*, created the Belgian Homœopathic School and started a Belgian Homœopathic Library. In 1976 this association was replaced by the "Federation Homoopathique Belge" (FHB).

During all this, homœopathic education was only possible in the Belgian School in Brussels. Students numbers were growing so fast different schools were created in different Belgian cities (Gent, Antwerp, Namur, Liege, Huy, Hechtel). During this period about 50 MDs achieved homœopathic education each year. In 1988 the "Unio Homoopathica Belgica" (UNIO) was recognized by the Belgian authorities. This professional union defended homœopathy on a political level. Today 300 homœopathic MDs belong to this union and 4,000 MDs (about 10% of all doctors) are prescribing homœopathic medications at least sometimes. One-fourth of the Belgian population uses homœopathy. As of 1998 only MDs could legally practice.

The country is represented in the LMHI.

Bahrain:

Homœopathy is not allowed to be practiced in Bahrain or the whole of middle east. The medicines cannot be imported because they are "manufactured by traditional methods which do not depend upon scientific clinical studies to improve their effacacy and safety." Since the World Health Organization has no regulations regarding homœopathy, it is not accepted.

There is one known homœopath in the country.

Bolivia:

One doctor in 1911. No further information.

Brazil:

In about 1810, Jose Bonifacio de Andrada e Silva, a politician and a student of natural science and mineralogy, knew about homœopathy through an exchange of letters with Hahnemann.

Dr. Antonio Ferreira Franca used homœopathy in Bahia in 1818, but found little support. In 1837, Dr. Duque Estrada learned homœopathy from a student, Frederick Emilius Jahn, who had come from Leipzig to study in Brazil. Although they were both interested in homœopathy as a science, neither took up the practice.

In 1836, the Academia Imperial de Medicina published articles against homœopathy.

The formal impetus to establish homœopathy in Brazil came from Benoit Mure, a Frenchman, who came to Brazil on business in 1840. With Vincent Jose Martins (from Lisbon)— they founded the Homœopathic Institute of Brazil in 1843. The first *Organon* in Portuguese was translated by Martins in 1846. The first journal, *The Hahnemannista*, was published in 1846.

After 1840, homœopathy was widely discussed by the press, and the discussion opened the doors to the works of Jose Martins and other homœopaths.

A three-year homœopathic school was founded in Rio in 1845, graduating the first class in 1847, making it the second homœopathic school (after Hering's Allentown Academy [1835-42]) in the world, but the Imperial Government did not allow the graduates clinical practice.

Some years later, after differences between Mure and Dr. Duque Estrada, there was a split resulting in two different institutes: the Instituto Hahnemanniano do Brasil (1859) and the Congregacio Médico-Homœopatica Fluminense. Weakened by the split, they soon ceased operation. In 1847, Benoit Mure returned back to France.

In spite of all the problems, homœopathy grew and spread in Brazil.

Many homœopaths, with a little pharmacy in hands, went from city to city, to fight several epidemic or endemic diseases, mainly cholera.

During the cholera epidemic in Rio in 1855, 388 cases were treated with homœopathy with a 2% death rate, while the allopathic infirmary had a 40-60% death rate.

In 1878, Saturnino de Meirelles and others re-created the old Instituto Homeopatico do Brasil and in 1880, changing the name to Instituto Hahnemanniano do Brazil, (IHB), which still exists.

In 1912, The IHB created the Homeopathic Hospital and the Faculdade Hahnemanniana, that taught homœopathy integrally with medicine. In 1918, the IHB was allowed to graduate homœopathic MDs and pharmacists. In 1924, the name was changed to Escola de Medicina e Cirurgia and in 1932 the National Council for Education ended the homœopathic teaching.

In the 1980s there was a resurgence of homœopathy. The AMHB (Brazilian Homeopathic Medical Association) and the council of medical specialties of the AMB (Brazilian Medical Association) began to discuss integration of specialties.

In Brazil, only MDs, veterinarians and dentists are allowed to prescribe both homœopathic and allopathic drugs. AMHB determined the homœopathy courses have a minimal curriculum and three years duration. It is offered as a postgraduate course for MDs. At the end of the course people have to take a test that AMHB gives each year, and have to pass the test to be registered as a homœopath in the Medicine Federal Council.

Homœopathy is taught in a few universities in different states. In Rio there are now five courses. In the last decade homœopathy has been mostly in the domain of pluralist prescribers. The AMHB has always promoted unicist "classical" homœopathy.

There are about 12,000 homœopaths in Brazil but few of them have the title from AMHB.

The country is represented in the LMHI.

Bulgaria:

Homœopathy was brought to Bulgaria by Georgy Mirkovich, MD. Born in a small Bulgarian village in 1828, Dr. Mirkovich graduated as a physician in 1856 from the Medical Faculty of The University of Montpellier in France. During his medical studies he has been trained also as a homœopath. Returning to Bulgaria, he established himself in private practice and joined the National Liberation Movement, for which he was imprisoned and deported by the Turk authorities (1865 -1878).

In 1893 Dr. Mirkovich edited and published the first homœopathic book in Bulgarian language: *Healing at Home with Homeopathy*. By that time he was a member of the newly-established Bulgarian Academy of Science.

From 1944 to 1989 homœopathy was strictly prohibited and practitioners prosecuted.

Systematic training according to ICCH standards was begun in 1993, in cooperation with the London College of Classical Homœopathy. The Bulgarian Homeopathic Association has 82 members. There are about 100 practicing homœopaths in the country.

Canada:

It is not clear who was the first practitioner in Canada. It is known that in 1842, James Lillie, a pupil of Federal Vandenburgh, settled in Toronto and began practicing homœopathy. Dr. Joseph J. Lancaster, who had studied in New York began practicing sometime in the 1840s in Ontario. He later attended the Homœopathic Medical College in Philadelphia and graduated in 1857.

A German named Von Schrader, settled in New Brunswick in about 1856. Although he had no diploma, he was joined by Dr. Peterson in 1858, and they established a practice in St. John.

In 1850, Dr. Lancaster petitioned the Legislative Assembly of Upper Canada (Ontario) on behalf of himself and other homœopaths to be given permission to practice. This resulted in the passage of "An Act Respecting Homœopathy" in 1859. Part of the Act was the creation of a board of examiners to qualify and license homœopathic physicians in Upper Canada.

The Homœopathic Medical Society of Canada was established in 1854 in Hamilton, Ontario, comprising all the prominent homœopaths in Upper (Ontario) and Lower Canada (Quebec).

The *Canadian Homœopathic Journal* was published in Hamilton in 1855-56.

In 1869, Ontario passed the Ontario Medical Act establishing a single unified College of Physicians and Surgeons of Ontario(CPSO) as the examining board for all medical practitioners. This united the three separate examining boards— eclectic, allopathic and homœopathic. Homœopaths were represented with five members on the council of the CPSO until 1934, when the number was reduced to one homœopath.

My database shows three practitioners from Western Canada graduating from The Homœopathic Medical College of Pennsylvania in 1856. King lists 90 graduates from Canada who studied at US schools between 1850 and 1905.

In 1931 there were 49 physicians listed.

The first female homœopath was Emily Stowe (1831-1903), who graduated from the New York Medical College for Women, in 1867. She founded the Women's College Hospital in Toronto.

The first homœopathic hospital opened as the Toronto Homœopathic Free Dispensary in 1888, followed by the Toronto Homœopathic Hospital in 1890 with 11 beds, later expanding to 32 beds.

All health care professions in Ontario are governed by the Regulated Health Professions Act which allows all health-care professions the same legal right to practice. This law upholds the belief that the public has the right to choose what health care it wishes. and that the government should only intervene to regulate where a profession poses a significant risk of harm to the public. Only allopathic professions are currently regulated.

All other provinces in Canada operate on the old medical licensing system, which grants an effective monopoly to allopaths. Doctors in Nova Scotia can practice homœopathy without fear of censure, but in Ontario, doctors are censured if they use homœopathy. A new law is being proposed which would allow doctors to practice alternative methods.

All schools of homœopathy in Canada offer diplomate status and all offer three-year, part-time courses (one or two weekends per month plus perhaps one or two evenings per week). There are no legal doctorate or university degree programs for homœopathy in Canada. A doctorate in any field other than allopathic medicine cannot legally be used while practicing alternative medicine. There are a few professional associations in Canada each with their own version of what constitutes competent standards. No single group speaks for the profession as a whole.

Canada (Québec):

John George Rosenstein, a German immigrant who had come from the United States, was allowed, in summer 1844 to "test" homœopathic therapy in the Montreal General Hospital, but not showing improvements on the patients, the experiments were stopped— satisfying the governors of the hospital and the Montreal press. This stopped homœopathy for the next 20 years in Québec.

Arthur Fisher began practicing homœopathy as soon as he obtained the right of medical practice in 1842, but he never publicly declared his homœopathic practice. Two other French-Canadian homœopathic supporters were Joseph Morrin, a physician in Québec City, and a Mr. Fargues who bequeathed to McGill University an amount of 6000 English pounds to establish a chair of homœopathy in his name. It is unknown where the money eventually went.

Joseph Morrin trained Pierre-Martial Bardy who became interested in homœopathy after a trip to the USA in 1847. The 1854 cholera epidemic gave him the opportunity to use homœopathy.

The Montreal Homœopathic Association (MHA) was founded by F. E. Grafton in 1863 and operated a homœopathic dispensary for the city's poor. In 1865, legal recognition for the MHA was granted. The dispensary ran for two years. In 1894 the Montreal Homœopathic Hospital was opened. A year later, a nurses' school was created in the hospital. In 1908, it was a 50-bed hospital. The hospital moved to Marlowe Avenue in 1931, and in 1952 changed its name to the Queen Elizabeth Hospital and, like other homœopathic hospitals in the USA, gradually became allopathic.

Most homœopaths of the MHA were English-speaking and trained in the UK and USA. Only one member was a French-Canadian (G.A.D. Delporte who received his diploma in 1912 and was still practicing in 1970, at 86 years old!). Seven women were members of the MHA; from Laura Müller in 1895 to Martha Graham Robson who was the last, in 1961, to obtain a licence. She died in London, England, in 1974. The MHA never exceeded 81 members.

At the end of the l970s, European French-speaking laymen re-introduced homœopathy in an eclectic way, combining osteopathy, naturopathy, "pluralistic," and "complexistic" homœopathy. Several pharmacies from France and Belgium established distribution outlets for their products in Quebec.

To insure legal protection, in November 1989, the Syndicat Professionnel des Homéopathes du Québec (SPHQ) was formed. The SPHQ established statutes and rules, an ethics code, and a 1500-hour training program. Pressured by the "college of doctors" who neither recognize homœopathy nor allow their members to practice it, the Government recently enacted new laws allowing homœopathy to be practiced only by MDs. The Québec courts have ruled the practice of homœopathy violated the law requiring a medical license. The SPHQ's future is in doubt, as part of its mandate was to help provide legal protection for its members, which now cannot happen.

Chile:

Homœopathy was first used in Chile in 1817 when General San Martin, the "liberator of Argentina," crossed the Andes with his homœopathic medicine chest. In 1848, Augusto Gusmao brought homœopathy into the country from Brazil. The *Organon* was translated by Dr. Benito Garcia Fernandez in 1855, and a Hering's *Domestic Physician*, translated by Dr. Roman Fernando del Rio, appeared the same year. There was a more modern Chilean translation of the *Organon* by Hochstetter in 1974, appearing in English in 1977.

There were six doctors, two chemists, and two veterinarians listed in 1931.

The practice of homœopathy is legal but restricted to MDs. There are many "unauthorized practitioners" using homœopathy as well. The Sociedad Médica Homeopática de Chile was founded in 1949, and The Sociedad de Medicina Homeopática de Valpariso was formed in 1990.

There are no journals or schools, although some universities teach homœopathy in their pharmacy schools' curriculum.

In 1998 there were fewer than 100 MDs practicing. There are five laboratories manufacturing homœopathic medicines.

China:

The 1911 *Directory* lists Dr. Emma J. Betow (Louisville, 1904) running a hospital in Shanghai. She commented, "The Chinese like homœopathy wherever it has been carried."

By 1931 four more hospital were under homœopathic management. A German Jewish refugee and homœopath, Dr. Galitzer, spent the World War II years in Shanghai.

The present status of homœopathy is unknown.

Colombia:

Homœopathy was introduced to Colombia in 1837. The Instituto Homeopatico de Colombia was established in 1865. There were 107 doctors listed in 1931. The Instituto still exists, although it has no regulatory or similar powers. It is now a school for homœopaths, all of them coming from allopathic practice.

In Bogotá, there are some 90 homœopaths listed in the yellow pages.

Although regulations say that only MDs can treat patients with homœopathy, many non-MDs are practicing homœopathy and they are tolerated.

There is an organization for homœopaths in Santa Fe de Bogotá, the Asociación Médica Homeopática de Colombia (ASMHOC).

There are two "official" schools, which only accept MDs: Escuela de Medicina Juan N. Corpas and Instituto Homeopático Luis G. Páez. There are others which teach homœopathy as a career (with no government recognition) or as a postgraduate medical course: Fundación Homœopática de Colombia, Fundación Colegio Nacional de Medicina Homœopática y Naturismo and a few more in Cali city.

There are some 30 homœopathic pharmacies in Bogotá, 10 in Medellín.

Costa Rica:

Homœopathy was introduced by a layman in 1889. There is a mention of a strong lay society in 1931. Homœopathy received official sanction in 1929, and further official recognition in 1987. It was in Costa Rica that Dr. Marcos Jiminez created a bilingual Spanish-English *Card Repertory* in 1925. Although it is legal only for MDs to practice, there are about 200 MDs and about 2,000 non-medical practitioners. "The Republican law forbids it, but everything when forbidden is practiced more." In July 1998 the congress turned down a bill to recognize non-medical practitioners.

There are several homœopathic schools which will teach both MDs and non-MDs. About 51% of the Costa Rican people use homœopathy as their first medicine.

Croatia:

Until the war in 1991, the only homœopathy practiced was anthroposophic in its direction. It was strongly influenced by Dr. Klara Zupic Dajceva, who learned Rudolf Steiner's methods from Steiner himself. After the war she began to teach homœopathy to medical students in Zagreb who were also interested in anthroposophy.

A group of people from a spiritual organization in Switzerland (Sathya Sai Organisation) that does service work came to Croatia in 1992. Two of the group were homœopaths, who came to Rijeka (a port town 65 kilometers from Trieste in Italy), and gave seminars in the evenings for two years, after helping refugees during the day.

After the first two years in this region, they presented a two-year series of seminars in Split where there were many medical doctors in the audience.

The London College of Homœopathy began a two-year

course of classical homœopathy in Zagreb and in Split. The Zagreb course recently finished and 100 certificates have been awarded to participants. About half the participants are doctors.

A course has been operating in Rijeka for three years, but its teaching combines acupuncture with homœopathic remedies.

There are two homœopathic associations in Zagreb, one in Split, and one in Rijeka.

The Croatian Association of Homeopaths was formed and registered in 1887. It plans to change the name to The Croatian Association of Classical Homeopaths to distinguish between them and other alternative healing practices.

Pharmacies have started to sell combination remedies. Labels state that "no curative effects have been proved."

There are no laws forbidding the practice of homœopathy, but that does not mean homœopathy has been legalized. Currently it can be practiced by both medical doctors and non-medical practitioners.

Cuba:

Homœopathy was introduced to Havana in 1842 by Dr. Francisco de P. Escopet from Spain. A journal, *La Bandera de la Homeopatia en la Habana*, was published in 1856. My database shows 12 graduates— all from the Hahnemann Medical College in Philadelphia— graduated between 1856 and 1889. In the 1931 *Directory* there is one doctor listed.

Homœopathy in Cuba all but vanished in the first decades of the 20th century. In 1958 only four physicians listed themselves as homœopaths in Havana. The most frequently used homœopathic drugs were combinations of Humphreys and were prescribed by lay people.

At the beginning of the Revolution, the official belief was that homœopathy wasn't scientific, and it was not recognized. The Cuban Society of Bioenergetic and Natural Medicine, served as a catalyst to have homœopathy incorporated into the National Health System in 1992.

Currently there are more than 300 physicians, 90 pharmacists, 70 dentists, and 100 veterinarians practicing homœopathy. Homœopathy is studied as postgraduate diploma course of 300 elective hours. You must be a physician to have a clinical practice.

The country is represented in the LMHI.

Czech Republic:

Until World War II only some German doctors practiced homœopathy on Czech territory. Dr. Quin, founder of British homœopathy, practiced a short time in Tisnov, a small town. A Catholic homœopathic hospital existed at Kromeriz since 1860. During the communist era of 1948-89 homœopathy was prohibited.

Until 1991 no books about homœopathy were published in the Czech language. The first books— about 20 titles including the *Organon*, Kent's *Repertory*, Boericke *Materia Medica*, Allen's *Keynotes*, Pulford's *Materia Medica*— were published by Alternativa Publishing house in 1991. A Czech translation of Murphy's *Repertory* will be published in 1999.

The Czech Homeopathic Medical Chamber is only for MDs and is focused on symptomatic prescribing according to Boiron's school. It has about 1000 members. The Czech Medical Homeopathic Society is focused on classical homœopathy and is only for MDs. It has about 300 members.

The only specialized journal is *Classical Homeopathy*, a quarterly published by Alternativa.

The School of Classical Homœopathy was organized by Alternativa six years ago. For the first three years it was run in conjunction with the Faculty of Homœopathy in London. It was only for MDs. Now it is open to anyone. The teachers are Czech, with overseas guests. It is a three-year weekend school.

There is a school at Kromeriz in Moravia, where Austrian doctors hold lectures for five days, once a year and in 1982 a course of Hahnemann's Foundation at Brno started, in conjunction with College of Classical Homœopathy in London.

Homœopathy is recognized by law and it is legal for both MDs and professionals to practice, but non-MDs cannot give a remedy directly, they can only recommend to buy and take.

About 3,000 doctors give symptomatic remedies. About 1,000 doctors and professionals practice classical homœopathy. None of the medical doctors use homœopathy exclusively because the insurance companies do not pay for homœopathic treatment.

Most pharmacies carry a line of remedies by Boiron.

Denmark:

Homœopathy was brought to Denmark by Hans Christian Lund, a pupil of Hahnemann, in 1821. Lund did a translation of the *Organon*, but the date is unknown. He was followed by Johann Pabst in 1830. A journal, *Homoeopathiken*, was published in Copenhagen in 1833.

The 1911 *Directory* says: "We have a report that homœopathy is not spreading amongst the profession because of a lack of organizing spirit." It lists six doctors (one graduating from Hahnemann, Philadelphia in 1888). "There are others who ask not to be known as homœopaths as there is no certain organization."

Homœopathic medicines could be prescribed only by medical doctors from 1936 until 1976, when homœopathy was re-established as an "alternative" practice.

The Danish Association of Classical Homeopathy (DSKH) was founded in 1987 along with the School of Classical Homoeopathy (SKH). As of 1998, the DSKH has 22 full members and 49 associate members. There are two MDs on the register. The journal *Hahnegal*, is published quarterly.

Egypt:

In Egypt, specifically in Cairo, there are four or five unlicensed homœopaths, all self-trained. In October 1998, The British Institute of Homœopathy started a two-year course in Cairo— three intensive days per month. There are 45 people enrolled, four of them doctors, a few pharmacists and the rest interested mothers. Homœopathy has no official recognition. There are no societies or journals.

Finland:

Homœopathy was first mentioned in Finland in 1888 by A. Pfaler in a history of Finnish healing practices. In the year 1921 Eino Suolahti made a research on the "Quackery in Finland," and mentioned that homœopathy was practiced mainly in the Swedish-speaking west coast areas of Finland. In other parts of Finland there had only been a couple of touring homœopaths, undoubtedly because of the country's remoteness.

A meeting to form a society of homœopaths was held in 1984 by seven homœopaths who had been studying in Sweden. The society was formally registered in 1986.

The number of members increased rapidly in 1991, when the first classical homœopaths graduated from the Kairon Institute in Helsinki. In the following years there were an increasing number of homœopaths coming also from Homeopatia Institute, the Finnish School of Classical Homeopathy in Helsinki, and the school named "Luontaislääkinnän edistämiskeskus" (Centre promoting naturopathic medicine) near the city of Tampere.

In the beginning of the 1990s there were two homœopathic societies, Suomen Homeopaatit ry, which became a member of ECCH and ICCH in 1991, and Suomen Klassiset Homeopaatit ry which formed in 1990, mainly by students of the Finnish School of Classical Homeopathy. The two societies merged in 1994, with its main aim to promote classical homœopathy.

The homœopaths who have graduated from the Luontaislääkinnän edistämiskeskus are still connected to a society called Pohjoismainen Homeopaattiyhdistys ry. (The Nordic Homœopaths). They have about 50 members; some of them are also members of the Suomen Homeopaatit ry.

In 1998 Suomen Homeopaatit ry had 400+ members, including students. There are about 160 homœopaths in the society who have been accepted on the list of regularly practicing homœopaths.

The society has published a magazine *Homeopatia* since 1992.

Homœopathic seminars are conducted twice a year with many speakers coming from abroad.

All the homœopaths have had a basic course in school medicine, anatomy, physiology, pathology etc. for at least 200 hours, and some have also been "co-educated" in school medicine in a two-year course (600 hours). The medical course (600 hours) was organized by the homœopathic society and IV Helsinki Medical Shool.

Finnish legislation provides no official status for homœopathy. There is no such thing as "registered" homœopaths, but the society is working on developing professional criteria, which would lead to a register of homœopaths and a guarantee of high quality among those practicing.

Also there are some restrictions in the Finnish legislation in regard to pharmacy: every homœopathic remedy has to be individually registered, be it registered in any other EU country or not, and every import company has to register their remedies individually. The cost of one remedy to be registered is 1000 FMK (about 110 English Pounds). Furthermore, the registration process takes 210 days.

France:

Homœopathy preceded Hahnemann's arrival in 1835. Count des Guidi, the Inspector of the University of Lyon, was visiting Italy and had his wife treated by de Romani and Horatiis. He then went to Köthen, staying some time with Hahnemann, and returned to Lyon in October 1830. That year, aged 61, des Guidi began practicing homœopathy.

Dr. Petroz, a physician of "high standing" in Paris, gathered homœopaths around him— Jahr, Curie, and Croserio among them. Curie moved to London in about 1835. The brother of Dr. Petroz opened Paris' first homœopathic pharmacy in 1833. The first *Organon* in French was by von Brunnow in 1824. The first journal in the French language was *Bibliothèque Homéopathique*, introduced in Geneva in 1832. Dr. Tessier introduced homœopathy to Paris hospitals in 1847.

King lists six graduates from France who studied at US schools between 1850 and 1905.

Non-medical people are NOT allowed to practice "healing" at all in France. They can (and are, usually) prosecuted by courts. It is *illegal* to practice "medicine" (i.e. therapeutics) of whatever kind, unless you are an MD.

While homœopathic remedies prescribed by MDs are (partially) reimbursed by the State Medical system (called Securite Sociale), anything beyond the 30C is not reimbursed and LMs do not legally exist. Whatever is legal you can buy OTC, but some remedies are not in the *Pharmacopoeia* e.g., all the newly-proved remedies and some "small" ones.

About 90% of the homœopaths are mixopaths, following in the wake of Léon Vannier who invented "French" homœopathy and whose son Philippe drew up the present regulations forbidding sale of potencies beyond the 30C.

In late 1998, the manufacture and sale of five nosodes was banned by French Law.

It is an interesting historical note that in the report to the AIH in 1906, a complaint was voiced about the growing use of polypharmacy in France.

There have been a number of French homœopaths whose work has been known to the international community— Pierre Jousset, J. Gallavardin, Duprat, Lathoud, Gilbert Charette, Maurice Fortier-Bernoville, and O.A. Julian. The influence of the French continues since two of the major manufacturers of homœopathic pharmaceuticals, Boiron and Dolisos, are located in France.

The country is represented in the LMHI.

Georgia:

The current status of homœopathy in the Republic of Georgia is unknown. The country is represented in the LMHI.

Ghana:

Homœopathy was brought to Ghana by Prince F. Hayford in the late 1960s. Further information was not forthcoming.

Germany:

The home of Hahnemann until 1835. After 1812 he had followers— Stapf, Gross, Horburg, Franz, Hartmann, and others who formed the prover's union.

There were efforts to start a homœopathic hospital in 1832, but Hahnemann disapproved of the person who was to run it, and in an article, called them "half–homœopaths." By 1834 the movement was splitting apart, and by 1837 there were those who believed that the writings of Hahnemann "can no longer be considered as expressing the standpoint of homœopathy of the day."

Isopathy was introduced by the veterinarian Wilhelm Lux in 1833-37. Guenther's *Homœopathic Veterinary Physician* was the first veterinary manual in 1836.

King lists 20 graduates from Germany who studied at US schools between 1850 and 1905.

There were few lay people using homœopathy prior to 1855 when Arthur Lutze's work described practice with double remedies— leading to the practice of "specifics" for domestic use.

The "single remedy, single dose, selected by similarity to the provings" had been virtually unknown for a long time, until Jost Kunzli translated Kent's *Repertory* into German in 1946. Most homœopathy in Germany was practiced on a very "pathological" basis. With the *Repertory* available, more people became interested in the Hahnemannian method.

Since George Vithoulkas began teaching in the USA in the 1970s, homœopathy has enjoyed a renewed interest and revival. Seminars with Vithoulkas and other American homœopaths were organized with up to 400 participants. Indian homœopaths also began coming to Germany to teach. In the 1980s some of the Heilpraktiker attending those seminars founded the Homöopathie-Forum, which is today

the biggest homœopathic non-profit organization in Germany with more than 1000 members.

Only medical doctors or heilpraktikers are allowed to treat patients in Germany. "Heilpraktiker" is a medical profession recognized by the German government, based on the Heilpraktikergesetz of 1939. A heilpraktiker is allowed to practice any unconventional therapy, for treatment of all diseases except certain infectious and venereal diseases. At this time there are no educational standards for heilpraktikers; the only requirement for earning the distinction "heilpraktiker" is the successful passage of an exam set by the Public Health Department.

A heilpraktiker is not allowed to treat a variety of infectious diseases such as venereal diseases, malaria, chicken pox, measles, and diseases of the sexual organs— which limits them in cases of pregnancy and childbirth.

About 10% of heilpraktikers are self taught but most are trained by private HP-schools, full time or part time. Because there are no mandatory guidelines, the school's quality varies greatly.

A heilpraktiker may not officially call themselves a homœopath, although they may indicate on their practice sign or calling cards that they practice homœopathy.

Medical doctors in Germany can identify themselves as specializing in homœopathy if they have gone through a six-week training program in homœopathy followed by an internship with a medical homœopath for 6 or 12 months.

In 1997, a professional organization especially for professional homœopaths in Germany was founded, the Verband Klassischer Homöopathen Deutschlands (VKHD). One of VKHD's primary objectives was to establish qualified guidelines for appropriate medical and homœopathic training. These standards are modelled on the ECCH guidelines.

Other organizations exist, the largest being Homöopathie-Forum (HF) and Deutsche Gesellschaft für Klassische Homöopathie (DGKH). These non-profit organizations are legally only allowed to work politically for public health (e.g. by promoting homœopathy as a therapy method), and not for the well-being of a group of professionals.

The umbrella organization for all other non-profit organizations is the Bund Klassischer Homöopathen Deutschlands (BKHD), with the HF, the DGKH, and Samuel-Hahnemann-Stiftung as its members. Together, the non profit-organizations in BKHD, and the professional organization VKHD are working to establish guidelines for medical and homœopathic training.

There are about 2,800 MDs with this qualification, although many other use homœopathy. About 600 practitioners are registered with the ICCH.

Polypharmacy is also very prevalent and many heilpraktikers and MDs use polypharmacy preparations with little or no training in classical homœopathic methods.

The ICCH lists 31 teaching institutions, five manufacturing pharmacies, seven journals, and three homœopathic hospitals: Robert-Bosch-Krankenhaus, Stuttgart; Waldhausklinik, Augsburg; Harlachinger Krankenhaus, München— most using complexes and low potency organopathic remedies, alhough the Harlachinger Krankenhaus has some MDs prescribing classical homœopathy with Rajan Sankaran as their supervisor.

The country is represented in the LMHI.

Greece:

In the late 1800s there was Dr. J Picramenos, about whom little is known. There was no mention of Greece other than the existence of one doctor being listed in the 1931 *Directory*.

The first *Organon* to be translated into Greek appeared in 1989. George Vithoulkas has a training clinic for MDs in Athens. In 1995 there were about 130 physicians using homœopathy.

In 1993 Gerasimos Stouraitis established the Hippocratean Center of Classical Homœopathy in Athens. It is both a clinic and a school for non-doctors. In 1997, Gerasimos Stouraitis established the Homœopathics' Association of Hellas which is an active member of the ECCH.

The country is represented in the LMHI.

Guatemala:

Homœopathy is known to be used in Guatemala, although no more information is available.

Honduras:

There was one homœopathic chemist in 1931. At present, there are a number of independent practitioners using homœopathy in Honduras, although there is no official recognition of the practice.

Hungary:

Joseph Mueller learned homœopathy from reading and came to Budapest in 1818. He was followed by George Forgo in 1820, and Joseph Bakody in 1831. Forgo translated the *Organon* into Hungarian in 1830.

In 1911 there were 100 practitioners listed. The 1931 Directory listed only 10 practitioners. In 1948 homœopathy was banned. It was made legal again in 1991. Between 1991 and 1997 the Hungarian Homœopathic Medical Association organized numerous courses and seminars, and some Hungarian doctors started to practice. In 1997 a law was passed regulating alternative medicines, and homœopathy was determined to be a "medical method of healing."

Only MDs are allowed to practice. In 1995 there were 302 physicians using homœopathy.

The country is represented in the LMHI.

Iceland:

Arthur Charles Gook (1883-1959) was the first formally-trained homœopath in Iceland, although there were probably a few "self-educated" people using the system. He was educated at the Missionary School of Homœopathy in London. He arrived in Akureyri, (after stopping in Denmark) in autumn 1905. He started a mission (he was first and foremost a missionary) and soon his homœopathic practice got going. He lived in Iceland for 50 years. He moved back to England in 1954 and died in 1959.

There are homœopaths in Iceland now but the status of homœopathy there has not been reported.

India:

Dr. John Martin Honigberger, from Transylvania, came to India in 1829. As an allopath, he treated Maharaja Ranjit Singh in Punjab. In 1834 he returned to Europe and made the acquaintance of Hahnemann. In about 1837 he was practicing in Constantinople, but received word that the Maharaja wished him to return. He returned to India in 1839 and introduced homœopathy.

A wealthy businessman, Rajendra Lall Dutt became interested in homœopathy in about 1850 and convinced an allopathic doctor, Mahendra Lal Sircar, to investigate the system. Dr. Sircar is considered the "Hering" of India. Many prominent Indian homœopaths studied with Dr. Sircar. Sircar's courageous conversion to homœopathy led to a constitutional crisis at the University of Calcutta which wished to rescind his medical degree— averted only when he resigned from the university.

Father Mueller, a Jesuit missionary, brought homœopathy to south India in 1878, but even before him homœopathy was practiced in the small princely states of Thanjavur and Pudukottai under the patronage of the respective Princes.

King lists 16 graduates from India who studied at US schools between 1850 and 1905.

The 1931 *Directory* reported there were "many mongrel homœopaths in Calcutta."

The Supreme court of India recently ruled that one can practice only the system for which he is licensed to practice. The homœopathic degree is the BHMS and DHMS— the Bachelor and Doctorate of Homœopathic Medical Science.

There are 110 institutes in India teaching homœopathy; all attached to universities. All teaching institutions have hospitals and dispensaries attached. In all government hospitals there are homœopathic wings. City Municipal Hospitals have a homœopathic wing. Whether all these are very active and what sort of homœopathy is practiced are different questions.

There are an estimated 150,000 homœopathic practitioners in India.

The country is represented in the LMHI.

The Faces of Homœopathy

Indonesia:

There is one homœopath practicing. Little else is known.

Ireland:

Homœopathy was first introduced to Ireland by Dr. Charles W. Luther in 1839. Dr. William Walter was instructing Dr. Joseph Kidd in Dublin in 1842. Kidd later had great success with homœopathy in the Irish potato famine of the 1840s, and later became the physician to Benjamin Disraeli.

Another important homœopath in Ireland was Dr. Michael Greene of Ennis, near Galway, who was the first to use *Crataegus* (Hawthorn).

The first English translation of the *Organon* was done by Devrient and edited by Samuel Stratten in Dublin in 1833.

The Irish Homœopathic Society was founded on April 10, 1845. A book published in 1848 lists 40 members of the Committee of the IHS and three medical attendants of the Homœopathic Institution: Drs. C. W. Luther, G. A. Luther, and W. Walter.

In the 1895 *Homœopathic Medical Directory* we find two homœopaths in Ireland. By 1930 the number rose to four. The Irish Society of Homœopaths was formed in 1990 to represent the professional homœopaths in Ireland. In the mid-1990s there were almost 30 physicians using homœopathy in Ireland, 89 professional homœopaths on the Society Register, and an unknown number of lay prescribers.

Israel:

There is no mention of homœopathy in Palestine in the 1931 *Directory*, yet Dr. Jarus had arrived in Israel from Germany in 1901, settling first in the north Rosh Pina and then in Tel-Aviv where he opened a clinic. In 1960 he built a Sanitorium in Rosh-Pina "Mizpe Hajamim." He died in the late 1970s aged over 90.

After Jarus died, Josef Reves (who learned homœopathy in Germany) began to teach a small group of people starting in 1976.

There have been a handful of people practicing some form of homœopathy since then, but only since 1990 has the volume and recognition of homœopathy risen to a substantial level.

The Israeli Association for Classical Homœopathy (IACH) was established towards the end of 1993 hoping to regulate the practice of classical homœopathy and form a body to further the interests of homœopathy among practitioners and with government bodies.

Starting with 12 founding members in 1994, it has 47 registered members in 1998— 11 of whom are MDs. In late 1998 there are an estimated 150 practitioners of classical homœopathy, about 50 of whom have a full-time practice. About 200 students are attending the courses offered.

The IACH maintains a register, represents homœopathic

interest in relations with the government authorities, and publishes a journal, *Homeopathic Times*, twice a year. The IACH organizes seminars with some of the world's most prominent homœopaths. Usually 120-140 people attend, including professional homœopaths and the few MDs who practice classical homœopathy.

Over the past few years homœopathy has been integrated into various allopathic clinics. At least three hospitals have taken on homœopaths (who are not necessarily MDs), to work within a "multi-therapy" clinic. Recently, the largest national health care provider, Kupat Cholim, has begun six alternative therapy clinics, in which classical homœopathy is one of the therapies available.

There is only one school in Israel which presently meets the standards of the ICCH— the Israeli School of Classical Homœopathy, run by Dr. Chaim Rosenthal, RCHom and Elia Onne, RCHom. This school offers a 4–year course, including one year of clinical training (internship).

There is no formal recognition of homœopathy as an accepted form of medicine, but neither are homœopaths persecuted for practicing as they see fit.

The first homœopathic pharmacy was opened in Tel-Aviv in 1941. Homœopathic remedies are at present readily available over-the-counter. Recently several large pharmaceutical companies have begun importing and distributing remedies, and the competition is strong in this rapidly growing market.

Italy:

Dr. Necker, from Austria, settled in Naples and began practicing homœopathy in 1821. He converted Drs. Romani, Mauro, and deHoratiis. The first journal, The *Archivio della Medicina Omiopatico*, was published in Lucca from 1827-30. The *Organon* was translated into Italian in 1833. Dr. Rubini of Naples used *Camphor* in 491 cases of cholera in 1855— saving all. The mortality rate for the homœopathic treatment was 8%, for the allopathic treatment 53%. The *Camphor* tincture became known as "Rubini's Camphor."

Homœopathy declined after the unification of the country in 1870.

King lists two graduates from Italy who studied at US schools between 1850 and 1905.

There are 46 homœopaths listed in the 1911 *Directory*.

After World War I, homœopathy came to a dead end. Homœopathy survived in a few areas of Italy thanks to single homœopaths, mainly in towns like Florence, Naples, Milan, and Rome. The revival of homœopathy only took place in the 1970s through students of Pierre Schmidt and by developing schools of homœopathy, such as the Free International University of Homœopathic Medicine (LUIMO).

A number of homœopathic pharmacies, mostly from France and Germany, also helped to spread homœopathy in Italy. By the end of the 1980s homœopathy has become quite well known among the general population.

The practice of homœopathy is restricted to MDs and veterinarians. There are some lay homœopaths, but they are not practicing legally. No formal registration of doctors as homœopaths exists, but the number is probably several thousand.

The LMHI helped the expansion of homœopathy when it organized two congresses: Rome (1980) and Capri (1996). Jacques Imberechts (Homoeopathia Europea), established different homœopathic groups and organized workshops in various Italian towns.

The largest organizations, that have several schools and associations each, are SIO (Società Italiana di Omeopatia) and FIAMO (Federazione Italiana delle Associazioni e dei Medici Omeopati).

There are many schools teaching homœopathy. Some are run by pharmacies like the French Dolisos and Boiron, or the German Heel, and others are privately run and independent. The three main "schools" are present: complex, pluralist, and classical.

Medicina Naturale is a journal that also deals with acupuncture and herbal medicine, and *Il Medico omeopata*, (published by FIAMO) is a classical homœopathic journal.

The country is represented in the LMHI.

Jamaica:

Jose J. Navarro came from Cuba in 1870. He taught a few people and returned to Cuba. The present status is unknown.

Japan:

Although the history of Japan is not mentioned in any sources, the 1911 *Directory* listed two homœopaths: Dr. Mary A. Suganuma (Cleveland 1883) in Nagasaki, and Herbert W. Schwartz, MD in Yokohama. There were also three graduates from Japan who attended homœopathic colleges in the USA between 1899 and 1902.

German old school officials convinced the Japanese Government to prohibit anyone with a homœopathic degree from practicing, so a "regular" degree was needed to practice.

The present status is unknown.

Latvia:

There were 20 homœopaths in 1921. There is no current information.

Luxembourg:

Homœopathy is not recognized by the goverment. There are both medical and professional homœopaths working. There are no societies or journals.

Malta:

Another country to which Dr. Benoit Mure introduced homœopathy in 1837.

Malaysia:

Homœopathy came to Malaysia during World War II, brought by the Indians through the British Army. The first Malay introduced to homœopathy was Dr Burhanuddin Al Hilmi in the mid-1950s. Among the oldest practitioners is Dr. Mohamed Yaakob, in his 70s, who is in Johore Bahru.

A study group was started by Al Hilmi in 1954 with 12 students. After Malaysian independence, Al Hilmi established the Persatuan Perubatan Homeopathy Malaysia (Homeopathic Medical Association of Malaysia) which became "official" in July of 1961.

Dr Nik Omar studied in Pakistan for five years and returned in 1977. In 1979 he started the Faculty of Homeopatyy in Malaysia with 7 students. Today the school, which conducts both full-time and distance learning, has about 1,000 students from Malaysia, Singapore, Thailand, Indonesia and the Philippines.

In 1984 Dr Omar started a homœopathic organization called The Registered Malaysian Homeopathic Medical Practitioners Association, although the actual register does not (as of this writing) exist, as standards have not been established.

At present there is no legislation governing homœopathy, but the Government and health ministry are receptive to all forms of alternative health, so this may change in the future.

Because of the lack of legislation, the standard of homœopathy practiced is variable. A few MDs are involved in homœopathy. There is a great deal of influence from India and a number of practitioners have trained there.

The Registered Malaysian Homeopathic Medical Practitioners has 500 members in Malaysia. There are about 100 full-time practitioners throughout the country and 500 part-time practicing although some of the practitioners diagnose using a pendulum and radionics methods.

There is one homœopathic journal, the *Homeopathic Newsletter*, published by The Malaysian Homeopathic Medical Practitioners Association, Johore Branch.

The public is getting better acquainted with homœopathy and many are requesting treatment. Homœopathy is popular in Kuala Lumpur and in Kota Bahru Kelantan.

Mexico:

Homœopathy was introduced in 1850 by Dr. P. Rafael Navarrete from Havana. In 1852 Salvador Riera, from Cuba, brought homœopathy to Yucatan. In 1853 Dr. Ramon Comellas came from Spain. Many conventional doctors were converted to homœopathic practice.

In 1863 the Instituto Homeopatica Mexicano was formed. Shortly after, the Sociedad Médico Homeopática Mexicana was founded and lasted 49 years. *La Gaceta* was the journal of the Society, while *El Propagador Homeopático* was the first Mexican journal and was published by the Instituto.

Another journal, *La Reforma Médica* was published from 1875-1892.

In 1889, the Academia Homeopatica was formed which became the National School of Homœopathy. The Instituto Homeopática lasted into the 1920s.

The first homœopathic pharmacy was founded in Mexico City in 1870.

King lists five graduates from Mexico who studied at US schools between 1881 and 1892.

Mexican president General Don Porfirio Díaz was attended by a homœopath with good results, and in 1895 the practice of homœopathy was officially recognized. In that same year, the first school, Escuela Nacional de Medicina Homeopática began, along with Hospital Nacional Homeopático— a homœopathic hospital.

Over the years the school survived many attacks from conventional medicine, but it has remained viable.

The homœopathic hospital still exists at the same location in Mexico City.

Dr. Higinio G. Pérez, founded la Escuela Libre de Homeopática de México in 1912. The school gained formal recognition in 1922, when Mexican president, Emilio Portes Gil, gave the school recognition and privilege under law as a free university.

Other schools like the Escuela Libre opened in both Guadalajara and the University in Yucatan. They met with moderate success.

Mexico, like other countries, saw interest in homœopathy decline during the 1930s until the 1950s. In 1960, seeing Hahnemannian ideals fading away, the "Homeopátia de México, AC" was founded by Drs. Proceso Sánchez Ortega, David Flores Toledo, and Ranulfo Romero Moreno. This group became the first to offer post-graduate education to MDs. It operates outside the national medical schools. It organizes conferences and does social work within the community with the students.

In 1982 a group was formed in Oaxaca as a part of "Homeopátia de México AC," and in 1985 it incorporated IESIO (Instituto de Estudios Superiores de Oaxaca) as a post-graduate educational program. A similar move happened in Guadalajara.

A few pharmacies manufacture homœopathic medicines, and many pharmacies sell remedies to doctors and patients alike.

Only two official schools offer training as a medical doctor and homœopath: the Polytechnic Institute and the Escuela Libre, both in Mexico City. The other schools (La Escuela Nacional de Medicina y Homeopátia in Mexico City, El Instituto Superior de Medicina Homeopática de Enseñanza e Investigación de Monterrey in Nuevo León and the Instituto de Estudios Tecnológicos y Superiores de Tepic Nayarit) offer postgraduate education for medical doctors.

The homœopathic hospital struggles to survive the pressure of the conventional medical machine. The saving grace is there are still homœopaths working there, and the Government still supports teaching homœopathy at the polytechnic.

Mexico is a Republic of States, and associations operating in each state need state approval. There are schools in the state of Jalisco that teach lay people, and they have spurred the Government to re-examine the classification of homœopathic practice. The outcome is not known at this time.

Legally, only MDs are allowed to practice, but there are many other people, many of them in pharmacies, who are prescribing. There are probably about 1,500-2,000 practitioners in Mexico.

The country is represented in the LMHI.

Myanmar (Burma):

King lists one graduate from Burma, Clara Lawrence-Davenport, who graduated from Boston in 1888.

Roy Ogden, a lay homœopath in the UK in the 1940s and 1950s, says he first learned homœopathy from a missionary when in Burma during World War II. The present status is unknown.

Netherlands:

The first homœopathic doctors were Johan Schonfield in Winshoten and a Dr. Schmid in Schiedam in 1834. Boenninghausen was born in Heringhaven in Overyssel, and was educated in Groningen. He moved to Westphalia (Germany) in 1816. He is credited with teaching many people, including some from Holland, but their names are unknown.

The first *Organon* in Dutch appeared in 1827. On request of patients who wanted homœopathic treatment, two German physicians immigrated to the Netherlands. The first, F. W. O. Kallenbach started his practice in 1857 in Rotterdam. In 1863, Dr. S. J. van Royen, the first Dutch homœopathic physician, settled in Utrecht. A journal, *Homœopathische Geneeskunst* was published in Rotterdam in 1859.

In 1914 the first homœopathic hospital opened in Oudenrijn.

Dr. A. Kuyper, the minister-president from 1901 to 1905, tried to establish a professorial chair at the University of Leiden, but failed.

Both *Directories* have a listing of physicians and associations. Dr. Hoyle (in 1931) comments in Holland there are 35 practitioners and 725 homœopathic chemist shops and "…the laity…knowing what they want, have taken the matter into their own hands, and aided by their family manuals, are treating themselves…." And the physicians who do come have to be good because "the clients would hardly be satisfied with an imitation or pretense to knowledge."

Homœopathy experienced a resurgence in the 1970s

when a group of doctors became interested in it and began teaching others. Since then, homœopathy has blossomed.

The VHAN (Vereniging van Homeopathische Artsen in Nederland) is the nation-wide association of homœopathic doctors, most of whom have trained at the SHO (Stichting Homeopathische Opleidingen), the training facility for homœopathic doctors in the Netherlands. There are currently about 400 MDs on the register.

Nederlandse Vereniging van Klassiek Homeopaten (NVKH) is the largest organization of non-medically qualified professional homœopaths. There are about 600 professional homœopaths operating with about 450 registered with the NVKH and the others registered with other health-related organizations. There are six schools teaching professional homœopaths, all using a six-year part-time (1-2 days a week) course, which includes practical training. All the schools will meet the ICCH/ECCH guidelines by 2002.

The KVHN (Koninklijke Vereniging ter bevordering der Homeopathie in Nederland) is a consumer organization.

The NVKH publishes a journal called *Dynamis*. The international journal *Homœopathic Links* is also published in the Netherlands.

VSM in Alkmaar, a member of the German Homint Group, is the only manufacturing pharmacy in the Netherlands.

The Netherlands has a complex system of public and private health insurance. The compulsory social insurance scheme (ZFW; Verplichte Ziekenfonds) is administered by approximately 40 "sickness funds" and covers about 60% of the Dutch population. Of the 40 funds, 14 cover homœopathy practiced by members of the NVKH in the supplementary insurance. Of the 63 private health insurance companies, 34 cover homœopathy.

Professional homœopaths do not have legal recognition, but since the BIG-law (Beroepen in de Individuele Gezondheidszorg/ Professions in the Individual Healthcare) in 1996, anybody is allowed to treat patients, within certain limits. The principle of the law is freedom for the patient to choose between a regular medical doctor and other therapists.

The country is represented in the LMHI.

New Zealand:

Although it is likely that immigrants from England brought homœopathy with them, the first homœopath recorded in New Zealand was William Purdie, MD, a graduate of Glasgow, who arrived in December, 1849, and settled in Dunedin. Shortly after, Dr. Charles F. Fischer, a medical graduate from Berlin, settled in Auckland. He published the first New Zealand homœopathic journal, *The Homœopathic Echo* — from 1855 to 1856. Fischer founded the Homœopathic Association in 1857, and a homœopathic hospital in 1858. The hospital saw 1047 patients from the time it opened until it closed in 1862. During the time it was open, the mortality

rate at the hospital was 2.2%. Fischer left New Zealand for Australia in 1869.

The Echo was published with the support of John Bell's Homœopathic Pharmacy in Auckland. Another pharmacy, J. A. Pond, was eventually taken over by Marriage's Pharmacy in 1880. In 1931, Marriage's reported that they "have a great trade, entirely with families."

In 1876 there was mention of Dr. Jahn in Auckland and Dr. Deck in Dunedin. By 1911 there were no doctors in Auckland, two were in Dunedin, one was in Levin (Henry Dundas MacKenzie; St. Louis, 1896). There were always chemist shops carrying remedies.

In 1931 the question was put: "Why don't the allopaths study homœopathy when the people demand it?"

Under Common Law, a medical degree is not needed to practice homœopathy.

The New Zealand Homœopathic Society was founded in 1951 by Alfred G. Grove, a lay practitioner. Grove died in 1974.

The New Zealand Institute of Classical Homœopathy was founded in 1987. There are, in 1998, about 90 professional homœopaths on an amalgamated register. There are several homœopathic physicians, some of whom are on the register as well. There is no separate register or organization for medically-qualified homœopaths.

There are four manufacturing homœopathic pharmacies in New Zealand and a number of chemist shops that offer the lower potencies.

New Zealand supports four part-time colleges offering training in homœopathy. There are two small journals: *Homœopathica* and *Homœopathy NewZ*.

Nigeria:

The All-Nigeria Homœopathic Medical Association was founded in 1961, shortly after the country gained its independence. The first practitioner , I. Okogeri, MD, the King of the Afikpo kingdom, began practice in 1962. He was trained in London. The practitioners have been trained abroad— many in India and Germany— or through overseas correspondence courses or are self-taught. There are a number of organizations, associations, and colleges. In 1989, Peter Fischer, from the Faculty of Homœopathy in London, described the standards as having "shortcomings, but these are not insuperable." The government is working on establishing professional and educational standards.

The Congress of Homoeopathic Medicine Practitioners was founded in 1972, along with the Nigerian College of Homeopathic Medicine— which is recognised by the government of the East Central State.

Both MDs and lay persons can practice homœopathy.

There is no journal published. The Congress has 30 MDs on its register. There are an estimated 2000 lay practitioners.

The Faces of Homœopathy

Norway:

In the historical record I found only a mention of a journal, *Homeopatisk Tidskrift,* published in 1916.

The pioneers in homœopathy were active in Norway at the end of the last century. One was O. M. Ohm (1848-1928) who, in 1892, published a small book; *Practical Homeopathy For Everyone.* Another pioneer was N. W. Anderschou who practiced in Oslo and, persecuted by the allopaths, moved to London.

The practitioners held an International Congress for Homœopaths and Natural healers in Kristiania (Norway) in August 1909.

The Norske Homeopaters Landsforbund (NHL) was founded in 1930. It had several hundred members. The society has, in 1997, about 350 full members and about 200 student members. *Dynamis* is published quarterly by the society.

"The Law of Quackery" passed in 1936, gives professional homœopaths, in principle, the possibility to treat all illnesses, except tubercular and venereal diseases, cancer, diabetes, epilepsy, dangerous anemias and pathological goitre.

In 1951 the Norwegian Homeopathic Patients Association (NHP) was founded. The NHP played a significant role in an important court case in the 1960s which involved prosecution of a homœopath. 15,000 signatures were collected on behalf of the homœopath, and the case was successfully resolved. The NHP has more than 1600 members in 1997.

The first school, the "Norwegian Academy of Natural Medicine" (NAN) was founded in 1975. In 1987 a second school was founded— the "Scandinavian Institute for Classical Homeopathy" (SIKH). Several international teachers have taught in Norway.

SIKH is a combined effort with a similar school in Sweden. NAN does a full homœopathy and medical training— but also includes one year of ear-acupuncture, reflexology and herbs. SIKH only takes students with a certain level of medical knowledge beforehand (even nurses have to learn more, and show they are OK by passing an exam). But they now offer an independent medicine course covering the field.

For a couple of years NHL was very active in ensuring most of the good international homœopaths came to Norway for seminars, and Jeremy Sherr had a full course of his Dynamis-school seminars, giving qualification to the ones pursuing it fully.

Pakistan:

The advent of homœopathy in Pakistan is practically the same as in India because India and Pakistan were a single country until 1947.

For 18 years after the creation of Pakistan, homœopathy was practiced widely but remained officially unrecognized. In 1965, the Government passed an act under which homœopathy and the indigenous herbal systems of medicine were regulated. Homœopaths wishing to continue their practice were assessed by a Government nominated Board of Senior Homœopaths. All practitioners with sufficient experience and knowledge of the system were formally registered and allowed to continue their practice. This Board of Homœopathic System of Medicine working under the Ministry of Health, was, in 1982, renamed the National Council for Homœopathy. This council is now responsible for conducting examinations, approving new homœopathic colleges, and registering practitioners.

All homœopaths are required to undergo four years of training. They are then awarded a diploma (DHMS). After a six-months apprenticeship with a qualified homœopath, they may be registered with the National Council for Homœopathy and become eligible to practice. The number of homœopaths registered with the council is about 70,000.

There are 84 recognized homœopathic colleges, with about another 30 awaiting recognition.

Any MBBS (MD) doctor may legally practice homœopathy if he can satisfy the council that he has done six-months apprenticeship in this field. There are a number of MBBS (MD) doctors practicing homœopathy.

Government hospitals also employ homœopaths. There are hundreds of free Government dispensaries in some provinces.

There are a number of local homœopathic manufacturing pharmacies. Most medicines are available in all standard potencies and many of them up to CM. All drugs except psychotropics and opiates are freely available without doctors' prescriptions.

The country is represented in the LMHI.

Peru:

Two doctors listed in 1931. The present status is unknown.

Philippine Islands:

King lists four graduates from the Philippine Islands who studied at US schools between 1850 and 1905. Reports indicate a number of people using remedies in the country today. There is one known classical homœopath in Iloilo City.

Poland:

A Dr. Mylo was in Warsaw in 1829. Dr. Bigel, of Warsaw, corresponded with Hahnemann in 1832. Joseph Podwigotzky, a nobleman, translated Hering's *Domestic* in 1856 and treated people without charge. A homœopathic society was founded in 1892. The 1931 *Directory* lists eight homœopaths. Homœopathy faded in Poland during World War II. In 1946 the Twarzystwo Zwolenników Homeopatii Rzeczypospolitej

Polskiej (The Republic of Poland Homœopathic Society) was formed. The number of physicians using homœopathy remained few until the 1970s, when interest in "alternative" disciplines grew strongly. In 1978 a re-formation of the older society took place in Danzig, and a school was established in 1980. The first new book on homœopathy in the Polish language was published in 1988. In the early 1990s, homœopathy continued to spread, and the 100th anniversary of the Homœopathic Society in 1992 saw more than 200 people attending. The legal practice appears to be limited to physicians and pharmacists.

Portugal:

In 1836, Dr. Florencio Galvao "taught his pupils discreetly." The first free clinic opened in 1852, and the first journal, *Gazeta Homoeopathica Portuense*, was published in 1853.

In 1911 there were about 30 practitioners, in 1931 there were nine.

The Portuguese Society of Homeopathy (SPH), has 18 MDs registered.

There are many non-MDs using homœopathy, but most are self-trained, and only a few call themselves practitioners.

Neither MDs nor non-MDs are recognized by the Portuguese Medical Association, which does not recognize homœopathy, however MDs are allowed to prescribe whatever they want.

The Government has no laws about the legality of homœopathic practice.

There are two homœopathic organizations: the SPH in Lisbon and the SPMH in Oporto. Both only accept MDs.

There are no existing journals.

Puerto Rico:

There were 2 physicians listed in 1931. The present status is unknown.

Romania:

Honigberger, who took homœopathy to India was Romanian, and Hahnemann had spent some of his early years in Sibu/Hermanstadt. A homœopathic society was formed in Romania in 1947. But shortly after, with the advent of the communist regime, homœopathy was made illegal because there was no scientific explanation making it compatible with materialism. A few homœopaths fled to other countries, but some stayed. By 1967 the practice was "tolerated" and some pharmacies began operating. The practice of homœopathy was legalized in 1969, and with the fall of the communist regime, it was no longer considered "witchcraft." A big influence on homœopathy in Romania was the wife of President Carstens of Germany— herself a homœopathic physician.

One must be a medical doctor to practice in Romania. As

of 1995 there were about 700 homœopaths.

The country is represented in the LMHI.

Russia:

Homœopathy was introduced in 1823 by laymen. Shortly after, Dr. Adam (a prover of *Carbo-v*), who had studied with Hahnemann in Germany, began practice in St. Petersburg. Dr. Bigel was practicing in St. Petersburg in 1827, and then removed to Warsaw.

Generally, only medical doctors were allowed to practice, but "the laity took it upon themselves to be instructed."

In about 1828, a nobleman, Iseman Korsakoff, learned of homœopathy and began the practice. It was he who suggested to Hahnemann the possibility of using a single vial for making remedies.

Alexander Peterson established a homœopathic pharmacy in Pensa in 1831.

The first *Organon* in Russian was translated by Wrassky in 1835.

The development of homœopathy in Russian was patronized by the Tsar's family. Homœopathy was often practiced by the village priest.

After the communist revolution in 1917, homœopathy was suppressed. In order to save homœopathy in Russia, homœopaths were forced to recognize the material doctrine and to refuse the spiritual basis.

Homœopathy did have its adherents but they were not state-supported. Most of the homœopathic prescribing was developed from Hughes' work and tended to be "clinical" in nature.

In 1992 homœopathy was officially allowed as a treatment method and clinical homœopathy was being taught for medical students of allopathic schools. There are several hundred homœopaths practicing.

The country is represented in the LMHI.

Singapore:

The Singapore Government recognizes homœopathy as an alternative medical practice. There is no legislation controlling alternative medicine directly or registering practitioners.

Practitioners are expected to keep within their area of practice, otherwise, they would be contravening the Medical Registration Act.

Several people in Singapore have recent BHMS degrees from India, but they are not organized. Several "mixopaths" run "homœopathic centers" since these can be registered as a business.

There are no colleges or journals, but health magazines do carry articles about homœopathy.

Conventional physicians are registered with the Ministry of Health, but none practice homœopathy.

The Registered Professional Homoeopathy Association, Singapore (RPHAS) was founded in 1992, and has approval from two prominent Government foundations, The Registry of Societies and the Ministry of Health. Some homœopathic practitioners are registered under this body and hence are issued Certificate of Registration and Certification of Membership. They can use "RPHAS" after their name. There are about 20 such homœopaths in Singapore.

Slovakia:

In 1993, Czechoslovakia was peacefully divided into two sovereign states— the Czech Republic and Slovakia. Homœopaths in both countries have open communication and share translated books. Homœopathy has been used since the 19th Century when Czechs and Slovaks were part of Austrian monarchy under Habsburgs. After World War I, Czechoslovakia was formed and homœopathy continued. After 1948 when the communists gained power, homœopathy was declared bourgeois quasi-science and homœopaths were persecuted. The last original homœopath in Slovakia died in the 1960s.

After the 1989 "Velvet Revolution" when socialism fell, homœopathy was revived. The Slovak Homeopathic Society was founded in 1991 in Bratislava, the capital of Slovakia. The society has about 500 members, mostly medical doctors, although there are several veterinary doctors and pharmacists interested in classical homœopathy.

The Slovak Homœopathic Society is oriented to classical homœopathy. It has sponsored several long-term teaching seminars: a two-year course from the London College of Classical Homeopathy organized by Peter Chappell; a two-year course from the Holland-Indian School of Classical Homeopathy, the teachers coming from the Boenninghausen Circle in Holland and homœopaths working with Rajan Sankaran; a two-year course from the Austrian School of Homeopathy; and a course of seminars by the sons of Dr. Sehgal from India.

However the first courses held in Slovakia were conducted by the Slovak Branch of Boiron. They created their own organization and taught about 2,500 students, but most followed the "French school" and are not doing classical homœopathy.

The development of homœopathy in Slovakia has been blocked by its unclear legal status. Because under EEC guidelines the remedies are considered "drugs," those who use homœopathy must have an allopathic practice, and non-medical homœopaths are not allowed, because the laws allow health care to be practiced only by medical doctors. As of this is writing, the Government is exploring new ways of regulating the health professions.

There are two homœopathic journals in Czech language: a translated *Homœopathic Links* and the journal *Homeopatie*. Both are published in Prague.

Slovenia:

Little is known of homœopathy in Slovenia. Slovensko Homeopatsko Drustvo (SHD— Slovenian Homeopathic Association) is associated with the homœopaths in Austria.

South Africa:

Homœopathy was introduced in the late 1820s by missionaries from Europe, chiefly the Germans, although many Dutch settlers brought it with them.

There were few doctors and many lay people with domestic books— mostly Hering's and Guernsey's. There was one doctor listed in Transvaal in 1931, but there were 15 chemists carrying homœopathic remedies. "The public demands homœopathy," said E. P. Hoyle in 1931.

The first homœopathic pharmacy in the Transvaal was opened in 1941 by Willem Last.

The Homœopathic Society of South Africa was started in 1949 by Barbara MacFarland who had studied homœopathy while in England.

In 1951 Bill Lilly, trained in England, started the first small learning group for lay people and by 1953 had produced the first crop of non-medical practitioners. Lilly helped form the South African Naturopathic and Homœopathic Association.

By the mid-1950s the few homœopathic physicians joined forces with the lay homœopaths to keep homœopathy alive.

In 1956, Lindlahr College was established and trained students in homœopathy, naturopathy, and osteopathy. It ran a 4-year part-time course. Noel Puddephatt lectured at Lindlahr in 1964.

The Homeopathic Medical College of South Africa (Johannesburg) was established soon after as a five-year resident school and "fully registered with the Ministry of Health in South and West Africa for the practice of Homœopathic Medicine." The course allowed successful students to register and practice in South Africa as homœopaths, and was run as a part-time series for three years.

By 1974 there were several colleges running, some of lesser repute. The Government stepped in, and under the Act of 1974, closed the colleges. The schools were given some time to close and to allow enrolled students to complete their studies. By 1980 all were closed.

In 1974, the government established a registration procedure for those already in practice, and about 400 homœopaths qualified, but it allowed no entrance to new practitioners. The register was re-opened in 1985.

In 1982 a new Act was passed, giving statutory guidelines for education and allowing for new educational institutions to open up.

After this time, Natal Technikon started the first Homœopathic course, a six-year qualification. Later on

(1992), Witwatersrand Technikon also started a course and the first students are now in their sixth and final year.

There are also a group of MDs studying with David Lilly, who runs the British Faculty of Homœopathy Course in South Africa.

In 1996 Lilly formed the South African Homœopathic Medical Association, along with medical doctors who had studied homœopathy under him.

Classical homœopathy is still in its infancy in South Africa, but there are some dedicated lay homœopaths who are classically oriented and some MD homœopaths practicing.

There are 443 registered homeopaths. David Lilly has trained 38 MFHom's and there atre another 57 students still in process.

Spain:

A layman named Zuarte, a merchant of Cadiz, met Necker in Italy. He visited Hahnemann, and then des Guidi. He began practicing in 1829.

In 1831, a group of doctors went to Germany to study cholera and Dr. Folch began homœopathic practice in Barcelona. Drs. Lopez Pinciano (Castile), Rino y Hurtado (Badajoz), and Purdentio Querol (Seville— then Madrid) began practice— all in 1833. Juan Manuel Rubiales had the first pharmacy in 1833. Dr. Lopez Pinciano is credited as the first translator of the *Organon* in 1835, although another source gives Augustin Lopez del Bano as a translator in 1833.

The first journal, *Gazeta Homoeopatica de Madrid*, was published in 1845.

The Sociedad Hahnemanniana Matritense was founded in 1845. The Hospital Homeopatico de San José, founded in Madrid in 1878, still operating with a geriatric department and an homœopathic outpatient department, is soon to be restarted in full.

The Academia Medico Homeopatica de Barcelona was founded in 1890, and the Hospital del Nen Deu, formerly completely homœopathic, still maintains a homœopathic outpatients department.

King lists three graduates from Spain who studied at US schools between 1850 and 1905.

By 1900, homœopathy was "tolerated" in Spain, although the number of practitioners was declining. An international meeting was held in Barcelona in 1924, but homœopathy continued to decline through the Spanish Civil War and World War II.

With the rise of interest in alternatives in the 1970s, interest in homœopathy began to grow. By 1980 there were a few groups with ties to South America, and Eizayaga and Ortega. There was an influx of pharmacies, run by the French and German industry— most of them selling complexes.

The Sociedad Española De Medicina Homeopatica was founded in 1996, to help make the practice of homœopathy official.

The Government recognizes homœopathic pharmacy, and the Spanish Medical Council supports homœopathy, provided it is practiced by physicians. There are about 1,000 homœopaths practicing. The remedies are sold only in pharmacies.

Homœopathy can be studied by physicians at these universities: Sevilla (master, 2 years), Valladolid (university specialist, 2 years), Murcia (university specialist, 2 years), Barcelona (postgraduate diploma, 3 years), and soon in Bilbao (university specialist, 2 years) and Málaga (college of physicians, 2 years), all of them after the completion of medical studies.

The country is represented in the LMHI.

Sweden:

Professor George Wahlenberg of Uppsala did not practice but knew Stapf in Germany. He discussed homœopathy with several others, including Peter Jacob Leidbeck of Stockholm who began practice and visited Hahnemann in 1832.

A journal was published in Stockholm in 1855-56. The first *Organon* in Swedish was translated by Liedbeck in 1835.

The practice of homœopathy was "almost unknown in 1902." There was one pharmacy with low potencies in the country. There were eight homœopaths listed in 1911.

In 1907, a journal called *Homoeopatiens Seger* (The Victory of Homœopathy) was published, under editor Dr. Helledag. It lasted five years.

In 1909 the first homœopathic association was established— Hahnemann-föreningen— in Göteborg. Its aim was to start a free clinic for poor people, and also to start a homœopathic hospital. However, for different reasons, it was never really established.

In 1912 Svenska homeopatiska Läkarföreningen (Swedish Homeopathic Society for Physicians) was started by Dr. Gröndal and Dr. Helledag. All practicing homœopathic doctors were members.

In 1912 the faculty of four medical schools refused to recognize homœopathy as a legitimate practice. Said the 1911 *Directory*: "Many allopaths use homœopathy on themselves and their families, but are afraid, due to inexperience, to try it on their patients."

During this time there were also conflicts between medical doctors practicing homœopathy and several practicing homœopaths who were not licensed physicians, and whose skill level was sorely questioned.

In 1915 Svenska föreningen for Vetenskaplig Homeopati (Swedish Association for Scientific Homœopathy) was established. The main aim was to make homœopathy reach the same status as allopathy. The association published a journal, called *Sigyn*. In 1919 the name was changed into *Homoeopatiens Seger* and the editor, once again, was Dr. Helledag, The association still exists and its journal today is called *Tidskrift för Homeopati* (Journal of Homœopathy).

In 1919, the Government decided homœopathic remedies could be sold freely, without a prescription.

In 1928 an association for non-medical homœopathic practitioners, Svenska Homeopaters Riksförbund, was established. Its name today is Svenska Homeopraktikers Riksförbund (SHR).

Three times— in 1944, 1952 and 1955— the Government attempted to ban the sale of homœopathic medicines, but all efforts to do so failed. In 1941 and 1950 there were attempts to forbid lay homœopaths practicing, but these also failed.

In January 1961 the prevalent law concerning the practice of homœopathy came into force. Even though there are limitations on practicing homœopathy, it was a victory for the homœopathic community. One of the laws forbids homœopaths (and other alternative practitioners) treating patients under eight years old.

Harald Ramme, wrote several short materia medicas based on his own experiences. In 1971 he founded the first school in Sweden, Arcanum in Göteborg, which is now run by his son. The school also runs a publishing enterprise, and has translated some homœopathic books into Swedish. The elder Ramme also started producing homœopathic remedies. The pharmacy is called DCG Farmaceutiska AB, and it is the main supplier of homœopathic remedies in Scandinavia.

In 1985 Svenska Akademin för Klassisk Homeopati (SAKH) was established with 15 members, growing to about 90 during its 13 years of existence.

Today, practicing homœopaths in Sweden can belong to the SAKH, the SHR, and the Hahnemann Collegium (HC), founded in 1988.

Two organizations whose members use different therapies including homœopathy are Svenska Naturmedicinska Sällskapet (SNS) and Svenska Naturläkarförbundet (SNLF).

The total members in the three homœopathic organizations is about 250 (some are members of two organizations). In Stockholm (one million population) 40 homœopaths are in the yellow pages.

Medicina Futura (MF), started in 1995, teaching from the ECCH guide lines. The homœopathic part of the school is a three-year, part-time course.

Nordiska Akademi för Klassisk Homeopati (NAKH), is a three year part time school of homœopathy. Students have to have a nurse's level medical training to be accepted. It started teaching in 1986.

Naturmedicinska Fackskolan (NMF), is a five-year part–time, or two-year, full-time, school of medicine and homœopathy and other alternative methods. It started in 1975.

Nordiska Hahnemann Institutet (NHI), is another course of homœopathy, associated with a school for medical studies.

Practical training for graduate homœopaths is a problem in Sweden, since there are few well-trained homœopaths with experience.

There are eight pharmacies, several of them making their own remedies.

The country is represented in the LMHI.

Switzerland:

Homœopathy developed "hand-in-hand with Germany." Dr. Franz Josef Siegrist was practicing in Basel in 1827. Pierre Dufresne began practicing in Geneva in 1831. In 1832 Charles Caspard Peschier, a pupil of Hahnemann and des Guidi began practice in Geneva. The first journal, *Bibliothèque homoeopathique*, was published in Geneva in 1832. The first homœopathic society was the Société Homoeopathique du Léman, founded in 1830 by a dozen Swiss and French homœopaths. The Schweizerischer Verein Homöopathischer Aerzte (SVHA) was founded in 1856.

The country's politics are based on local laws. In the cantons (districts) where there is legislation about medical practice by non-MDs— you have to be a heilpraktiker and have passed an exam where the Government check that you "don't have any serious misconception about the basis of medical knowledge."

The only homœopathy covered in the basic health insurance is that done by MDs. There are some 200 MDs practicing homœopathy, and there are probably around 500 lay-homœopaths, some being heilpraktikers.

The Verband Klassischer Homöopath Innen (VKH) was founded in 1992 as an professional organization for classical homœopaths. There are several other organizations: Associazione per l'omeopatia unistica classica (AOUC); Homöopathie Verband Schweiz (HVS); Schweizerische Homöopathie Gesellschaft (SHG); Schweizerischer Verein für Homöopathie (SVH); Schweizerischer Verband homöopathischer Ärzte (SVHA)

At present there are many MDs who claim to practice homœopathy but many are using combination remedies after taking three week courses. Several schools teach homœopathy in the country.

Prescriptions (from an MD) for any homœopathic remedies above the 6C or 12X potency are not needed.

The country is represented in the LMHI.

Tunisia:

A society of alternative medicine was founded in 1982 and it taught homœopathy through a series of seminars, mostly to medical doctors, dentist, and veterinarians. About 10 people graduated every year from these seminars. There are now about 200 MDs using homœopathy along with their allopathy, or who use homœopathy according to the "French school" of more than one remedy based on pathology, and using only low potencies with 30c as the top limit. In the major cities almost every pharmacy has about 20 or 30 major polychrest remedies in stock.

Turkey:

John Arschagouni, MD (HMC 1891) was listed as being in Constantinople in the 1911 *Directory*. My data base shows another homœopath there in 1875. The present status is unknown.

Ukraine:

Development of homœopathy in the Ukraine is closely related with the spread of homœopathy in Russia. Homœopathy was under the patronage of Grand Dukes Konstantin Pavlovich and Michail Pavlovich, Emperor Nikolas I, his daughter Olga Nikolaevna, Queen of Wurtemberg. The peculiarity of development of homœopathy in the Ukraine in the 19th century was that homœopaths were supported by the most prominent men of that period. Societies of Followers of Homœopathy were founded in Kiev, Kharkov, Odessa, Poltava, and Chernigov. There were hospitals in Kiev and Kharkov, and many pharmacies. The Kiev Society of Followers of Homœopathy was formed in 1891.

Historic events in Russia had an unfavorable effect on further development of homœopathy. Mass repressions of the 1930s and World War II resulted in discontinuance of the Societies. However, homœopaths remained in all the cities of the Ukraine.

The new stage of development of homœopathy began in 1985, when Dr. N. K. Bulach opened The Homœopathic Department in Kharkov, and the Homœopathic Society of Kharkov was formed by Dr. V. D. Karamyshev. The Centre of Homœopathy was formed in Kiev by Dr. T .D. Popova. Development of homœopathy has been supported by the Ministry of Public Health of the Ukraine. Postgraduate teaching in homœopathic medicine was started in Kiev and Kharkov in 1990-92.

The country is represented in the LMHI.

United Arab Emirates:

King lists one graduate, Marian Wells Thoms, from "Arabia" who graduated Ann Arbor in 1898.

Homœopathy is not recognized in the UAR, with a few homœopaths (mostly from India) practicing privately. Most patients are expatriate Indians and not Arab nationals.

Uruguay:

Dr. Juan Christiano Korth, who received his diploma in 1847 from Rio de Janeiro set up practice in that year in Montevideo. A journal, *Revista Homeopatica*, was published from 1881-1888, and *Boletin de Homeopatia* was published from 1889-1896. The present status is unknown.

Venezuela:

The first person to use homœopathy in Venezuela was Dr. Manuel Porras in 1860. In 1880, Dr. Fernando de la Ville founded the first school that taught homœopathy. A year later, the government recognized the practice of homœopathy, but homœopathy never grew much after that. Only seven practitioners were listed in the 1931 Directory.

In 1934, Dr. Risquez attended a homœopathic meeting in Europe and returned to Venezuela to begin teaching others. Shortly after the Centro Amigos de la Homeopathia was formed and this organization carried homœopathy through the 1940s and 1950s.

In 1959, Dr. Martin Kelber began teaching a one year course for physicians. One of the physicians from the course attended a Congress in Mexico, and this began a long standing relationship between the two countries. Over the next ten years, Proceso Sánchez Ortega, and David Flores Toledo came from Mexico to teach homœopathy in Venezuela.

Risquez attended the 1961 Liga meeting in Amsterdam and made a number of international contacts. Shortly after Tomás Paschero from Argentina began teaching in Venezuela.

In 1969 La Asociación Médica Homeopática Venezolana was formed and in 1975 the Fundación Venezolana de Medicina Homeopática was formed. Both teach classical homœopathy. The Sociedad Venezolana de Medicina Homeopatica is the umbrella organization representing homœopathic interests.

In 1971 La Escula Médica Homeopática Venezolana was established, and by 1991 had graduated 51 doctors.

In 1975 Dr. Mathias Dorcsi, from Austria, began teaching in Venezuela, and in 1977 the first Venezuelan homœopathic conference was held in Caracas.

At this time, about 700 MDs have completed post-graduate study in homeopathy.

Non-MDs can not study or practice homœopathy in Venezuela.

A journal, *Gaceta Homeopatica de Caracas*, is published twice yearly.

There are about 50 homœopathic pharmacies.

The country is represented in the LMHI.

Bibliography and References

Bibliography and Credits

The Following works were used to obtain much of the information contained in this work. Other titles used appear within the specific chapter listings:

Bradford, Thomas Lindsley, MD. *Homeopathic Bibliography*. Philadelphia: Boericke and Tafel, 1892.

Bradford, Thomas Lindsley, MD. *Biographies of Homœopathic Physicians* Philadelphia: Hahnemann Collection, Allegheny University of Health Sciences, 1916. *[Bradford's Scrapbooks* (35 volumes)]

Bradford, Thomas Lindsley, MD. *The Pioneers of Homeopathy*. Philadelphia: Boericke and Tafel, 1897.

Cleave, E. *Biographical Cyclopedia of Homœopathic Physicians and Surgeons*. Philadelphia: Galaxy Publishing Co. 1873.

Coulter, Harris Livermore, PhD. *Divided Legacy, Science and Ethics in American Medicine 1800-1914*. Berkeley: North Atlantic Books, 1982.

Coulter, Harris Livermore, PhD. *Divided Legacy, The Bacteriological Era. A History of the Schism in Medical Thought*, Volume IV. Berkeley: North Atlantic Books, 1994.

Haehl, Richard, MD. *Samuel Hahnemann, his Life and Work*. (2 volumes) Translated by M. L. Wheeler and W. H. R. Grundy. London: Homœopathic Publishing Company, 1922.

Homœopathic Physician, Philadelphia 1881-1899.

Homœopathic Recorder, published at several locations, 1886-1959.

Journal of the American Institute of Homeopathy, published at several locations, 1909-1998.

Kaufman, Martin. *Homeopathy: The Rise and Fall of a Medical Heresy*. Baltimore: Johns Hopkins Press, 1971.

King, William Harvey, MD. *The History of Homeopathy and Its Institutions in America*, (4 volumes). New York: Lewis Publishing Company, 1905.

Knerr, Calvin, MD. *The Life of Hering*. Philadelphia: Magee Press, 1940.

Transactions of the American Institute of Homœopathy, published at several locations, 1845-1909.

Transactions of the International Hahnemannian Association, published at several locations, 1880-1946.

Wood, Matthew. *The Magical Staff The Vitalist Tradition in Western Medicine*. Berkeley: North Atlantic Books, 1992.

Hahnemann Collection, Allegheny University of Health Sciences, Philadelphia, Pennsylvania.

Introduction

page iii. Photograph of Raymond Seidel. Collection of the author.

page xiv: Photograph of NCH Summer School. Collection of the author.

page xvi. Letter from Elizabeth Wright Hubbard to Julia M Green. Collection of the author.

Chapter 1. The Beginnings

page 2. Flow chart. Work in progress by the author.

page 3. Quote from Richard Grossinger. Grossinger, Richard. *Planet Medicine*. Boulder and London: Shambhala, 1982; Photograph of Samuel Hahnemann. Haug Verlag, Heidelberg. Used with permission. Hahnemann signature. *Journal of the American Institute of Homeopathy*, November-December 1964. The biography was assembled from information in Haehl's two volumes and from Bradford, Thomas Lindsley, MD. *The Life and Letters of Samuel Hahnemann*. Philadelphia, PA: Boericke and Tafel, 1895.

page 4. Cullen's *Materia Medica*. From the Library of Boericke and Tafel, Santa Rosa, CA

page 5. First Edition *Organon*. Hahnemann Collection, Allegheny University of Health Sciences, Philadelphia, Pennsylvania.

page 6. "A" or "E." Discussion drawn from the lyghtforce mail-list.

page 10. Pictures of the stages of Hahnemann's life. From the Hahnemann Monument, Washington DC. Photographs by the author.

page 11. Picture of Johanna Hahnemann. From Haehl. Page 158; Biographical information from Haehl. Picture of Melanie Hahnemann. Collection of the author. Signature of Melanie Hahnemann from Haehl, Page 225.

page 12. Portrait of Hahnemann. Robert Bosch Institute, Stuttgart. Used with permission.

page 13. Photograph of Hahnemann Grave by Philip Robbins.

page 14. Medallion of Melanie. Picture from *Hahnemann, Die abenteuerlichen Schicksale eines altlichen Rebellen und seiner Lehre, der Homöpathie*. by Martin Gumpert, Berlin: Fischer, 1934 Collection of Christopher Ellithorp.

page 15. Elderly Madam Hahnemann. Robert Bosch Institute, Stuttgart. Used with permission. The generalized biography of Melanie was developed from Handley, Rima. *A Homeopathic Love Story, The Story of Samuel and Mélanie Hahnemann*. Berkeley: North Atlantic Books, 1990 and Haehl's work. The specific quotes by Melanie are from Haehl's.

page 17. Friedrich Hahnemann. Information from Bradford's *Pioneers*, pages 35-51; Knerr, pages 27, 83-84, 120.

page 19. Picture of Gross. Haehl page 377. Biographical information from Bradford's *Pioneers* pages 20-31.

page 20. Picture of Stapf. Haehl page 385. Biographical information from Bradford's *Pioneers* pages 117-122.

Chapter 2: Homœopathy Comes to the USA

page 22. Gram. *U. S. Medical and Surgical Journal*, July 1867, page 449. Collection of Christopher Ellithorp. Biographical information from Bradford's *Pioneers* pages 288-300, King Vol. I pages. 60-64; Morris, S. Brent. *The Folger Manuscript The cryptoanalysis and interpretation of an American Masonic manuscript*. Ft. George G. Meade, Maryland, 1991. Draft copy.

page 23. Folger Manuscript. From S. Brent Morris. collection of the author.

page 24. Picture and signature of John Gray. Line engraving by "Galaxy Press, Philadelphia." Collection of the author. Biographical information from Bradford's *Pioneers* pages 300-317, King Vol. I, pages 67-68.

page 24. Picture of Federal Vanderburgh. King Vol. I, page 81. Signature of Vanderburgh. Collection of Christopher Ellithorp. Biographical information from Bradford's *Pioneers* pages 631-637.

page 26. Picture and signature of Hempel. Line engraving by "Galaxy Press, Philadelphia." Collection of the author. Biographical information from *Transactions of the American Institute of Homœopathy,* 1880, page 150; Knerr's *Life of Hering*.

page 27. Silhouette of Wesselhoeft and signature from the Hahnemann Collection, Allegheny University of Health Sciences, Philadelphia, Pennsylvania. Biographical information from Bradford's *Pioneers* page 644-662; King Vol. I. 132-134.

page 28. Detwiller. photograph and signature from the Hahnemann Collection, Allegheny University of Health Sciences, Philadelphia, Pennsylvania. Biographical information from Bradford's *Pioneers* page 226-232; King Vol. I, pages 128-131; *Homœopathic Physician,* Vol. 7, page 212; *Transactions of the American Institute of Homœopathy,* 1889, pages 193-198.

page 28. Pulsatilla. From A. von Villers and F. von Thümen. *Die Pflanzen des Homöopathischen Arzneischatzes.* Dresden 1893. Collection of author.

page 29. Leipzig Kit. Collection of the author.

page 29. *American Botanist.* Collection of the author.

page 30. Hering. An engraving by Sartain from a Daguerreotype by G. H. Weeks. National Center for Homeopathy. Signature. Collection of the author. The biographical information about Hering can be found in Knerr's *Life of Hering* and in: Raue, Charles, MD. *A Memorial to Constantine Hering.* Philadelphia: Globe printing, 1880; Faber, Herman. *Constantine Hering, MD, A Biographical Sketch.* Reprinted from the *Journal of the American Institute of Homœopathy,* June, July, August 1915; Hering, Carl. "Chronology of Events in the life of Constantine Hering." *Transactions of the International Hahnemannian Association,* 1919, pages 11-38.

page 31. Hering as a student. Knerr, page 26 facing.

page 32. Surinam 1828. Moravian Library, Bethlehem, Pennsylvania.

page 33. Hering and Snake. *Life of Hering,* Page 168.

page 34. Hering and Book. Hahnemann Collection, Allegheny University of Health Sciences, Philadelphia, Pennsylvania.

page 35. George Bute. Collection of author. Biographical information from Cleave's *Biography* page 202-206.

page 36. Allentown. Line translation of photo in King Vol. 1, page 115. Collection of author.

page 37. List of Graduates. Hahnemann Collection, Allegheny University of Health Sciences, Philadelphia, Pennsylvania.

page 38. Lippe. Hahnemann Collection, Allegheny University of Health Sciences, Philadelphia, Pennsylvania. Signature. Cleave's, page 26. Biography from *Homeopathic Physician,* Volume 8, page 186, 1888.

page 39. Neidhard. Cleave's *Biography* page 58. Biographical information from Cleave's *Biography* page 58.

page 40. Pulte. King Vol. II, page 225 signature from Hahnemann Collection, Allegheny University of Health Sciences, Philadelphia, Pennsylvania. Biography from Cleave's 28-30; *Biographical Sketch of J. H. Pulte, M.D.* Cincinnati: Miami Printing and Publishing, 1868; Bradford's *Pioneers,* pages 520-531; *Homœopathic Survey,* January 1929, page 31.

page 40. Sturm. Collection of the author.

page 41. Jahr. From *Revue Belge d'Homoeopthie,* Volume 3, 1958 pages 375-380. Collection of author. Biographical information from Bradford's *Pioneers* page 366-386.

page 42. Jahr's Manual. Collection of author.

page 43. Boenninghausen. Frontispiece, from C. M. Boger, *Characteristics and Repertory.* Parkersburg, 1905. Biographical information from Bradford's *Pioneers* page 167-191. "Maria" quote from Bruce Barwell, a New Zealand homœopath.

page 46. Boenninghausen. Found in Mazzini Stuart, *The Life of Peter Stuart, the "Ditton Doctor."* London: Books, Ltd. 1921. From the collection of Francis Treuherz.

Chapter 3: 1835-1870

page 48. William Leo-Wolf Frontispiece. National Center for Homeopathy.

page 49. AIH seal. Minutes of the Meeting. *AIH Transactions* 1844-46. Collection of the author.

page 50. Application for Membership. Collection of the author.

page 52. The Founders. King Vol. II page 54.

page 52. Jacob Jeanes. photo and signature from Hahnemann Collection, Allegheny University of Health Sciences, Philadelphia, Pennsylvania. Biographical information King Vol. I, page 144, Vol. II. page 55; Knerr, page 41-42.

Page 53. Walter Williamson. King Vol. II page 47, signature from Hahnemann Collection, Allegheny University of Health Sciences, Philadelphia, Pennsylvania. Biographical information from Cleave's *Biography* page 30; King, Vol. II page 55-56.

Page 53. James Kitchen. Picture and Signature Cleave's page 129. Biographical information from Cleave's page 129; King Vol. I, page 147.

page 54. Alvan E. Small. Photograph from the Faculty of Homeopathy, London. Signature from Hahnemann Collection, Allegheny University of Health Sciences, Philadelphia, Pennsylvania. Biographical information from Cleave's page 23; *Transactions of the American Institute of Homœopathy,* 1889, pages 198-200.

page 54. H. N. Guernsey. photograph and signature from Hahnemann Collection, Allegheny University of Health Sciences, Philadelphia, Pennsylvania. Biographical information from Cleave's page 9; Homeopathic Physician, Volume 5, 325; *Transactions of the American Institute of Homœopathy,* 1888 pages 115-118.

page 55. H. N. Guernsey. Collection of Christopher Ellithorp. Quote from Guernsey, H. N., MD. *Plain Talks on Avoided Subjects.* Philadelphia: F. A. Davis, 1882. Collection of the author.

page 56. Hahnemann (Filbert Street). Catalog cover. Collection of Chris Ellithorp. Hahnemann 1884. King Vol. II page 36 Information from Bradford, T. L., MD, *The History of the Homœopathic Medical College of Pennsylvania and the Hahnemann Medical College. Philadelphia:* Boericke and Tafel, 1898.

page 57. Tullio Verdi. Cleave's Page 17. Biographical information from Cleave's page 17; *Transactions of the American Institute of Homœopathy,* 1903 pages 730-731.

page 58. Politics in Washington DC. *Divided Legacy,* page 291-294.

Chapter 4: Hering

page 60. Hering in his Study. Original photo in the collection of the author.

page 61. Augustus Korndoerfer. Photo and signature from Hahnemann Collection, Allegheny University of Health Sciences, Philadelphia, Pennsylvania. Biographical information from King Vol. IV, page 249

page 61. E. A. Farrington. Photo from Hahnemann Collection, Allegheny University of Health Sciences, Philadelphia, Pennsylvania. Signature from a copy of Lilienthal's *Therapeutics* that was presented by the author to E. A. Farrington, from the collection of Larry Malerba, DO. Biographical information from *Homœopathic Physician,* Vol. 6, page 42; Farrington, E. A. *Clinical Materia Medica.* Philadelphia: Hahnemann Publishing House, 1890, pages 2-15; *Transactions of the American Institute of Homœopathy,* 1888, pages 134-137.

page 62. C. G. Raue. Picture and signature from Cleave's page 52 Biographical information from Cleave's page 51; *Homœopathic Physician,* volume 16, page 413, pages 422-483.

page 63. Calvin B. Knerr. Hahnemann Collection, Allegheny University of Health Sciences, Philadelphia, Pennsylvania. Signature *Journal of the American Institute of Homeopathy,* November-December 1964. Biographical information from *Homœopathic Recorder* November 1940, page 2.

page 63. Charles Mohr. photo and signature from Hahnemann Collection, Allegheny University of Health Sciences, Philadelphia, Pennsylvania. Biographical information from King, Vol. IV page 89

page 64. Hering Portrait. National Center for Homeopathy; the information about Hering can be found in Knerr's *Life of Hering;* in Raue, Charles, MD. *A Memorial to Constantine Hering.* Philadelphia: Globe printing, 1880; and in Faber, Herman. *Constantine Hering, MD, A Biographical Sketch.* Reprinted from the *Journal of the American Institute of Homœopathy,* June, July, August 1915.

page 65. Hering. National Center for Homeopathy.

page 67. Hering at table. *Life of Hering,* page 22.

page 68. Letter from Hering. Collection of the author.

page 69. Gelsemium. From A. von Villers and F. von Thümen. *Die Pflanzen des Homöopathischen Arzneischatzes.* Dresden 1893. Collection of author.

page 70. Tickets from Globe Ticket Company (with thanks to Linda Lorrie Gross).

page 71. Jenichen. Bradford's *Pioneers,* pages 392-410; Interview with Frederick Schmid, Santa Barbara, CA April 1987.

page 72. Hering Grave. Photo by the author.

Chapter 5: The Division

page 75. Dunham. photo from the Faculty of Homœopathy, London; Signature appears in the flyleaf of an *American Homeopathic Review* Vol. 6, 1866 in the Collection of the author. Biographical information from Dunham, Carroll, MD, *Lectures on Materia Medica.* Philadelphia: Boericke and Tafel, 1880 "A Memoir of the Author" by E. M. Kellogg, MD, pages vii-xxiii; *Homœopathic Recorder,* July 1938, MacAdam, E. Wallace, MD, "Carroll Dunham." pages 10-17; *United States Medical Investigator,* Volume 3, pages 57-60, pages 103-107.

page. 76. Dunham. Hahnemann Collection, Allegheny University of Health Sciences, Philadelphia, Pennsylvania.

page 76. Graves. Photo by the author.

page 77. The Retrenching *Transactions of the American Institute of Homœopathy,* 1870, pages 570-589; 1879, page 1180ff; 1880, pages 144ff, 163 ff.

page 78. IHA Seal. Collection of the author.

page 76. The formation of the IHA *Transactions of the International Hahnemannian Association,* 1880-83.

page 79. IHA Journals. Collection of the author.

page 80. H. C. Allen photo from the Faculty of Homeopathy, London; signature from William Kirtsos. Biographical material King Vol. III, page 397-98; *Transactions of the International Hahnemannian Association,* 1909, pages 6-10.

page 82. Lippe Grave. Photo by the author.

Chapter 6: Homœopathic Pharmacy

page 84. Sears Kits From *Sears Catalog Number 110,* circa 1900, page 25; B&T Kits *Boericke and Tafel Catalog 1875* ; Radde *Hull's Jahr, 1853,* all from the Collection of the author.

page 85. Humphreys picture from *Humphreys' Mentor.* New York: Humphreys Publishing, 1898. Collection of the author; Signature from Christopher Ellithorp. Veterinary Product. *Veterinary Catalog,* circa 1890 Catalog. Collection of the author. Biographical information *Humphreys' Mentor.* New York: Humphreys Publishing, 1879, pages iii-vi.

page 86. Wedding Picture. Collection of Gretchen Worden; Photo of Boericke and Tafel. Bradford's Scrapbook, Hahnemann Collection, Allegheny University of Health Sciences, Philadelphia, Pennsylvania. Biographical information Cleave's page 369; "Boericke and Tafel's Homœopathic Pharmacies," *Homœopathic Recorder* 1893, pages 66-69; "A Sketch of Francis Edmund Boericke" by John Pitcairn, *New Church Life,* 1902.

page 87. Boericke Machine. Drawing by author after *Organon*, 1878, page 420. Mention of MM potency on page 347.

page 88. F. E. Boericke photograph from Boericke and Tafel; Signature from the contract between F. E. Boericke and William Boericke and W. A. Dewey to write *The Twelve Tissue Salts of Schuessler*, Dated October 26, 1887. Collection of the author; Family tree information from Gretchen Worden.

page 89. Fincke. Photograph *Homœopathic Recorder*, December 1930. Signature from a 7th edition of Hering's *Domestic Physician*. signature dated 1857. Collection of the author. Fincke label. Collection of author. Biographical information *Transactions of the American Institute of Homœopathy*, 1907, pages 25-27, 307-317.

page 90. Fincke with Horn. Hahnemann Collection, Allegheny University of Health Sciences, Philadelphia, Pennsylvania.

page 91. Fluxion drawing from United States Patent No. 93,980. Collection of the author. Fincke bottles Collection of author. Fincke process description. Kaercher, William, MD, "The Fincke Process of Potentization, A Reprint from *The Homœopathician*, November, 1914; United States Patent No. 93,980; Hering quote from *Life of Hering*, page 97.

page 92. Fincke Letter to Bradford in Bradford's Scrapbooks, Hahnemann Collection, Allegheny University of Health Sciences, Philadelphia, Pennsylvania.

page 93. Fincke photograph from A. J. Gross, Brooklyn, NY. Identified on back as "Uncle Doctor Fincke." Collection of author; Fincke letter to Dr. Edmund Carleton. Collection of author.

page 94. Dunham remedy bottles. Collection of author. Dunham Remedy Process: Lippe, Adolph, MD, "The Preparation of High Potencies," *Hahnemannian Monthly*, Volume 3, Page 497- 501; Jones, Samuel A. MD, "Book Notices" [review of Dunham's two books], *American Observer Medical Monthly*, Volume 16, pages 343-344.

page 96. Skinner Photograph and signature, Clarke, J. H., *Thomas Skinner, MD, A Biographical Sketch*, London: Homœopathic Publishing Company, 1907. Collection of the National Center for Homeopathy.

page 96. Skinner Machine *The Organon*, Vol. I page 45.

page 97. Kent Letter *Homœopathic Recorder*, September 1928, page 562. The original letter is in possession of Dr. Hayes' grand daughter. The letter, as a copper printing plate, is in the collection of the author.

page 98. Swan. Hahnemann Collection, Allegheny University of Health Sciences, Philadelphia, Pennsylvania; signature from *Jahr's Manual*, printed by Balliere, 1847 in the Collection of the National Center for Homeopathy. Biographical information *Homœopathic Physician*, Volume 13, page 557; Volume 14, page 26.

page 99. *List of Swan's High Potencies: Morbific Products and Nosodes*, Philadelphia: Boericke and Tafel, circa 1900. Collection of the author. Swan letter to Bradford in Bradford's Scrapbooks, Hahnemann Collection, Allegheny University of Health Sciences, Philadelphia, Pennsylvania.

page 100. Santee Potentizer Nash, E. B., MD, "A New Potentizer." *Homeopathic Physician*, Volume 9, page 106. Signature from the Collection of Christopher Ellithorp.

page 101. Ehrhart and Karl photographs from *List of High Potencies*. Chicago: Ehrhart and Karl, circa 1915. Collection of the author. Kent Potentizer. Drawing by author from a photo of the machine taken by the author. Kent bottle. Collection of author.

page 102. Burdick Potentizer. Deschere, Martin, MD, "Microscope and Potency, with a Review of the Modes of Potentizing Drugs, and the Introduction of a New Potentizer. *North American Journal of Homœopathy*, May 1879. page 491.

page 102. B&T Skinner Machine. Photo by the author, 1987; Robinson, W. W., MD "The High Attenuation: Its History and Mode of Preparation." *Homœopathic Recorder*, February 1941. pages 51ff. Winston, Julian. "A Brief History of Potentizing Machines." *British Homœopathic Journal*, April, 1989, pages 59-68.

Chapter 7: The Second Generation

page 104. E M. Hale photograph from the Faculty of Homœopathy, London; Signature from Cleave's, page 24. Biographical Information from Cleave's pages 24-25; *Transactions of the American Institute of Homœopathy*, 1899, pages 927-928.

page 105. Ludlam Picture King Volume II page 348, Signature from William Kirtsos. Biographical Information from Cleave's page 11; *Transactions of the American Institute of Homœopathy*, 1899, pages 930-931.

page 105. T. F. Allen picture from College of Physicians and Surgeons, Philadelphia, signature from *Journal of the American Institute of Homeopathy*, November-December 1964. Biographical Information from Cleave's page 427, *Transactions of the American Institute of Homœopathy*, 1903, pages 725-727.

page 106. *Allen's Encyclopedia* page. Collection of the author.

page 107. *Millspaugh* Cover and drawing from the collection of the author. Biographical Information from *The Dictionary of American Biographies* Volume 8, Charles Scribner and Sons, 1934 (from Chris Ellithorp).

page 108. Helmuth picture and signature from *Transactions of the American Institute of Homœopathy*, 1902 page 829. Biographical Information from *Transactions of the American Institute of Homœopathy*, 1902 pages 829-831 Poem from Helmuth, W. T., MD, *With the "Pousse Cafe," Being a Collection of Post-Prandial Verses*. New York: Boericke and Tafel, 1892, pages 105-112.

page 111. T. C. Duncan photo from King Volume 1 page 350; signature from Christopher Ellithorp. Biographical Information from the *Hahnemannian Advocate*, 1902, page 277. "Cultural Standards" from Duncan, T. C., MD. *How to be Plump*. Chicago: Duncan Publishing, 1878. Collection of the author.

page 112. Gregg. Signature from Hahnemann Collection, Allegheny University of Health Sciences, Philadelphia, Pennsylvania. Book illustration from Gregg, Rollin R., MD, *An Illustrated Repertory of Pains in Chest, Sides, and Back; Their Direction and Character*. Chicago: Duncan Brothers, 1879. Collection of the author. Biographical information, *Homœopathic Physician*, Volume 6 page 327; *Transactions of the American Institute of Homœopathy*, 1889, pages 202-204.

page 113. Yingling Picture from *Homœopathic Recorder* February 1931; book cover from the collection of the author. Biographical information *Emporia Daily Gazette*, obituary, April 3, 1933. Furnished by Jay Yasgur.

page 114. E. B. Nash Picture from the *Homœopathic Recorder* August 1938. Signature from inscription on flyleaf of *Leaders in Typhoid*, collection of the author. Biographical Information from the *Homœopathic Recorder*, February 1917 pages 67-68.

page 115. S. A. Jones picture from King Vol. I page 254, Signature from a manuscript in the Samuel Jones Collection, University of Illinois, Champaign-Urbana, Illinois. Copy in the collection of the author. Biographical information from King Vol. III page 97; Wood, James C, MD, *An Old Doctor of the New School* Caldwell, Ohio: Caxton Press, 1942 , pages 121-123; information in the Samuel Jones Collection, University of Illinois, Champaign-Urbana, Illinois.

page 116. "Science in Medicine" original corrected manuscript in the Samuel Jones Collection, University of Illinois, Champaign-Urbana, Illinois. Copy in the collection of the author.

page 117. E. E. Case. Photo collection of the author, signature, collection of the National Center for Homeopathy. [The photo was found in a "History of Hartford, Connecticut." André Saine found a reference, and I found the volume at the New York Public Library. Sorry to say, I did not keep further details.] Biographical Information from *Homœopathic Recorder*, December 1918, pages 572-573.

page 118. Stuart Close. Photo from collection of Chris Ellithorp, signature from the collection of the Richard Moskowitz; Close, older. *Homœopathic Recorder*, July 1929. Biographical Information from the *Transactions of the International Hahnemannian Association*, June 1930, page 26-27.

page 119. E. P. Anshutz. Photo and signature from Hahnemann Collection, Allegheny University of Health Sciences, Philadelphia, Pennsylvania. Biographical Information from *Homœopathic Recorder*, February 1918, pages 44-52.

page 119. A. L. Monroe. Picture *The American Institute of Homœopathy, Section on Materia Medica and General Therapeutics*, 1894. page 34. Signature from Hahnemann Collection, Allegheny University of Health Sciences, Philadelphia, Pennsylvania. poem from Monroe, A. L., MD, *A Materia Medica Memorizer*. Louisville: J. P. Morton, 1882. Biographical Information from King's Vol. III, pages 361-362.

page 120. W. H. King. Photo from King's Vol. III, page 336, Biographical Information from King's Vol. III, pages 346-348.

page 120. T. L. Bradford. Photo from King's Vol. III, page 349, signature from Hahnemann Collection, Allegheny University of Health Sciences, Philadelphia, Pennsylvania. Biographical Information from King's Volume 3, pages 344-351.

page 121. Lilienthal. Picture, Faculty of Homœopathy, London; signature from a copy of Lilienthal's *Therapeutics* that was presented "by the author to E. A. Farrington," Collection of Larry Malerba, DO. Biographical Information from King's Vol. IV, page 139; *Homœopathic Recorder*, November 1891, pages 244-248; O'Neil, F. Gordon, *Ernest Reuben Lilienthal and his Family*. San Francisco: Stanford University Press, 1949, Collection of author (with thanks to Lourdes Gonzaga).

page 122. Young Lilienthal. From Frances Stern, great-granddaughter of Samuel Lilienthal. (with thanks to Lourdes Gonzaga).

page 124. William Boericke. Graduation photograph, Hahnemann Archives. Signature, collection of the author. Biographical Information obituary, *Journal of the American Institute of Homœopathy*, June 1929, pages 564-5; unpublished interview with Jean Barnard by Greg Bedayn.

page 124. Oscar Boericke. Photo and signature from the 1898 Hahnemann Yearbook, Hahnemann Collection, Allegheny University of Health Sciences, Philadelphia, Pennsylvania.

page 125. W. A. Dewey. Photo from Faculty of Homœopathy, London. Signature in collection of the author. Older Dewey photo found in a botany book, collection of Chris Ellithorp. Biographical Information from King's Vol. III, pages 351-2 *Essentials of Homœopathic Therapeutics*. Collection of author.

page 126. J. W. Ward. picture from King's Vol. III, page 393 Biographical Information from King's Vol. III, page 393; *The Laboratory*, Vol. 3, March 1936, pages 5-12, 17-18, 20-29, 30-1, 39-41. Collection of Dana Ullman.

page 127. Letter in the Collection of the author. Photo of older Ward from Ward, J. W., MD, *Unabridged Dictionary of Sensations As If*. San Francisco: Wobbers, 1939.

page 128. Florence Ward photo from *Journal of the American Institute of Homœopathy*, January 1920, page 688. Biographical Information from *The Journal of the American Institute of Homœopathy*, January 1920, page 688, *Pacific Coast Journal of Homœopathy*, 1920, pages 39-41; letter from John Erskine (Ward's grandson), collection of Dana Ullman.
Picture of the Ward Sanatorium *Hospitals and Sanatoriums of the Homœopathic School of Medicine*, Council on Medical Education of the American Institute of Homœopathy, 1916. page 92.

Chapter 8: The Mental Hospitals

page 130. The information about the mental hospitals was gleaned from King's, Vol. I; *Hospitals and Sanatoriums of the Homœopathic School of Medicine*, Council on Medical Education of the American Institute of Homœopathy, 1916; *The International Homeopathic Directory 1931*, American Institute of Homeopathy, edited by E. Petrie Hoyle; the 1941 *Directory of United States Homeopathic Physicians*, American Institute of Homeopathy, 1941.

page 130. Picture of Middletown gates and building from a postcard. Collection of Christopher Ellithorp. Picture of the Pharmacy from *Centennial Chronicle 1874-1974*, Middletown, 1974. Collection of the author.

page 131. Picture of Gowanda State from a postcard. Collection of Christopher Ellithorp. Picture of Allentown from *Hospitals and Sanatoriums of the Homœopathic School of Medicine*, Council on Medical Education of the American Institute of Homœopathy, 1916, page 69.

page 134. Information about Patton from Asa Hershoff, ND; Norwich by Nancy Adams; Westboro by Albrik Avanessian.

page 135. Pictures from *Hospitals and Sanatoriums of the Homœopathic School of Medicine*, Council on Medical Education of the American Institute of Homœopathy, 1916. Patton, page 91; Norwich, page 21; Westboro, page 17.

page 136. Fergus Falls information from Lynn Lammer and Allen Vickstrom.

page 136. Talcott. Picture and signature from the *Transactions of the American Institute of Homœopathy*, 1902 page 832. Biographical Information from *Transactions of the American Institute of Homœopathy*, 1902 page 832-833.

page 137. Poem from *Transactions of the American Institute of Homœopathy*, 1902 page 832. "On Prognosis of Insanity" A paper delivered to the Homœopathic Medical Society of the State of New York, 1878.

page 138. Admission form to Middletown. Copy of original. Collection of the author (with thanks to Janet Madow).

Chapter 9: The Women

page 140. Melanie. Picture from *The American Homeopath,* used with permission. Other information in the introduction from: Mitchell, Kristin M., *Her Preference was to Heal* History Department, Yale University, 1989. 74 pages; Leavitt, Judith W, ed. *Women and Health in America* Madison: University of Wisconsin Press, 1984, pages 422-427; Barlow, William and Powell, David, "Homeopathy and Sexual Equality, The Controversy over Coeducation at Cincinnati's Pulte Medical College, 1873-1879." [Ms. Mitchell's thesis is one of the clearest and concise expositions about the history of women in medicine, specifically from the homœopathic standpoint. I have done little but condense and summarize her findings.]

page 142. Cleveland King's Vol. III, page 17. Cleveland college history, King's Vol. III, pages 13-15.

page 143. New England Female. King's Vol. III, page 160. Historical information from King's Vol. III, pages 159-169; Interview with Anne Kirshman.

page 144. Lozier. King's Vol. III, page 152. Signature from Archives and Special Collections, Special Collections on Women in Medicine, Allegheny University of the Health Sciences, Philadelphia, Pennsylvania. Biographical information from King's Vol. III, pages 125, 151-156; Lozier, Abraham *In Memoriam: Clemence Sophia Lozier, MD* New York: (Private Printing) 1888 at the New York Historical Society; Mitchell, pages 46-48.

page 145. NY Medical College Announcement. Collection of Christopher Ellithorp.

page 146. Cady Stanton. Picture and biography from Lutz, Alma. *Created Equal— a Biography of Elizabeth Cady Stanton,* New York: John Day Co., 1940.

page 147. Bayard. Picture from Cleave's page 51. Biographical information from Cleave's page 51; *Transactions of the American Institute of Homœopathy*, 1890 pages 129-131; *Transactions of the International Hahnemannian Association*, 1890 pages 85-89. Hering Story, Knerr, page 79. Mrs. Bayard's Cocker Spaniel, Carleton, Edmund *Homœopathy in Medicine and Surgery*, Philadelphia: Boericke and Tafel, 1913 pages 28-29.

page 141. Anthony and Stanton suffrage picture. Johnstown Historical Society, Johnstown, New York.

page 148. Stanton at school. King's Vol. 3, pages 154-155.

page 149. Edson. Picture from an article about Edson in the New York Times, February 27, 1961 (uncredited). Biographical Information *Transactions of the American Institute of Homœopathy*, 1898. page 726. Furman, Bess, "Garfield had Woman Doctor, Setting Precedent for Kennedy," *New York Times,* February 27, 1961.

page 149. Mercy B. Jackson. Cleave's page 443.

page 150. Carolyn E. Hastings. Cleave's, page 497.

page 151. Mary Florence Taft. Frontispiece in *The Homœopathician,* May 1912. Collection of the author; Signature Collection of Richard Moskowitz. Biographical Information *The Homœopathic Survey*, Volume 2, Number 1, October 1927, pages 7-8. Bookplate, Collection of the author.

Chapter 10: The Arrival of Kent

page 154. Kent. 1882 Photograph labeled "Guerin, St. Louis" and in pencil, "Dr. Kent." It was found in the pages of an old Jahr's *Repertory*. It is from this likeness that the line-engraving of Kent, found in the 1885 *Transactions of the International Hahnemannian Association*, appears to be derived. The original source of the photo is unknown. Collection of the author. Signature from the *Medical Advance,* December 1884 (Courtesy of Christopher Ellithorp). Biographical Information from *The Homœopathician,* Volume 1; *Medical Advance*, December 1884, pages 306-307; *Journal of the American Institute of Homœopathy*, July 1916; King Volume 4, page 156; *Homœopathic World,* August 1916, pages 348-351, "The Death of Dr. Kent," by Margaret L. Tyler, MD; Michot-Dietrich, Hela PhD, *Zeitschrift für Klassische Homöopathie,* November-December, 1985 "In Search of James Tyler Kent's Ancestors"; Michot-Dietrich, Hela PhD, *Homeopathy Today* June, 1990, "In Search of James Tyler Kent's Ancestors"; Kent, J. T. MD, *Final General Repertory* edited by Pierre Schmidt, MD, and Diwan Harish Chand, MD. New Delhi: National Homœopathic Pharmacy, 1982. pages iii-xi.

page 155. Kent never wrote about his conversion through Phelan. The information we have has been transmitted by Pierre Schmidt, who undoubtedly heard it from Gladwin, who heard it from Kent. We know that Kent resigned his position at the eclectic college in 1879. At that time he had studied homœopathy with Phelan. His wife's illness must have been between 1878 and 1879. No closer date is available.

Letter from John Pitcairn to Reverend Robert J. Tilson, November 23, 1893. The John Pitcairn Archive, Bryn Athyn, Pennsylvania (with thanks to Klaus-Henning Gypser, MD)

page 156. Bearded Kent. *Medical Advance*, Ann Arbor, Michigan, December 1884. Frontispiece.

page 156. Photo of William Wilson Sherwood. Collection of author.

page 157. Phelan *St. Louis Post Dispatch*, St. Louis Library, St. Louis, Missouri. Biographical Information obituary, *St. Louis Post Dispatch*.

page 158. Rectal Applicator. From the collection of Andrew Lange, Boulder, Colorado; Kent, J. T., MD, *Sexual Neuroses*, St. Louis: Maynard and Tedford 1879. Collection of Christopher Ellithorp. Commentary on Scudder and Kent from a letter from Matthew Wood to the author, September 8, 1998.

page 160. Kent Arrival in Philadelphia. *Medical Advance*, Volume 19, 1887, page 186; *Medical Advance*, Volume 20, 1888, page 386; *Medical Advance*, Volume 21, 1888, page 82; *Medical Advance*, Volume 21, 1888, page 481; *Medical Advance*, Volume 33, 1895, page 315-318.

page 161. Spring Garden Street photo from the Archives of the German Society, Philadelphia, Pennsylvania. Postgraduate school information from the Minutes of the Post Graduate School, Hahnemann Collection, Allegheny University of Health Sciences, Philadelphia, Pennsylvania.

page 163. Gladwin. Photograph from the National Center for Homeopathy, signature from Chris Ellithorp. Biographical information *Homœopathic Recorder* June, 1931 pages 460-463.

page 164. H. Farrington. Photograph. Collection of the author, signature Collection of Chris Ellithorp. Biographical Information *Journal of the American Institute of Homœopathy*, July 1957, page 215; *Homœopathic Recorder*, July/August/September 1957, pages 30-31. The Development of the Repertory *The Homœopathician*, July/August, 1914; *The Critique*, Volume 16, 1909 pages 160-61, "Kent's Repertory" by R. Gibson Miller.

page 165. Kent Oval. From Kent, J. T., MD, *The Repertory of the Homœopathic Materia Medica*, Chicago: Ehrhart and Karl, 4th edition, 1922.

page 166. Swedenborg and Kent. material gleaned from the following sources:
Emanuel Swedenborg, A Continuing Vision, A Pictorial biography and anthology of Essays and Poetry, Edited by Robin Larsen, Stephen Larsen, James Lawrence, William Woofenden, New York 1988, articles by Peebles, Whitmont and Moskowitz are on pages 468- 477; Treuherz, Francis "The Origins of Kent's Homœopathy" in the *Journal of the American Institute of Homeopathy*, December 1984 pages 130-147; Van Dusen, Wilson *The Presence of Other Worlds: The Findings of Emmanuel Swedenborg*. New York: Harpers and Row, 1974; Trobridge, G. *Swedenborg Life and Teaching*. London: Swedenborg Society, 1945; Swedenborg, Emmanuel *Divine Love and Wisdom* New York: Swedenborg Foundation, 1982; Mack, Gwyn Dresser "The Non-Material Healing Agency: What Can the New Church Contribute?" *The New Church Messenger*, May 14, 1955 pages 147-150; "Homeopathy and the New Church, a Symposium." c. 1950 Unknown publication and date. pages 40-41. Block, Marguerite Beck *The New Church in the New World*,
New York: Henry Holt, 1932, page 161-162; Swank, Scott Trego, Chapter XII, "Swedenborgianism and Homeopathy," *The Unfettered Conscience: A Study of Sectarianism, Spiritualism, and Social Reform in the New Jerusalem Church, 1840-1870*, Philadelphia: University of Pennsylvania, Doctoral Thesis; Interview with Eleanor Peebles, 1988.

page 168. Kent Letter. Collection of the author.

Chapter 11: Great Britain: I

page 170. Turner Bookplate. Collection of Chris Ellithorp.

page 171. Quin. Photo and Signature from the British Homœopathic Association, London. Biographical information from Bradford's *Pioneers* pages 532-548. Young Quin. Photo of painting at the Faculty of Homœopathy, London. Courtesy of Peter Fischer, MD

page 172. Cartoon of Quin, Collection of the author (a gift from Francis Treuherz).

page 173. Dudgeon. Photo from Faculty of Homœopathy, London; signature from Hahnemann Collection, Allegheny University of Health Sciences, Philadelphia, Pennsylvania. Biographical information from *Journal of the British Homœopathic Society* 1904-05 New Series Vol. 13, pages 55-68.

page 174. Dudgeon photo, mounted portrait labeled "Lizzie Caswell Smith, The Gainsborough Studio, 309 Oxford Street" Collection of the author.

page 174. Hughes. Photo and signature from Hughes, Richard, MD *Principles and Practice of Homœopathy* London: Leath and Ross, 1902, Collection of the National Center for Homeopathy. Biographical information *Transaction of the American Institute of Homœopathy*, 1902, pages 834-836.

page 175. Kent Quote in a letter bound in a copy of Kent's *Materia Medica*, at the Ontario Naturopathic College Library.

page 176. Cooper photograph. Found in Cooper, R. LeHunte, *The Cancer Problem* London: John Bale and Sons, 1927. Photo mounted on first page of the book. Collection of the National Center for Homeopathy. Biographical material from Bonnard, Jean, 1994, "Robert Thomas Cooper and Arborivital Medicine," *Student Homeopath #21*, September 1994, pp22-24; Cooper, Robert T, *Cancer and Cancer Symptoms*, London, 1900; Cooper, R. LeHunte, *The Cancer Problem* London: John Bale and Sons, 1927; Tyler, Margaret *Homœopathic Drug Pictures*, Devon: Health Science Press. page 617; Margaret Tyler, in *British Homœopathic Journal*, 1932, p.136.

page 178. Burnett. Photograph and signature frontispiece in Clarke, J. H. MD *The Life and Work of James Compton Burnett, MD* London: Homœopathic publishing Company, 1904. Biographical information from same; Wood, Matthew *The Magical Staff: The Vitalist Tradition in Western Medicine* Berkeley: North Atlantic Books, 1992 pages 167-172; Spurling, Hilary *Ivy When Young: The Early Life of I. Compton-Burnett 1884-1919* London: Allison and Busby, 1983, pages 18-29, 32-33, 93-112. (The Clarke book is the base from which both Wood and Spurling get much of their information, yet both have looked at it in a very different manner. The Spurling book also contains information gleaned from conversations with Dr. Frank Bodman who knew Burnett.)

page 180. Burnett. Photograph from Faculty of Homœopathy, London.

page 181. Burnett book. Collection of the author.

page 183. Clarke. Photograph from Faculty of Homœopathy, London. Signature from an Interleaved Lippe's *Repertory*, Annotated "J. H. Clarke, 30 Clays S W, April 1893" Collection of the author. Biographical information *Homœopathic Recorder*, March 1932, pages 157-60.

page 185. "Dr. Clarke and Mr. Hyde." Treuherz, Francis RSHom, *Resonance*, July/August 1991, pages 14-15.

page 186. Bach. Portrait by Matthew Wood, taken from a photograph; signature from Weeks, Nora *The Medical Discoveries of Edward Bach* London: C. W. Daniel Co. 1976. Biographical information from Weeks, Nora *The Medical Discoveries of Edward Bach* London: C. W. Daniel Co. 1976; Wood, Matthew *The Magical Staff: The Vitalist Tradition in Western Medicine* Berkeley: North Atlantic Books, 1992 page 185-192; Personal communication with the Stefan Ball, Bach Centre, Oxon, UK.

page 187. Bach. Photograph in Weeks, Nora *The Medical Discoveries of Edward Bach* London: C. W. Daniel Co. 1976. Much information about the context of Hughes, Clarke, and British practice was gleaned from Campbell, Anthony *The Two Faces of Homœopathy* London: Jill Norman, 1984.

Chapter 12: Kent in Chicago

page 190. Dunham College. Picture King's Vol. III, page 119. History of Dunham/Hering Colleges King's Vol. III, pages 118-122. Kent and Wife in Garden. Original photograph in the collection of the author.

page 191. Kent the Teacher. *Dunham Medical College Journal* 1900, pages 99-106.

page 192. Letter from Kent to Sugden. Reproduced in the *Homœopathic Recorder*, February 1929, page 117.

page 193. Kent letter to Bradford. Hahnemann Collection, Allegheny University of Health Sciences, Philadelphia, Pennsylvania. The term "keynote prescribing" was first used by Guernsey in a talk to the Philadelphia Homœopathic Medical Society in 1867 during an explanation of why he prescribed *Crocus* in a case. He said the long black string of blood dropping from the nose let him think of *Crocus* and all the other symptoms of the patient agreed. In 1868 he presented the paper "The Key-Note System" in which he explained that the keynote is just a hint for a remedy and the other characteristic symptoms must fit as well.

page 194. *The Homœopathician*. Collection of the author. Information about the Society of Homœopathicians from the collection of Christopher Ellithorp.

page 195. Kent. Frontispiece in Kent, J. T., MD *Lectures on Homœopathic Philosophy*, (Memorial Edition) Chicago: Ehrhart and Karl, 1926. Information from Kent, J. T., MD *Lectures on Homœopathic Philosophy*, (Memorial Edition) Chicago: Ehrhart and Karl, 1926. page 12-13; Interview with David Wember, MD.

page 196. Information about Stevensville and picture of the Bitterroot Inn from Bitterroot Valley Historical Society, Hamilton, Montana.

page 197. Old Kent House. Photographer unknown, presented to the author by the owners of the Kent property, Collection of the author; New Kent house. Photograph by Greg Bedayn.

page 198. Kent's Grave. Photograph by the author.

Chapter 13: Great Britain: II

page 200. Gibson Miller. Photo from the Collection of the National Center for Homeopathy; Signature from Miller's copy of Hering's *Guiding Symptoms*. Collection of the Glasgow Homœopathic Library. Biographical information *British Homœopathic Journal*, 1919, volume 9, page 107; *Homœopathic World*. June 2, 1919, pages 230-235.

page 201. Tyler. Picture from the collection of the author (with thanks to John Ainsworth); signature from Chris Ellithorp. Biographical information *Homœopathic Recorder*, September 1943, pages 140-141. In a memorial to Kent, Tyler says that one of her great regrets is that she never heard Kent lecture in person.

page 201. Wheeler. Biographical information from the *British Homœopathic Journal*, April 1947, pages 2-10.

page 201. The Card Repertory Letter. Printed in Currim, Ahmed, MD, *Guide to Kent's Repertory* New Haven: Hahnemann Institute for Homeopathic Documentation, 1966 pages 191-193.

page 202. Lewin, Octavia, "Cases Illustrating Constitutional Treatment" *The Journal of the British Homoeopathic Society* Vol. XI Session 1902-1903, pages 130-139.

page 205. Shepherd. Photograph from Gweneth Robinson (thanks to Roger Savage, RSHom). Biographical information, Shepherd, Dorothy *Why I Became a Homœopath* London: Homœopathic Publishing Co. 1940 pages 1-3; *Homœopathy*, Volume 2, 1952, page 256.

page 206. Weir. Photograph *Homœopathic Recorder*, May, 1932; Signature from a letter to Dr. Alexander Klein, collection of the author. Biographical information *Journal of the American Institute of Homœopathy*, September 1955; *Journal of the American Institute of Homœopathy*, June 1971; Smith, Constance Babington *Champion of Homœopathy; The Life of Margery Blackie* London: John Murray, 1986, page 64.

page 207. Borland. Photograph, poem, and reminiscences from Smith, Constance Babington *Champion of Homœopathy; The Life of Margery Blackie* London: John Murray, 1986, page 64.(no credit on the photo). Biographical information *Homœopathy*, January 1961, page 6.

page 208. Fergie Woods. Photograph from Faculty of Homœopathy, London; signature *Journal of the American Institute of Homœopathy*, November-December 1964. Biographical information *Homœopathy*, February 1961, page 26, *Homœopathy*, March 1961, page 35.

page 208. Blackie. Photo and biographical information from Smith, Constance Babington *Champion of Homœopathy; The Life of Margery Blackie* London: John Murray, 1986.

page 209. Anthroposophical information from: Yasgur, Jay *Homeopathic Dictionary* (4th edition), Greenville: Van Hoy Press, 1998, pages 16-17; Klunker, Will, "Anthroposophy and Homœopathy," *Classical Homeopathic Quarterly, 1988*, Heidelberg: Karl F. Haug, pages 3-12; "Anthroposophical Medicine," Peter Hinderberger, MD, unpublished article in the collection of the author.

Chapter 14: The Decline

page 212. Bernard. Photo from the Philadelphia Free Library, Philadelphia, Pennsylvania. Biographical information from the *Encyclopedia Brittanica*. "Modern Medicine." Lecture by Richard Moskowitz at the National Center Summer School, circa 1988.

page 213. "Bayer Man" from *Life Magazine* ad circa 1950.

page 214. *Upjohn Catalog* Collection of the author; *Squibb Catalog*, College of Physicians, Philadelphia, Pennsylvania. The drug companies. Coulter, Harris *Divided Legacy*, Volume 3. pages 402-419.

page 215. French ad. College of Physicians, Philadelphia Pennsylvania. "The AMA Opens." The summary is condensed from Coulter, *Divided Legacy*, Volume 3. pages 419-442 and from Kaufman, pages 156-170. The quotes are from *Divided Legacy.*, which in turn quoted the *Homœopathic Recorder*.

page 217. Menninger. Photo from the Collection of the author. Quote from "Some Reflections Relative to the Symptomotology and Materia Medica of Typhoid Fever," C. F. Menninger, *American Institute of Homœopathy Transactions 1897*, page 430.

page 218. Coulter. Photo (uncredited) and signature. Collection of the author. Biographical Information from an interview by the author.

page 219. Coulter and Popova. Photo by the author.

page 220. Flexner Photo from *Life Magazine*, "The 100 Most Important Americans of the 20th Century," Fall 1990, page 99. (the photo is identified only as "1929." no credit has been established. Time-Life could not locate a credit.) Flexner, Abraham *Medical Education in The United States and Canada* New York: The Carnegie Foundation, 1910 pages 158-161.

page 222. Chicago Hahnemann. King's Vol. II, page 346; New York Homœopathic, King's Vol. II, page 261

page 223. Southwestern Homœopathic. King's Vol. II, page 319; Detroit Homœopathic King's Vol. II, page 174. Information on schools from King's Vol. II and III.

page 224. White House. Credited to "Scherer, Washington, DC" Collection of Christopher Ellithorp. The original is about a foot high and five feet long. Information about the schools was gleaned from many of the journals of the time; *The Ohio State University College of Medicine* Blanchester, Ohio: The Brown Publishing Co. 1934, pages 439-441; Ohio State University, Proceeding of the Board of Trustees, May 3, 1922; *Ohio State University Monthly*, July 1922, pages 33.

page 225. Letter by Dr. James William Ward Collection of the author.

page 225. Montgomery Ward. *Hospitals and Sanatoriums of the Homœopathic School of Medicine,* Council on Medical Education of the American Institute of Homœopathy, 1916, page 96.

page 226. Myth and Fact. Cook, Daniel, MD, and Naude, Alain *Journal of the American Institute of Homeopathy* Autumn, 1996 pages 125-141.

page 230. AIH Definition. Kent, James T., MD Kent, J. T., MD *Clinical Cases, Lesser Writings, Aphorisms and Precepts* Chicago: Ehrhart and Karl, 1926, pages 229-232.

page 232. Wood. photo and signature *Transactions of the American Institute of Homœopathy*, 1902 frontispiece. Biographical information from Wood, James C, MD, *An Old Doctor of the New School* Caldwell, Ohio: Caxton Press, 1942.

page 233. Wood photo. Wood, James C, MD, *An Old Doctor of the New School* Caldwell, Ohio: Caxton Press, 1942, rear of dust-jacket. Collection of the author.

page 234. Royal Copeland. Photo *Transactions of the American Institute of Homœopathy*, 1908. Biographical Information Wood, James C, MD, *An Old Doctor of the New School* Caldwell, Ohio: Caxton Press, 1942, pages 205-206.

page 235. Young Copeland from Wood, James C, MD, *An Old Doctor of the New School* Caldwell, Ohio: Caxton Press, 1942, page 207. Copeland election poster Collection of Christopher Ellithorp. "Homeopathy and Expediency" from Copeland, Royal, MD *The Scientific Reasonableness of Homeopathy* reprinted from the *Chironian*, 1909, pages 51-52. Collection of the author.

page 236. The Flu Epidemic *Journal of the American Institute of Homœopathy* May 1921 page 1038; *Homœopathic Recorder*, August 1919, pages 345-348 "Epidemic Influenza Treated by Homœopathic Physicians" by William A. Pearson, MD.

Chapter 15: The Keeping

page 240. IHA Photo. Collection of the author.

page 242. Assorted biographies from obituaries in the *Homœopathic Recorder*.

page 243. Julia M. Green. Photograph from *Homœopathic Recorder*, November 1928; signature from a letter in the collection of the author. Biographical material Vargo, Kay *Julia M. Green; a Master Prescriber* unpublished manuscript in the Collection of the author; *Journal of the American Institute of Homeopathy*, March 1964, page 58; Interviews with Maesimund B. Panos and Sandra M. Chase.

page 244. AFH Library Postcard. Collection of the National Center for Homeopathy.

page 245. AFH Office Postcard. Collection of the National Center for Homeopathy. Vargo, Kay *The American Foundation for Homeopathy,* unpublished manuscript, Collection of the author; AFH minutes. Collection of the National Center for Homeopathy.

page 246. Schmidt. Photograph by Robert Schore, signature from Kent, J. T. MD, *Final General Repertory* edited by Pierre Schmidt, MD, and Diwan Harish Chand, MD. New Delhi: National Homœopathic Pharmacy, 1982. Biographical information *Journal of the American Institute of Homeopathy,* March 1988, pages 34-37.

page 247. Volstead act *Jottings*, Philadelphia: Boericke and Tafel, December 1919, page 6; April 1921, page 3; December 1921, page 5; May 1930, page 5; Records of the Washington Homeopathic Pharmacy (courtesy of Joseph Lillard).

page 248. Twilight Sleep Movement. Information courtesy of Anne Kirschmann.

page 249. The ERA *Jottings*, Philadelphia: Boericke and Tafel, January 1923 page 2; *Homœopathic Recorder*, May, 1921, "The Electronic Reaction of Abrams" by J. W. King, page 198-207; *Journal of the American Institute of Homeopathy*, August 1919, "Hahnemann Doctrine of Attenuation" by Albert Abrams, pages 402-406; *Transaction of the International Hahnemannian Association* 1925, pages 16-39; Russell, Edward W., *Report on Radionics* Suffolk: Neville Spencer, 1973, pages 17-40.

page 251. The Work of William Boyd, Russell, Edward W., *Report on Radionics* Suffolk: Neville Spencer, 1973, pages 142-49; *British Homœopathic Journal*, January 1954; picture of Emanometer *British Homœopathic Journal*, 1923, pages 458-493.

page 252. Stearns. Photograph in *Homœopathic Recorder*, June 1930; signature on cover of *Physics of High Dilutions* in collection of author. Biographical information *Journal of the American Institute of Homeopathy*, May 1947, Page 175, 179-180.

page 253. Boger. Photograph in the collection of the author, signature from a letter to Dr. Carleton, January 17, 1907, collection of author. Biographical information *Homœopathic Recorder*, fourth quarter 1935; *Transactions of the International Hahnemannian Association*, 1936; Interview with Jean Giles, Boger's grand-daughter, April 1998.

page 254. Boger Card. Collection of the author.

page 255. Boger's Electrical Potentizer. *Homœopathic Survey,* published by the American Foundation for Homœopathy, January, 1929, pages 12-13. Interview with George H. Nitsche, MD, 1991.

page 256. Boger Letter. Collection of the author.

Chapter 16: The Final Blows

page 258. Chicago Hospital. *Jottings*, February 1929, page 2. Collection of the author.
page 259. Camden Hospital. Postcard. Collection of Christopher Ellithorp. Editorial by H. A. Roberts, *Homœopathic Recorder*, January 1936, pages 46-48.
page 260-261. Postcards. Collection of the author.
page 262. "Strange Bed-fellows" A number of articles by Lucy Stone Herzog, MD, appeared in the *Journal of the American Institute of Homeopathy* from 1937 to 1941. They included "The Embattled Physician" August 1937; "What Is To Be Done About it" November 1937; "The Outlook to Date" April 1939; "A Summary of Activities" August 1940; "The Menace" March 1941, etc. An excellent summary is offered in Kaufman, pages 178-179.

Chapter 17: 1930-1940

page 266. Rabe photograph. *Jottings* December 1919, page 15. Collection of the author; signature found in a copy of Burnett's *Enlarged Tonsils*. Dated 1901, collection of the author. Biographical information *Journal of the American Institute of Homeopathy*, May 1952, page 112.
page 269. Roberts photograph from *Homœopathic Recorder*, March 1928; signature found in a copy of Ward's *Dictionary*. Dated 1939, collection of the author. Biographical information *Homœopathic Recorder*, November 1950, page 123.
page 270. Hayes photograph *Transactions of the International Hahnemannian Association*, 1926; signature from a letter to Julia M. Green, March 3, 1947, collection of the author. Biographical information *Homœopathic Recorder*, August 1952, page 54; Interview with Hayes' grand-daughter, Dorothy DiCecco, May 1995.
Page 273. Hayes at desk. Original belonged to the American Foundation for Homeopathy. Whereabouts unknown. Copy from printing screen. Collection of the author.
page 275. Pulford photograph from *Homœopathic Recorder*, October 1930; signature from the collection of William Kirtsos. Biographical information, *Homœopathic Recorder*, October 1948, pages 101-102.

Chapter 18: The Final Closings

page 278. *The Medic*. Collection of the author. Rogers, Naomi. *An Alternative Path: The Making and Remaking of Hahnemann Medical College and Hospital*. New Brunswick: Rutgers University Press 1998, pages 83-210.
page 279. Quote from Bertram Brown. Related to me by Henry Williams.
page 280. Garth Boericke. Photo courtesy of Jean Bernard. Cartoon from *The Medic* 1931 page 200. Biographical information *Journal of the American Institute of Homeopathy*, September/October 1967 page 272. [much can be inferred about the state of the AIH at this time by the fact that Boericke died in January 1968, and the obituary is in the October 1967 *Journal*! The *Journals* were, obviously, coming out on a very delayed schedule!].
page 281. John A. Borneman. Photograph from *The Medic*, 1933 page 50. Biographical information from Jay Borneman.
page 282. Borneman Family. Photograph by the author. Jay is "John Paul" but his grand-dad always called him "John IV."
page 285. Pharmacy Drawing from Borneman catalog, circa 1950. Collection of the author.
page 286. AFH Class. Unidentified photographer. Collection of the author.
page 287. Shupis Address. *Homœopathic Recorder*, November 1948. pages 123 ff.
page 288. Shupis. *1938 The Medic*.
page 289. Injectable ad. 1941 *AIH Directory of Homeopathic Physicians*. Collection of the author.
page 290. Directory. *AIH Directory of Homeopathic Physicians* Collection of the author.

Chapter 19: The Links

page 292. Hubbard. Photograph from *Homœopathic Recorder* June 1928; signature from the collection of the author. Biographical information *Journal of the American Institute of Homeopathy*, July/August 1959, pages 130-131; *Journal of the American Institute of Homeopathy*, May/June 1967, pages 130-136; Interviews with Harris Coulter, Catherine Coulter, Maesimund Panos, Henry Williams, Allen Neiswander.
page 293. Bookplate. Found in Bradford's *Logic of Figures*, collection of the author.
page 294. Letter from Hubbard to Green; Kit card, collection of author.
page 295. Dixon Photograph. *Homœopathic Recorder* September 1939; signature *Journal of the American Institute of Homeopathy*, November-December 1964. Biographical information *Journal of the American Institute of Homeopathy*, November/December 1959, page 205; Interview with Celeste Beckwith Chapman, 1981; several informal discussions with Maesimund B. Panos over the years.
page 296. Dixon. Photographer unknown. Collection of the author.
page 297. Dixon. Photographer unknown. Courtesy of Michael Garn, MD.
page 298. T. K. Moore. Photographer unknown. Courtesy of Michael Garn, MD.
page 299. Grimmer photograph from *Homœopathic Recorder* August 1932; signature from a letter to Julia M. Green, January 2,1947, collection of the author. Biographical information from *Journal of the American Institute of Homeopathy*, July 1953, pages 216-217; *Journal of the American Institute of Homeopathy*, July/August 1959, "57 years in the Practice of Homeopathic Medicine," pages 125-126; *Journal of the American Institute of Homeopathy*, January/February 1967, pages 58-59.

page 300. Grimmer photograph from *Journal of the American Institute of Homeopathy* July 1953, page 216.
page 302. Musings. Original letters in the collection of the author.
page 306. *Homœopathic Recorder.* Collection of the author.

Chapter 20: Drawing Together

page 308. AFH Photograph. Uncredited. Collection of the author.
Information for this section is gleaned from the *Journal of the American Institute of Homeopathy.* The issues were so important that almost every journal between 1948 and 1955 had something about it. I would have to list them all. Reading through the journals from this time gives a full sense of the times. The major articles were: *Journal of the American Institute of Homeopathy*, February 1944, pages 35-36; *Journal of the American Institute of Homeopathy*, March 1946, pages 80-81, Rabe, Rudolph, "What Homeopathy Needs"; *Journal of the American Institute of Homeopathy*, July 1949, pages 1-4, Rabe, Rudolph, "Can the School of Homeopathy Survive?"; *Journal of the American Institute of Homeopathy*, January 1951, pages 11-15, Crutcher, Lewis, "Retrospect and Prospect"; *Journal of the American Institute of Homeopathy*, January/February 1960, pages 17, 22.
page 310. "The Merger" Information for this section is gleaned from: *Journal of the American Institute of Homeopathy*, October 1955, pages 35-36, Gladish, Donald, "A Time for Decisions"; *Journal of the American Institute of Homeopathy*, January 1957, pages 25 "President's Message"; *Journal of the American Institute of Homeopathy*, March 1957, page 85; *Homœopathic Recorder,* July/August/September 1959. Pages 3-6; *Journal of the American Institute of Homeopathy*, May/June 1960, page 69. Troup, Ronald, "International Notes."
page 311. AIH Board. Uncredited. Collection of the author.
page 312. Gladish. Photograph uncredited. Collection of the author. Signature and biographical Information *Journal of the American Institute of Homeopathy*, July 1957, page 212; *Journal of the American Institute of Homeopathy*, July/August 1967, page 195.
page 313. Eikenberry. Photograph, signature, biographical information from *Journal of the American Institute of Homeopathy*, August 1956, page 219.

Chapter 21: Keeping it Alive

page 316. Rood. Photograph by Jane Hale, published in the *Flint Journal*, Flint, Michigan, July 13, 1986. Used with permission. Biographical Information from *The American Homeopath*, Layfayette, CA: Greg Bedayn, editor, 1997, pages 98-99; and conversations with many of her patients and colleagues.
page 317. Rood and Panos. Photograph. uncredited. Collection of author.
page 318. Baker photograph from *The Medic*, 1930 page 66; signature from the National Center for Homeopathy, photo with Clark Baker by Jay Yasgur. Biographical information from an interview with Baker, 1994.
page 319. Young. Photograph uncredited. Collection of the author. Signature and biographical information from *Journal of the American Institute of Homeopathy*, June 1974, pages 67-70.
page 320. Boyson. Photograph by Walter Telep. Collection of the author. Signature from the AFH files (thanks to Anne Kirschmann); drawing in the collection of the author. Biographical information from *Journal of the American Institute of Homeopathy*, June 1972, page 66; conversations with patients and colleagues including Maesimund Panos, Henry Williams, Harris Coulter, David Hufford.

Chapter 22: The New Leaders

page 322. State Society. Photographer unknown. Collection of the author.
page 323. Dinner. Photographer unknown. Collection of the author.
page 324. Neiswander. Photograph from *Homœopathic Recorder*, October 1950; signature from AFH Files (thanks to Anne Kirschmann); Allan and Georgiana photo by Tess Nossaman. Biographical information from personal interview.
page 325 Williams. Photo from *Journal of the American Institute of Homeopathy*, September 1974, page 160; Signature from collection of the author. Williams (older) photograph by Paula Leligdon. Biographical information from personal interview.
page 326. Stephenson. Photograph uncredited, from the National Center for Homeopathy. Signature collection of the author. Biographical information *Journal of the American Institute of Homeopathy*, September 1985, page 130.
page 327. Panos. Photograph courtesy of the National Center for Homeopathy; signature collection of the author. Biographical information from *The American Homeopath*, Layfayette, CA: Greg Bedayn, editor, 1997, pages 53-56; and several personal interviews over the years.
page 328. Panos and dad photograph. Courtesy of Maesimund B. Panos; Panos, Whitmont, and Williams, photograph by Tess Nossaman.
page 329. Panos and Green. Collection of the author; Banning Brace ad. Collection of Christopher Ellithorp.
page 330. Green Letter. Original in the collection of the author.

Chapter 23: The Resurgence

page 332. 1972 Class. Photographer unknown. Collection of the author.
page 333. Bill Gray. photograph by the author (1994). Biographical information from two interviews.
page 334. Dean Crothers. Photograph by the author (1988). Biographical information from an interview.
page 336. Nick Nossaman. Photograph by the author (1988). Biographical information from an interview.

page 337. Karl Robinson. Unknown photographer (1988). Collection of the author. Biographical information from an interview.

page 338. Chase. Photographer unknown (1988). In the Collection of the author. Biographical information from several interviews.

page 339. Wember. Photograph by the author (1994). Biographical information from several interviews.

page 340. Moskowitz and Kirtsos. Photograph by the author (1987). Biographical information from several interviews.

page 341. Moskowitz in Santa Fe. Photograph by the author (1982).

page 342. Letter from Moskowitz. Collection of the author.

page 343. The "Boston Ladies." Photograph by the author (1987).

page 344. Peebles. Biographical information from a personal interview and from an unpublished interview by Louise Woofenden in the collection of the author.

Chapter 24: Revitalization

page 346. Packman. Photographer unknown. *Homeopathic Heartbeat*, December 1978. The information about the AFH and the NCH was gleaned from an unpublished manuscript by Kay Vargo "The History of the American Foundation for Homeopathy"; three interviews with Ralph Packman; interviews with Harris Coulter; many documents from the AFH in the collection of the author.

page 347. *Layman Speaks.* From the Collection of the author.

page 349. Vargo. photograph by Walter Telep. Collection of the author.

Chapter 25: 1970s The Bay Area

page 352. Neustaedter. Photo (1991) and signature from Dana Ullman. Biographical information from an interview.

page 354. Morrison and Herrick. Photo by Greg Bedayn.

page 355. Morrison. Signature from Roger Morrison. Biographical information from an interview. Herrick. Signature from Nancy Herrick. Biographical information from an interview.

page 356. Ullman. Photo by the author (1989). Signature from Dana Ullman. Biographical information from an interview.

page 357. Vithoulkas. Photo by the author (1987). Signature courtesy of Dana Ullman. Biographical information from several interviews.

page 358. Ticket. Collection of Dana Ullman.

page 360. Krishnamurti information from George Vithoulkas and Alain Naudé. "Essence" information from interviews with Bill Gray, Roger Morrison, and George Vithoulkas.

page 361. Doctors group. Photographer unknown. published in the *IFPH Newsletter*, Spring 1980. page 2.

page 362. Kunzli quote: *Journal of the American Institute of Homeopathy*, March 1982, pages 42-43.

page 363. Naudé. Biographical information from an interview.

page 364. Organon information from a correspondence with Robert Schore and interview with Naudé. Photo. unknown photographer. *Journal of the American Institute of Homeopathy*, September 1976.

pages 365, 366, 367. IFH Mastheads. Collection of the author. Much of the information in this segment was gleaned from conversations with Dana Ullman, Bill Gray, Roger Morrison, Dean Crothers, and Alain Naudé, as well as the records printed in the IFH publications.

Chapter 26: 1970-85: The Naturopaths

page 370. The Naturopaths. Boyle, Wade and Kirchfeld, Friedhelm, *Nature Doctors: Pioneers in Naturopathic Medicine*. Portland: Medicina Biologica, 1994.

page 371. NCNM. Photo and information from NCNM.

page 372. Bastyr University. Photo and information from Bastyr University; Southwest College. Photo and information from Southwest College.

page 372. Bastyr. Photo by Karen Boyle from *Nature Doctors,* page 302. Biographical information from *Nature Doctors*, pages 302-312; interview with Melanie Grimes.

page 373. King and Kipnis (1988). Photo by the author. Signatures from King and Kipnis. Biographical information from an interview.

page 374. Messer. Photo by Mitzi Lebensorger (1995). Signature from the National Center. Biographical information from an interview.

page 375. Murphy. Photo by the author (1987). Signature from Jim Klemmer. Biographical information from an interview.

pages 376,377. Ullman. Photo by the author (1990). Signatures from the Ullmans. Biographical information from an interview.

pages 378-382. Herscu/Rothenberg Photo by the author (1992). Signatures from Herscu/Rothenberg. Biographical information from an interview.

page 382. Saine. Photograph by the author (1992). Signature from Andre Saine. Biographical information from an interview.

Chapter 27: 1975-1990: Divisions and Healings

page 387. AFH Dinner. Photographer unknown. Collection of the author. The information on "The Great Unpleasantness" was gleaned from *The Homeopathic Heartbeat* (1979-1981); *Homeopathy Today* (1981-1985); *The American Homeopath* (April-July, 1981; *American Homeopathy* (August 1981-1985); from letters from the National Center, now in the collection of the author; several interviews with Ralph Packman, Maesimund Panos, Sandra M. Chase, Elaine Ryan, Forrest Murphy, Jr., David Wember, Richard Moskowitz, Nick Nossaman, Glen Hill, Jack Borneman, Wyrth Post Baker, Christine Zack DeZutel, and Harris Coulter; and through personal experiences during the time period.

page 388. DeZutel. Photographer unknown. From *American Homeopathy*, April 1982, page 2. Signature from *American Homeopathy*, page 3, January 1986.

page 389. Florida Course. Photographer unknown. From *American Homeopathy* June 1982.
page 390. Haviland and Vargo. Photographer unknown. Collection of the author.
page 391. Mastheads from the collection of the author; Lillard photo by the author.
page 392. Kunzli and Shore. Photo (1987) and signature from Robert Schore. Biographical information from an interview.
page 393. Eizayaga photo by the author (1986).
page 394. MacLeod (1986), Imberechts (1987), Sherr (1991) photos by the author. Creasy photo from *The American Homeopath*, 1997, page 21; Ghegas photo by Douglas Hoff; Sankaran photo by Melissa Fairbanks.
pages 395- 398. Commentary. The information here has been gleaned from discussion with a number of homœopaths, from information posted to the lyghtforce internet mailing list, and from personal experience at an untold number of seminars.
page 398. Lay Education. The information has been gleaned from an unpublished manuscript by Kay Vargo "The History of the American Foundation for Homeopathy"; *The Qualifying Course for Layman*. Washington: American Foundation for Homeopathy, 1946; letters written by Vargo, Williams, Boyson, and others in the "Post-Graduate" file at the National Center for Homeopathy and in the personal collection of the author; issues of *The Layman Speaks* (1965-77), *The Homeopathic Heartbeat* (1977-1981); *Homeopathy Today* (1981-1985); and personal experiences at the NCH Summer Course between 1980 and 1990.
page 402. Quote from James Whitney from an unpublished article. Used with permission.
page 405. Renner. Photograph by the author. Signature collection of the author. Biographical information from a personal interview, 1984.
page 406. John Collins story from Stephen Messer, ND. Letter from Renner, collection of the author.

Chapter 28: Great Britain: III

page 410. Maughan photo courtesy of Grieg Follas; Damonte photo in the collection of the author (from Liz Dancinger). The information for this chapter was gleaned from "A Brief History of British Lay Homœopathy" by Peter Morrell in *The Homœopath*, number 59, 1995; from discussions with Misha Norland, Kay Samuels, and Elizabeth Dancinger; and from e-mail correspondence with Peter Morrell, Francis Treuherz, and Jerome Whitney.
page 411. The Staines Crash. Those aboard were: Dr. E Stewart, Dr. T Stewart, Dr. Isobel Campbell, Dr. S Kadleigh, Mr. and Mrs. D. W. Everitt (head of Nelson's Pharmacy), Dr. J. Rubin, Mr. P. Glennie-Smith, Dr. Golomb, Dr. Joan Mackover, Dr. Mary Stevenson, Dr. V. L. Lanza, Dr. S. Linger, Dr. L. Kandalla, Dr. S. Kandalla.
page 411. The summary of the Druid Order is from an unpublished manuscript by Jerome Whitney. Used with permission.
page 412. Information about the UKHMA from private correspondence with Trevor Cook, Frank Meredith, and Stephen Gordon. Quote from *(SH) Student Homœopath*, Issue 73, November 1998. Figures of practitioners from Stephen Gordon of the ECCH/ICCH.

Chapter 29: The Diploma Peddlers

page 414. *The Journal of the American Institute of Homeopathy,* April 1957 Editorial by A. D. Sutherland "A Warning" page 117 November/ December 1957 W. P. Baker, "The Place of Homeopathy in American Medicine" page 296-298; July/ August 1958 Donald Gladish, "President's Message" page 108.
page 415. Reddick. Photo from *The Medic* 1937.
page 416. Maryland State Certificate. Collection of the author.
page 417. Freemont College Diploma. Collection of the author. The information about the Maryland Board and the "Approved Schools" was gleaned from files in the possession of Harris Coulter and from interviews with Coulter and Henry N. Williams.
page 419. Florida State Certificate. Collection of the author.
page 420. Florida Board Certificate. Collection of the author. The information was gleaned from letters between Statham and Packman in the collection of the author; A file from the NCH labeled "Fla. Col. Baker", now in the collection of the author; from several interviews with Harris Coulter; and from a visit by the author to Statham's facility in Florida in the spring of 1982.
pages 423-425. The information about Arizona was gleaned from letters between Statham and Packman in the collection of the author; Articles appearing in *The Homeopathic Heartbeat* (1980)and *American Homeopathy* (September 1983); interviews with Harvey Biegelsen and Lester Steward.

Chapter 30: The Detractors

page 428. There were a number of sources for the information in this section. The specific articles in the magazines: The "four Steps" were in "The Paradigm Dispute in Medicine" by Harris L. Coulter, *The American Homeopath*, Layfayette, CA, 1998, pages 8-27; *Nautilus Magazine*, July 1983, "Homeopathy Hokum and Bunkum" by Stephen Barrett, MD; *Consumer Reports*, January 1987; *Alternative Therapies*, March 1995 page 55-56, David Hufford; *Consumer Reports*, March 1994, "Homeopathy: Much Ado About Nothing?" Information about the "Barrett Petition" and about the "Driscoll Suits" was gleaned from information that was current on *HomeoNet* at the time and subsequently printed in *Homeopathy Today*. Information about the National Council Against Health Fraud was taken from their position paper and other information found on the web site <www.quackwatch.com>. Further information was gleaned from personal correspondence with Stephen Barrett (1986-1987) and in 1998 over the Internet.

Chapter 31: The Legal Battles

page 440. The North Carolina Case. Information gleaned from *Homeopathy Today* (1985-1990) and from discussions with George Guess.
page 441. Guess. Photo by Mitzi Lebensorger (1995). Signature collection of the author. Biographical information from an interview.

page 443. Parsons Case. *Homeopathy Today* (1989-91) and telephone interview with Philip Parsons. Brinkley Case. information from a letter from Elizabeth Brinkley, April 4, 1997 and a letter from the National Center for Homeopathy, June 1998.

page 444. Legal information from Monica Miller, May 1998.

Chapter 32: Research

page 446-448. Research information gleaned from Kaufman, pages 157-159; Dunn, Charles Wesley. *Federal Food, Drug, and Cosmetic Act: A Statement of its Legislative Record.* New York, G. E. Stechert and Sons, 1938; Coulter, Harris, *The Clinical Trial: An Analysis.* Washington DC: The Center for Empirical Medicine, 1991. Quotes from pages 1- 13; *Homeopathy Today*, March 1994, pages 8-11, Talks by Michael Carlston, MD and Ted Chapman, MD at the 1993 Ohio Conference; private correspondence with Dr. Christian Kurz, PhD.

page 449. Clinical Research. Reilly Quote from BBC program, *Homœopathy: Medicine or Magic?*; Jacobs, J. and Jonas W. *Healing with Homeopathy* New York: Warner Books, 1996, pages 275-331.

page 450. Reilly. Photo and signature from David Reilly (1998). David Reilly, Morag A. Taylor, Neil G.M. Beattie, et al., "Is Evidence for Homoeopathy Reproducible?" *The Lancet*, 344, December 10, 1994: 1601-6; Letters to the Editor: "Is Evidence for Homoeopathy Reproducible?" *The Lancet*, 345, January 28, 1995: 251-3; personal correspondence with David Taylor Reilly, 1989-present.

page 453. Jacobs. Photo by Phil Schofield from the cover of *Resonance*, May 1994. Signature from Jennifer Jacobs. Biographical information from an interview with Jennifer Jacobs.

page 454. Nicaragua. Information condensed from an interview by the author with Jennifer Jacobs which appeared in both the May 1994 *Homeopathy Today* and *Resonance*.

page 456-460. Non-Clinical information from *Journal of the American Institute of Homeopathy*, September/October 1963 pages 363-366, Modern Aspects of Homeopathic Research by Garth Boericke and Rudolph B. Smith; *Journal of the American Institute of Homeopathy*,October-December 1968, pages 197-212, Changes Caused by Succussion on NMR Patterns by Garth Boericke and Rudolph B. Smith; Bellevite, Paolo and Signorini, Andrea, *Homeopathy: A Frontier in Medical Science.* Berkeley: North Atlantic Books, 1995, pages 260-262; Conte, Roland R., Berliocchi, Henri, Lasne, Yves, Vernot, Gabriel, *Theory of High Dilutions and Experimental Aspects,* West Yorkshire: Dynsol, 1996; Resch G., Gutmann V., *Scientific Foundations of Homeopathy*, Germany: Barthel & Barthel Publishing, 1987; P. C. Endler and J. Schulte, editors, *Ultra-High Dilution-Physiology and Physics.* Boston: Kluwer Academic Publishers. 1998; Bastide, Madeleine.*Signals and Images.* Boston: Kluwer Academic Publishers. 1997; Lo, Shui-Yin, Lo, A, Chong, Li Wen, Tianzhang, Lin, and others. "Physical Properties of Water with I/sub e/ Structures." *Modern Physics Letter B*, August 20, 11996, Volume 10(number 19): pages 921-30; conversations with Dr. Christian Kurz, PhD. "Ie." Shui-Yin Lo marketed his "Ie water" in two different areas: as a laundry detergent and as an automotive accessory claiming to significantly increasing the fuel mileage of any car. As a result of the former, the Oregon Department of Justice prohibited the sale of his product and fined him $190,000. They had several of his products as well as "Ie water" samples supplied by Lo's company investigated by an independent laboratory. The lab was familiar with Lo's research and tried to reproduce some of the very measurements he reported in his paper, unsuccessfully.

page 461. Benveniste photo by the author (1989). Signature from Dana Ullman. Information from *Nature*, 30 June, 1988, page 787, 816-818; *Nature*, 28 July, 1988, pages 287-291; *Boston Globe*, July 27, 1988 "Insults, Incredulity among Scientists" Richard Saltus, *New Scientist*, July 23, 1988 "Nature Sends in the Ghost Busters to solve the riddles of the antibodies," O'Regan, Brendan, "*Nature* vs. Nature: Science Censorship and New Ideas, *Noetic Sciences Review*, Autumn 1988, pages 10- 29; information posted at the time on HomeoNet; BBC discussion (viewed by the author while in Scotland, 1988); Butler, Declan, "Nobel Laueates face libel suit from 'water memory' researcher" *Nature* 389 (October 2, 1997) page 427; Lecture by Benveniste at Temple University, Philadelphia, PA, spring 1994.

Chapter 33: Pharmacy

page 466. The information in this chapter was gleaned from discussions with Jay Borneman, Jack Borneman, Glen Hill, and Willard Eldridge, as well as documents generated by the Homeopathic Pharmacopoeia Convention; The "Homeopathic Guidelines" in the *Congressional Record* of May 31, 1988; and articles written by Jay Borneman for *Resonance*. Background of the FD&C Act was gleaned from Dunn, Charles Wesley. *Federal Food, Drug, and Cosmetic Act: A Statement of its Legislative Record.* New York, G. E. Stechert and Sons, 1938.

page 469. The information about "Questionable Pharmacy and Slick Marketing" has been gleaned from the Author's collection of homœopathic ephemera. Illustration from the *Irving Homœopathic Institute Catalog*, 1892. Collection of the author.

page 470. Liv-u-mor illustration from the collection of the author.

Chapter 34: The Literature

page 474. Summary information gleaned over the years through many discussions and correspondence with Dana Ullman of "Homeopathic Educational Services" and Greg Cooper of "Minimum Price." The books left off the list are: Fincke *On High Potencies*, Lippe's *Repertory*, Field's *Symptom Register*, Shedd's *Clinical Repertory*, Gram's *Characteristics*, Worcester's *Repertory to the Modalities*.

page 475. Vermeulen. Photo by Gwyneth Evans. Holland, 1998. (He's holding a New Zealand apple). Scholten. Photo by the author. Auckland, New Zealand, 1997.

page 476. Coulter. Photograph by the author (1989). Signature from the collection of the author. Biographical information culled from several interviews.

page 478. "The Treasures That Were Lost." information gleaned from the "library bequests" folder of the AFH now in the collection of the author; Cowperthwaite letter in the collection of the author (found by Corey Weinstein, MD); interviews with Harris Coulter and Christine Zack DeZutel. Quote about Colt from Wilson, R. L., *The Colt Heritage*. New York: Simon and Schuster, 1978. page 116.

Chapter 35: The Electronic Age

page 484. Farley Card. Collection of the author.

page 486. Warkentin. Photo courtesy of David Warkentin (1996), signature collection of the author. Biographical information from several interviews.

page 487. Main screen of *MacRepertory*. From the author.

page 488. Graphing screen of *MacRepertory* and screen of *ReferenceWorks*, from the author.

page 489. VanZandvoort. Photo and biographical information from *American Homeopath* Volume 1, 1994, pages 51-62. Signature from Roger VanZandvoort.

page 489. Witko. Photo by the author, Nottingham, 1988. Biographical information from an interview with the author.

page 490. Main screen and Graphic screen of *CARA* from CARA

page 491. RADAR information from the *Synthesis Repertory,* pages 1726-1727. Schroyens photo and signature courtesy of Frederick Schroyens. Biographical information from an interview with the author.

page 492. Main screen and Graphic screen of *RADAR* from Frederick Schroyens.

page 494. *HomeopathyOnline* image from the author.

Chapter 36: Epilog

page 496. CCH information from Harry Swope and Richard Pitt; NASH Information from Miranda Castro.

page 497. Smithsonian photo by the author.

page 499. Winston, Julian, *Some Notes and Observation: American Homeopathy* 1982. Philadelphia: privately published.

page 500. Guizot quote from Haehl, Volume 1, page 231

Appendix A:

page 502. Ellithorp photo by the author; "Ugly Sam" *Irving Homœopathic Institute Catalog*, 1892. Collection of the author.

page 503. Beckwith photo from King's Vol. III, page 19.

page 505. Information from Wood, *An Old Doctor of the New School.*

page 506. Conversion from King's Vol. I, page 196.

page 507. Divine Healing. Information from the collection of the author.

page 508. The Kits. Information from the collection of the author.

page 509. Humphreys' from the collection of the author.

page 510. The Gavel Book. Photo by the author.

page 511. The Gavel. Photo by the author; letter courtesy of the National Center for Homeopathy.

page 512. Middletown Cases from the collection of the author, with thanks to Janet Madow who obtained them.

page 514. Powder Papers drawings by the author.

page 515. The AIH Two Step. From the collection of William Kirtsos.

page 520. Pharmacy Chart prepared by the author from information contained in Bradford's *Bibliography*, and from interviews with Jay Borneman, Forrest Murphy, and Joe Lillard.

Appendix B:

page 522. "The Great Unpleasantness" information gleaned from interviews with all those involved; from the contents of *The Layman Speaks, Homeopathic Heartbeat, Homeopathy Today, American Homeopath, American Homeopathy*; and papers and letters in the collection of the author. Mastheads from the collection of the author.

page 526. Mastheads from the collection of the author.

page 528. Kent's School. All information gleaned from the Post-Graduate Minutes in the Hahnemann Collection, Allegheny University of Health Sciences, Philadelphia, Pennsylvania.

page 533. New York. Information from the personal files of the author.

page 534. ABHM Letterhead. Collection of the author.

Appendix C: The Graduates

The information from this section was gleaned from a database constructed by the author which references all the graduates of homeopathic colleges listed in King's Vol. III and IV, and all the homeopathic practitioners listed in the *Directory of Practitioners* published by the AIH in 1925, 1941, and 1963. Additional information was gleaned from a listing of graduates of Ohio State University, and a number of Hahnemann Medical College yearbooks. All materials are in the collection of the author.

Appendix D: The States

The information in this section was developed from the brief histories found in King's Vol. I. The number of practitioners was gleaned from the 1941 and 1963 *AIH Directory of Practitioners*, and the 1996 *Directory of Practitioners* published by the National Center for Homeopathy.

Appendix E: The Hospitals

page 556. The Wesson Memorial Hospital and the National Homœopathic Hospital photos from *Hospitals and Sanitariums of the Homœopathic School of Medicine* published by the Council on Medical Education of the American Institute of Homœopathy, 1916. Collection of the author.

The information for this section was assembled from data found in the above book and from the "hospital and sanitarium" sections in Bradford's *Bibliography*, published in 1892, the listing of hospitals in the *International Homœopathic Directory* of 1911, the chart of hospitals and data in the *International Homœopathic Directory of 1931*, the list of hospitals in the *AIH Directory of 1941* and a publicity pamphlet issued by the Hahnemann Hospital in Brighton, Massachusetts. All volumes in the collection of the author.

Appendix F: The World

Personal correspondents are listed in the acknowledgments in the front of the book. Sources for other information is listed in the introduction to the section.

page 569. Nosodes. "Pursuant to viral safety guideline modifications, the Medicines Agency voted to place a one year moratorium, beginning on October 27, 1998, on certifications for sioncle homeopathic medicines prepared from biological strains of human origin (*Luesinum, Medorrhinum, Morbillinum, Pertussinum, Psorinum*) in all different types of forms and formats."

page 632. Photo of Gwyneth Evans and Julian Winston by William Kirtsos, at his library, July 4, 1994.
page 633. The Scale. Cover of *Irving Homœopathic Institute Catalog*, 1892. Collection of the author.

For more information about homœopathy as a system of medicine, these are my four favorite introductory books:

Homeopathy: Beyond Flat Earth Medicne by Timothy Dooley, ND, MD.
San Diego, CA: Timing Press, 1995, 112 pages, $9.00

Homeopathy: An Introduction for Skepics and Beginners by Richard Grossinger.
Berkeley, CA: North Atlantic Books, 1993, 162 pages, $12.95

Discovering Homeopathy: Medicine for the 21st Century by Dana Ullman
Berkeley, CA: North Atlantic Books, 1988, 271 pages, $12.95

The Organon of the Medical Art by Samuel Hahnemann, edited and annotated by Wenda Brwester O'Reilly. PhD.
Redmond, WA: Birdcage Books, 1996, 407 pages, $55.00

For even more information about homœopathy, look at this web site which has links to take you to **all** the others):

http:// www.homeopathyhome.com

for information in the USA, write to:

The National Center for Homeopathy 801 N. Fairfax St. #306, Alexandria, VA 22314

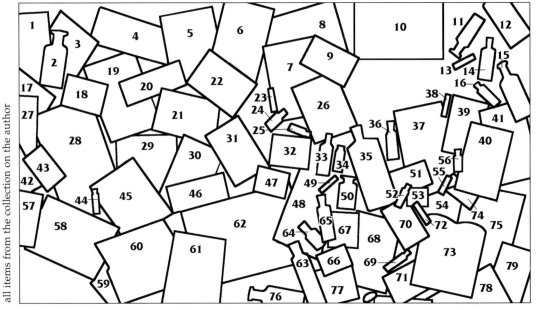

1. Original proving notebook from Donald Macfarlan, MD. Circa 1930

2. Tincture bottle from Boericke and Tafel, unlabelled.

3. *Medical Advance*, Volume XXXIX, Number 1. January 1911

4. Envelope addressed to Sir John Weir, postmarked London, 26 January 1955

5. *Homœopathic Recorder*, Vol. XL, Number 3. March 15,1925.

6. Program for the 82nd Session of the American Institute of Homeopathy, Philadelphia, 1926

7. Letter from Cyrus M. Boger to Edmund Carleton. January 17, 1907.

8. Subscription blank for the Hahnemannian Monthly. Circa 1885

9. Post Card. Pittsburgh, PA. Homeopathic Hospital. Circa 1915

10. Board of Trustees, American Foundation for Homœopathy. October 4, 1952.

11. Boericke and Tafel Tablet Triturates (*Ferrum iodatum* 2X) circa 1910.

12. Boericke and Tafel trituration bottle. (*Strontium brom* 1/100). Circa 1900.

13. A. Nelson and Co. (Polyvalent 12c/Bach)

14. Boericke and Tafel Tablet Triturates (*Natrum jod* 3X) circa 1940.

15. Boericke and Tafel Triturates (*Lacturcarium* 4X) circa 1890.

16. Remedy bottle from Royal E. S. Hayes. (*Ruta* 6) Circa 1950

17. Receipt from Boericke and Tafel to Dr. A. LeBar, Stroudsberg, PA October 29, 1888

18. Elizabeth Wright. Announcement of opening of practice in Boston.

19. *Journal of Homeopathic Practice*, Volume 1, Number 1, Spring 1978

20. Receipt of payment for *Medical Advance* to Edward Rushmore. May 1878.

21. The Boericke Potentizer. Circa 1915

22. *Enlarged Tonsils, cured by medicine* by James Compton Burnett. Boericke and Tafel, 1901

23. Skinner potency from Boericke and Tafel. (*Causticum* CM) Circa 1900

24. Swan potency from Ehrhart and Karl. (*Thuja* CM). Circa 1900.

25. Sulphur 4MM. Prepared by Dr. Rabe.

26. Portrait of Hahnemann from John B. Young, Clinton, Iowa. Circa 1890.

27. *List of 969 Homœopathic Remedies* prepared by the late Dr. B. Fincke.

28. *Journal of the American Institute of Homœopathy*, February 1909, Volume I, number 2.

29. *The Homœopathician, A journal for Pure Homœopathy*. Volume I, Number 5, May 1912

30. Catalog for the Tenth Annual Session of the AFH Postgraduate School. 1931.

31. *Leaders in Typhoid* by E. B. Nash. Boericke and Tafel, 1900

32. Package of 1000 Powder Papers from Boericke and Tafel

33. Trituration bottle from Boericke and Tafel. Labeled: Human hair. Capillaria. 2 1/00 Dr. Swan 21-4-88. (1888)

34. Dunham Potency from Smith's Pharmacy. (*Cicuta virosa* 200) Circa 1900.

35. John A. Borneman triturate bottle (11X *Calc Flour*) circa 1920

36. Boericke and Tafel trituration (small bottle) (*Ambra grisia* 24X) circa 1910.

37. Letter from J. T. Kent. Dated September 21. Early 1890s.

38. "Boericke and Tafel" printing cut.

39. Photograph of Dr. Kent from Guerin, St. Louis. Circa 1882.

40. *The Grounds of a Homœopath's Faith* by Samuel A. Jones. Boericke and Tafel, 1880.

41. Letter from Royal E. S. Hayes, MD to Julia M. Green. 3 March 1947

42. Receipt from Middletown State Homeopathic Hospital, November 27, 1897.

43. Remedy Envelope. Maesimund B. Panos, MD. Washington, DC. Circa 1960.

44. *Pulsatilla* 200 (Jenichen graft)

45. Telegram from Elizabeth Wright Hubbard to Dr. Julia M. Green. May 2, 1947

46. Stock box of Fincke remedies (*Magnetis polus austr.*) labeled "6, 30-1m-10m-cm. 1874"

47. Senexet House, Putnam Connecticut— the site of the AFH Postgraduate school during the 1930s.

48. Program of the Commencement Exercises, New York Homœopathic Medical College, May 3, 1894.

49. *Ornithogalum* 30. Cork marked "SK" (Skinner).

50. Bottle from Carl Gruner homöopath. Dresden. (*Franzensbad* 2X) Circa 1900

51. Card describing the contents of "Whitmont's Kit." From Boericke and Tafel. Circa 1950.

52. Remedy bottle from Dr. Margaret Burgess Webster (*Sulphur* 200)

53. Printing cut for Boericke and Tafel. Circa 1925.

54. Boericke and Tafel letterhead on onionskin paper. Circa 1965.

55. *Proteus* 50M. (B&T)

56. Kent Potency from Ehrhart and Karl (*Secale* 10M), circa 1930.

57. Original printing plate for Boericke's *Materia Medica*.

58. *Materia Medica with Repertory* by William Boericke. Original 9th edition, 1927.

59. Boericke and Tafel envelope for douche powders.

60. Pocket case containing 16 remedies, 30th potency. Circa 1890.

61. List of Swan's High Potencies from Boericke and Tafel, Grand Street, New York. Circa 1900.

62. *Physician Catalog of Homœopathic Medicine and Books*, Boericke and Tafel, 1894

63. John A. Borneman. Tablet Triturates (*Calc carb.* 17X) circa 1950

64. *Mygale* 2X. Dr. Wilmar Schwabe, Leipzig. (unopened)

65. Boericke and Tafel trituration. (*Crotalus horridus*, 39X). circa 1900

66. Calling Card of Pierre Schmidt. Circa 1930

67. Dr. J. W. Waffensmith. New Haven, Connecticut. Circa 1915

68. Letter from Hering. August 16 1877

69. Ehrhart and Karl bottle. (*Phosphorus* CMM) Allen Potency. circa 1920

70. Post Card. Boericke and Tafel. Collecting Rhus toxicodendron. Circa 1920.

71. Post Card: Yonkers, NY, Homeopathic Hospital. 1929

72. Fincke bottle (*Rathania* 200) circa 1890

73. Pocket case with 40 remedies, mostly 200's. Belonged to Dr. Louise Ross.

74. Receipt for delivery of a load of hay to Dr. Benjamin Woodbury, Patten, Maine. October 17, 1890

75. Letter from Elizabeth Wright Hubbard to Dr. Julia M. Green. August 29, 1947

76. bottle from C. V. Dorman, Washington, DC

77. Post card. Utica, NY. Homeopathic Hospital. 1912

78. Letter from H. A. Roberts, MD to Julia M. Green. September 30, 1946.

79. *Jottings*, by Boericke and Tafel. May 1930.

Index

A

O

P

About the Author

Julian Winston
May 31, 1941 —

Born in the Bronx, New York and growing up in Yonkers, New York, I spent Sundays at Washington Square Park in Greenwich Village, playing banjo and guitar.

Always interested in design, I attended Pratt Institute, gaining my degree, Bachelor of Industrial Design (B.I.D.) in 1963. I worked for several product and packaging design offices in New York City before moving to New Jersey to work for Creative Playthings.

I accepted a position as an Associate Professor of Design at the Philadelphia College of Art (now The University of the Arts) in 1969.

While in Philadelphia, I began to play pedal steel guitar in 1971, built two pedal steel guitars of my own, and wrote *the* instruction book, *Pedal Steel Guitar,* (with Bill Keith) in 1976. I recorded with several "folk" artists (Steve Goodman, Jim Ringer and Mary McCaslin, Saul Broudy, David Bromberg, Rosalie Sorrels) and did a solo recording for Philo Records in 1978, titled *Steel Wool.*

I met Dr. Raymond Seidel in 1971, attended Millersville in 1980, became registrar of the NCH Summer School in 1981, and dean of the program in 1988. I was elected to the board of directors of the National Center in 1982, and became the editor of the National Center's newsletter, *Homeopathy Today,* in 1984.

In 1992, I accepted an invitation from the Wellington College of Homœopathy in New Zealand to assist it in establishing a "summer school." I fell in love with the country *and* with the principal of the college.

After two years of spending six months in the USA and six months in New Zealand, I put all my belongings in a 20–foot container, and moved to New Zealand in June 1995.

I live in Tawa, just a short drive from Wellington, with my archives of over 2,000 homœopathic books,

4,000 remedies, and a large, yet to be catalogued amount of homœopathic ephemera.

In 1997 I became board member emeritus of the National Center for Homeopathy. I continue to edit *Homeopathy Today* from New Zealand. I am co-director of the Wellington College of Homœopathy with my wife, Gwyneth Ann Evans, a full–time homœopathic practitioner. I edit *Homœopathy NewZ,* a small newsletter devoted to things homœopathic in New Zealand.

I still play steel guitar and banjo, and teach design, part-time, at the local Polytechnic.
I can be reached at:

PO Box 51-156
Tawa, Wellington, NZ
e-mail at <jwinston@actrix.gen.nz>

Dr. Maesimund Panos, upon finding out my degree was a B.I.D., asked: "twice a day?"

633

The Faces of Homœopathy

A Timeline of H

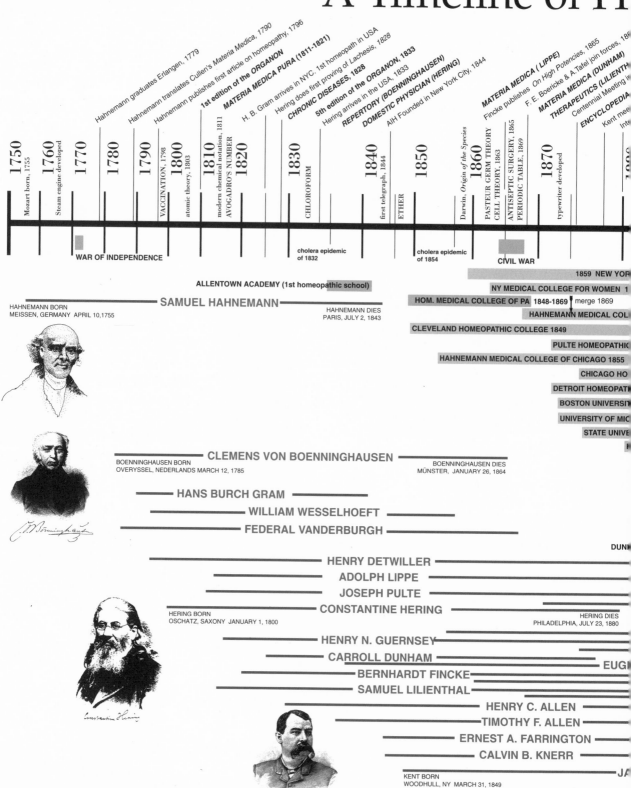

Timeline dates (top axis): 1750 · 1760 · 1770 · 1780 · 1790 · 1800 · 1810 · 1820 · 1830 · 1840 · 1850 · 1860 · 1870 · 18—

Events along the top:
- Mozart born, 1755
- Steam engine developed
- Hahnemann graduates Erlangen, 1779
- Hahnemann translates Cullen's Materia Medica, 1790
- Hahnemann publishes first article on homeopathy, 1796
- VACCINATION, 1798
- atomic theory, 1803
- 1st edition of the ORGANON
- modern chemical notation, 1811
- AVOGADRO'S NUMBER
- MATERIA MEDICA PURA (1811-1821)
- H. B. Gram arrives in NYC. 1st homeopath in USA
- Hering does first proving of Lachesis, 1828
- CHRONIC DISEASES, 1828
- 5th edition of the ORGANON, 1833
- Hering arrives in the USA. 1833
- REPERTORY (BOENNINGHAUSEN)
- DOMESTIC PHYSICIAN (HERING)
- AIH Founded in New York City, 1844
- first telegraph, 1844
- CHLOROFORM
- ETHER
- Darwin, Origin of the Species
- PASTEUR GERM THEORY
- CELL THEORY, 1863
- ANTISEPTIC SURGERY, 1865
- PERIODIC TABLE, 1869
- MATERIA MEDICA (LIPPE)
- Fincke publishes On High Potencies, 1865
- F. E. Boericke & A.Tafel join forces, 186—
- MATERIA MEDICA (DUNHAM)
- MATERIA MEDICA (LILIENTH—
- THERAPEUTICS (DUNHAM)
- Centennial Meeting i—
- ENCYCLOPEDIA
- Kent mee—
- Inte—
- typewriter developed

Bottom axis bands:
- WAR OF INDEPENDENCE
- cholera epidemic of 1832
- cholera epidemic of 1854
- CIVIL WAR
- 1859 NEW YOR—
- NY MEDICAL COLLEGE FOR WOMEN 1—
- HOM. MEDICAL COLLEGE OF PA 1848-1869 — merge 1869
- HAHNEMANN MEDICAL COL—
- CLEVELAND HOMEOPATHIC COLLEGE 1849
- PULTE HOMEOPATHIC
- HAHNEMANN MEDICAL COLLEGE OF CHICAGO 1855
- CHICAGO HO—
- DETROIT HOMEOPAT—
- BOSTON UNIVERSI—
- UNIVERSITY OF MIC—
- STATE UNIVE—

ALLENTOWN ACADEMY (1st homeopathic school)

HAHNEMANN BORN
MEISSEN, GERMANY APRIL 10,1755

SAMUEL HAHNEMANN

HAHNEMANN DIES
PARIS, JULY 2, 1843

BOENNINGHAUSEN BORN
OVERYSSEL, NEDERLANDS MARCH 12, 1785

CLEMENS VON BOENNINGHAUSEN

BOENNINGHAUSEN DIES
MÜNSTER, JANUARY 26, 1864

HANS BURCH GRAM

WILLIAM WESSELHOEFT

FEDERAL VANDERBURGH

DUN—

HENRY DETWILLER

ADOLPH LIPPE

JOSEPH PULTE

CONSTANTINE HERING

HERING BORN
OSCHATZ, SAXONY JANUARY 1, 1800

HERING DIES
PHILADELPHIA, JULY 23, 1880

HENRY N. GUERNSEY

CARROLL DUNHAM

BERNHARDT FINCKE

EUG—

SAMUEL LILIENTHAL

HENRY C. ALLEN

TIMOTHY F. ALLEN

ERNEST A. FARRINGTON

CALVIN B. KNERR

JA—

KENT BORN
WOODHULL, NY MARCH 31, 1849